LIQUID CRYSTALS WITH NANO AND MICROPARTICLES
Volume II

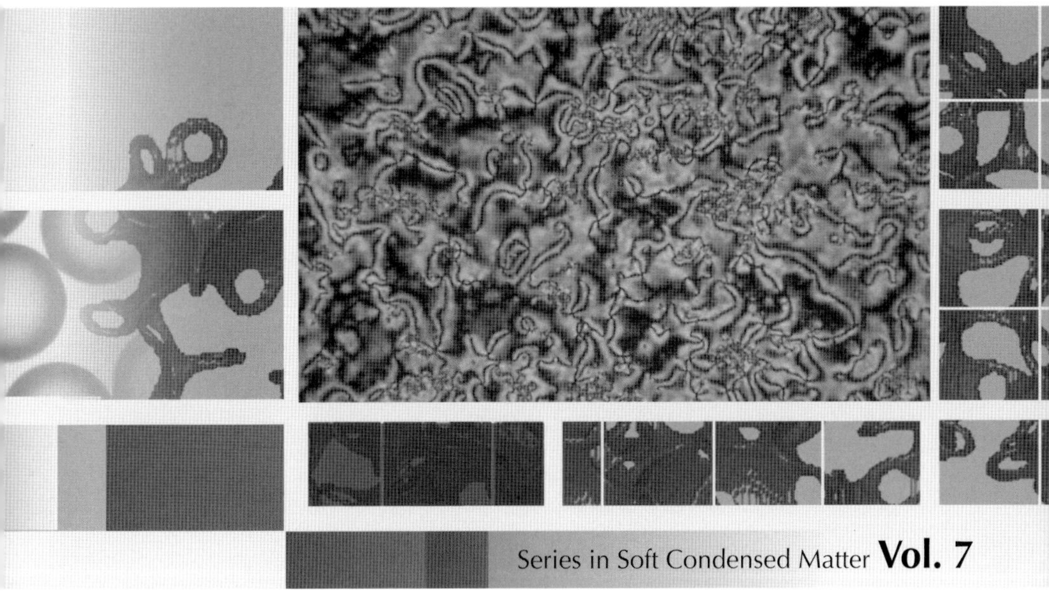

Series in Soft Condensed Matter **Vol. 7**

LIQUID CRYSTALS WITH NANO AND MICROPARTICLES

Volume II

Editors

Jan P F Lagerwall • Giusy Scalia

Seoul National University, South Korea

NEW JERSEY · LONDON · SINGAPORE · BEIJING · SHANGHAI · HONG KONG · TAIPEI · CHENNAI · TOKYO

Published by

World Scientific Publishing Co. Pte. Ltd.

5 Toh Tuck Link, Singapore 596224

USA office: 27 Warren Street, Suite 401-402, Hackensack, NJ 07601

UK office: 57 Shelton Street, Covent Garden, London WC2H 9HE

Library of Congress Cataloging-in-Publication Data
Liquid crystals with nano and microparticles / [edited by] Jan P.F.
    Lagerwall (Seoul National University, South Korea), Giusy Scalia
(Seoul National University, South Korea).
        pages cm. -- (Series in soft condensed matter ; vol. 7)
    Includes bibliographical references and index.
    ISBN 978-981-4619-25-7 (hardcover-set : alk. paper) -- ISBN 978-981-3203-67-9
    (hardcover-Vol. I : alk. paper) -- ISBN 978-981-3203-68-6 (hardcover-Vol. II : alk. paper)
    1. Liquid crystals. 2. Colloidal crystals. 3. Nanoparticles. I. Lagerwall, Jan P. F.
II. Scalia, Giusy.
    TA418.9.L54L58 2015
    530.4'29--dc23
                                                                2014020840

British Library Cataloguing-in-Publication Data
A catalogue record for this book is available from the British Library.

Desk Editor: Christopher Teo

Printed in Singapore

Preface

Liquid crystals and colloids are traditional soft condensed matter research fields with well-known applications ranging from displays of all kinds to cosmetic and food products that are with us in the everyday life. In the last century the coupling of the two research fields was sporadic, while the last 10 years brought a change: the interest in the merged field, a segment of anisotropic soft matter covering liquid crystal colloids and colloidal liquid crystals, became a hot topic.

The maturity of traditional fields with many skilled researchers, new experimental techniques, new materials, more efficient application of mathematical tools, and better computing facilities fostered a fast growth of this new field. It is important to list some new or upgraded experimental approaches that have been crucial for these developments: multiphoton confocal polarization microscopy, use of markers such as fluorescent dyes and quantum dots, atomic force microscopy, particle and defect manipulation with laser tweezers based on complex light beams, microfluidic techniques, high resolution lithographic techniques, 3D printing of submicrometer objects, emerging new materials like graphene etc. On the modelling and theoretical side, one can identify more proficient use of mathematical tools originating from topology and geometry. This together with efficient numerical computation schemes supported by multicore and graphic processors enable to numerically solve equations of complex physical models and visualize predicted structures. The synergy of experimental and modelling approaches allows to understand observed complex superstructures in liquid crystal colloids and design new ones for particular applications.

The liquid crystal colloids can be roughly divided in two classes depending on the size of the inclusions: mesoscale ranging from supra- to sub-micron, and nanoscale ranging from supra-nanometer to nanometer inclusion sizes. In case of mesoscale objects, the particles are surrounded by an area where nematic order is substantially perturbed and possibly accompanied by topological defects. This provides strong effective interactions among inclusions that allows the formation of colloidal particle assemblies. The effect that depends on surface anchoring properties and shape asymmetry, in general decreases upon approaching nanoscale. The sharing of liquid crystal deformations accompanying mezo-size inclusions leads to fascinating colloidal structures that include singular and nonsingular defects, which comply with topological properties of the orientational ordering field. In the nematic liquid crystals effective interactions based on localised or entangling disclination line defects provide the stability of colloidal structures with 1D, 2D, and 3D particle arrangements that can partially self-assemble or can be assembled by the assistance of laser tweezers. In nematic colloids the disclination networks may include also knots and links or can be accompanied by solitons. The resulting robust arrays of inclusions in liquid crystals lead to tuneable colloidal crystals that, when adding also the functionality of particles, may further lead to interesting photonic or metamaterial applications.

For the nanoscale inclusions there are at least three different situations that need to be recognised. The first situation is covering homogeneous dispersions with low concentrations of nanoparticles of different shapes and functionalities in the thermotropic liquid crystal solvents. In the second situation a high concentration of cylinder or disc-like nano-particles in an isotropic solvent directly leads to a lyotropic kind of a liquid crystal phase. In both cases physical properties of the resulting homogenous liquid crystal phases can be designed by selecting properties of nano-colloidal particles and their concentrations. The third situation covers the cases where constrained thermotropic liquid crystals have inhomogeneous orientational order that provides general spatially depended force fields that affect nano inclusions. This is reflected in the tendency of nanoparticles to concentrate in areas of depressed liquid crystalline order. Particularly singular point and line defects attract the particles and provide a means to self-assemble complex spatial distributions of nano-colloidal inclusions which again may find a way to photonic applications.

The editors have done an excellent and timely job in collecting 27 chapters written by the experts working on the front of the new field. In the 900 pages practically all relevant aspects of this fast developing anisotropic soft matter research field are addressed. The book starts with fundamentals of liquid crystals and colloidal dispersions and then continues with characterisation methods including advanced polarization microscopies, atomic force microscopy, spectroscopic & scattering techniques. It concludes with optical tweezers as a micron scale manipulation tool. The rest of the collection is devoted to different colloidal systems. The first segment covers structures based on micron scale particles dispersed in nematic and smectic solvents where topological properties of the media play crucial roles and includes examples of electrically driven dynamics of such colloidal systems. In the next segment numerous liquid crystal nanocolloids from inorganic to organic particles dispersed in calamitic, discotic, lyotropic, polymeric, elastomeric and polymer stabilised liquid crystals are described. The last segment is devoted to the colloidal liquid crystals constituted by tiny anisotropic objects ranging from carbon nanotubes to cellulose nanocrystals, dispersed in isotropic solvents.

This impressive book, devoted to the fast developing field of anisotropic soft matter, is covering the whole span from basic science to applications of liquid crystalline colloids and thus provides a much needed overview. It addresses a broad audience from physicists, chemists, material scientists, to engineers, and will be welcome by the readers ranging from experienced researchers to beginners in the field and students.

Ljuldjana, June 2016

Slobodan Žumer
University of Ljuldjana
and
Jozef Stefan Institute

Contents

Part 4
Nanoparticles in liquid crystals

Chapter 13

Nanoparticles in discotic liquid crystals

Sandeep Kumar

Raman Research Institute,
C.V. Raman Avenue, Bangalore 560 080, India
skumar@rri.res.in

The self-assembly of disc-shaped molecules creates discotic liquid crystals (DLCs). These nanomaterials of the sizes ranging from 2-6 nm are emerging as a new class of organic semiconducting materials. The unique geometry of columnar mesophases formed by discotic molecules is of great importance to study the one-dimensional charge and energy migration in organized systems. A number of applications of DLCs, such as, one-dimensional conductor, photoconductor, photovoltaic solar cells, light emitting diodes and gas sensors have been reported. The conductivity along the columns in columnar mesophases has been observed to be several orders of magnitude greater than in perpendicular direction and, therefore, DLCs are described as molecular wires.

On the other hand, the fields of nanostructured materials, such as gold nanoparticles, quantum dots, carbon nanotubes and graphene, have received tremendous development in the past decade due to their technological and fundamental interest. Recently the hybridization of DLCs with various metallic and semiconducting nanoparticles has been realized to alter and improve their properties. These nanocomposites are not only of basic science interest but also lead to novel materials for many device applications.

This article provides an overview on the development in the field of newly immersed discotic nanoscience. After a brief introduction of DLCs, the article will cover the inclusion of various zero-, one- and two-dimensional nanoparticles in DLCs. Finally, an outlook into the future of this newly emerging intriguing field of discotic nanoscience research will be provided.

Contents

1. Introduction

1.1. *Discotic liquid crystals*

The self-assembly of appropriately functionalized disc-shaped molecules leads to the formation of discotic liquid crystals (DLCs).[1,2] The phenomenon of liquid crystallinity in organic materials was discovered more than a century ago when in 1888 Friedrich Reinitzer, an Austrian botanist, noticed the unusual melting behavior of cholesteryl benzoates.[3] Otto Lehmann, a German physicist, explained the existence of "double melting" in these materials[4] and called them as "fluid crystals" which become "liquid crystals" in later years. During the early stage, major work on liquid crystals was carried out by a German chemist Vorländer who in 1908 established his rule that liquid crystalline compounds must have a molecular shape as linear as possible. After almost a century, in 1977, Chandrasekhar and his colleagues reported "...what is probably the first observation of thermotropic mesomorphism in pure, single component systems of relatively simple plate like, or more appropriately disk-like molecules".[5] From thermodynamic, optical, and X-ray studies carried out on newly synthesized benzene hexa-n-alkanoates, it was established that these materials form a new class of liquid crystals (LCs) in which molecules are stacked one on top of the other in columns, and the columns in turn constituted a 2D hexagonal arrangement. The disk-like molecules spontaneously self-assemble into 1D stacks, which in turn self-organize on various 2D lattices; the third dimension has no translational order (Fig. 1).

There are two contrasting units in DLCs; a rigid core which provides crystalline character, and peripheral flexible aliphatic chains surrounding the core which are responsible for the liquid like nature of the mesophase.

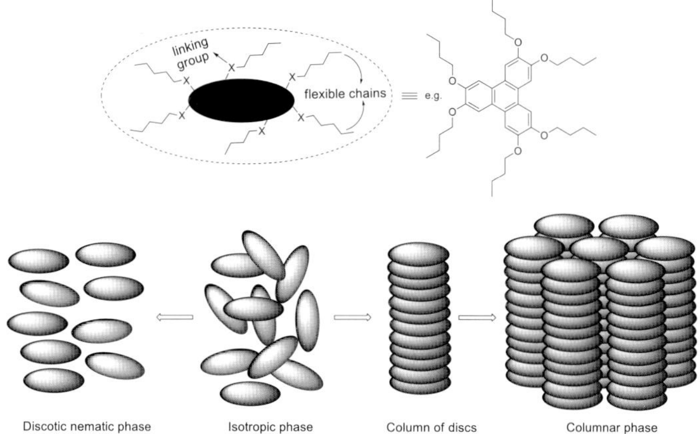

Fig. 1.   General template for discotic mesogens (top) and self-organization of disc-like molecules into discotic nematic and columnar mesophases (bottom).

Commonly, these materials are crystalline at ambient temperature and display mesomorphism on elevated temperature. However, the mesophase can be stabilized at or below room temperature via careful molecular engineering. When the molecular crystals of such discotic molecules are heated, the peripheral alkyl chains start melting first and provide fluidity to the mesophase while preserving the order due to core–core stacking. This is defined as the melting point of the discotic liquid crystalline material. On further heating, the unstacking of the central cores takes place leading to an isotropic liquid state, known as the clearing point of the discotic liquid crystalline material. Discotic liquid crystals usually exhibit either nematic phases having only orientational order of the molecules or columnar phases having both orientational and long-range positional order.

A majority of discotic liquid crystals exhibits ordered columnar phases probably because they are derived from central aromatic cores such as, triphenylene, hexabenzocoronene, phthalocyanine, etc., (Fig. 2) which possess strong $\pi - \pi$ interactions favoring columnar stacking of the molecules. About 95% discotic mesogens exhibit columnar phases. It may be noted that though columnar phases are most characteristic for discotic (disc-shaped) mesogens, they are by no means unique to the supramolecular assembly of disc-shaped molecules. Several other molecular architectures, such as, surfactants (forming lyotropic columnar phases), polycatenar molecules, dendrimers and bent-core mesogens are also known to exhibit

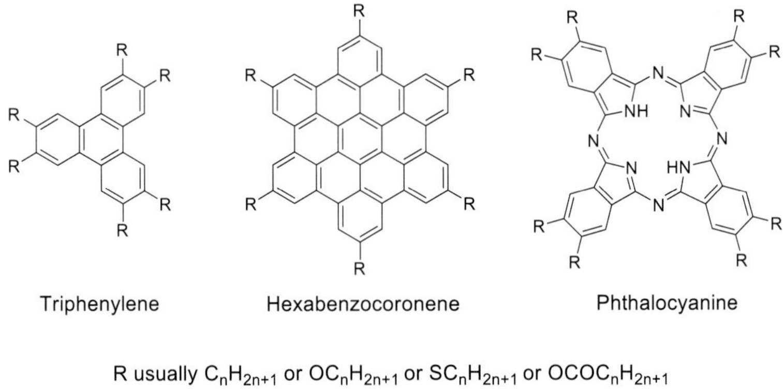

Fig. 2. Molecular structures of some discotic mesogens.

columnar phases. However, they are not being considered as discotic liquid crystals and, therefore, they are not covered in this article.

The columnar mesophases of discotic molecules are of great importance to study the one-dimensional charge and energy migration in organized systems. In the columnar mesophase of DLCs, aromatic cores are oriented in columns separated by molten aliphatic hydrocarbon chains. The intracolumnar (core-core) separation in a columnar mesophase, depends on the core structure, is usually of the order of 0.35 nm while the intercolumnar (neighboring columns) separation is generally in the range of 2-4 nm, depending on the length of flexible chains. Therefore, intracolumnar interactions are much stronger than intercolumnar interactions. Like any other organic material, DLCs are also insulators in their pure state; however, they can be made conducting by generating charges via chemical or photochemical doping. The columnar arrangement of aromatic cores can transport charge efficiently along the columns in quasi one dimension (Fig. 3). The conductivity along the columns in columnar mesophases has been observed to be several orders of magnitude greater than in perpendicular direction. As the charge migration is extremely important in many opto-electronic devices like, photovoltaic solar cells, light emitting diodes, and gas sensors, the use of DLCs in such devices could be highly beneficial. Due to their fundamental and technological importance, impressive research work is going on all over the globe, which has been reviewed in several articles, e.g., see references.[6-30]

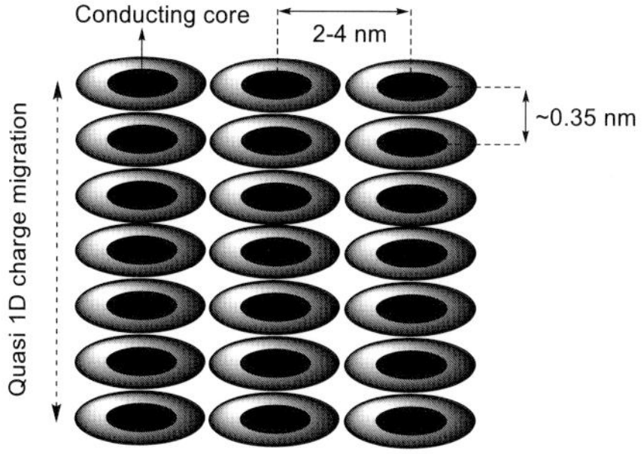

Fig. 3.   Quasi-one-dimensional charge migration in the columnar mesophase of DLCs.

1.2. *Nanoparticles*

Materials below 100 nm in one-, two- or all the three-dimensions are commonly referred to as nanomaterials. They may possess unique properties which differ from those of individual atoms or molecules and from those of bulk material. Several phenomena become pronounced as the size of the particles decreases; for example, the conductivity of metal NPs decreases significantly as their size decreases to one billionth of a meter; silver nanoparticles (NPs), but not bulk silver, possess antibacterial activity; bulk gold is inert and not soluble in common solvents but gold NPs exhibit catalytic properties and can be dissolved in solvents; the optical absorption and fluorescence properties of metal NPs are very different than in the bulk materials, etc.[31–33]

Though nanomaterials are known for centuries, the field of nanoscience and nanotechnology saw explosive development during the past two decades, primarily because of our ability to see and touch nanoscale objects with the help of modern instruments, such as scanning tunneling microscope (STM), atomic force microscope (AFM), high-resolution transmission electron microscope (HRTEM) and field emission scanning electron microscope (FESEM). In recent years, there has been tremendous development in the fields of nanostructured materials, including metallic NPs and nanorods (NRs), semiconducting quantum dots (QDs), carbon nanotubes (CNTs), fullerenes and graphene. The science and technology dealing with nanomaterials have received immense interest in nearly every field of science. The potential applications of nanomaterials in the fields of energy, computing, optics, catalysis, biosciences and medical sciences have been extensively discussed.[33] Keeping pace with topical sciences, the field of liquid crystals

(LCs) has recently entered into the fascinating domains of nanoscience and nanotechnology.[34–39]

One of the current research areas worldwide in nanoscience field is to design nanomaterials that are able to self-assemble into functional superstructures in multiple directions. Nanoparticles assembly has been induced by several methods; however, using liquid crystals as an organizing medium to induce the self-assembly of nanoparticles is a powerful tool. A number of LC-NP hybrid systems have been explored. Calamitic mesogens (liquid crystals formed by rod-shape molecules) are the most commonly employed materials in the preparation of these hybrids.[34–39] However, recently some efforts have been made to incorporate various NPs in the supramolecular order of discotic liquid crystals.[40,41]

In this chapter, we describe dispersion of: (*i*) metallic nanoparticles; (*ii*) semiconducting nanoparticles and, (*iii*) carbon nanoparticles in DLCs. Each variety of NPs could be of: (a) spherical or quasi-spherical morphology (commonly described as zero-dimensional NPs); (b) rod-shaped morphology (commonly known as one-dimensional NPs) and, (c) sheet-shaped morphology (commonly called as two-dimensional NPs). In the case of carbon NPs, all the three varieties; spherical (C60); rod-shaped (carbon nanotubes) and sheet-shaped (graphene) NPs have been dispersed in DLCs. While the dispersion of spherical and rod-shaped metallic NPs in DLCs has been successfully achieved, only spherical semiconducting NPs have so far been dispersed in DLCs.

2. Metallic NPs in DLCs

2.1. *Spherical or quasi-spherical metallic NPs*

Among all metallic NPs, gold nanoparticles (GNPs) have received much attention of scientists due to their interesting properties such as, surface plasmon resonance (SPR), surface-enhanced Raman scattering (SERS), nonlinear optical (NLO), electronic and magnetic properties. They are likely the best understood NPs from chemical properties and stabilizing techniques point of views, and therefore, by far the most extensively investigated NPs. GNPs have found applications in catalysis, optics, sensors, biological imaging, etc.[32,42,43]

The existence of gold fine particles is known to humans since ancient times and their uses in medicine and decoration are documented for centuries.[44] Michael Faraday, an electrochemist, reported the synthesis of colloidal gold in 1857[45] and after that the scientific evaluation of GNPs received increased attention. During the past few years, a large number of methods have been developed to prepare GNPs with various shapes and sizes. Among various methods such as, electrochemical, gas phase and liquid phase synthesis, the preparation of GNPs in the liquid phase has received much attention due to its many advantages, such as large-scale production and good yield. Under controlled reaction conditions, it is not difficult to produce mono-disperse and uniform geometry NPs in good yield. These NPs are typically prepared via the reduction of gold salts in aqueous or organic media in the presence of surface stabilizers.

Though the synthesis of alkanethiols protected GNPs has been reported by Mulvaney and Giersig in 1993,[46] the Brust–Schiffrin methods of monolayer-protected GNPs in organic solvent appeared in 1994[47,48] have become the most popular methods for the synthesis of smaller gold particles. These NPs are commonly referred to as monolayer-protected GNPs or gold clusters (particles smaller than 2 nm in size are often referred to as gold clusters). Usually, sodium borohydride (a strong reducing agent) is used to reduce gold(III) salt in the presence of an alkanethiol capping agent to produce 1–3 nm GNPs. The sizes of NPs can be controlled between 2 and 5 nm by varying the thiol concentration.[47–49] Sodium borohydride, being a strong reducing agent, causes more nucleation, and alkanethiol, being a strong capping agent, drastically inhibits growth of NPs.

Subsequently, several other reducing agents, capping ligands and reaction conditions (e.g., single phase, biphase reactions, low temperature) have been used to prepare a variety of GNPs. Additionally, several other methodologies such as photochemical, electrochemical, radiolytic, microwave and sonochemical methods have been developed to prepare GNPs.[42] Moreover, the ligand-exchange methodology allows incorporation of various surface functionalities on NPs. These monolayer-protected gold metal clusters are promising materials, since they can be handled in a similar manner as general organic compounds due to their high stability under ambient conditions and solubility in conventional organic solvents. Further, a variety of chemical reactions can be performed on functionalized gold NPs.

2.1.1. *Liquid crystal-GNP hybrids*

Though homogeneous mixing of anisotropic LCs with isotropic spherical or quasi spherical NPs seems difficult, several efforts have been made to disperse these NPs in various liquid crystals in small amount. Efforts have also been made to create liquid crystalline NPs via attaching anisotropic mesogens on the surface of NPs, with the idea that if the anisotropic ligands impart sufficient anisotropy into the hybrid system, these NPs may display mesomorphism. A number of LC-GNP hybrids have been prepared to study their physical properties.[39] Primarily three methods have been used to prepare LC-GNP hybrid systems. The simplest one is mixing of GNPs and LC in a solvent followed by removal of the solvent. To ensure good mixing of NPs in LC media, usually organic soluble monolayer-protected metallic NPs are used (often alkanethiol-protected GNPs) to prepare nanocomposites. Because of the non-compatibility of systems, only a very small amount of spherical NPs can be homogeneously mixed in LCs.

The ligand exchange of such alkanethiol-protected GNPs with desired thiol-terminated mesogens provides mixed monolayer-protected GNPs having both alkane thiols and mesogens attached to the gold surface. Such mixed monolayer-protected GNPs may have better compatibility with liquid crystalline media and can be obtained easily without using huge access of thiol-terminated mesogen which is usually difficult to prepare. On the other hand, reduction of gold salt in the presence of an excess of thiol-terminated mesogens affords GNPs passivated with mesogens only. A flexible spacer is commonly used to attach mesogenic ligand with GNPs. A few such systems have been reported to be liquid crystalline in virgin state.[37]

Ensuring the purity of final isolated GNPs is very important. As the ligand is used in huge excess in the reaction, the unreacted ligand must be completely removed. If the ligand is not removed completely, the system may act as monolayer-protected GNPs dispersed in the ligand and if the ligand is itself liquid crystalline, it may give spurious results. Further, it is noteworthy that though the thiol-terminated ligand may not be liquid crystalline itself but its dimer (disulphide), formed in the reaction, could be liquid crystalline. Therefore, ascertaining the purity of liquid crystalline NPs through the use of spectral and analytical techniques is quite important. Purification of the monolayer-protected GNPs is usually carried out through repeated precipitation (taking the NPs in nonpolar solvent like dichloromethane and then adding an excess of a polar solvent like ethanol followed by centrifugation) or via chromatography or through a combination of these methods. However, unlike any organic material, it is generally difficult to get monolayer-protected NPs of very high purity.

Metallic NPs of gold, silver and palladium have been dispersed in various calamitic LCs to study the effects of these NPs on various physical properties of LCs.[36–39] While studying physical properties of LC nanocomposites, care should be taken in selecting the LC having low isotropic temperature (preferably below 160°C) as alkanethiol-coated NPs often start decomposing above this temperature. Further, nanocomposites should be prepared by mixing two components (LC and NPs) in a low boiling solvent such as dichloromethane or diethyl ether which can be removed easily at room temperature. Treatment of small NPs at high temperature may increase their size significantly via migration of alkanethiols on the NPs. Therefore it is better, though difficult, to determine the size of NPs via imaging in the composite.

2.1.2. *GNPs in discotic liquid crystals*

GNPs are the only metallic NPs which have so far been dispersed in DLCs. We initiated this work by doping simple hexanethiol-passivated GNPs in triphenylene and benzene-based DLCs.[50] GNPs with a core diameter of about 1.6 nm were prepared by reduction of gold salt ($HAuCl_4$) with sodium borohydride in the presence of hexanethiol. These NPs were dispersed in three different DLCs, namely hexakis(hexylthio)triphenylene (HHTT), hexakis(pentyloxy)triphenylene (HPT) and hexakis(4-nonylphenylethynyl)benzene, by mixing (sonication) the two components, i.e., DLC and GNPs, in dichloromethane followed by removal of the solvent and drying under vacuum at room temperature. In all the experiments DLC and NPs were mixed by weight; for example 1% doped system means 1 mg of NPs were mixed with 99 mg of DLC.

Virgin HHTT exhibits a highly ordered helical phase at low temperatures, in addition to a hexagonal columnar mesophase at higher temperature[51] whereas HPT displays only an ordered hexagonal columnar phase.[52] The hexakis(4-nonylphenylethynyl)benzene is a nematic phase forming DLC.[53] While the dispersion of GNPs in calamitic nematic LCs has been extensively studied,[36–39] discotic nematic phases have not yet received much attention. In a single experiment, hexakis(4-nonylphenylethynyl)benzene and GNPs were mixed in 1:1 ratio which resulted in the macroscopic phase separation of two components. This is not surprising as NPs in such a high concentration cannot be dispersed homogeneously in any LC. Because of the paucity of nematic phase forming DLCs, other experiments could not be realized. Therefore, it is of paramount importance to look the dispersion of GNPs in small amounts and particularly in a room temperature discotic nematic LC. It is noteworthy that discotic nematic liquid crystals have been used to fabricate wide-viewing liquid crystal displays (LCDs)[6] and it is well established that the dispersion of GNPs in calamitic nematic LCs improves the electro-optical properties significantly.[39] Therefore, it would be quite interesting to study NP doped discotic nematic systems.

On the other hand, smooth dispersion of hexanethiol-passivated GNPs in columnar phases of DLCs could be realized.[50] Several binary mixtures of GNPs and HHTT were prepared and characterized from their spectral and thermal analysis. Increasing the amount of NPs in DLCs decreases the mesophase to isotropic temperature but the crystals to mesophase or mesophase to mesophase (helical phase to columnar phase) temperatures do not change significantly. Investigations performed by X-ray diffraction (XRD) studies on a GNPs-doped HHTT system described the formation of self-assembled superlattices of GNPs in the helical phase of HHTT.[54] An increase in the electrical conductivity of the nanocomposite was observed due to the presence of GNPs in the matrix.

Subsequently, gold nanoparticles fully covered with triphenylene discotics were synthesized with the idea that such a functionalization could yield liquid-crystalline NPs.[55] These triphenylene-capped GNPs were prepared by reduction of $HAuCl_4$ in the presence of a thiol-functionalised triphenylene derivative as shown in Fig. 4 (Scheme 1). TEM studies revealed that on surfaces the discotic functionalized nanoparticles self-assemble into hexagonal patterns believed to arise from the strong – interactions between the triphenylene ligands of adjacent nanoparticles. Shen *et al.* prepared triphenylene-protected GNPs with different spacer lengths and investigated the self-assembled 1-D stripes and hexagonal close packed or disordered organization of GNPs as a function of the size of GNPs, alkyl chain lengths, interparticle – interaction and solvent hydrophilicity.[56] It is interesting that the self-assembled structure of these NPs could be controlled (hexagonal or 1D nanochain) just by altering the ratio of methanol to toluene in the solvent.

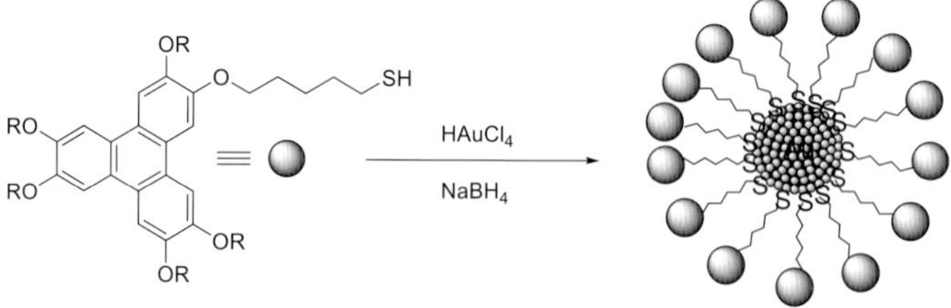

Fig. 4. Scheme 1: Synthesis of discotic-decorated GNPs.

Though mesomorphism was not observed in these discotic decorated gold nanoparticles, they could be dispersed in large quantities into the columnar phase of a related triphenylene derivative, owing to their chemical compatibility with one another. XRD studies of the bulk composites suggested random distribution of gold nanoparticles between the domain gaps of the columnar phase in a disordered fashion (Fig. 5). The dispersion of just 1% (by weight) hexaalkoxytriphenylene-capped GNPs in a hexagonal columnar phase forming triphenylene DLC exhibits remarkable six orders of magnitude enhancement in the electrical conductivity of the system.

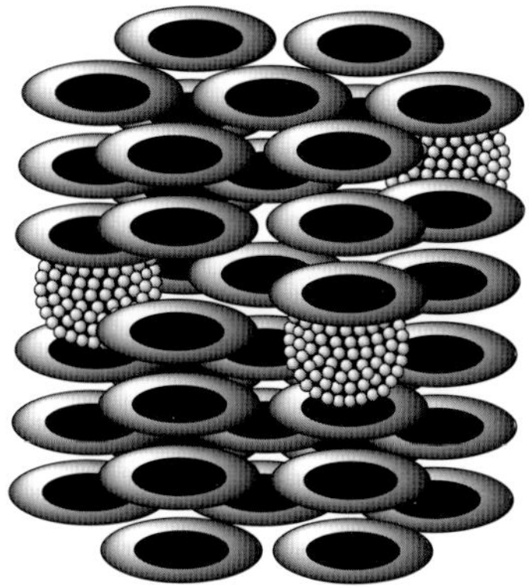

Fig. 5. A simplified illustration of the NPs dispersion in a hexagonal columnar matrix.

The DC electrical conductivity values measured, while cooling from isotropic temperature, for pure hexakis(heptyloxy)triphenylene (H7TP) and the mixture of 1% triphenylene-coated GNPs and H7TP are shown in Fig. 6.[55] At about 46°C a change in the slopes of the conductivity–temperature plots are observed which indicate a phase transition from crystalline to columnar mesophase. Similar enhancement in the conductivity has also been observed when a triphenylene-based DLCs was doped with about 1% of an electron-deficient molecule, trinitrofluorenone (TNF).[57] In the case of H7TP-GNP composites, GNPs can act as electron deficient moiety. The large electrical conductivity of the nanocomposites could be due to the highly delocalized electron density of triphenylene molecules covalently bonded to gold nanoparticles which provide a facile path for electronic conduction. Holt *et al.* confirmed the six orders of magnitude enhancement in electrical conductivity in the hexagonal columnar phase of a triphenylene-based DLC doped with 1% methylbenzene thiol-covered GNPs.[58] The for-

                                    S. Kumar

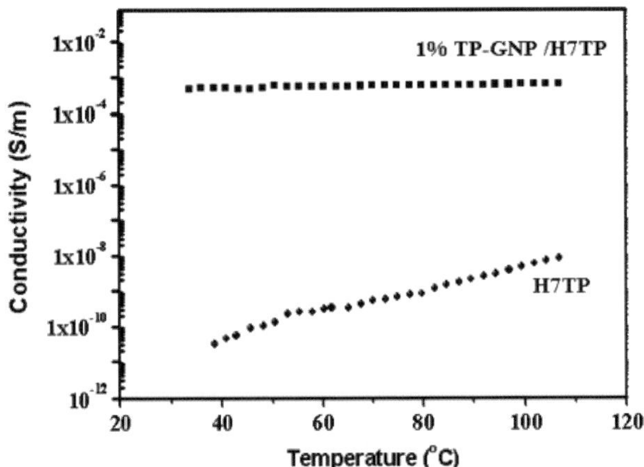

Fig. 6.   The variation of measured DC conductivity values as a function of temperature for 1% TP-GNPs mixed with H7TP and neat H7TP. The conductivities shown are obtained while cooling from the isotropic phase.[55]

mation of small chain-like aggregates of GNPs upon applying a DC field was proposed.

Very recently, Basova *et al.*[59] reported nanocomposites of discotic tetrasubstituted nickel phthalocyanine (NiPcR4) with hexadecylamine coated gold nanoparticles (AuNP-HA). Four composites of NiPcR4/AuNP-HA containing 0.1, 1, 2 and 5 wt.% of AuNP-HA were prepared and studied for their mesomorphic and electrical properties. All NiPcR4/AuNP-HA composites containing 0.1-5 wt.% of Au nanoparticles were found to be liquid-crystalline in nature. Nanocomposites exhibit two orders of magnitude higher conductivity compared to pure discotic liquid crystal. The lateral conductivity tends to increase with the increase of AuNP concentration.

Supreet *et al.* studied effect of dispersion of gold nanoparticles on the optical and electrical properties of a polar nitro-functionalized triphenylene (MNTP4) discotic liquid crystal.[60] Dispersions of hexanethiol-passivated GNPs of core diameter in range 1.2–2 nm in MNTP4 were prepared with 0.25% to 1% GNPs in DLC. A decrease in orientational order parameter (S), an increase in relaxation time (τ) for disc motion with GNPs in a columnar plastic phase (Col_p) and enhancement in dc electrical conductivity by several orders of magnitude at ambient conditions was observed upon doping GNPs.

2.2. *Elongated metallic NPs in DLCs*

Elongated NPs like, nanorods, nanofibres, nanoribbons, etc., are anisotropic one-dimensional nanomaterials which possess unique thermal, electrical, optical and mechanical properties. These nano architectures have many potential applications such as, nonlinear optical materials, photo-sensors, memory devices, etc. Similar to LCs, physical properties of elongated NPs are direction dependent. Therefore, control over their orientation in the desired direction is very important for many device applications. Because of their structural similarity, dispersion of elongated NPs in rod-shaped LCs is quite favorable and various metallic and semiconducting nanorods (NRs) have been dispersed in a variety of calamitic LCs.[36–39] However, gold nanorods (GNRs) are the only one-dimensional metallic nanoparticles which have so far been dispersed in DLCs.[61]

GNRs of different aspect ratios can be prepared via several methods,[62,63] however, the seed-growth methods developed by Murphy and El-Sayed groups[64,65] have received much attention due to their simplicity, better yield and formation of well-defined nanostructures. As prepared NRs are generally coated with a cetyltrimethylammonium bromide (CTAB) layer which prevents aggregation of NRs. To make these NRs compatible with hydrophobic liquid crystalline media, these NRs may be treated with alkanethiol. Unlike thiol-functionalized quasi-spherical NPs, thiol-passivated GNRs cannot be prepared in a single step. The replacement of CTAB by alkanethiol usually needs several rounds of ligand exchange reaction. GNRs display two plasmon bands; a weak transverse band in the visible region, like spherical GNPs, and a strong longitudinal band in the near-infrared region. The position of the longitudinal band red-shifts as the aspect ratio increases. This tunability of the plasmon band offers several applications for GNRs.[62,63]

To investigate the dispersion of GNRs in DLCs, we prepared GNRs[61] following the procedure of El-Sayed.[65] These NRs were found to be approximately 15 nm wide and 40 nm long with an aspect ratio of 2.7. The CTAB-coated GNRs were treated with dodecanethiol to obtain organic-soluble GNRs. Hexakis(pentyloxy)triphenylene (HPT), an archetypal DLC, was used to disperse these GNRs. Several nanocomposites of HPT and GNRs were prepared by mixing the two components in an organic solvent (dichloromethane), followed by removal of the solvent under vacuum. UV-vis spectroscopy, polarizing optical microscopy, differential scanning calorimetry, XRD and conductivity studies indicate that GNRs are dispersed in between the columns of discotic molecules. The nanocomposites exhibit a marked increase in electrical conductivity compared to pure triphenylene DLC. Conductivity of undoped HPT varies from $4.7 \cdot 10^{-10}$ Sm^{-1} at 65°C to $4.5 \cdot 10^{-9}$ Sm^{-1} at 122°C. The dispersion of 1% GNRs in HPT increases conductivity to $1.22 \cdot 10^{-6}$ Sm^{-1} at 121°C. Increasing the concentration of GNRs to 5%, increases the conductivity further by about one order of magnitude. In all the cases the conductivity in the mesophase increases with increase in temperature.

In the columnar phase, disc-shaped molecules can form a ribbon-like structure with the π planes of the aromatic molecules stacking in the direction of the long axis of the ribbon (Fig. 7). These ribbons are formed due to the association of many hexagonal columns.[66–69] Such molecular nanoribbons have recently gained importance because of their potential applications in electronic devices. Xiao *et al.* reported that a discotic contorted hexabenzocoronene derivative organizes into molecular stacks and that these stacks organize into cables or fibers.[69] A field effect transistor was constructed using an isolated nanofibre. Nanowires derived from triphenylene, perylene and decacyclene discotics have been used for explosive sensing.[66–68]

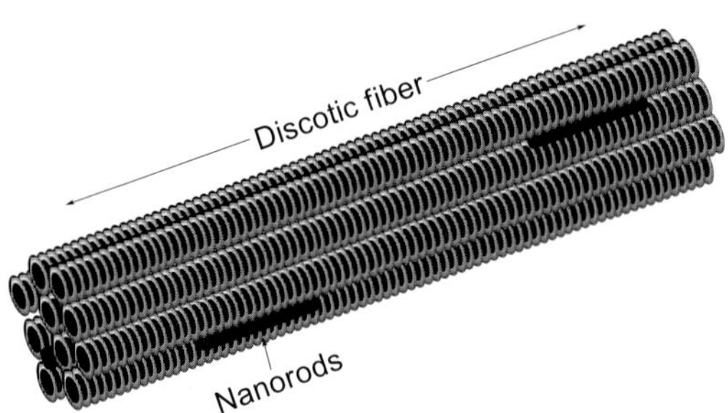

Fig. 7. Schematic illustration of the formation of ribbon-like structure by disc-shaped molecules and dispersion of elongated NPs in a columnar matrix.

With the idea that ribbon of discotic incarcerated GNRs may provide better 1D conducting properties, we looked into the formation of nanoribbons of undoped as well as GNRs doped triphenylene DLCs.[61] These nanoribbons are easily prepared when a chloroform solution of HPT or GNR-dispersed HPT was added to methanol. SEM images clearly demonstrate the formation of long ribbon like structures for both HPT and GNR-HPT composites. In the GNRs doped HPT nanoribbons, the GNRs are aligned with its long axis parallel to length of the ribbon (Fig. 7) as evident from the dark field scanning transmission electron microscopy (STEM) image. As GNRs imbedded discotic nanocomposites show enhanced conductivity, due to the insertion of NRs along the columnar axis, such nanocomposites could be better materials for devices like field effect transistors.

3. Semiconducting NPs in DLCs

3.1. *CdSe QDs in DLCs*

Nanoparticles made of semiconductor materials, often referred to as Quantum Dots (QDs), are the other quasi spherical NPs that have been extensively studied during the past decade because of their potential applications in the life sciences and materials science.[70–72] Compared to pure metallic NPs, much larger variety of QDs can be prepared via the combination of various elements, for example, QDs belonging to group II and VI elements (e.g., CdSe, CdS, CdTe, ZnO, ZnSe and so on), group IV and VI elements (e.g., PbS, PbSe, SnS and so on), and group III and V elements (e.g., InP, InS, InN and so on) have been prepared and extensively studied for various properties. Among all the QDs, CdSe QDs have received much attention in materials science due to their interesting photoluminescence properties.

High-quality monodisperse Cd-based QDs can be easily prepared by several methods.[73–75] Liquid crystalline media can also be used to prepare these NPs.[76] With the hope that excellent optical and electronic properties of CdSe QDs can be coupled with the self-organizing behavior of LCs and such LC-QD nanocomposites may exhibit mutually beneficial effects on various electro-optical properties, a number of QDs have been dispersed in various calamitic LCs.[77]

Kumar and Sagar studied the dispersion of CdSe QDs in DLCs.[78] Organic soluble, octadecylamine passivated CdSe QDs of two different sizes, 2.4 and 3.5 nm, were prepared and dispersed in a columnar matrix of hexabutyloxytriphenylene (H4TP) DLC. The formation of spherical particles with uniform sizes and shapes was confirmed by transmission electron microscopy (TEM). The narrow size distribution of the particles was inferred from the photoluminescence spectra of the QDs. The absorption and emission spectra show an apparent red-shift, as expected, with the increase in the size of the particle. Nanocomposites of DLC and CdSe QDs were prepared by mixing the two components in a low boiling solvent via sonication followed by removal of the solvent and drying in vacuum. Several composites with 1%, 2%, 3% and 5% of CdSe QDs in H4TP were prepared and analyzed using POM, DSC and XRD. No significant change in POM, DSC and XRD was observed indicating that the dispersion of QDs in small amount does not disturb the columnar phase of H4TP. Like metallic GNPs dispersion in DLCs, CdSe QDs also get dispersed in columnar matrix of DLCs. The hexagonal columnar lattice of the DLC remains unaffected by the insertion of QDs. Similar to GNPs (Figure 5), a random distribution of QDs in the columnar phase was visualized. The electrical conductivity of the composites was found to be enhanced by two orders of magnitude. The enhancement in the conductivity could be a result of the formation of electron donor–acceptor interactions between the electron-rich organic triphenylene and the inorganic semiconductor. The enhancement in the conductivity due to the formation of charge transfer complex has been well documented in TP donor and other acceptor like $AlCl_3$.[57]

3.2. *ZnO nanoparticles in DLCs*

Zinc oxide (ZnO) is a wide band gap semiconductor of the II–VI semiconductor group. It possesses a direct band gap of 3.37 eV and large excitonic binding energy of about 60 meV at room temperature.[79] ZnO NPs can be employed as a non-toxic alternative to metal chalcogenides. They have great application potential in devices like, light-emitting diodes, field-effect transistors, photo diodes, ultraviolet photo detectors, solar cells, UV light emitters, sensors and lasers.[80] The dispersion of ZnO NPs into calamitic ferroelectric liquid crystal (FLC) and nematic liquid crystal (NLC) have been investigated.[81,82] The addition of ZnO NPs in the SmC^* phase improves the optical contrast and reduces the threshold voltage of liquid crystal display devices. A physical model describing an interaction of ZnO NPs with the surrounding FLC molecules was proposed.[83] Doping of ZnO NPs in surface-stabilized FLCs was found to improve the alignment of the FLC molecules, and a field-induced reorientation process was also observed.[84] The role of ZnO NPs in ordering the liquid crystalline systems that can be used for photovoltaic applications was studied by Martinez-Miranda *et al.*[85] An improvement in the alignment of the liquid crystal with increasing weight percentage of ZnO nanoparticle was observed and a three orders of magnitude enhancement in the current generated was reported.

Supreet *et al.* studied the dispersions of ZnO nanoparticles (NPs) in the columnar matrix of discotic liquid crystals for the first time.[86] The inclusion of ZnO NPs into the columnar matrix enhances the orientational order in the columnar phase without affecting the two-dimensional hexagonal lattice of the mesophase. The alignment in homeotropic samples was also found to be better with the addition of the NPs. The real (ϵ') and imaginary (ϵ'') parts of the permittivity increase by a small amount in the dispersions (Fig. 8). The order parameter measured using the IR dichroism technique in the face-on geometry (homeotropic alignment) shows an enhancement for the composite system. The dc conductivity was also found to increase, albeit only by an order of magnitude, on addition of the NPs.

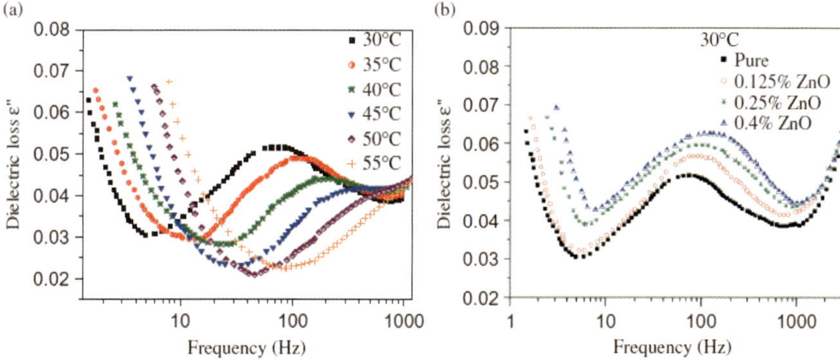

Fig. 8.   (a) Dielectric loss (ϵ'') verses frequency at different temperature for pure DLC. (b) ϵ'' as a function of frequency for pure and dispersed systems at 30°C. Reproduced with permission from Ref. 86

Chen *et al.* reported the preparation of self-assembled ZnO NPs modifed with a thiolated triphenylene (TP-S)-based DLC ligands (TP-S@ZnO) (Fig. 9).[87] Solar cells with a conventional device configuration "Indium tin oxide (ITO)/Poly(3,4-ethylenedioxythiophene) polystyrene sulfonate (PEDOT:PSS)/active layer/Lithium fluoride (LiF)/Aluminum (Al)" (Fig. 9) were prepared. The bulk heterojunction devices based on poly(3-hexylthiophene) (P3HT)/ZnO film showed a power conversion efficiency (PCE) of 0.46% which improves to 0.51% on annealing the sample at 130°C. The device based on TP-S@ZnO/P3HT showed an improvement with a PCE of 0.70%, which further improves to 0.95% on annealing the sample at 130°C.

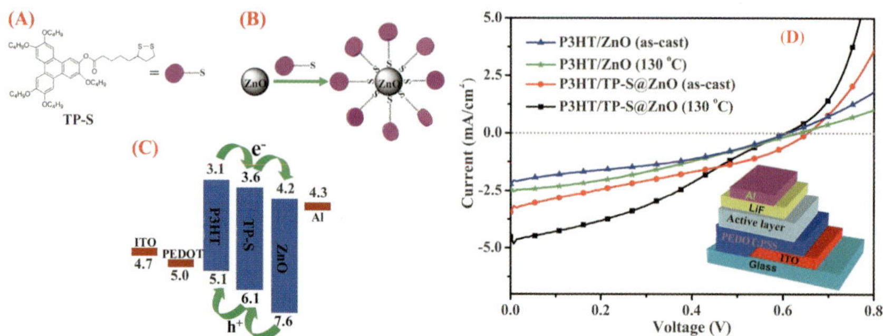

Fig. 9.   (A) Chemical structures of 2-[(5-(1,2-dithiolan-3-yl)pentanoate)]-3,6,7,10,11-pentakis(butoxy)triphenylene (TP-S), (B) a ZnO nanoparticle modified with triphenylene ligands (TP-S@ZnO) and (C) the energy level diagram for P3HT, TP-S and ZnO; (D) $J-V$ characteristics of photovoltaic cells based on P3HT/ZnO hybrid films with and without TP-S interfacial modifications before and after thermal treatment. The inset shows a schematic device configuration of the solar cell. Reproduced with permission from Ref. 87

4. Carbon NPs in DLCs

Carbon is an essential part of life. This sixth element of the periodic table has ability to form covalent bonds with the same (catenation) and other elements of the periodic table in almost countless variety.[88] Carbon occurs in all forms; zero-, one-, two- and three-dimensional geometry with insulating to conducting properties. While 2-D graphite and 3-D diamond are the known naturally occurring allotropes; 0-D fullerene and 1-D nanotubes can be synthesized. Carbon allotropes possess many exciting superlative properties, such as, diamond is the hardest substance, CNTs are the mechanically strongest materials, graphite exhibits the highest electric and heat conductivities, etc. Recently, synthetic nanocarbons (fullerene, CNTs and graphene) have received much attention in materials science due to their fascinating properties.[88] All the three types of carbon NPs (zero-dimensional fullerene, one-dimensional CNTs and two-dimensional graphene) have been coupled with LCs to hybridize their properties.

4.1. Quasi spherical carbon NPs in DLCs

Quasi spherical carbon NPs, commonly known as fullerenes or buckminsterfullerenes or buckyballs, are hollow spheres composed of carbon atoms. After the discovery of this new allotrope of carbon in 1985, a huge amount of work has been carried out on fullerenes in the fields of supramolecular chemistry and materials science. Among the various fullerenes, such as C_{60}, C_{70}, and C_{76}, the C_{60} ([60]fullerene) has been studied extensively. The C_{60} molecule is a strong electron acceptor capable of accepting from one to six electrons to form the corresponding anions. The donor-acceptor conjugates of C_{60} with various organic donors have recently been extensively studied as photo-induced electron and/or energy transfer systems, and highly efficient photovoltaic cells have been prepared from these conjugates.[89,90] Fullerenes can be easily functionalized to yield various organic soluble C_{60} derivatives. To improve the physical properties of various thermotropic liquid crystals, efforts have been made to attach C_{60} covalently to mesogens as well as to disperse in liquid crystalline media. Both calamitic and discotic liquid crystals have been used to study the effects of C_{60} doping on phase behavior, however, in this chapter only the dispersion of fullerenes in DLCs and their covalent attachment with discotic mesogens is presented briefly.

To attach C_{60} covalently with discotic molecules, primarily two synthetic routes have been explored. The first involves the Bingel reaction in which various discotic malonate derivatives are used.[91–93] The Prato reaction, using 1,3-dipolar cycloaddition reaction of C_{60} with an aldehyde terminated discotic molecule, is the other route to functionalize discotics with fullerenes (Fig. 10; Scheme 2).[94] A number of C_{60}–discotic adducts involving either one mesogen or two mesogens attached to a C_{60} molecule or two C_{60} molecules attached to one discotic molecule have been synthesized and studied for various properties.[91–104] The formation of adducts has been verified by usual spectroscopic, analytical and thermal techniques. Some representative examples are shown in Figure 11. A number of dendrimers

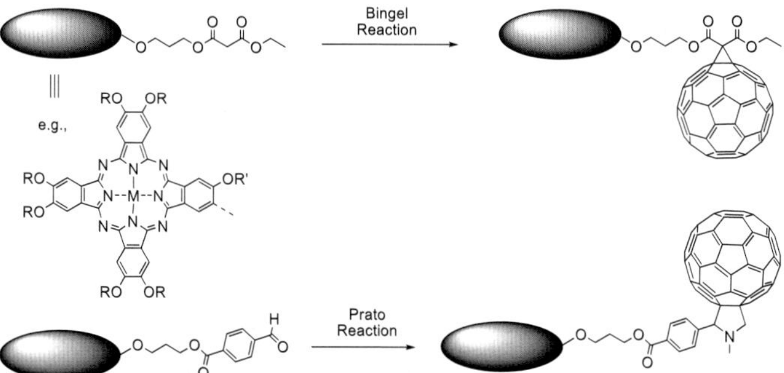

Fig. 10. Scheme 2: Functionalization of discotic molecules with C60 via Bingel and Prato reactions.

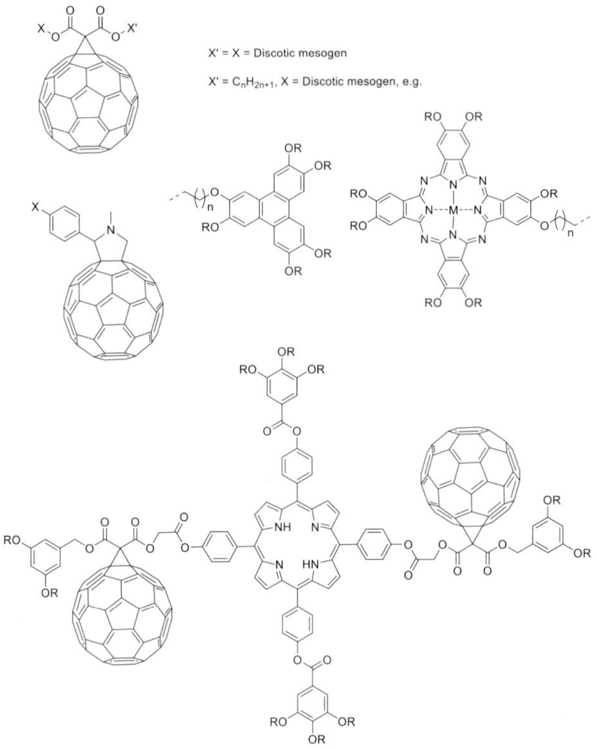

X' = X = Discotic mesogen

X' = CnH2n+1, X = Discotic mesogen, e.g.

Fig. 11. Some representative examples of discotic-C_{60} adducts.

have been attached to C_{60} which display nematic, smectic and columnar phases.[105–107] The attachment of optically active mesomorphic groups leads to the formation of chiral nematic phase. Liquid-crystalline hexa-adduct of C_{60} with chiral mesogens displays supramolecular helical organization.[106] These molecules have been considered as chiral nanoparticles having poles at the top and bottom of the structure, i.e. a molecular boojom. This could arise from spiralling of the local director of the chiral mesogens around the C_{60} core.

While a few C_{60}-discotic adducts were reported to be liquid crystalline in virgin state, other can be dispersed in small amount in a columnar matrix without disturbing the mesophase behavior of the host. Bushby and co-workers observed a two-dimensional hexagonal superlattice from the ordering of fullerenes within the hexagonal columnar liquid-crystal matrix formed by a fullerene derivative and a hexaphenyl hexaazatriphenylene discotic. It is proposed that to maximize fullerene–fullerene contact, the fullerenes form chains that wrap around the central column in every group of seven columns.[91] The dispersion of C_{60}–derivatives in DLCs may improve the order of the mesophase due to the formation of supramolecular structures.[91,103] A few C_{60}–discotic nanocomposites have been successfully used to fabricate efficient solar cells.[95,101,102]

4.2. *Carbon nanotubes in DLCs*

After the discovery of spherical synthetic carbon allotrope, fullerene, the existence of quasi-one-dimensional carbon nanotubes (CNTs) was reported by Iijima in the early 1990s.[108] CNTs are seamless hollow cylinders of graphite with a high aspect ratio. A CNT formed by rolling up a single graphene sheet is called as single wall CNTs (SWNTs), while nanotubes formed by several graphene layers are defined as multi wall CNTs (MWNTs). CNTs are either metallic or semiconducting, depending on their helicity. Accordingly their applications in the field of molecular electronics have been sought. Mechanically, CNTs have been reported to be the strongest material. Due to their remarkable electrical, mechanical and thermal properties, CNTs have emerged as one of the most widely studied nanomaterials during the past two decades.

Both, SWNTs and MWNTs have been dispersed in many LCs and their effects on the electro-optical properties of LCs are extensively studied by several researchers.[109–116] DLCs and CNTs exhibit many similarities, e.g., both are anisotropic materials which self-assemble in to hexagonal aggregates and exhibit 1D conducting properties. With the idea that cylindrical CNTs can be aligned in the cylindrical columns of discotic molecule (columnar mesophase), acid-purified SWNTs were tried to disperse into the columnar matrix of a triphenylene-based DLC.[117] However, it was observed that these purified SWNTs form aggregates in the mesophase even in a very small quantity. This could be due to noncompatibility of their chemical nature; DLCs are non-polar hydrophobic molecules while acid-purified SWNTs are polar hydrophilic materials.

Can functionalization of SWNTs with discotic mesogens create liquid crystalline SWNTs? To verify this hypothesis, SWNTs were covalently coupled with hexaalkoxytriphenylene mesogens.[117] Carboxylic acid functionalities of acid-purified SWNTs were first converted to reactive acid chlorides which on classical esterification with a hydroxyl functionalized triphenylene derivative yields discotic-functionalized nanotubes (f-SWNTs)

(Fig. 12; Scheme 3). Spectral and thermal analysis confirmed the formation of discotic-functionalized nanotubes. The number of discotic molecules attached to CNTs were not sufficient to bring the entire system liquid crystalline, however, these f-SWNTs were freely soluble in common organic solvents and therefore, they could be easily dispersed in organic-soluble DLCs. Accordingly, several composites of f-SWNTs and H4TP (having 1-10% of f-SWNTs in H4TP) were prepared and analyzed using POM, DSC and XRD. Results indicate insertion of the f-SWNTs in the columnar matrix occupying the space between the disc columns (Fig. 12; Scheme 3).

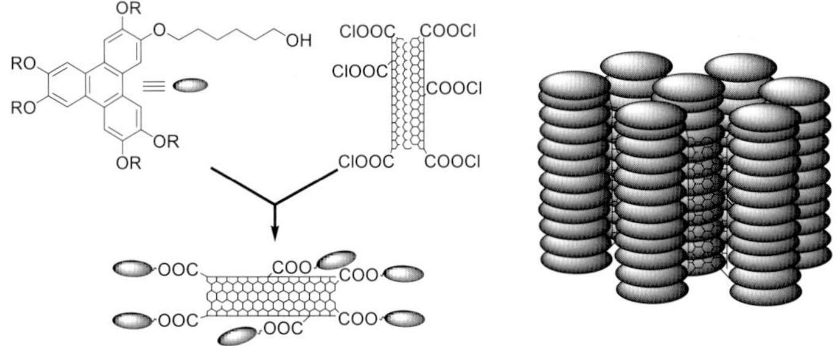

Fig. 12.   Scheme 3: Functionalization of SWNTs with discotics and their dispersion in a columnar matrix.

Organic soluble CNTs can also be prepared by attaching simple long aliphatic chains with acid functionalized CNTs. Octadecylamine (ODA)-functionalized SWNTs soluble in common organic solvents are now commercially available. Their dispersion in columnar phases of triphenylene and rufigallol-based discotic monomers and polymers was looked by Kumar and Bisoyi.[118] However, unlike discotic-functionalized SWNTs, which are more compatible with a discotic columnar phase, only a maximum of 2 wt% of SWNTs could be homogeneously dispersed in the columnar matrix of these room-temperature DLCs. The $\pi - \pi$ interactions of triphenylene molecules surrounding the SWNTs with the columnar phase forming triphenylene molecules likely stabilize the dispersion of f-SWNTs. As the columnar phase of DLCs can be aligned parallel or perpendicular to the surface, the CNTs present in the composites would also be oriented in the desired direction. It has recently been reported by Lee *at al.* that discotic ionic liquid crystals derived from triphenylene core serve as excellent dispersants for pristine SWNTs.[119] The nanocomposites exhibit anisotropic conducting properties upon shearing the sample, and the shear-induced orientation of the SWNTs was maintained for a long period at room temperature. Kilinc *et al.* studied electrical properties of mesomorphic bis[tetrakis(alkylthio)phthalocyaninato]lutetium(III) double decker complexes [(CnS)$_4$Pc]$_2$Lu(III) doped with SWNTs.[120] The conductivities of [(CnS)$_4$Pc]$_2$Lu(III)-SWNT composites increased in the order of 10^1 to 10^4 and the conduction mechanism also changed from ohmic to space charge limited conduction. The conductivity of the ordered film of [(C$_6$S)$_4$Pc]$_2$Lu(III) increases from $6.9 \cdot 10^{-6}$ Scm^{-2} to $3.5 \cdot 10^{-6}$ Scm^{-1} upon SWNT dispersion.[120]

Zilberman *et al.* prepared discotic hexa-peri-hexabenzocoronene-functionalized CNTs based sensors for the analysis of volatile organic compounds (VOCs), useful for detecting cancer.[121,122] The sensors were prepared on p-type Si wafers capped with a 2 μm thick thermally grown SiO$_2$ insulating layer. Ti/Pd interdigitate electrodes with an inter-electrode spacing of 100 μm were formed on the substrates by evaporation. Single wall CNTs dispersed in dimethylformamide were coated over electrodes by drop-casting followed by drying slowly at room temperature and finally solvent was removed at elevated temperature. The random networks of carbon nanotubes (RN-CNTs) so formed were then functionalized with discotic hexa-peri-hexabenzocoronene (HBC) derivatives. HBC-functionalized and unfunctionalized RN-CNT chemiresistors were electrically tested under exposure to various nonpolar alkanes like, octane, decane, etc. as well as to polar compounds like, alcohol and water (Fig. 13). The chemiresistors responses upon exposure to the analyte vapors were rapid and fully reversible upon switching back to dry air. Swelling of the organic film during exposure was observed. It was proposed that the expansion of the sponge-like organic overlayer creates scattering centers in the underlying RN-CNTs by physically distancing the CNTs at their intersections. The exact sensing mechanism has yet to be deduced.[122]

MWNTs have been mixed with naphthalene polymer based mesophase pitch.[123] Cho *et al.* mixed MWNTs with mesophase pitch (in the molten state) and successfully melt-spun into fibers containing 0.1 and 0.3 wt.% MWNTs.[124] Microstructural examination reveals that whereas the carbon fibers obtained from pure mesophase pitch had a radial texture of graphene layers, the nanotube-modified fibers had a random texture. Crawford and co-workers looked the capillary infiltration of naphthalene polymer, which exhibits a discotic nematic liquid crystal phase at elevated temperature, into multiwall carbon nanotubes.[125] The MWNTs were first oxidized at 700°C to open the nanotube tips. When a mixture of tip-opened MWNTs

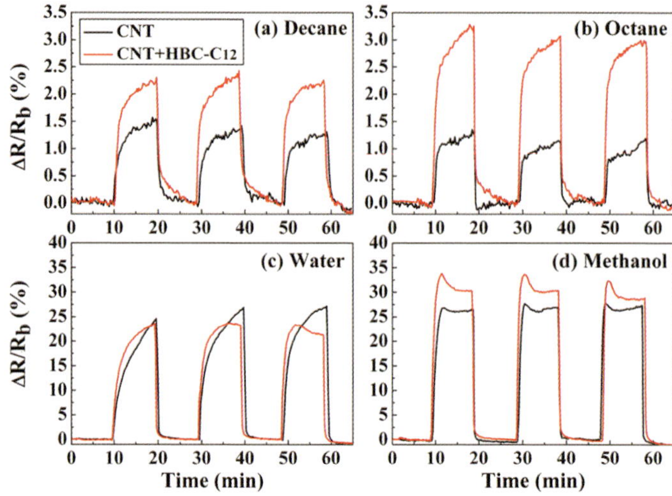

Fig. 13. Normalized resistance, $\Delta R/R_b$, of a RN-CNT sensor before and after the functionalization with a discontinuous HBCC12 layer drop cast from 10^{-4}M solution in toluene upon exposure to (a) decane and (b) octane in the vapor phase at $p_a/p_o = 1$, and to (c) water and (d) methanol in the vapor phase at $p_a/p_o = 1$. Reproduced with permission from Ref. 118

and finely ground solid naphthalene polymer were heated to 300°C, the polymer in the discotic nematic phase infiltrates into the nanotube cavities (Figure 14). High resolution transmission electron microscopy (HRTEM) was used to visualize the director profile inside the 5 nm cavity of a multiwall carbon nanotube. The discotic planes lie approximately parallel to the tube sidewalls due to strong - interactions at the interface.

4.3. Graphene in DLCs

Though the presence of graphene layers in graphite is known for a long time, its synthesis and characterization could be achieved only recently. Graphene, the two-dimensional allotrope of carbon, is a monolayer of carbon atoms arranged in a honeycomb lattice. This nanomaterial has recently been found to display outstanding electrical, optical, mechanical, transport and thermal properties and, therefore, its applications in many devices has been sought.[126,127] As mentioned earlier, most of the DLCs are derived from polycyclic aromatic hydrocarbon (PAH) cores. Benzene is the first and smallest PAH core, while graphene may be considered as

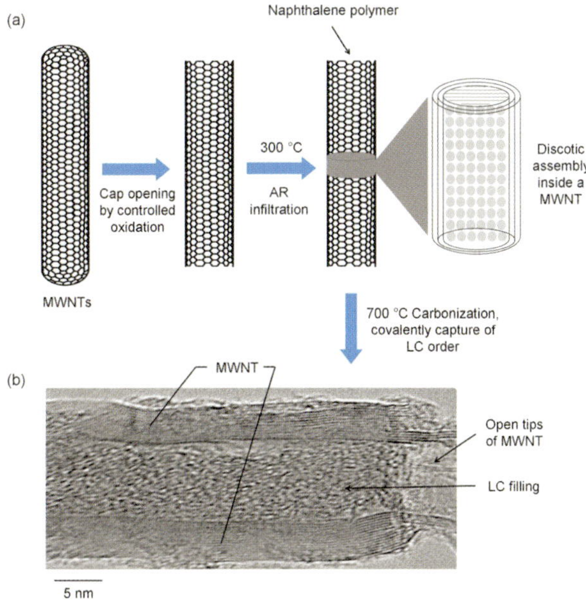

Fig. 14. Schematic illustration of fabrication process to infiltrate naphthalene polymer into carbon nanotube cavities (a) and the corresponding HRTEM image of the liquid crystal director field (b). Reproduced with permission from Ref. 121

the ultimate member. In between them, there exist several PAH cores such as, naphthalene, phenanthrene, pyrene, triphenylene, perylene, dibenzopyrene, truxene, decacyclene, hexabenzocoronene, etc., which form DLCs on appropriate peripheral substitution.[2] As graphene is a sheet-like nanoobject with very high aspect ratio, it was anticipated that upon dispersion in sufficiently high concentrations it would exhibit liquid crystalline phase behaviour. This has indeed been proved by Pasquali and co-workers.[128] Graphite spontaneously exfoliates into single-layer graphene in chlorosulphonic acid and dissolves at isotropic phase as high as 2 mg/mL. When the precipitated soluble graphene powder was re-dispersed in about 20 mg/mL concentration and centrifuged, the spontaneous formation of liquid crystalline phase was observed. The observed liquid crystalline Schlieren texture was very similar to typical discotic nematic mesophase texture. A number of studies have been carried out to prepare discotic lyotropic LCs from graphene oxide.[129–132] However, here we have covered only the dispersion of graphene in thermotropic DLCs.

Kumar and co-workers looked the dispersion of functionalized reduced graphene oxide in a rufigallol-based room-temperature DLC namely 1,5-dihydroxy-2,3,6,7-tetrakis(3,7-dimethyloctyloxy)-9,10-anthraquinone.[131] This material is not only liquid crystalline at room temperature and therefore easy to handle but also electron deficient which can help the self-assembly via donor-acceptor interactions. Organic soluble, octadecylamine-functionalized reduced graphene oxide (f-graphene) was prepared and characterized from spectral, thermal and X-ray diffraction studies. Dispersion of f-graphene (1% and 5%) in DLC was carried out by sonicating a dichloromethane solution of DLC and f-graphene for 30 min followed by removal of the solvent under vacuum. These DLC–graphene nanocomposites were analyzed by UV-Vis spectroscopy, POM, DSC, XRD, Raman spectroscopy, scanning electron microscopy (SEM) and conductivity studies. An ordered sandwich like structure, where the discotic molecules form columnar structures on graphene sheets was observed in these nanocomposites. Cryo-SEM and SEM images provide evidence for this ordering (Fig. 15).

5. Summary and outlook

The dispersion of NPs in self-organizing supramolecular architectures is currently a subject of great importance. Liquid crystalline state represents a fascinating state of matter which combines order and mobility at molecular level to macroscopic levels. Due to their ordered dynamic nature, liquid crystals are very sensitive to external stimuli such as, boundary conditions, temperature, magnetic field, electric field, mechanical stress, etc. LCs in the form of liquid crystal displays (LCDs) have become part and parcel of our everyday life. There are several other applications of LCs. Recently, they have entered in the fascinating domains of nanoscience and nanotechnology. NPs exhibit interesting physical properties. Designing nanomaterials which are able to self-assemble into functional superstructures in multiple directions is a subject of great interest and using liquid crystals as an organizing medium to induce the self-assembly of nanoparticles could be an attractive methodology. A variety of LCs have been used to disperse zero-, one- and two-dimensional NPs.

Though the dispersion of NPs in DLCs has emerged in the scientific literature only 10 years ago, the topic has made significant advances during this period. All types of NPs; zero-dimensional, one-dimensional, two-dimensional, metallic, semiconducting and carbon NPs, have been dis-

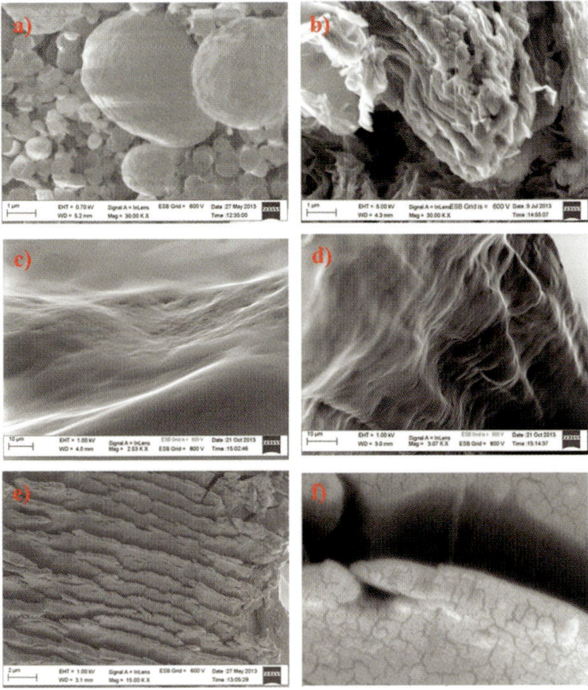

Fig. 15.   (a) Cryo-SEM image of RTAQ. (b) SEM image of f-graphene showing layered structures forming crumpled bundles. (c) SEM image of RTAQ (shows no prominent features). (d) SEM image of 1GrAQ showing a layered arrangement. (e) Cryo-SEM image of the 1GrAQ composite also showing a layered structure. (f) Enlarged portion of (e) showing graphene layers covered by a layer of discotics.[130]

persed in monomeric and polymeric DLCs displaying mesophases at room-temperature or at elevated temperatures. These hybrid systems can find applications in a wide range of fields, including photovoltaic solar cells, thin film transistors, photoconductors, sensors and so on. The dispersion of NPs in DLCs imparts significant changes in their physical properties, for example, the electrical conductivity of the system increases by several orders of magnitude compared with the pure discotic system. As hundreds of DLCs and NPs can be prepared, limitless hybrids are possible to explore their physical properties. However, only a few physical studies, such as the electrical conductivity and dielectric behavior of a few DLC-NP composites have so far been explored. Many other studies, such as charge mobility, alignment and anisotropic physical properties, of DLC-NP hybrids have to be undertaken to realize their full potential for application in various devices. No doubt, DLCs will play more prevalent roles in nanoscience and nanotechnology in the near future. However, there are several difficulties associated with these hybrid systems such as, phase segregation, decomposition of NPs at higher temperature, alignment, enhancement of ionic conductivity, etc., which have to be solved to materialized their applications.

References

1. J. W. Goodby, P. J. Collings, T. Kato, C. Tschierske, H. Gleeson, and P. Raynes, eds., *Handbook of Liquid Crystals.* vol. III, Wiley-VCH (2014).
2. S. Kumar, *Chemistry of discotic liquid crystals: from monomers to polymers.* CRC press (2010).
3. F. Reinitzer, Beiträge zur kenntniss des cholesterins, *Monatshefte für Chemie/Chemical Monthly.* **9**(1), 421–441 (1888).
4. O. Lehmann, On flowing crystals, *Zeitschrift für Physikalische Chemie.* **4**, 462 (1889).
5. S. Chandrasekhar, B. Sadashiva, and K. Suresh, Liquid crystals of disc-like molecules, *Pramana.* **9**(5), 471–480 (1977).
6. H. K. Bisoyi and S. Kumar, Discotic nematic liquid crystals: science and technology, *Chem. Soc. Rev.* **39**(1), 264–285 (2010).
7. H. K. Bisoyi and S. Kumar, Liquid-crystal nanoscience: an emerging avenue of soft self-assembly, *Chem. Soc. Rev.* **40**(1), 306–319 (2011).
8. N. Boden, R. Bushby, J. Clements, and B. Movaghar, Device applications of charge transport in discotic liquid crystals, *J. Mater. Chem.* **9**(9), 2081–2086 (1999).
9. R. J. Bushby and O. R. Lozman, Discotic liquid crystals 25 years on, *Curr. Opin. Colloid Interface Sci.* **7**(5), 343–354 (2002).
10. R. J. Bushby and O. R. Lozman, Photoconducting liquid crystals, *Current Opinion in Solid State and Materials Science.* **6**, 569–578 (2002).
11. R. J. Bushby and K. Kawata, Liquid crystals that affected the world: discotic liquid crystals, *Liq. Cryst.* **38**(11-12), 1415–1426 (2011).
12. S. Chen and S. H. Eichhorn, Ionic discotic liquid crystals, *Isr. J. Chem.* **52**(10), 830–843 (2012).
13. B. Donnio, D. Guillon, R. Deschenaux, and D. Bruce. Metallomesogens, chapter 7.9. In eds. J. McCleverty and T. Meyer, *Comprehensive Coordination Chemistry II, Vol. 7*, pp. 357–627. Elsevier: Oxford, UK (2003).
14. J. W. Goodby, I. Saez, S. Cowling, V. Gortz, M. Draper, A. Hall, S. Sia, G. Cosquer, S. Lee, and E. Raynes, Transmission and amplification of information and properties in nanostructured liquid crystals, *Angew. Chem. (Int. Ed.).* **47**(15), 2754–2787 (2008).
15. B. R. Kaafarani, Discotic liquid crystals for opto-electronic applications, *Chem. Mater.* **23**(3), 378–396 (2010).

16. T. Kato, N. Mizoshita, and K. Kishimoto, Functional liquid-crystalline assemblies: Self-organized soft materials, *Angew. Chem. (Int. Ed.).* **45**(1), 38–68 (2006).

17. S. Kumar, Recent developments in the chemistry of triphenylene-based discotic liquid crystals, *Liq. Cryst.* **31**(8), 1037–1059 (2004).

18. S. Kumar, Triphenylene based discotic liquid crystal dimers, oligomers and polymers, *Liq. Cryst.* **32**(9), 1089–1113 (2005).

19. S. Kumar, Self-organization of disc-like molecules: chemical aspects, *Chem. Soc. Rev.* **35**(1), 83–109 (2006).

20. S. Kumar, Rufigallol-based self-assembled supramolecular architectures, *Phase Transitions.* **81**(1), 113–128 (2008).

21. S. Kumar, Hierarchical discs, *Liq. Cryst. Today.* **18**(1), 2–27 (2009).

22. S. Kumar, Playing with discs, *Liq. Cryst.* **36**(6-7), 607–638 (2009).

23. S. Kumar, Functional discotic liquid crystals, *Isr. J. Chem.* **52**(10), 820–829 (2012).

24. S. Laschat, A. Baro, N. Steinke, F. Giesselmann, C. Hägele, G. Scalia, R. Judele, E. Kapatsina, S. Sauer, A. Schreivogel, and M. Tosoni, Discotic liquid crystals: From tailor-made synthesis to plastic electronics, *Angew. Chem. (Int. Ed.).* **46**(26), 4832–4887 (2007).

25. K. Ohta, K. Hatsusaka, M. Sugibayashi, M. Ariyoshi, K. Ban, F. Maeda, R. Naito, K. Nishizawa, A. M. Van de Craats, and J. M. Warman, Discotic liquid crystalline semiconductors, *Mol. Cryst. Liq. Cryst.* **397**(1), 25–45 (2003).

26. S. K. Pal, S. Setia, B. Avinash, and S. Kumar, Triphenylene-based discotic liquid crystals: recent advances, *Liq. Cryst.* **40**(12), 1769–1816 (2013).

27. W. Pisula, X. Feng, and K. Müllen, Charge-carrier transporting graphene-type molecules, *Chem. Mater.* **23**(3), 554–567 (2010).

28. S. Sergeyev, W. Pisula, and Y. Geerts, Discotic liquid crystals: A new generation of organic semiconductors, *Chem. Soc. Rev.* **36**(12), 1902–1929 (2007).

29. C. Tschierske, Liquid crystal engineering - new complex mesophase structures and their relations to polymer morphologies, nanoscale patterning and crystal engineering, *Chem. Soc. Rev.* **36**(12), 1930–1970 (2007).

30. J. Wu, W. Pisula, and K. Müllen, Graphenes as potential material for electronics, *Chem. Rev.* **107**(3), 718–747 (2007).

31. C. Burda, X. Chen, R. Narayanan, and M. A. El-Sayed, Chemistry and properties of nanocrystals of different shapes, *Chem. Rev.* **105**(4), 1025–1102 (2005).

32. M.-C. Daniel and D. Astruc, Gold nanoparticles: assembly, supramolecular chemistry, quantum-size-related properties, and applications toward biology, catalysis, and nanotechnology, *Chem. Rev.* **104**(1), 293–346 (2004).

33. C. N. R. Rao, A. Müller, and A. K. Cheetham, *The chemistry of nanomaterials: synthesis, properties and applications.* John Wiley & Sons (2006).

34. H. K. Bisoyi and S. Kumar, Carbon-based liquid crystals: art and science, *Liq. Cryst.* **38**(11-12), 1427–1449 (2011).

35. Y. A. Garbovskiy and A. V. Glushchenko, Liquid crystalline colloids

of nanoparticles: preparation, properties, and applications, *Solid State Physics.* **62**, 1–74 (2010).

36. J. P. F. Lagerwall and G. Scalia, A new era for liquid crystal research: Applications of liquid crystals in soft matter nano-, bio- and microtechnology, *Curr. Appl. Phys.* **12**(6), 1387–1412 (2012).

37. G. L. Nealon, R. Greget, C. Dominguez, Z. T. Nagy, D. Guillon, J.-L. Gallani, and B. Donnio, Liquid-crystalline nanoparticles: Hybrid design and mesophase structures, *Beilstein J. Org. Chem.* **8**, 349–370 (2012).

38. O. Stamatoiu, J. Mirzaei, X. Feng, and T. Hegmann, Nanoparticles in liquid crystals and liquid crystalline nanoparticles, *Topics Current Chemistry.* **318**, 331–393 (2012).

39. S. Umadevi, V. Ganesh, and T. Hegmann. Nanoparticles: Additives and building blocks for liquid crystal phases. In eds. J. W. Goodby, P. J. Collings, T. Kato, C. Tschierske, H. Gleeson, and P. Raynes, *Handbook of Liquid Crystals, vol. VI*, pp. 27–76. Wiley-VCH, Weinheim, Germany (2014).

40. S. Kumar, Discotic liquid crystal-nanoparticle hybrid systems, *NPG Asia Materials.* **6**(1), e82 (2014).

41. S. Kumar, Nanoparticles in the supramolecular order of discotic liquid crystals, *Liq. Cryst.* **41**(3), 353–367 (2014).

42. C. Louis and O. Pluchery, *Gold nanoparticles for physics, chemistry and biology.* World Scientific (2012).

43. P. Zhao, N. Li, and D. Astruc, State of the art in gold nanoparticle synthesis, *Coord. Chem. Rev.* **257**(3), 638–665 (2013).

44. W. Paul and C. Sharma, Blood compatibility studies of swarna bhasma (gold bhasma), an ayurvedic drug, *International journal of Ayurveda research.* **2**(1), 14 (2011).

45. M. Faraday, The bakerian lecture: experimental relations of gold (and other metals) to light, *Philosophical Transactions of the Royal Society of London.* **147**, 145–181 (1857).

46. M. Giersig and P. Mulvaney, Preparation of ordered colloid monolayers by electrophoretic deposition, *Langmuir.* **9**(12), 3408–3413 (1993).

47. M. Brust, J. Fink, D. Bethell, D. Schiffrin, and C. Kiely, Synthesis and reactions of functionalised gold nanoparticles, *J. Chem. Soc., Chem. Commun.* (16), 1655–1656 (1995).

48. M. Brust, M. Walker, D. Bethell, D. J. Schiffrin, and R. Whyman, Synthesis of thiol-derivatised gold nanoparticles in a two-phase liquid-liquid system, *J. Chem. Soc., Chem. Commun.* (7), 801–802 (1994).

49. M. J. Hostetler, J. E. Wingate, C.-J. Zhong, J. E. Harris, R. W. Vachet, M. R. Clark, J. D. Londono, S. J. Green, J. J. Stokes, and G. D. Wignall, Alkanethiolate gold cluster molecules with core diameters from 1.5 to 5.2 nm: core and monolayer properties as a function of core size, *Langmuir.* **14**(1), 17–30 (1998).

50. S. Kumar and V. Lakshminarayanan, Inclusion of gold nanoparticles into a discotic liquid crystalline matrix, *Chem. Commun.* (14), 1600–1601 (2004).

51. S. Marguet, D. Markovitsi, P. Millie, H. Sigal, and S. Kumar, Influence of disorder on electronic excited states: an experimental and numerical study

of alkylthiotriphenylene columnar phases, *J. Phys. Chem. B.* **102**(24), 4697–4710 (1998).

52. S. Kumar and M. Manickam, Oxidative trimerization of o-dialkoxybenzenes tohexaalkoxytriphenylenes: molybdenum (v) chloride as a novel reagent, *Chem. Commun.* (17), 1615–1666 (1997).

53. S. Kumar, S. K. Varshney, and D. Chauhan, Room-temperature discotic nematic liquid crystals, *Mol. Cryst. Liq. Cryst.* **396**(1), 241–250 (2003).

54. D. Vijayaraghavan and S. Kumar, Self-assembled superlattices of gold nanoparticles in a discotic liquid crystal, *Mol. Cryst. Liq. Cryst.* **508**(1), 101/[463]–114/[476] (2009).

55. S. Kumar, S. K. Pal, P. S. Kumar, and V. Lakshminarayanan, Novel conducting nanocomposites: synthesis of triphenylene-covered gold nanoparticles and their insertion into a columnar matrix, *Soft Matter.* **3**(7), 896–900 (2007).

56. Z. Shen, M. Yamada, and M. Miyake, Control of stripelike and hexagonal self-assembly of gold nanoparticles by the tuning of interactions between triphenylene ligands, *J. Am. Chem. Soc.* **129**(46), 14271–14280 (2007).

57. V. Balagurusamy, S. K. Prasad, S. Chandrasekhar, S. Kumar, M. Manickam, and C. Yelamaggad, Quasi-one dimensional electrical conductivity and thermoelectric power studies on a discotic liquid crystal, *Pramana.* **53**(1), 3–11 (1999).

58. L. A. Holt, R. J. Bushby, S. D. Evans, A. Burgess, and G. Seeley, A 106-fold enhancement in the conductivity of a discotic liquid crystal doped with only 1%(w/w) gold nanoparticles, *J. Appl. Phys.* **103**(6), 063712 (2008).

59. T. V. Basova, R. G. Parkhomenko, I. K. Igumenov, A. Hassan, M. Durmu, A. e. G. Gürek, and V. Ahsen, Composites of liquid crystalline nickel phthalocyanine with gold nanoparticles: Liquid crystalline behaviour and optical properties, *Dyes and Pigments.* **111**, 58–63 (2014).

60. Supreet, R. Pratibha, S. Kumar, and K. Raina, Effect of dispersion of gold nanoparticles on the optical and electrical properties of discotic liquid crystal, *Liq. Cryst.* **41**(7), 933–939 (2014).

61. B. Avinash, V. Lakshminarayanan, S. Kumar, and J. Vij, Gold nanorods embedded discotic nanoribbons, *Chem. Commun.* **49**(10), 978–980 (2013).

62. X. Huang, S. Neretina, and M. A. El Sayed, Gold nanorods: from synthesis and properties to biological and biomedical applications, *Adv. Mater.* **21**(48), 4880–4910 (2009).

63. C. J. Murphy, L. B. Thompson, D. J. Chernak, J. A. Yang, S. T. Sivapalan, S. P. Boulos, J. Huang, A. M. Alkilany, and P. N. Sisco, Gold nanorod crystal growth: from seed-mediated synthesis to nanoscale sculpting, *Curr. Opin. Colloid Interface Sci.* **16**(2), 128–134 (2011).

64. N. R. Jana, L. Gearheart, and C. J. Murphy, Seed-mediated growth approach for shape-controlled synthesis of spheroidal and rod-like gold nanoparticles using a surfactant template, *Adv. Mater.* **13**(18), 1389 (2001).

65. B. Nikoobakht and M. A. El-Sayed, Preparation and growth mechanism of gold nanorods (NRs) using seed-mediated growth method, *Chem. Mater.* **15**(10), 1957–1962 (2003).

66. Y. Che, X. Yang, G. Liu, C. Yu, H. Ji, J. Zuo, J. Zhao, and L. Zang, Ultrathin n-type organic nanoribbons with high photoconductivity and application in optoelectronic vapor sensing of explosives, *J. Am. Chem. Soc.* **132**(16), 5743–5750 (2010).

67. H. Wang, X. Xu, L. Li, C. Yang, and H.-F. Ji, Optoelectronic property and sensing applications of crystalline nano/microwires of decacyclene, *Micro & Nano Letters, IET.* **6**(9), 763–766 (2011).

68. H. Wang, X. Xu, A. Kojtari, and H.-F. Ji, Triphenylene nano/microwires for sensing nitroaromatics, *J. Phys. Chem. C.* **115**(41), 20091–20096 (2011).

69. S. Xiao, J. Tang, T. Beetz, X. Guo, N. Tremblay, T. Siegrist, Y. Zhu, M. Steigerwald, and C. Nuckolls, Transferring self-assembled, nanoscale cables into electrical devices, *J. Am. Chem. Soc.* **128**(33), 10700–10701 (2006).

70. D. Bera, L. Qian, T.-K. Tseng, and P. H. Holloway, Quantum dots and their multimodal applications: a review, *Materials.* **3**(4), 2260–2345 (2010).

71. X. Michalet, F. Pinaud, L. Bentolila, J. Tsay, S. Doose, J. Li, G. Sundaresan, A. Wu, S. Gambhir, and S. Weiss, Quantum dots for live cells, in vivo imaging, and diagnostics, *Science.* **307**(5709), 538–544 (2005).

72. O. E. Semonin, J. M. Luther, and M. C. Beard, Quantum dots for next-generation photovoltaics, *Mater. Today.* **15**(11), 508–515 (2012).

73. B. L. Cushing, V. L. Kolesnichenko, and C. J. O'Connor, Recent advances in the liquid-phase syntheses of inorganic nanoparticles, *Chem. Rev.* **104**(9), 3893–3946 (2004).

74. C. Murray, D. J. Norris, and M. G. Bawendi, Synthesis and characterization of nearly monodisperse cde (e= sulfur, selenium, tellurium) semiconductor nanocrystallites, *J. Am. Chem. Soc.* **115**(19), 8706–8715 (1993).

75. C. Rao, S. Vivekchand, K. Biswas, and A. Govindaraj, Synthesis of inorganic nanomaterials, *Dalton Transactions.* (34), 3728–3749 (2007).

76. *Block Copolymer Templated Synthesis and Organization of Semiconductor Nanocrystals*, vol. Macromolecular symposia 289(1). Wiley Online Library (2010).

77. J. Mirzaei, M. Reznikov, and T. Hegmann, Quantum dots as liquid crystal dopants, *J. Mater. Chem.* **22**(42), 22350–22365 (2012).

78. S. Kumar and L. K. Sagar, Cdse quantum dots in a columnar matrix, *Chem. Commun.* **47**(44), 12182–12184 (2011).

79. Ü. Özgür, Y. I. Alivov, C. Liu, A. Teke, M. Reshchikov, S. Do an, V. Avrutin, S.-J. Cho, and H. Morkoc, A comprehensive review of zno materials and devices, *J. Appl. Phys.* **98**(4), 041301 (2005).

80. J. L. Gomez and O. Tigli, Zinc oxide nanostructures: from growth to application, *J. Mater. Sci.* **48**(2), 612–624 (2013).

81. H. Jiang and N. Toshima, Low driving voltage of a liquid crystal device fabricated from 4'-pentyl-4-biphenylcarbonitrile doped with environmentally friendly zno nanoparticles, *Chem. Lett.* **38**(6), 566–567 (2009).

82. T. Joshi, A. Kumar, J. Prakash, and A. M. Biradar, Low power operation of ferroelectric liquid crystal system dispersed with zinc oxide nanoparticles, *Appl. Phys. Lett.* **96**(25) (2010).

83. L.-S. Li and J. Y. Huang, Tailoring switching properties of dipolar species in

ferroelectric liquid crystal with zno nanoparticles, *J. Phys. D: Appl. Phys.* **42**, 125413 (2009).

84. J. Huang, L. Li, and M. Chen, Probing molecular binding effect from zinc oxide nanocrystal doping in surface-stabilized ferroelectric liquid crystal with two-dimensional infrared correlation technique, *J. Phys. Chem. C.* **112**, 5410–5415 (2008).

85. L. Martinez-Miranda, K. M. Traister, I. Meléndez-Rodríguez, and L. Salamanca-Riba, Liquid crystal-zno nanoparticle photovoltaics: Role of nanoparticles in ordering the liquid crystal, *Appl. Phys. Lett.* **97**(22), 223301 (2010).

86. Supreet, S. Kumar, K. Raina, and R. Pratibha, Enhanced stability of the columnar matrix in a discotic liquid crystal by insertion of zno nanoparticles, *Liq. Cryst.* **40**(2), 228–236 (2013).

87. X. Chen, L. Chen, and Y. Chen, Self-assembly of discotic liquid crystal decorated zno nanoparticles for efficient hybrid solar cells, *RSC Advances.* **4**(7), 3627–3632 (2014).

88. A. Hirsch, The era of carbon allotropes, *Nat. Mater.* **9**(11), 868–871 (2010).

89. C.-Z. Li, H.-L. Yip, and A. K.-Y. Jen, Functional fullerenes for organic photovoltaics, *J. Mater. Chem.* **22**(10), 4161–4177 (2012).

90. L. K. Shrestha, Q. Ji, T. Mori, K. Miyazawa, Y. Yamauchi, J. P. Hill, and K. Ariga, Fullerene nanoarchitectonics: from zero to higher dimensions, *Chemistry - An Asian Journal.* **8**, 1662–1679 (2013).

91. R. Bushby, I. Hamley, Q. Liu, O. Lozman, and J. Lydon, Self-assembled columns of fullerene, *J. Mater. Chem.* **15**(41), 4429–4434 (2005).

92. R. Deschenaux, B. Donnio, and D. Guillon, Liquid-crystalline fullerodendrimers, *New J. Chem.* **31**(7), 1064–1073 (2007).

93. M. Manickam, A. Smith, M. Belloni, E. J. Shelley, P. R. Ashton, N. Spencer, and J. A. Preece, Introduction of bis-discotic and bis-calamitic mesogenic addends to c60, *Liq. Cryst.* **29**(4), 497–504 (2002).

94. F. Yang, H. Guo, J. Xie, Z. Liu, and B. Xu, Synthesis and mesomorphic property of novel discotic c60-triphenylene derivative, *Letters in Organic Chemistry.* **8**, 599–602 (2011).

95. Q. D. Dao, T. Hori, K. Fukumura, T. Masuda, T. Kamikado, A. Fujii, Y. Shimizu, and M. Ozaki, Efficiency enhancement in mesogenic-phthalocyanine-based solar cells with processing additives, *Appl. Phys. Lett.* **101**(26), 263301 (2012).

96. A. de la Escosura, M. V. Martínez-Díaz, J. Barberá, and T. Torres, Self-organization of phthalocyanine-[60] fullerene dyads in liquid crystals, *The Journal of organic chemistry.* **73**(4), 1475–1480 (2008).

97. T. Kamei, T. Kato, E. Itoh, and K. Ohta, Discotic liquid crystals of transition metal complexes 47: synthesis of phthalocyanine-fullerene dyads showing spontaneous homeotropic alignment, *J. Porph. Phthalocyanines.* **16**(12), 1261–1275 (2012).

98. Y. H. Geerts, O. Debever, C. Amato, and S. Sergeyev, Synthesis of mesogenic phthalocyanine-c60 donor - acceptor dyads designed for molecular heterojunction photovoltaic devices, *Beilstein J. Org. Chem.* **5**(1), 49 (2009).

99. H. Hayashi, W. Nihashi, T. Umeyama, Y. Matano, S. Seki, Y. Shimizu, and H. Imahori, Segregated donor-acceptor columns in liquid crystals that exhibit highly efficient ambipolar charge transport, *J. Am. Chem. Soc.* **133** (28), 10736–10739 (2011).

100. M. Ince, M. V. Martínez-Díaz, J. Barberá, and T. Torres, Liquid crystalline phthalocyanine-fullerene dyads, *J. Mater. Chem.* **21**(5), 1531–1536 (2011).

101. M. Jurow, B. Hageman, E. DiMasi, C. Nam, C. Pabon, C. T. Blackc, and C. M. Drain, Controlling morphology and molecular packing of alkane substituted phthalocyanine blend bulk heterojunction solar cells, *J. Mater. Chem. A* (2013).

102. Q. Sun, L. Dai, X. Zhou, L. Li, and Q. Li, Bilayer- and bulk-heterojunction solar cells using liquid crystalline porphyrins as donors by solution processing, *Appl. Phys. Lett.* **91**(25), 253505 (2007).

103. C.-L. Wang, W.-B. Zhang, C.-H. Hsu, H.-J. Sun, R. M. Van Horn, Y. Tu, D. V. Anokhin, D. A. Ivanov, and S. Z. D. Cheng, A supramolecular structure with an alternating arrangement of donors and acceptors constructed by a trans-di-c-60-substituted zn porphyrin derivative in the solid state, *Soft Matter.* **7**(13), 6135–6143 (2011).

104. C.-L. Wang, W.-B. Zhang, H.-J. Sun, R. M. Van Horn, R. R. Kulkarni, C.-C. Tsai, C.-S. Hsu, B. Lotz, X. Gong, and S. Z. D. Cheng, A supramolecular "double-cable" structure with a 129(44) helix in a columnar porphyrin-c-60 dyad and its application in polymer solar cells, *Adv. Energy Mater.* **2**(11), 1375–1382 (2012).

105. S. Campidelli, R. Deschenaux, J. Eckert, D. Guillon, and J. Nierengarten, Liquid-crystalline fullerene-oligophenylenevinylene conjugates, *Chem. Commun.* (6), 656–657 (2002).

106. S. Campidelli, T. Brandmueller, A. Hirsch, I. M. Saez, J. W. Goodby, and R. Deschenaux, An optically-active liquid-crystalline hexa-adduct of [60]fullerene which displays supramolecular helical organization, *Chem. Commun.* (41), 4282–4284 (2006).

107. J. Lenoble, S. Campidelli, N. Maringa, B. Donnio, D. Guillon, N. Yevlampieva, and R. Deschenaux, Liquid-crystalline janus-type fullero-dendrimers displaying tunable smectic-columnar mesomorphism, *J. Am. Chem. Soc.* **129**(32), 9941–9952 (2007).

108. S. Iijima, Helical microtubules of graphitic carbon, *Nature.* **354**(6348), 56–58 (1991).

109. R. Dhar, A. S. Pandey, M. B. Pandey, S. Kumar, and R. Dabrowsi, Optimization of the display parameters of a room temperature twisted nematic display material by doping single-wall carbon nanotubes, *Appl. Phys. Express.* **1**(12), 121501 (2008).

110. S. Jeon, K. Park, I. Baik, S. Jeong, S. Jeong, K. An, S. Lee, and Y. Lee, Dynamic response of carbon nanotubes dispersed in nematic liquid crystal, *Nano.* **2**(1), 41–49 (2007).

111. M. Kimura, N. Miki, N. Adachi, Y. Tatewaki, K. Ohta, and H. Shirai, Organization of single-walled carbon nanotubes wrapped with liquid-crystalline pi-conjugated oligomers, *J. Mater. Chem.* **19**(8), 1086–1092 (2009).

112. J. P. F. Lagerwall and G. Scalia, Carbon nanotubes in liquid crystals, *J. Mater. Chem.* **18**(25), 2890–2898 (2008).

113. V. Manjuladevi, R. K. Gupta, and S. Kumar, Effect of functionalized carbon nanotube on electro-optic and dielectric properties of a liquid crystal, *J. Mol. Liq.* **171**, 60–63 (2012).

114. P. Sureshkumar, A. K. Srivastava, S. J. Jeong, M. Kim, E. M. Jo, S. H. Lee, and Y. H. Lee, Anomalous electrokinetic dispersion of carbon nanotube clusters in liquid crystal under electric field, *J. Nanosci. Nanotechnol.* **9**(8), 4741–4746 (2009).

115. O. Trushkevych, N. Collings, T. Hasan, V. Scardaci, A. Ferrari, T. Wilkinson, W. Crossland, W. Milne, J. Geng, B. Johnson, and S. Macaulay, Characterization of carbon nanotube-thermotropic nematic liquid crystal composites, *J. Phys. D-Appl. Phys.* **41**(12), 125106 (2008).

116. P. van der Schoot, V. Popa-Nita, and S. Kralj, Alignment of carbon nanotubes in nematic liquid crystals, *J. Phys. Chem. B.* **112**(15), 4512–4518 (2008).

117. S. Kumar and H. Bisoyi, Aligned carbon nanotubes in the supramolecular order of discotic liquid crystals, *Angew. Chem. (Int. Ed.).* **46**(9), 1501–1503 (2007).

118. H. K. Bisoyi and S. Kumar, Carbon nanotubes in triphenylene and rufigallol-based room temperature monomeric and polymeric discotic liquid crystals, *J. Mater. Chem.* **18**(25), 3032–3039 (2008).

119. J. J. Lee, A. Yamaguchi, M. A. Alam, Y. Yamamoto, T. Fukushima, K. Kato, M. Takata, N. Fujita, and T. Aida, Discotic ionic liquid crystals of triphenylene as dispersants for orienting single-walled carbon nanotubes, *Angew. Chem. (Int. Ed.).* **51**(34), 8490–8494 (2012).

120. N. Kilinc, A. S. Ahsen, D. Atilla, A. G. Guerek, S. E. San, Z. Z. Oeztuerk, and V. Ahsen, Electrical properties of mesomorphic phthalocyanine-carbon nanotube composites, *Sensor Lett.* **6**(4), 607–612 (2008).

121. Y. Zilberman, U. Tisch, W. Pisula, X. Feng, K. Muellen, and H. Haick, Spongelike structures of hexa-peri-hexabenzocoronene derivatives enhance the sensitivity of chemiresistive carbon nanotubles to nonpolar volatile organic compounds of cancer, *Langmuir.* **25**(9), 5411–5416 (2009).

122. Y. Zilberman, U. Tisch, G. Shuster, W. Pisula, X. Feng, K. Muellen, and H. Hoick, Carbon nanotube/hexa-peri-hexabenzocoronene bilayers for discrimination between nonpolar volatile organic compounds of cancer and humid atmospheres, *Adv. Mater.* **22**(38), 4317–4317 (2010).

123. J. G. Park, N. G. Yun, Y. B. Park, R. Liang, L. Lumata, J. S. Brooks, C. Zhang, and B. Wang, Single-walled carbon nanotube buckypaper and mesophase pitch carbon/carbon composites, *Carbon.* **48**(15), 4276–4282 (2010).

124. T. Cho, Y. Lee, R. Rao, A. M. Rao, D. Edie, and A. A. Ogale, Structure of carbon fiber obtained from nanotube-reinforced mesophase pitch, *Carbon.* **41**(7), 1419–1424 (2003).

125. K. Jian, R. Hurt, B. Sheldon, and G. Crawford, Visualization of liquid crystal director fields within carbon nanotube cavities, *Appl. Phys. Lett.* **88**

(16), 163110 (2006).

126. V. Georgakilas, M. Otyepka, A. B. Bourlinos, V. Chandra, N. Kim, K. C. Kemp, P. Hobza, R. Zboril, and K. S. Kim, Functionalization of graphene: Covalent and non-covalent approaches, derivatives and applications, *Chem. Rev.* **112**(11), 6156–6214 (2012).

127. T. Hasobe and H. Sakai, Molecular nanoarchitectures composed of porphyrins and carbon nanomaterials for light energy conversion, *J. Porph. Phthalocyanines.* **15**(5-6), 301–311 (2011).

128. N. Behabtu, J. Lomeda, M. Green, A. Higginbotham, A. Sinitskii, D. Kosynkin, D. Tsentalovich, A. Parra-Vasquez, J. Schmidt, E. Kesselman, Y. Cohen, Y. Talmon, J. Tour, and M. Pasquali, Spontaneous high-concentration dispersions and liquid crystals of graphene, *Nat. Nanotechnol.* **5**(6), 406–411 (2010).

129. B. Dan, N. Behabtu, A. Martinez, J. Evans, D. Kosynkin, J. Tour, M. Pasquali, and I. Smalyukh, Liquid crystals of aqueous, giant graphene oxide flakes, *Soft Matter.* **7**(23), 11154–11159 (2011).

130. J. E. Kim, T. H. Han, S. H. Lee, J. Y. Kim, C. W. Ahn, J. M. Yun, and S. O. Kim, Graphene oxide liquid crystals, *Angew. Chem. (Int. Ed.).* **50**(13), 3043–3047 (2011).

131. A. B. Shivanandareddy, S. Krishnamurthy, V. Lakshminarayan, and S. Kumar, Mutually ordered self-assembly of discotic liquid crystal-graphene nanocomposites, *Chem. Commun.* **50**(6), 710–712 (2014).

132. Z. Xu and C. Gao, Graphene chiral liquid crystals and macroscopic assembled fibres, *Nat. Commun.* **2 571 571** (2011).

Chapter 14

Metallic and semiconducting nanoparticles in LCs

Anshul Sharma,[a] Martin Urbanski,[b] Taizo Mori,[a,c]
Heinz-S. Kitzerow[b] and Torsten Hegmann[a,*]

*[a] Chemical Physics Interdisciplinary Program, Liquid Crystal Institute,
Kent State University, Kent (OH) 44242 USA*
*[b] Dept. of Chemistry, University of Paderborn, 33098 Paderborn,
Germany*
*[c] World Premier International (WPI) Center for Materials
Nanoarchitectonics (MANA), Nat. Inst. for Materials Science (NIMS),
Tsukuba, & Japan Soc. for Promotion of Science (JSPS), Tokyo, Japan*
**thegmann@kent.edu*

This chapter provides an overview of recent advances in nanoparticle-liquid crystal dispersions with a particular focus on bulk versus surface effects. Surface effects will include the role of surface functionalization of metal and semiconducting nanoparticles as well as interfacial effects, alignment and anchoring in thin liquid crystal films related to nanoparticle segregation. We will also try to provide a practical guide for experimental work on nanoparticle-liquid crystal dispersions, including tips and best practices for preparing dispersions, detecting and preventing inhomogeneities as well as Dos and Don'ts for handling samples and filling test cells for electrooptic, spectroscopic, and other experiments critical for research in this area.

1. Introduction

With the many advances in nanoscience and nanochemistry over the past two decades, incorporation of functionalized metal nanoparticles (NPs) and quantum dots (QDs) in liquid crystals (LCs) has emerged as a promising approach to create LC nanocomposites where the properties of at least one or even both constituent(s) are tuned, enhanced, or sensed.[1–6] Recent research on metal NPs (mainly gold and silver) and QDs in LCs largely focuses on LC-guided self-assembly and alignment of NPs as well as on

497

modulating the properties of different LC phases using small quantities of a nanoscale additive. The bulk of research on the latter is devoted to nematic LC phases (N-LCs), because of their use in display and other optical and electro-optical applications such as lenses or light shutters. It has been shown that doping N-LCs with low concentrations of NPs is an effective way to tune the optical and electro-optic properties of LCs, both in N-LC[1–6] and ferroelectric SmC* LC (FLC) phases.[7–16]

Numerous tests focusing on the electro-optic properties of LCs with NP (QD) additives reported new or improved electro-optical properties including lower threshold voltage (V_{th}), altered dielectric anisotropy ($\Delta\epsilon$), or faster response time.[5] In addition to metal NPs and semiconductor QDs other types of NPs such as magnetic and ferroelectric NPs have been reported to effectively alter LC properties such as bulk ordering, phase transition temperatures, birefringence, dielectric anisotropy, response to external fields, and the chirality of N-LCs.[17–19] Likewise, substantially altered properties of FLCs were reported after the addition of small quantities of metallic, semiconductor or metal oxide NPs.[7–16]

Considering all the positive current and future prospects for LC-NP dispersions, research in this area has suffered from the unavailability of design principles for NPs that are (1) well dispersed, (2) purposefully and completely segregated, or (3) somewhere in between these two scenarios. To formulate such design principles, one needs to know more about the interactions between LC molecules and NPs, especially their ligand shell. Key aspects to take into consideration are not only the chemical nature of these capping molecules and the composition of the capping monolayer (one, two or more different molecules are used to protect the surface of the NP), but also the shape and size of the nanomaterial as this relates to the NP curvature and consequentially the density of the capping ligands. Finally, another key element is the ability of the experimenter to prepare either well dispersed or perfectly segregated NP in LC samples with high fidelity. The chemical stability of the NPs plays here a significant role.[20] Therefore it seems reasonable to tackle these major obstacles facing LC nanocomposites. One obstacle is the low miscibility or dispersibility of NPs in LCs that is exacerbated in the absence of compatible functional groups on the surface of NPs. It is worth noting here that dispersibility of NPs in any liquid crystalline phase is expected to be lower than in the isotropic liquid phase by virtue of intrinsic limited miscibility in any partially ordered medium. The tendency of NPs to aggregate can also be viewed as the compensation of the system for distortions in the local order parameter in the presence of NPs smaller than 100 nm.[21] Another obstacle is the weak stability of NPs in LC composites arising from the lack of robust capping ligands or inadequate coverage on the surface of NPs, which depends on the NP size and shape (*vide infra*).

Since the results of optical and electro-optical tests critically depend on the nature (well dispersed, fully segregated, or intermediate) and the quality of the NP dispersion (or segregation) several problems frequently occur. Commonly used methods to measure the bulk properties of an LC material are affected by both surface and bulk properties and require known, well-defined boundary conditions, which are typically achieved by high quality alignment layers such as rubbed polyimide. However, when NPs reside at (or segregate to) the LC-alignment layer interface, these well-defined boundary conditions are obscured and any theoretical assumption no longer matches the experimental conditions.[22]

Using representative examples for each case (well dispersed, partially dispersed, and fully segregated, Fig. 1) we will attempt to devise some principle design rules for NPs that should allow research teams active in this field to perhaps synthesize or select the most promising NP for their specific purpose. In due course, based on our own experience working with various types of NPs in LC phases, we will provide some Dos and Don'ts, i.e. best practices to follow and mistakes to avoid.

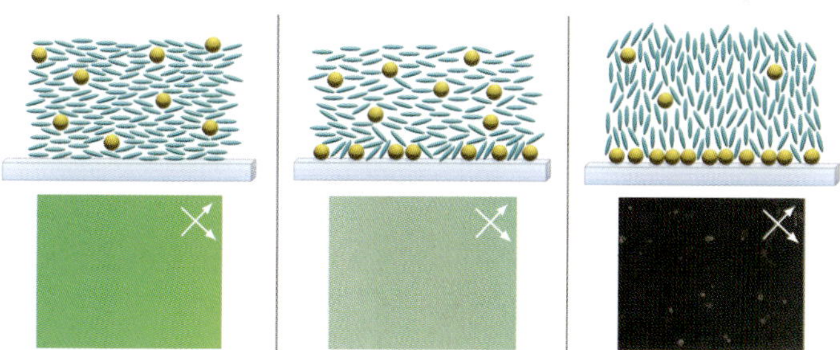

Fig. 1. Illustrations of the three possible degrees of surface interactions of NPs at the interface between N-LCs and the substrate: (a) no surface coverage of NPs, therefore no influence on the initial alignment layers. The bulk properties can be determined using simple models, (b) partial segregation influencing initial tilt angle and anchoring strength, and (c) fully segregated NPs that may or may not induce homeotropic LC alignment. Reproduced with permission from Ref. 22, Figure 11.

2. Role of NP surface chemistry

Inadequate colloidal stability of NPs in LC phases increases the risk of NP aggregation and irreversibly phase-separation in NP-LC system that can range from the nanoscale to the bulk. Both of the aforementioned obstacles, i.e. limited colloidal and chemical stability, are directly linked to the surface chemistry of the NP and therefore any attempt to achieve for example well-dispersed and stable colloidal LC dispersions should be addressed together. Once the surface of NPs is covered with organic ligands or surfactants featuring mesogenic or pro-mesogenic motifs close or comparable to those of host LC molecules, interactions of NPs with the LC matrix will be more specific,[23] but this alone does not guarantee well-dispersed NP in a given LC host.[24] A mixed ligand shell, created for example by using longer functional and shorter aliphatic hydrocarbon chains (spacers) or more space between functional ligands would additionally enable insertion of host LC molecules (*via* inter-digitation) in order to minimize the disturbance of the local director in the LC phase caused by the presence of the NPs. This also relates to the size, i.e. curvature, of the nanomaterial and its shape.[25]

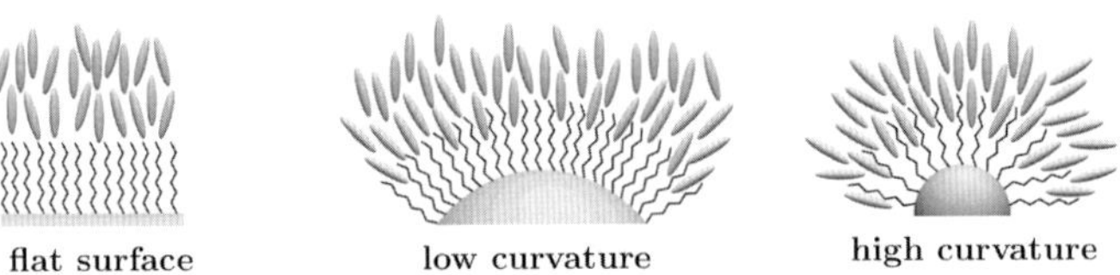

Fig. 2. Schematic drawings illustrating the influence of radius of curvature on the possible degree of interdigitation between ligand shell and host molecules. Reproduced with permission from Ref. 26 and adapted from Coursault *et al.*[25]

Even with all factors carefully selected, homogeneous dispersions of NPs are usually limited to lower NP concentrations in most LC systems, often just a few wt.-%. Our own experiments revealed that well-defined boundary conditions with high anchoring energies, for example rubbed polyimide coated planar cells, enhance the colloidal stability of NPs in N-LCs, but this may not matter much in cases with diminished long-term thermal or chemical stability of the NPs used. Starting with the scenario of well-dispersed NPs, we will use specific examples of mesogenic or chiral functional group decorated NPs to explain how bulk LC properties such as their response to applied electric fields (electro-optic response) or chirality are not only affected by the presence of well-dispersed NPs but also used to assess the dispersions' homogeneity.

2.1. *Well-dispersed NPs*

While it is perhaps easy to disperse lower NP concentrations in LC hosts, say 0.1 wt.-%, for many types of NPs significant optical, electro-optical or other effects are expected or seen only for higher NP concentrations, e.g. 1wt.-% or higher. The design and synthesis of NPs that disperse well in any given LC host is likely the most challenging, but we will use a few key examples to demonstrate what concepts are the most likely road to success. Before, however, we need to address problems concerning the thermal and chemical stability particularly of Au and Ag NPs that are the most frequently studied.

Figure 3 provides a graphical overview of the reactivity of Au NPs and the thiolate ligand shell in the presence of various types of reagents and at elevated temperatures. This is by no means an exhaustive list of effects and potentially detrimental reactions of Au NPs, but highlights the most critical. We have previously described these processes regarding Au NP

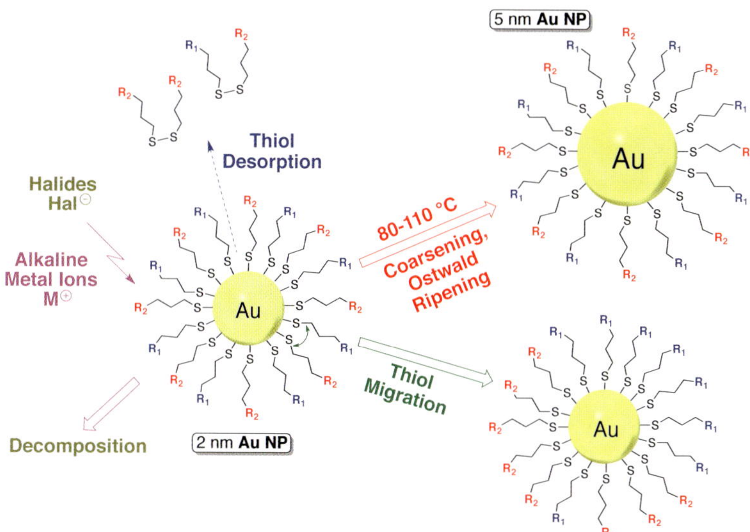

Fig. 3. The reactivity of mixed monolayer-capped Au NPs in the presence of halides, alkaline metal ions, and at elevated temperatures. Larger Au NPs (about 5 nm in core diameter) are frequently synthesized by stirring a solution of smaller NP seeds (e.g., 1.5 to 2 nm) in boiling toluene for several hours.

                     A. Sharma et al.

reactivity in great detail and would like to refer the reader to these two references.[6,20] Elevated temperature is perhaps the most important aspect particularly when dealing with LC hosts with clearing points near or above 90°C, when both thiol migration and thiol desorption have been observed. Temperature effects also play a role during sample preparation using sonication, which we will discuss briefly in the Dos and Don'ts section.

At lower sample preparation as well as LC host clearing temperatures the use of mesogenic and pro-mesogenic ligands (often thiols) appears to be the most successful strategy. We are not discussing the self-assembly of these types of NPs here; a recent review by Górecka and co-workers provides a comprehensive overview of recent research in this area.[27] The first example we discuss are Au NPs capped with cyanobiphenyl-based ligands bound to the NP surface via Au-S bonds as reported by several groups. Aiming for an enhanced compatibility with cyanobiphenyl N-LC hosts such as 5CB[#] or 8CB, our group first investigated mixed monolayer capped Au NPs, where aliphatic thiols and cyanobiphenyl-based thiols simultaneously cover the surface of the Au NPs (Fig. 4). We surprisingly found, however, that the mixed monolayer, cyanobiphenyl-capped Au NPs severely aggregated in both N-LC hosts at concentrations up to 5 wt.-%. Optical microscopy (both polarized and bright field) clearly indicated that larger, several μm-sized aggregates formed in the bulk (i.e. in a vial) and then settled to the glass-LC interface in thin N-LC films between plain, untreated glass and in unidirectionally rubbed polyimide-coated ITO-glass cells. The aliphatic thiol-capped Au NPs appeared well dispersed in the bulk, but were also expelled by the N-LC host to the interface in thin film preparations (Fig. 5).[24]

Goodby and co-workers, however, reported a contrasting study using Au NPs capped exclusively with cyanobiphenyl ligands (**Au3-Au7**, Fig. 4), which formed stable, homogeneous dispersions up to 20 wt.-%.[28] This seems surprising for various reasons. Most notably, in this case the dense cyanobiphenyl-coated Au NPs should present a fairly polar interface to the surrounding 5CB host molecules and perhaps not permit interactions or interdigitation between host N-LC molecules and N-LC ligands. Later careful EO and alignment studies by Urbanski *et al.* could not confirm the high miscibility and showed that NPs such as **Au3-Au7** belong into the category of partially dispersed NPs (vide infra).[26]

Both types of Au NPs are also fairly similar in size (2.0 vs. 2.4 nm in core diameter), which means effects of NP surface curvature should not result in such dramatic differences with respect to miscibility.

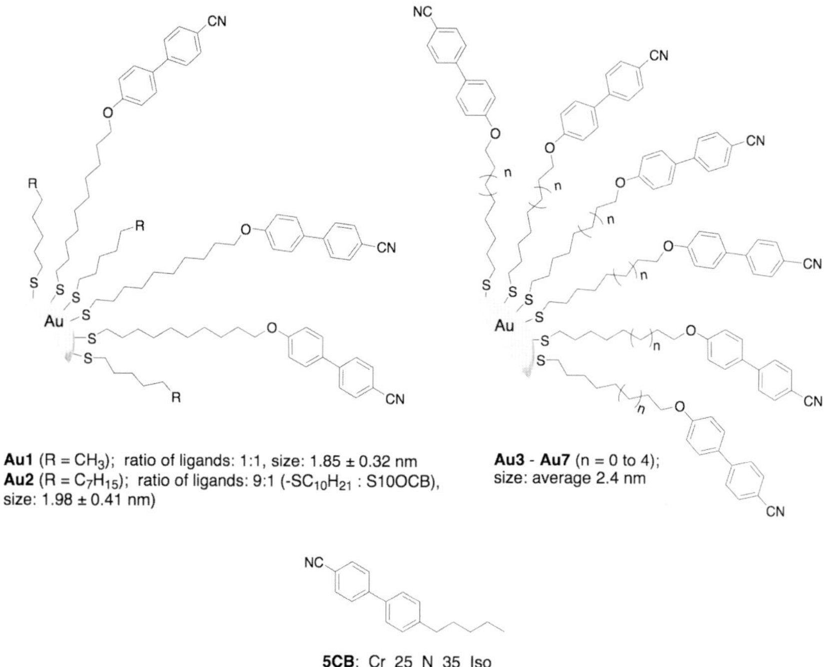

Au1 (R = CH₃); ratio of ligands: 1:1, size: 1.85 ± 0.32 nm
Au2 (R = C₇H₁₅); ratio of ligands: 9:1 (-SC₁₀H₂₁ : S10OCB), size: 1.98 ± 0.41 nm)

Au3 - **Au7** (n = 0 to 4); size: average 2.4 nm

5CB; Cr 25 N 35 Iso

Fig. 4. Au NPs capped with cyanobiphenyl-based thiol ligands: mixed monolayer-capped Au NPs reported by our group (**Au1** and **Au2**)[24] and fully covered by cyanobiphenyl ligands (**Au3** - **Au7**) reported by Goodby and co-workers[28] in cyanobiphenyl N-LC hosts such as 5CB, 8CB, or E7.

The model shown in Fig. 6 proposed by Goodby's team schematically shows the possibility of a tactoidal deformation of the NP ligand shell surrounding the core, which should facilitates the incorporation into N-LC host media. Based on arguments including the π-π stacking between neighboring cyanobiphenyl ligands and the greater density of packing at the poles (assuming a tactoid) such tactoidal deformation would be easier realized with Au NPs only capped by mesogenic ligands. Additionally, x-ray and neutron diffraction studies combined with molecular modeling led to the conclusion that these NPs form smectic-type LC phases as neat materials, providing additional support for the tactoidal ligand shell deformation that may improve miscibility in a structurally similar N-LC host.[28]

To follow up on this concept and additionally avoid problems with ligand migration and desorption highlighted in Fig. 3, we prepared Au NPs

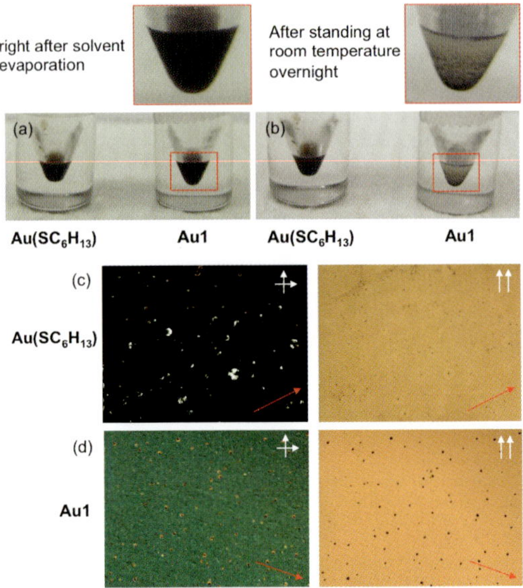

Fig. 5.   V-vials containing 5CB doped with two types of Au NPs, hexanethiol-capped Au NPs and mixed monolayer cyanobiphenyl-thiol capped Au NPs (**Au1**), (a) right after solvent evaporation showing what appear to be well-dispersed mixtures and (b) after storing the mixtures in the N-LC phase overnight with **Au1** almost completely settled to the bottom of the vial. Optical photomicrographs with crossed (left) and parallel (right) polarizers of 5 wt.-% of (c) $Au[SC_6H_{13}]_x$ and (d) **Au1**(red arrows indicate the rubbing direction of the polyimide in these cells). Adapted with permission from Ref. 24.

capped with mesogenic ligands using a silane conjugation approach. Here, Au NPs capped with MPS (3-mercaptopropyltrimethoxysilane) are used as precursor for the subsequent conjugation with reactive N-LC molecules featuring trimethoxysilane end-groups. Considering the results of several earlier studies on NPs in N-LCs by our group, we also selected mesogenic moieties for this silane conjugation that are similar to non-polar N-LCs such as Felix-2900-03[#], an LC with phenylpyrimidine core flanked by two terminal hydrocarbon chains, which has frequently shown to accommodate higher concentrations of NPs with hydrophobic ligand shell than polar cyanobiphenyl-based N-LC hosts.[30]

These LC silane-functionalized Au NPs (**Au8-Au10**) were shown to be chemically and thermally very robust, surviving prolonged heat treatment at 190°C as well as pulsed sonication due to the nature of the conjugated siloxane ligand shell. Colloidal dispersions of these NPs with mesogenic lig-

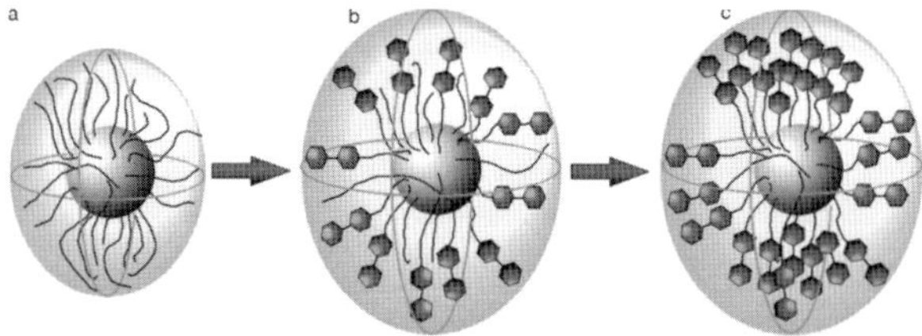

Fig. 6.   The model of the tactoidal deformation of the ligand shell proposed by Goodby and co-workers, which demonstrates the effect of decorating the surface of Au NPs with mesogens.   An increase of the particle diameter would increasingly cause a splay of the mesogens that, in turn, results in conformational changes with a greater density of packing at the poles: (a) NP with aliphatic coating, (b) NP with a mixed monolayer (as **Au1** and **Au2**), and (c) NP with N-LC mesogen coating only as **Au3-Au7**. Reproduced with permission from Ref. 28 (Figure 5).

ands that are structurally identical (**Au8** and **Au9**) or compatible (**Au10**) with molecules of the N-LC host showed superior colloidal stability and dispersibility at concentrations up to 5 wt.-%. For some mixtures doped with 1wt.-% of the Au NPs POM studies and DSC data showed an increase of the clearing point of the N phase ($T_{Iso/N}$). All dispersions showed lower values for the rotational viscosity and elastic constant (K_{eff}), but only **Au10** with a dissimilar structure between the NP ligand and the host displayed the most drastic thermal effects and overall strongest impact on the electrooptic properties of the host. The observed electrooptic results (lower rotational viscosity γ_1, lower effective elastic constant K_{eff} and lower threshold voltage V_{th}) were explained considering both the structure and the density of the surface ligands of each Au NP and led us to conclude on a model that builds upon the model proposed by Goodby and co-workers.[28] Assuming there is sufficient interaction between the LC molecules and the ligands of the NPs, the anisometric N-LC host will impose a tactoidal deformation of the ligand shell. This anisometric shape presumably originates from ligand chains in the axial position of the NP that fold and coil, whereas ligands in the equatorial region fully extend or unfold (Fig. 8). Upon applying external electric fields, small distortions in the surrounding director field could induce a flip in the equatorial and axial orientation, for which coils unfold and unfolded ligands fold up. In this way, the reorientation of the host molecules is facilitated by the presence of the NPs even without a rotation of the NP core by anisometric interactions of ligands and host molecules. This model would best explain the reduced V_{th} values and

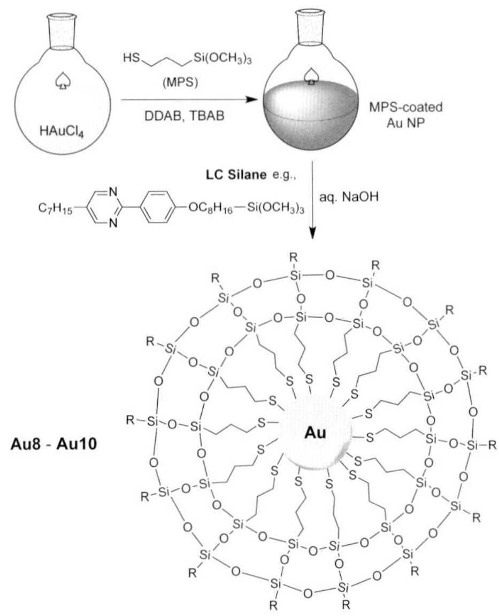

Au NP	R =	size / nm	# of ligands
Au8	C₇H₁₅—...—OC₈H₁₆-	4.1	728
Au9	C₇H₁₅—...—OC₁₁H₂₂-	6.9	4538
Au10	C₆H₁₃O—...—OC₆H₁₂O—...	7.1	2602

Fig. 7. Synthesis and idealized 2D structure of the Au NPs with phenylpyrimidine or phenylbenzoate mesogenic ligands (**Au8-Au10**). The NP size was determined by TEM and the number of mesogenic ligands using the combined data from TEM and TGA (thermogravemetric analysis). Abbreviations: DDAB...didodecyldimethylammonium bromide, TBAB...tetrabutylammonium borohydride. Adapted from Ref. 29.

the reduced γ_1 values in dispersions with **Au10** and high concentrations of **Au9**. It seems that for the latter particles, although the surface ligands are fairly compatible with the host molecules, for reasons such as larger NP size in comparison to **Au8** and higher density of organic ligands in comparison to the similar sized **Au10**, this compatibility is not sufficient to cause similar EO effects as **Au10**. Hence, the easier it is to achieve a distorted

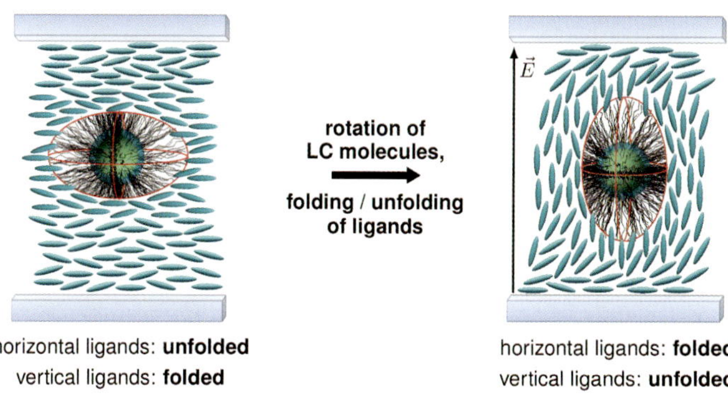

Fig. 8. Schematic of the expected mechanism of facilitated switching due to NP doping: (left) the ligand shell is deformed to a tactoidal shape due to anisometric interactions with the N-LC host, (right) upon applying an electric field, the LC molecules rotate, whereas the NP does not rotate. The previously folded ligands unfold, and the formerly unfolded ligands fold. Reproduced with permission from Ref. 29, Figure 17.

ligand shell, the more likely it will be to observe an altered EO response, which is why **Au10**, despite the structurally dissimilar ligand induced the most drastic changes in the EO response of the host. We can interpret this as a dynamic feedback system, in which the effectiveness of a NP to alter the EO response depends on how it can be affected by the LC host.

Detailed EO measurements in combination with numerical simulations of the **Au10** in Felix-2900-03 confirmed that these NPs are bulk-active and do not segregate to the glass (or alignment layer)/N-LC interface at least for concentrations up to 2.5 wt.-%.[22] This is in contrast to CdSe QDs with 4.1 nm core diameter capped with aliphatic amines ($C_{16}H_{33}NH_2$) reported earlier,[31] which settle to the interface inducing homeotropic alignment of otherwise planar cells affecting the pre-tilt and hence the EO response (increase in pretilt and lower anchoring energy W).[22] Hence, despite the larger surface curvature, the incorporation of mesogenic ligands with a low enough density to allow for effective interactions with the N-LC host molecules (unless they are polar as in the case of **Au1** and **Au2**) appears to be a good strategy to achieve well-dispersed NPs in N-LC hosts. In addition, thermally robust ligand shells will allow the experimenter to sonicate the mixtures for sufficiently long periods of time to facilitate homogeneous dispersion of the NPs in N-LCs.

For example, Au NPs synthesized following the method presented in Fig. 7 but using a simple aliphatic trimethoxysilane to conjugate to MPS-coated Au NP allowed the preparation of well-dispersed NP/LC mixtures with the NPs featuring the same size (**Au11**: 4.1± 0.7 nm) as the CdSe QDs described above. These NPs also enhanced the clearing point and induced similar trends in the EO response of the Felix-2900-03 N-LC host (Fig. 9).[20]

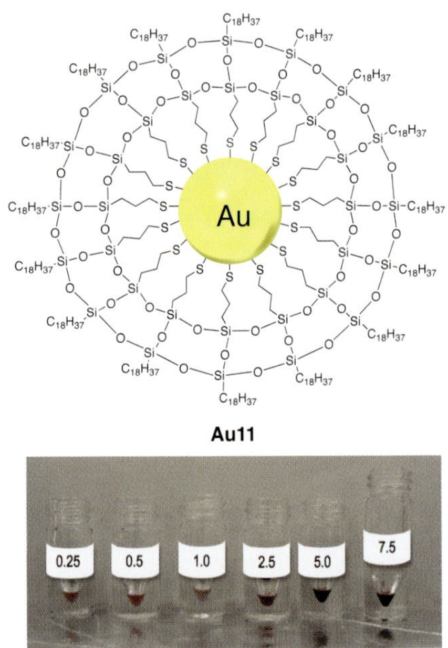

Fig. 9.   2D representation of the aliphatic silane-conjugated **Au11** NPs and dispersions of **Au11** in Felix-2900-03 at concentrations ranging from 0.25 to 7.5 wt.-%. Reproduced with permission from Ref. 20, Figure 3.

In addition to EO measurements and microscopy observations of the N-LC alignment, the bulk induction of chirality into an N-LC can also be used to demonstrate how a careful choice of the nature of the ligand shell affects the quality of NP dispersions in N-LCs. In fact, we have recently shown that N-LCs can be used to understand, visualize, and measure the chirality of chiral ligand-capped Au NPs. The chiroptical effects of NPs and QDs either assembled in a chiral fashion using a chiral template or decorated with chiral ligands is a hot topic in nanoscience, but will not be discussed here. We would like, however, to refer the reader to a couple of leading articles and reviews on this topic.[32–40] To obtain well-dispersed chiral ligand-capped Au NPs that can transfer their chirality to an achiral

N phase, we replaced a common chiral dopant structure (S)-naproxen[18,41] with chiral cholesterol mesogenic ligands, which form a chiral nematic (N*) phase as neat materials, using both Au-S linkages and silane conjugation as shown earlier (Fig. 10).

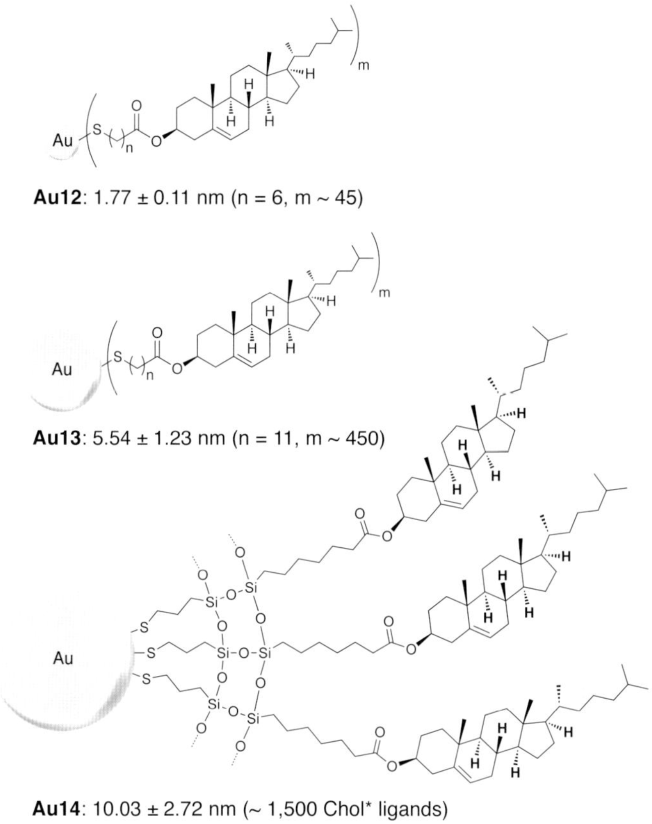

Au12: 1.77 ± 0.11 nm (n = 6, m ∼ 45)

Au13: 5.54 ± 1.23 nm (n = 11, m ∼ 450)

Au14: 10.03 ± 2.72 nm (∼ 1,500 Chol* ligands)

Fig. 10. 2D idealized structures of cholesterol-thiol capped Au NPs **Au12**, **Au13** and **Au14** synthesized via silane conjugation.

The key findings from this study were that Au NPs synthesized in the presence of a chiral ligand (**Au12** and **Au13**) are more potent chiral inducers than NPs prepared in the absence of a chiral bias (a chiral cholesterol disulfide), **Au14** synthesized via silane conjugation.

Because these two sets of Au NPs were not identical in diameter, it is difficult to speculate how significant the additional contribution of the higher surface curvature of the smaller NPs was, since higher curvature would facilitate interactions (chirality transfer) between ligand and host molecules. That this effect might be small, however, can be understood from a comparison between **Au12** and **Au13**. At the same concentration ranging from 2.5 to 10 wt.-%), the larger **Au13** induces a tighter helical pitch p in 5CB (e.g., 5.33 μm for **Au13** vs. 6.23 μm for **Au12** at 5 wt.-%) with an overall lower number of NPs but a larger volume fraction of the NPs in this mixture compared to **Au12** in 5CB. Standardizing these two mixtures based on the overall number of chiral ligands leads to the conclusion that the smaller **Au12** outperforms the larger **Au13** based on calculations of the helical twisting power β_M.

These Au NPs dispersed so well showing no sign of aggregation or phase separation in N-LC hosts such as 5CB or Felix-2900-03 that helical pitch measurements using Grandjean-Cano wedge cell method could be done (Fig. 11).[19]

Another example of mesogen-coated NPs showing a reduced tendency of phase separation and segregation to the interfaces in thin films were perhaps recently reported by Hirst *et al.* focusing on CdSe and CdSe/ZnS core/shell QDs with side-on linked mesogenic ligands (Fig. 12).[42] The structure of the ligand is closely related to those used for self-assembly studies by Mehl *et al.* for Au NPs[43–45] as well as by our group for Au nanorods.[46] The authors report on mixtures containing up to 0.15 wt.-% of these QDs in 5CB, and it is not clear if higher QD concentrations would have dispersed well in 5CB as well or if the tactoidal deformation of the ligand shell is active considering the difference in ligand connectivity (side-on vs. end-on). For the Au nanorods reported by our group, this side-on fixation of mesogenic ligands resulted in nanorods with excellent miscibility in hosts such as 5CB well above 10 wt.-%.[46] Several examples of mesogen-coated metal NPs and QDs were discussed in an earlier review.[6]

2.2. *Partially dispersed NPs*

Partially dispersed NPs is possibly the most loosely defined category among the three described here. Partial dispersion of NPs in LC host phases depends on many factors such as NP concentration, temperature, and preparation conditions to list the three likely most important. We have seen earlier that tests performed with different setups, perhaps the time NP suspension are kept right after preparation/solvent evaporation, and boundary conditions affect the quality of NP dispersions in LC hosts. We will again

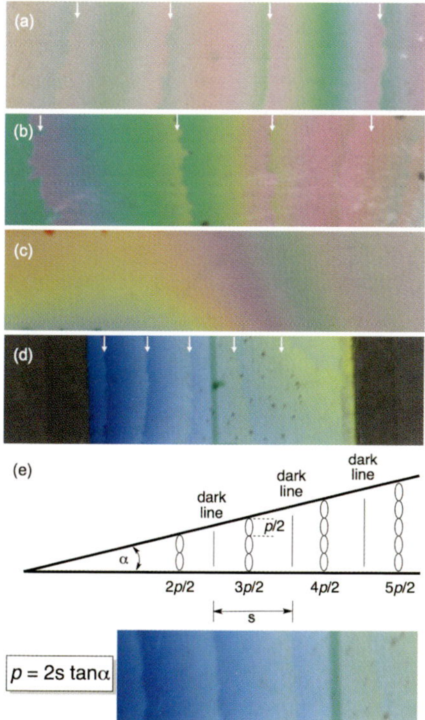

Fig. 11. Images of Grandjean-Cano wedge cells (crossed polarizers) showing Grandjean steps (lines) of the induced N* phase of 5CB after doping with: (a) 5 wt.-% of **Au12**, (b) 5 wt.-% of **Au13**, and (c) 5 wt.-% of **Au14** (showing no evidence for Grandjean steps), and (d) 10 wt.-% of **Au12**. (e) Grandjean-Cano wedge cell method to determine the helical pitch (p) of an N* phase (s = distance between two disclination lines). Reproduced with permission from Ref. 19, Figure 3.

use a few examples to highlight when and how NPs belong into this particular category, starting with the connectivity of mesogenic ligands, following the discussion of the previous section.

Zubarev *et al.* for example reported on mixed monolayer capped Au NPs (**Au15**), where the mesogenic ligands are directly connected to the Au NP surface via a phenylmercaptan moiety (Fig. 13).[47]

Using absorption spectroscopy in the visible part of the electromagnetic spectrum and calculated absorption spectra from Mie theory, the authors were able to confirm the maximum concentration of 0.2 wt.-% in 5CB of these **Au15** NPs with a core diameter of 6 nm. While 0.2 wt.-% in 5CB

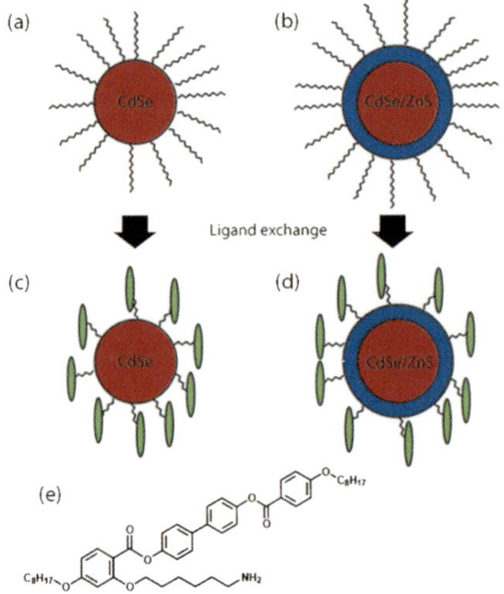

Fig. 12.   a-d) Schematic representation of the QDs before and after ligand exchange with a side-on mesogenic ligand. (e) Chemical structure of the used mesogenic amine. Reproduced with permission from Ref. 42, Figure 1.

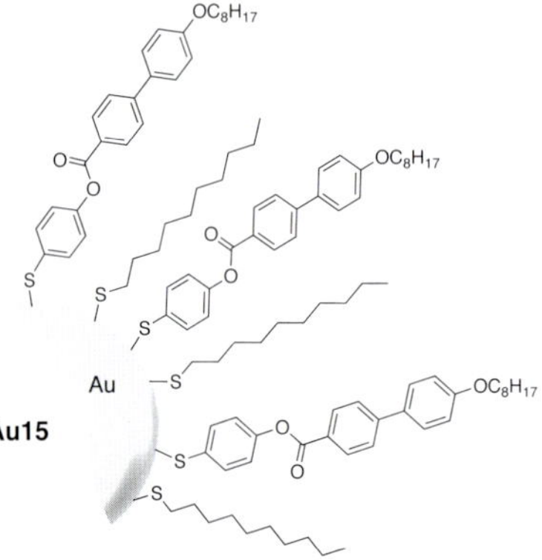

Fig. 13.   Mixed monolayer-capped Au NPs (**Au15**) with pro-mesogenic ligands directly connected to the Au NP surface via a phenylmercaptane unit.

appears quite low in comparison to several of the Au NPs highlighted in the previous section, their solubility in 5CB is higher when compared to alkanethiolate monolayer-protected Au NPs,[47] which is in agreement with earlier work by our group.[17,30] Two key factor are likely responsible for the low tendency of **Au15** to form homogenous bulk suspensions in 5CB compared to, for example, **Au12** and **Au13**. First, the larger size results in a small curvature and second, the mesogenic ligands are not tethered to an alkyl chain but rather embedded in the surrounding hydrocarbon chains of the aliphatic thiols. As a result, the mesogenic ligands have less chance to interact with the host molecules diminishing the likelihood of a tactoidal ligand shell deformation.

Applying an electric field to a N-LC filled in an electro-optic test cell usually leads to a reorientation of the LC material only, but does not alter the alignment layer. The boundary conditions remain unchanged, and after removing the external electric field the N-LC shows the same alignment as before the switching experiment. Applying an electric field to NP/LC dispersions, however, was shown to modify the surface anchoring of the LC on the substrate interface of EO test cells. For example, dispersions of **Au6**,[28] $Au(SC_{12}H_{25})_m$,[30] $CdSe_{590}$ or $CdSe_{610}$[31] in 5CB show homogeneous planar alignment induced by rubbed polyimide alignment layers after filling into EO test cells. Dispersions of **Au11**[20] and low concentrations of the magic sized msCdSe and msCdSe:Zn[48] QDs in Felix-2900-03 filled in test cells also exhibit homogeneous planar alignment, besides the appearance of birefringent stripes[49] in dispersions with msCdSe particles. As a consequence of the homogeneous planar alignment, all samples appear bright between crossed polarizers with the easy axis of the test cells oriented under an azimuthal angle of $\varphi = 45°$ to the plane of polarization of incident light. However, after one EO measurement cycle we found that dispersions of **Au6** and $Au(SC_{12}H_{25})_m$ in 5CB show gradual color changes within the electrode area between crossed polarizers. Dispersions containing **Au6** even change to a non-birefringent black state after 10 cycles. In contrast, dispersions of QDs $CdSe_{590}$ and $CdSe_{610}$ in 5CB as well as dispersions of msCdSe and msCdSe:Zn QDs in Felix-2900-03 do not show such field induced alignment changes. Dispersions of the **Au11** NPs in Felix-2900-03 are found to be stable under the influence of an electric field, and do not alter the effect of the cell's polyimide alignment layers (Fig. 14).

These field-induced alignment changes occur only within the active ITO-electrode areas of the EO test cells, and exhibit a sharp boundary line to the unaltered planar alignment in the surrounding.

Finally, we will use two series of QDs differing in size and in the type of ligand (hydrophobic aliphatic amine vs. hydrophilic thioglycolic acid) to show how delicately either size of QDs (i.e. radius of curvature) or chemical nature of the ligand affects the quality of dispersions in a given LC host.

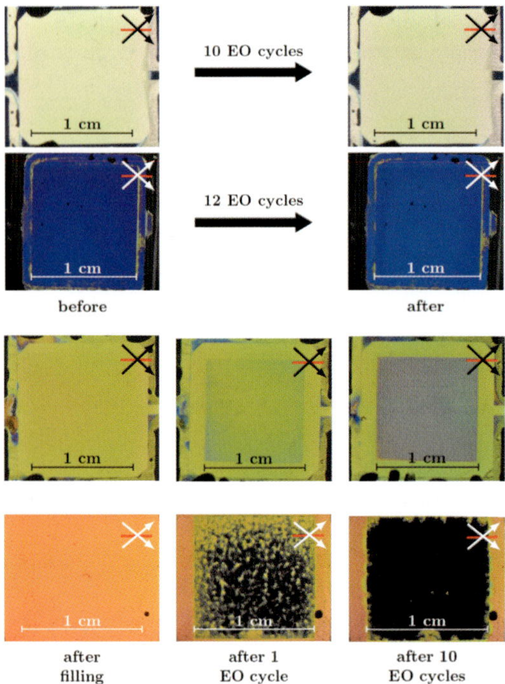

Fig. 14. Macroscopic photographs of EO test cells filled with dispersions of (top to bottom) 0.5 wt.-% CdSe$_{590}$ in 5CB, 0.5 wt.-% **Au11** in Felix-2900-03, 0.5 wt.-% Au(SC$_{12}$H$_{25}$)$_m$, and 1.0 wt.-% **Au6**NPs before and after cycles of measurements in an applied electric fields. Images were taken at $T_{Iso/N} - T = 8$ K using a white light source between crossed polarizers. The orientation of the cell's rubbing direction with respect to the crossed polarizers is indicated by the bars and arrows, respectively. Reproduced with permission from Ref. 26.

Considering a series of CdSe QDs all capped with the same aliphatic mine (C$_{16}$H$_{33}$NH$_2$) differing only in size, the POM images of planar cells filled with mixtures of 1wt.-% of these QDs in the N-phase of Felix-2900-03 (Fig. 15) show at least some trend with respect to size and radius of curvature (assuming identical ligand density). The QD with the smallest size (CdSe$_{480}$) overwrites the boundary conditions initially set by the rubbed polyimide alignment layers, i.e. they phase separate, segregate to the interface, and induce homeotropic alignment. This effect principally continues as the size of the QD and the radius of curvature increases (CdSe$_{610}$, $\varnothing = 5.0$ nm), at which point the domains with planar alignment dominate. This would indeed indicate that the largest QDs in this series allow for the

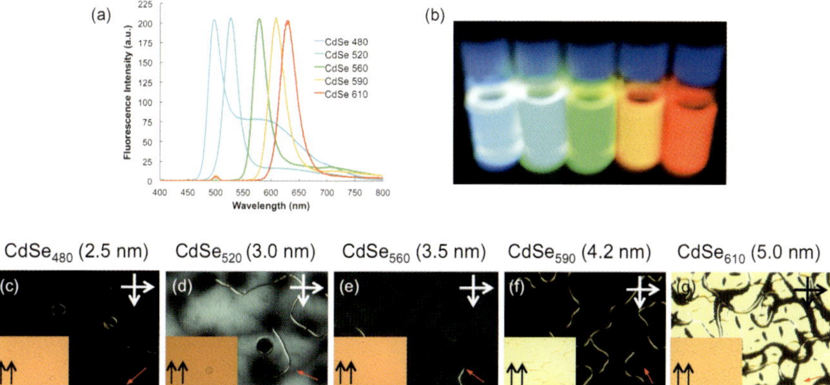

Fig. 15. (a) Fluorescence emission spectra of the size-separated CdSe QDs capped with hexadecylamine in toluene and (b) photograph of the fluorescing QDs ($\lambda_{exc.} = 366$ nm). (c-g) POM images of 1wt.-% mixtures in the N-LC phase of Felix-2900-03 at $T_{Iso/N} - T = 9°C$ in planar rubbed polyimide-coated cells. The inset shows the same area with parallel polarizers (white arrows show polarizer orientation, red arrows show rubbing direction of the cell). Reproduced with permission form Ref. 31, Figure 11.

preparation of the most homogenous bulk dispersion. Once the concentration of each of these QDs increased any further (2-5 wt.-%), macroscopic aggregation is observed, which is then, however, less severe for the smaller QDs.[31]

Interestingly, changing the surface chemistry from aliphatic amines in this CdSe series to hydrophilic functional groups in a related CdTe series (capped with thioglycolic acid, $HSCH_2COOH$) allows for the creation of homogenous dispersions in the bulk up to 2 wt.-% as shown in the POM images of planar cells in Fig. 16)

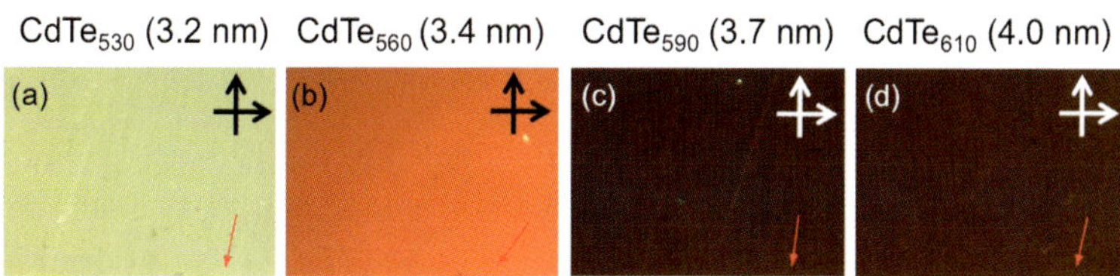

Fig. 16. (a-d) POM images of 2wt.-% mixtures of the CdTe QDs in the N-LC phase of Felix-2900-03 at $T_{Iso/N} - T = 9°C$ in planar rubbed polyimide-coated cells (white or black arrows show polarizer orientation, red arrows show rubbing direction). Reproduced with permission form Ref. 31, Figure 12.

The reason for this behavior is not immediately obvious, but perhaps a tangential anchoring of the N-LC molecules to the surface of these polar QDs favor the overall planar alignment in thin films and a better dispersion in the bulk. Assuming this to be correct, it should then be easy to design NPs that would favor phase separation and segregation to the interfaces of thin, sandwiched N-LC films by using small NPs with dense ligand coatings that do not contain any (pro-)mesogenic groups, which is what we will discuss in more detail in the next section.

2.3. *Segregated NPs*

Using such small Au NPs capped with aliphatic thiols (Ø= 1.9± 0.5 nm for hexanethiol-capped and Ø=2.1± 0.7 nm for dodecanethiol-capped Au NPs), we reported a thermal history dependent, unprecedented dual alignment mode, in which a planar alignment cell filled with mixtures containing 5 wt.-% of these NPs in Felix-2900-03 ($\Delta\epsilon = +0.62$ at $T_{Iso/N} - T = 10°C$) can be switched from homeotropic to planar alignment on applying an electric field ($E < E_{th,pureLC}$). The cell is filled with mixture at $E = 0$ and then slowly cooled to N phase. Upon gradually increasing the voltage of the applied AC field ($E \geq 2.0$ Vμm^{-1}) the area of bright birefringent domains increases (Fig. 17). However, heating the cell above $T_{Iso/N}$ and cooling the cell to the N-LC phase in the field-ON state, a reverse switching phenomena is observed. Upon switching the electric field OFF, all dark domains became bright, indicating change to planar alignment. In cells with larger cell gaps (6.8± 0.5 μm) the 5wt.-% mixtures of these Au NPs in Felix-2900-03 showed initially less uniform homeotropic domains due to an increase of bulk-to-interface ratio, which was overcome by increasing concentration to 10 wt.-%.

We postulated that this homeotropic alignment was the result of NPs residing at the LC-glass interface. Upon applying an electric field, the charged NPs act as local capacitors and dipoles and hence alter the anchoring conditions.[30]

A systematic investigation of this phenomenon helped shine more light on the mechanism behind this unusual switching and alignment behavior. Detailed electrooptic test ultimately revealed the formation of convection rolls (electrohydrodynamic instabilities or Williams-Kapustin domains), leading to the conclusion that electro-convection plays a major role in the reverse EO switching of these N-LC/NP mixtures at lower frequencies of the applied AC electric field (Fig. 18).[50]

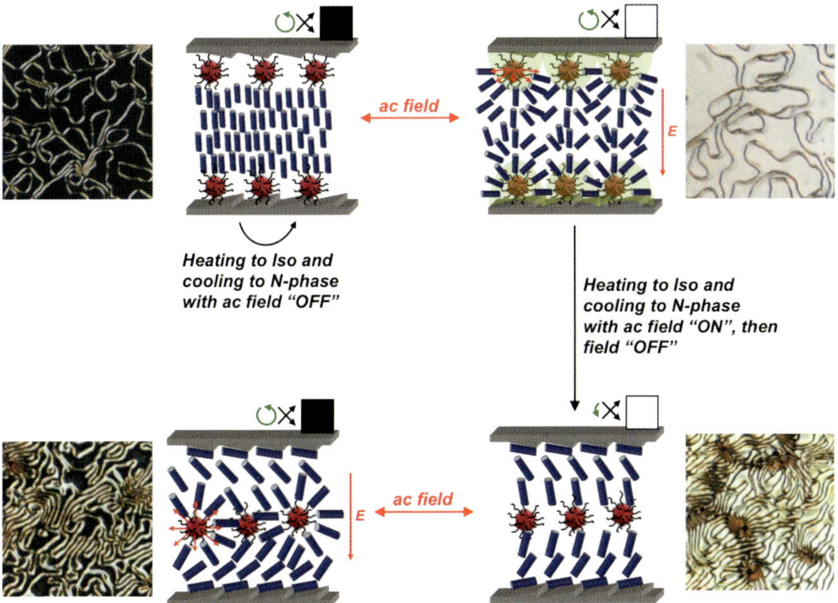

Fig. 17. Schematic representation of the dual alignment and electro-optic mode of an N-LC doped with small NPs capped with aliphatic thiols. Reproduced with permission from Ref. 30, Figure 10. The origin of the birefringent stripes (which are p-walls) was solved by fluorescence confocal polarizing microscopy studies.[49]

Further studies on the effects of NP size, length of the hydrocarbon chains of the capping thiols, and the concentration on the alignment of N-LC hosts with either positive or negative dielectric anisotropy revealed the following. Using higher concentrations of such Au NPs in the N-LC produces homeotropic alignment, but leads to NP aggregates. Reducing the NP concentration results in less perfect homeotropic alignment with the aforementioned birefringent stripes. While investigating the role of lower concentrations (1 and 2 wt.-%) of the same Au NPs with aliphatic thiol capping in Felix-2900-03 and 8CB, we also observed a rather interesting temperature-dependent alignment switch.

As shown in Fig. 19 for Felix-2900-03, on decreasing the temperature from 64°C to 56°C, the typical Schlieren texture (Fig. 19a) changes gradually to homeotropic alignment (Fig. 19d). This effect is attributed to temperature dependent solubility of NPs in LC. At higher temperatures the Au NPs are well dispersed in LC host and the LC molecules interact

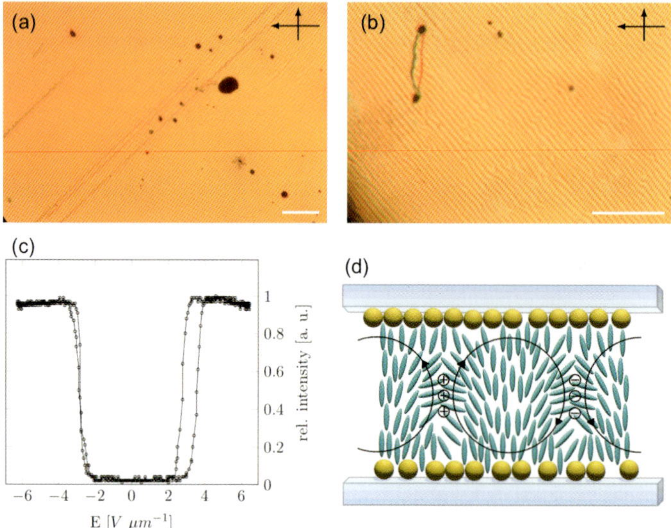

Fig. 18. Parallel convection rolls due to electrohydrodynamic instabilities in Felix-2900-03 doped with 5 wt.-% of $Au(SC_{12}H_{25})_m$ at an applied DC bias of 30 V. The white bar represents 100 μm, the arrows the position of polarizer and analyzer, respectively: (a) magnification 10X, (b) magnification 32X. The convection rolls have a spacing of 8-9 μm. (c) EO characteristic of the Au NP doped mixture at an AC frequency of 0.01 Hz. The measurement was performed with an interference filter for monochromatic light ($\lambda = 579$ nm). (d) Simplified model of electroconvection rolls in a Au NP/LC dispersion with NP induced homeotropic alignment. Reproduced with permission from Refs. 26 and 50.

with the glass surface governing the overall alignment. By lowering the temperature more and more of the NPs are expelled from the bulk LC to glass-LC interface. Our group found that this thermal alignment change is concentration dependent as by reducing the concentration to 1 wt.-%, the temperature at which this alignment switch occurs dropped by 10°C (Fig. 19g-i). We also showed that such thermal alignment change from planar to homeotropic could be created even when cells are preloaded with NPs and then filled with LC. Ag NPs and CdSe QDs in the same size regime will show the same effect as long as they are protected with a dense monolayer of aliphatic ligands.[51]

To test the limit of these effects for applications in devices as well as the efficacy of homeotropic alignment generated by segregated NPs we first succeeded in patterning of LCs by a simple process of stenciling.[4] The success of this rather simple alignment patterning approach was the motivation for

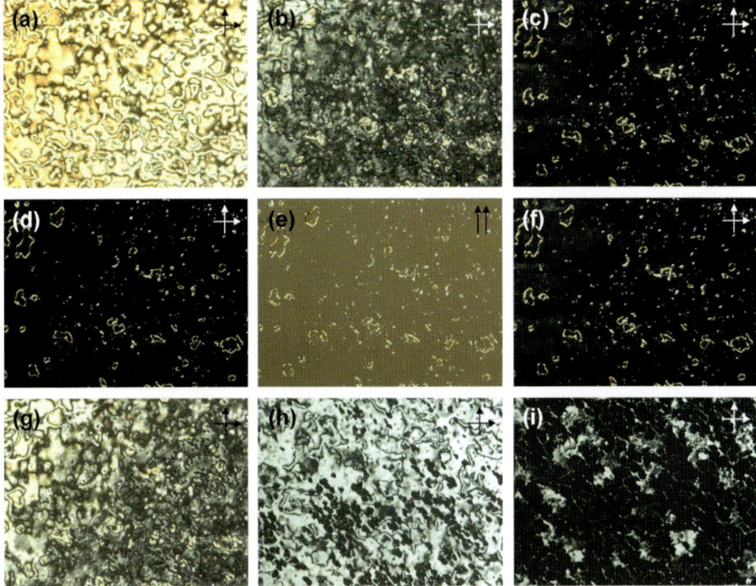

Fig. 19.   POM photomicrographs: Felix-2900-03 doped initially with 2 wt.-% of Au NPs capped with dodecanethiol, Ø=2.1± 0.7 nm) from cooling at (a) 64.0, (b) 61.0, (c) 58.9, and (d) 56.0°C with crossed polarizers and at (e) 56.0°C with parallel polarizers (lower light intensity).   The same area observed on heating at (f) 59.0 and (g) 62.0°C. Felix-2900-03 doped initially with 1 wt.-% of the same Au NP from cooling at (h) 49.8 and (i) 48.5°C (white or black arrows indicate polarizer and analyzer position). Reproduced with permission from Ref. 51, Figure 2.

developing ink-jet printing of small NPs as a versatile and easy tool for the patterned alignment of LCs.[52] Optimization of the NP ink parameters according to printer and cartridge requirements using dodecanethiol-capped Au NPs (Ø= 1.9± 0.4 nm) dispersed in a carrier fluid for printing. Commercially available neat N-LCs and N-LC mixtures with both positive and negative $\Delta\epsilon$ were used to test the quality of patterned homeotropic alignment layers. The polar anchoring energy of the homeotropic alignment induced by the printed NPs was found to be comparable to commercially available homeotropic polyimides (the value we obtained was $W = 6.8 \cdot 10^{-4} \mathrm{Jm}^{-2}$).[52]

As seen in Fig. 20, the homeotropic alignment of the LC is controlled by the printed NP features and in the other areas the director orientation is governed by the still exposed surface of the substrate. It was important to set director boundary also in the non-printed areas as well as the top substrate of cells. The solution was to use an alignment "underlayer"

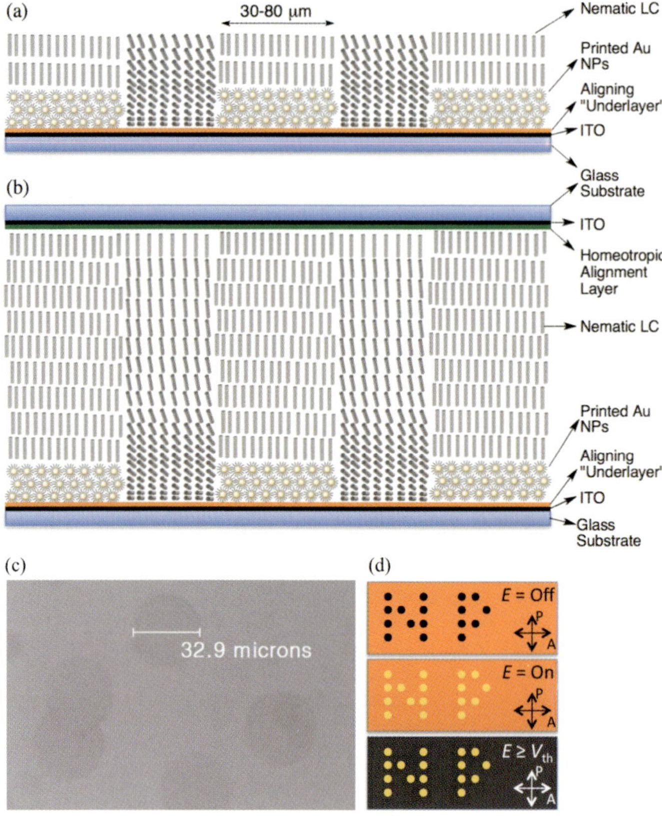

Fig. 20. (a) Schematic image of the substrate design of an LC cell with ITO electrodes and alignment layers (continuous layer of $30°$ SiO_x and patterned printed layer of Au NPs). (b) Schematic image of the hybrid structure of the cell with NPs printed on one of the surfaces featuring a homogeneous alignment layer (bottom), and a second surface with a homeotropic alignment layer (NP induced homeotropic -hybrid patterning). The rubbing direction or easy axis of orientation of the SiO_x alignment "underlayer" determines the direction of planar alignment in the non-printed domains in (a) and (b). (c) Spherical pixels (droplets) printed using Au NPs (bright field micrograph). (d) Possible alignment/electro-optic pattern (homeotropic pixels in planar cell and vice versa using applied electric fields). Reproduced with permission from Ref. 52, Figure 1.

that allows maximum amplitude of the optical axis modulation in the cell with homogenous alignment of the LCs. We explored various alignment layer materials with different polar anchoring energies like polyimide PI-2555#, polyvinyl alcohol and SiO_x films evaporated at $30°$ with respect to evaporation direction (Fig. 21). The traces of NP droplets observed when PI-2555 (Fig. 21c) or PVA$^{\#}$ (Fig. 21d) were used as "underlayer" clearly indicated that the anchoring of the LC to the polymer alignment layer is overpowering the NP-induced anchoring and that an alignment layer with lower anchoring energy such as obliquely deposited SiO_x is needed. To set the boundary conditions for the second substrate, the best option appeared to be an alignment layer that generated homeotropic director configuration over printed areas and a hybrid configuration over the non-printed areas (Fig. 20b). Using SE-1211$^{\#}$ on a pre-cleaned ITO-coated glass was one option for this purpose. As shown in Fig. 21 for MLC-6610$^{\#}$ (with $\Delta\epsilon < 0$), the patterned NP-induced alignment also works on just bare ITO (Fig. 21a). The quality of the homeotropic alignment in the printed areas is high and clear sharp edges surrounded by Schlieren texture in the non-printed areas clearly indicate that it is not necessarily required to print on other alignment substrates.

As demonstrated by the images in Fig. 22, we can print any imaginable pattern with excellent quality. The aforementioned dual alignment mode for LC cells with printed NPs was also observed. When NPs were printed only on one substrate with ITO, 30° SiO_x as 'underlayer' and with ITO/

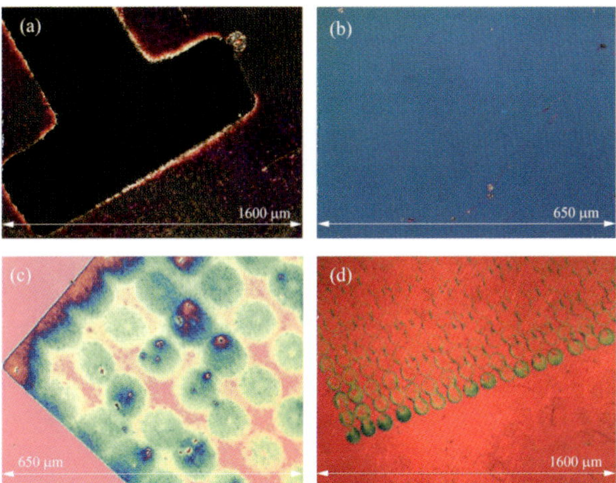

Fig. 21. LC textures and alignment patterns in cells (cell gap: 5 μm) created by printed NPs (crossed polarizers): (a) MLC-6610 on bare ITO (top + bottom substrate); (b) MLC-6610 on the rubbed polyimide PI-2555 - homogeneous alignment; (c) MLC-6610 on rubbed polyimide PI-2555 - distorted (tilted) alignment; (d) 5CB on rubbed polyvinyl alcohol. In all cells, two identical surface alignment layers are used, and the NPs are only printed on one of the substrates. Reproduced with permission from Ref. 52, Figure 2.

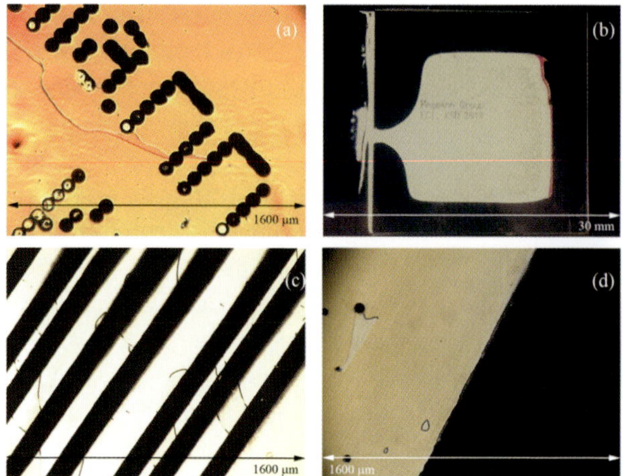

Fig. 22.   LC texture and alignment patterns of MLC-6610 in cells (cell gap: 5 μm) with the NPs printed on the surface of 30° SiO$_x$ (crossed polarizers): (a) alpha-numerical pattern; (b) alphanumerical pattern (entire cell); (c) linear pattern; (d) large-feature, square pattern. The opposite surface of these cells is covered with polyimide SE-1211 inducing homeotropic anchoring. Reproduced with permission from Ref. 52, Figure 3.

SE-1211 on the other substrate, an asymmetrical dielectric response was observed in the field-ON state (Fig. 23a).

The cell returned to initial homeotropic state on both applying negative DC field and switching the electric field OFF (Fig. 23a). However, when both substrates had similar alignment "underlayers" (ITO, 30° SiO$_x$ and printed NPs), the cell switched from homeotropic to parallel alignment on applying positive DC field (Fig. 23b). These cells did not switch back to the homeotropic state on switching the electric field OFF, which does support the involvement of convection rolls in this process.

Printing the NPs on both surfaces eliminates this irreversibility as shown in field OFF and negative DC field states (Fig. 23c). We were also able to show reversible switching with both AC (1 kHz) and DC-applied field for an N-LC with negative dielectric anisotropy, which is important for vertical alignment based display modes.

By adjusting the LC, the ink formulation, and the alignment of the printed surface, any desired pattern is possible with excellent contrast between homeotropic and homogeneous (planar) director configuration. Using advanced sub-femtoliter ink-jet printers it should be possible to generate patterns with comparable size and resolution to photoalignment and pho-

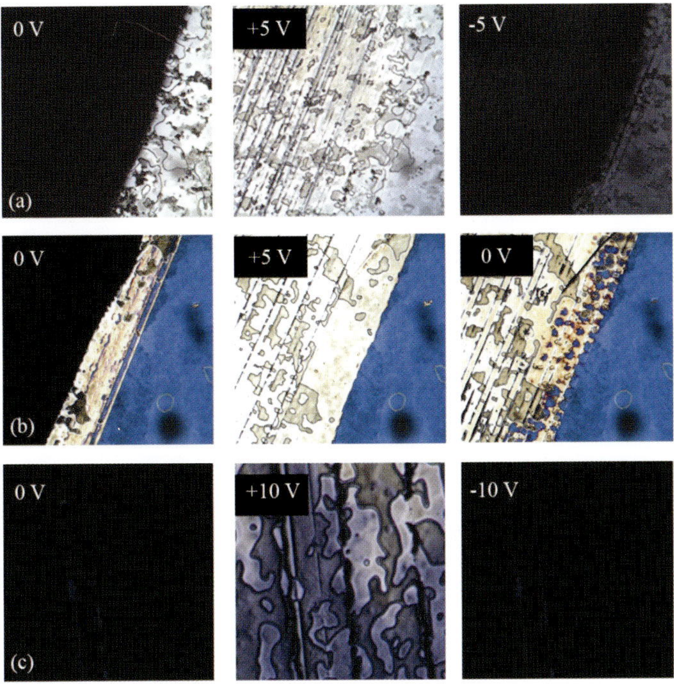

Fig. 23. EO response of the LC cells under an applied DC electric field; LC material: Felix-2900-03; NPs printed on the various surfaces: (a) Substrate 1: ITO + 30° SiO$_x$ + printed NPs, Substrate 2: ITO + PI-1211 substrate; (b) two ITO + 30° SiO$_x$ + printed NPs substrates; (c) Substrate 1: ITO + 30° SiO$_x$ + printed NPs, Substrate 2: ITO + PI-1211 + printed NPs. Reproduced with permission from Ref. 52, Figure 4.

tolithography techniques, with ink-jet printing as the overall simpler, more versatile, and scalable process providing unmatched flexibility to use any material and substrate in numerous applications.

3. Dos and Don'ts

Before drawing some general conclusions on NP dispersions in LCs, we thought it might be useful to share some Dos and Don'ts (tips and tricks) with the experimental chemists, physicists and engineers working in this area of research. Over the last ten years, we worked with various types of NPs and LC dispersions of NPs, and found that many research groups face a common set of problems when dealing with these materials. In this section we will briefly highlight some of these and provide potential solutions that have worked for us.

3.1. *Characterization and storage of NPs*

First, many research teams rely on commercially available NP samples for their experiments. These are often expensive and come ready in some sort of a carrier fluid. Be vigilant and characterize them before beginning to prepare mixtures with LC hosts. Run NMR, UV-vis, FT-IR, elemental analysis, or whatever other technique is suitable for the type of NP you purchased, to familiarize yourself with the material you are planning on using. Many suppliers of NPs stabilize their products using an excess of the ligand used to monolayer-protect the surface of the NPs. Similar to the purification steps needed to obtain pure NP samples without excess free ligand, you will need to purify these samples prior to using them. Carefully check the thermal and chemical stability, particularly at temperatures slightly above the clearing point of your LC host. You will need to heat your LC/NP mixtures above that temperature if you are hoping to achieve well-dispersed samples. Run a TGA and check for long-term chemical and colloidal stability in organic solvents or aqueous suspensions. Figure 24 shows a typical TGA trace of Au NPs capped with an aliphatic thiol.

Pay attention to the proper storage of your NPs. Some NPs are stable when stored at low temperatures (fridge, freezer) in dry powdered form in pre-cleaned glass vials under a protective atmosphere of an inert gas (nitrogen or argon); others are stable (colloidal stable) only in solution. Make sure you only use solvents of high purity and deionized (DI) water.

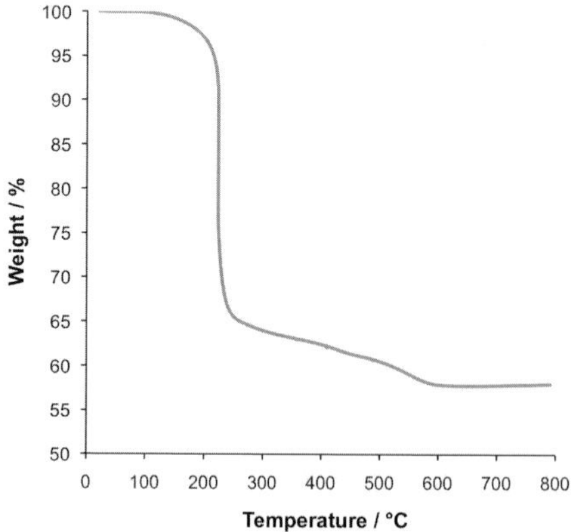

Fig. 24. TGA thermogram of the dodecanethiolate-capped Au NPs showing an onset of weight loss (desorption and decomposition) at 140°C (Ø= 2 nm)[52] confirming XPS data obtained by Joseph and co-workers.[53]

3.2. *Preparation of mixtures*

The preparation of NP/LC suspension is more of an art form than real science, and should not be rushed. Most importantly, familiarize yourself with the chemistry and the chemical nature of the NP you wish to use. Check the solubility of both the NP and the LC in a common solvent to be used for the preparation of mixtures. Each combination will have its most appropriate solvent, so check as many as you can and find the best possible.

Clean your vials and spatulas with aqua regia and/or piranha solution. Completely dissolve both NP and LC in a common solvent and then mix them with a clean stirrer (magnetic or small, clean glass rod). Sonicate the mixture, but only after you have established that sonication does not affect your NPs surface chemistry. Remove the solvent completely under a steady flow of a dry inert gas, which may also help prevent oxidation of certain types of NPs and ligands. This may take time (sometimes between 24 to 48 hours) and is best done at a temperature where the LC host is in the isotropic phase. To get rid of any trace amounts of solvent dry your sample additionally under high vacuum, but only if your LC mixture survives such prolonged vacuum drying without change in composition. Figure 25 shows some key steps of the typical procedure we follow.

For many NPs or QDs LCs careful observation of color changes or color inhomogeneities are helpful during the sample preparation and useful indicators of either homogeneous suspensions or NP phase separation. For QDs, check under UV irradiation as well to detect inhomogeneities of the QD emission in your suspension. Visual inspections of mixtures give a first indication whether to go ahead and fill an electro-optic cell or discard the mixture. Even for mixtures that pass this visual inspection, use microscopy (polarized and bright field) to check for NP aggregates in the micron-size regime. Such aggregates or self-assembled arrays (if you are lucky) might be what you are looking for, but perhaps not, which means, start over finding a better solvent or using a lower concentration of the NPs you are interested in.

3.3. *Filling LC test cells*

It is always good idea to fill EO test cells with NP/LC dispersions with the LC in the isotropic liquid phase. Most NPs are just better soluble in the isotropic liquid phase of LCs. One of three methods is commonly used to fill cells, some of which work better than others, as we will see. Using

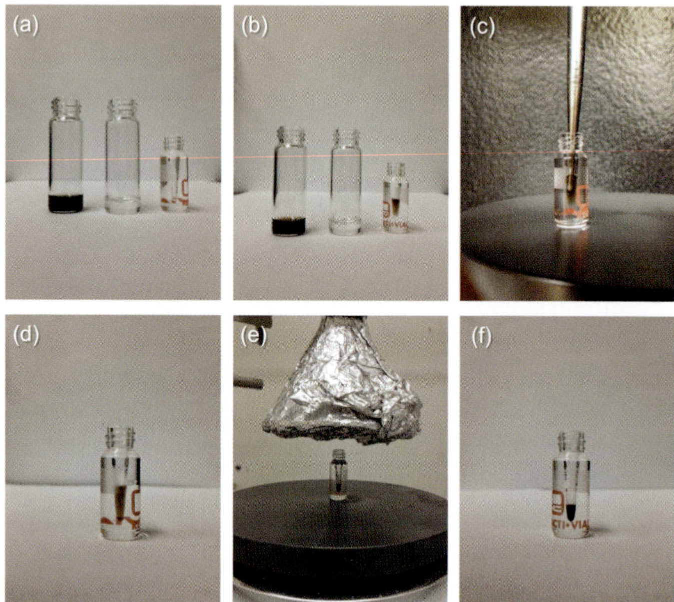

Fig. 25. (a) Preparing solutions of both NP and LC in a common solvent, (b) mixing them in a V-vial, (c) sonicate the solution, (d) homogeneous colloidal dispersion, (e) drying under a flow of dry nitrogen, and (f) final homogeneous LC dispersion (after sonication with the LC in the isotropic liquid phase if necessary and possible considering the thermal stability of the used NPs.

capillary forces to fill test cells for example sometimes creates concentration gradients of the NP or QD with a high concentration at the filling site to a rather low concentration at the opposite end of the cell as shown in Fig. 26.

This de facto creates three independent zones in one and the same cell that correspond to each of the three scenarios we described in detail in Sec. 2.1 to Sec. 2.3. This, of course, makes reliable EO measurements impossible (Fig. 27).

Potential solutions to this problem is the use of another set of techniques, which are either making use of vacuum filling of test cells, the rapid thermal quenching into the LC phase range of cells initially filled with the NP/LC suspension in the isotropic liquid phase (vacuum filling), or a technique that has been working well for our group. Here, the entire path from V-vial to pipette to cell is temperature controlled with the temperature maintained just above the clearing point of the LC mixture (Fig. 28). For many stubborn mixtures, this method works well.

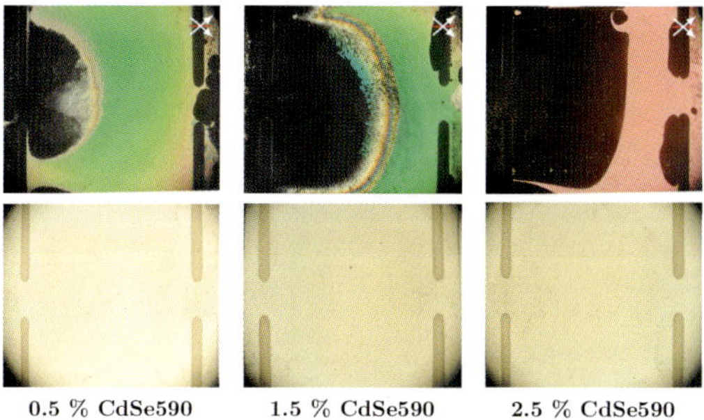

Fig. 26.   Macroscopic images of 4 μm EO test cells filled with dispersions of CdSe$_{590}$ in Felix-2900-03. Test cells were filled from the left side. Images were obtained without polarizers (bottom) or between crossed polarizers (top) at a temperature $T_{Iso/N} - T = 7$ K. White arrows represent the orientation of polarizer and analyzer; the red bar indicates the easy direction of the test cell. Reproduced with permission from Ref. 26.

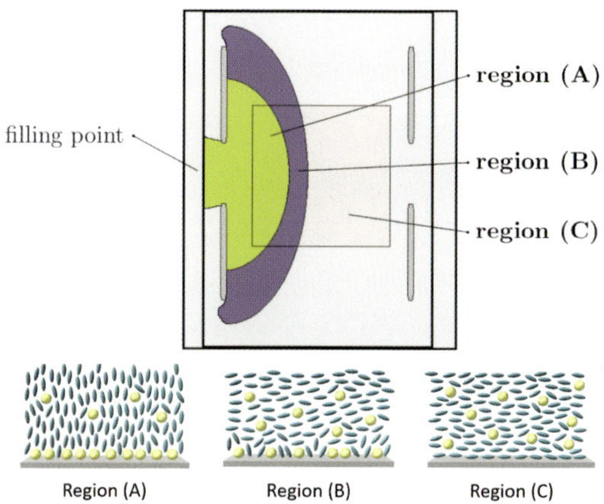

Fig. 27.   A concentration gradient within an EO test cell sometimes arising by filling cells using capillary forces with the LC for example in the N phase. For some aliphatic ligand capped NPs, the three regions correspond to fully segregated (region A, Sec. 2.3), partially dispersed (region B, Sec. 2.2), and well dispersed (region C, Sec. 2.1). Reproduced and adapted with permission from Ref. 26.

Finally, we also successfully use the vacuum filling method, which is shown in Fig. 29. The method allows for rapid filling of test cells with precise temperature control, and is shown here for both a NP-doped N-LC mixture and a cell with patterned ink-jet printed NP alignment layers.

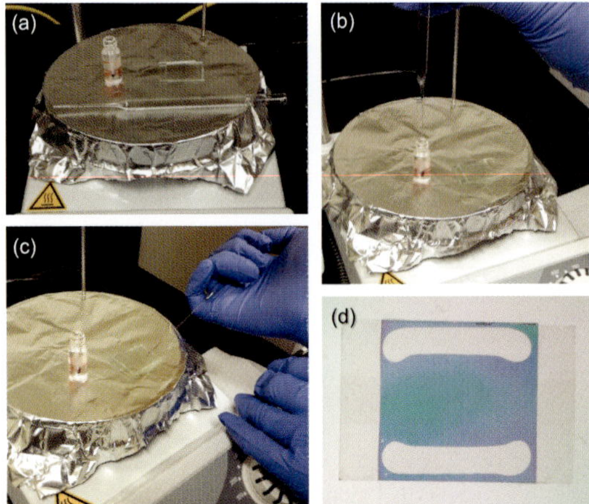

Fig. 28. (a) Heat all glassware, EO test cell and V-vial with mixture on a hot plate to a temperature just above the clearing point, (b) mixture is then transferred quickly from the V-vial to the EO test cell using a draw capillary from a glass pipette, (c) which rests on the hot plate while injecting the mixture rapidly into the EO test cell. (d) The cell filled between crossed polarizers.

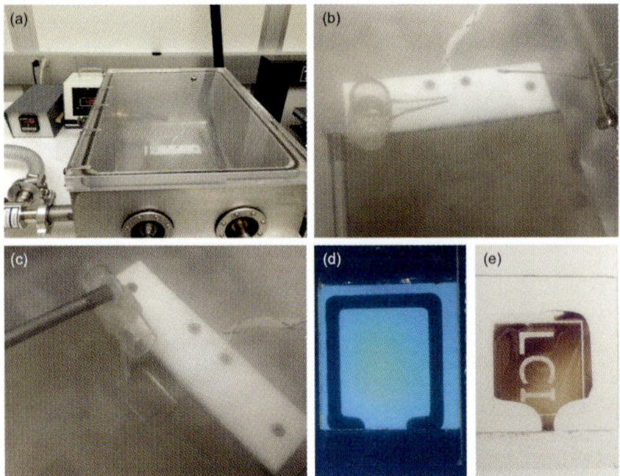

Fig. 29. Vacuum filling of EO test cells with NP/LC mixtures: (a) system equipped with vacuum pump, temperature controller, and hot stage, (b) N-LC mixture is degassed, (c) once desired vacuum is achieved a drop of the mixture is poured on open side of cell, (d, e) filled cells between crossed polarizers.

4. Summary

Research in the area of NP dispersions in LCs has come a long way, and the few examples described in this chapter do not do justice to the large, increasing number of articles published in recent years. Potential device applications will perhaps only arise from either well-dispersed NPs in LC phases or from perfectly segregated NPs serving as alignment layers. The bulk of the data suggests that NP inclusions and NP alignment layers can positively affect the electrooptic response of LCs, both N-LCs and FLCs.

Considering available data from LC dispersions containing NPs other than certain types of metal NPs and semiconductor QDs such as carbon nanotubes or ferroelectric NPs, LC phase stabilizing effects appear to be a key piece of evidence for mixtures with well-dispersed NPs. Including anisometric metal NPs discussed here (due to tactoidal deformations, Fig. 30), spherical ferroelectric NPs that create an anisometrically shaped electric field within the surrounding N-LC molecules,[54] and anisometric carbon nanotubes[55] we assume that anisometric interactions between particles and host are the underlying cause for the LC phase stabilization, which, in turn, is only possible if these particles are well dispersed (Fig. 31).

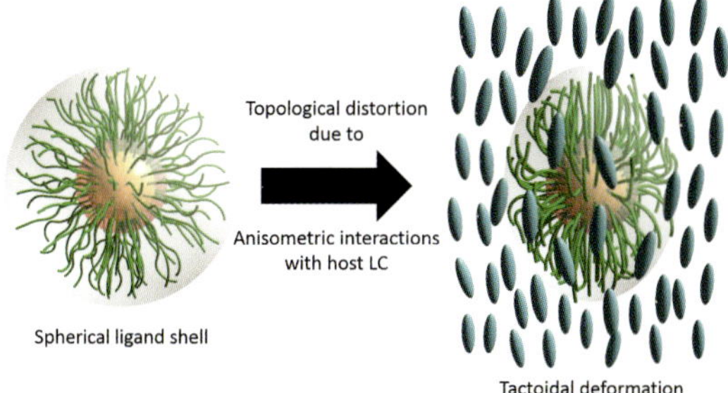

Fig. 30. Tactoidal deformation of the ligand shell proposed for well-dispersed NPs in N-LC host phases. The green ligands protecting the surface of the NP include mesogenic groups, carefully designed mixed monolayer-capped NPs, and NPs with a well-defined silane ligand shell. Adapted from Ref. 26.

We have also established that the radius of curvature of the NP core and, coupled to this, the density of the ligand shell are perhaps the most important factors in deciding if a NP stays well dispersed in a LC host (limited to a certain concentration interval) or if the NPs are expelled to the interfaces in thin films (depending on the anchoring conditions of the underlying substrates). Such NP alignment layers that additionally affect the electrooptic response of a LC on a positive and reproducible manner are most likely to find use in display applications, particularly if the NP are emissive, but could also find unique uses in various types of sensors.

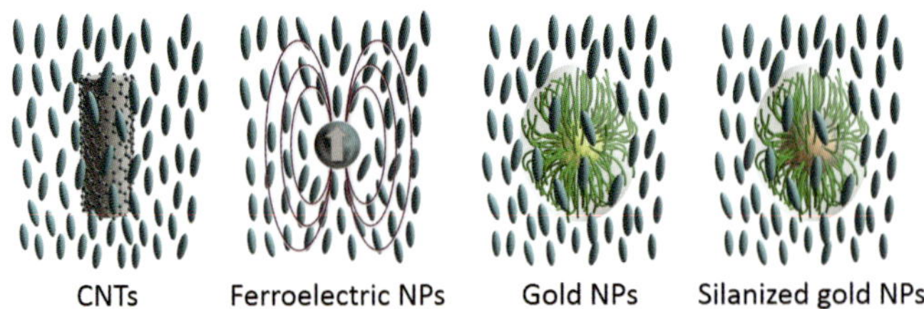

Fig. 31. Schematic drawings of NPs dispersed in a nematic LC host. The examples shown are NPs with assumed anisometric particle / host interactions that stabilize the N-phase and increase the onset temperature of the nematic to isotropic phase transition. Adapted from Ref. 26.

Last but not least, LC materials will play an increasing role in solving various nanomaterial related puzzles such as NP chirality and assembly of NPs in linear, zigzag, helical and other non-trivial 3D fashions.

An important and rapidly emerging field of LC-NP research focuses on the development of metamaterials, i.e. artificial materials which may exhibit rather unusual optical properties owing to plasmonic resonances of metal NPs.[27,56–63] Unlike the dilute dispersions of functionalized NPs described in this chapter, plasmonic metamaterials require a very high volume fraction of the metal component and may be formed by self-assembled NPs with mesogenic shells even without any LC solvent.[56]

Acknowledgments

TM acknowledges financial support (postdoctoral scholarship) from the Japan Society for the Promotion of Science (JSPS). TH acknowledges the support by the National Science Foundation under Grant No. DMR-1506018 for parts of this work and the Ohio Third Frontier (OTF) Program for Ohio Research Scholars "Research Cluster on Surfaces in Advanced Materials", which also supported the TEM facility at the Liquid Crystal Institute at Kent State University, where some of the TEM studies were performed. MU and HSK acknowledge financial support by the Deutsche Forschungsgemeinschaft (DFG, KI 411) and the European Science Foundation (ESF-EURO- CORES, SONS II program, LCNANOP project).

Notes

Materials suppliers: PI-2555 (HD microsystems (Hitachi DuPont, New Jersey), SE-1211 (Nissan Chemical Industries, Ltd., Japan), PVA (Sigma Aldrich, USA), MLC-6610 and E7 (E. Merck KG, Darmstadt, Germany), Felix-2900-03 (Synthon Chemicals GmbH & Co. KG, Germany), 5CB and 8CB (TCI America, USA).

References

1. T. Hegmann, H. Qi, and V. M. Marx, Nanoparticles in liquid crystals: Synthesis, self-assembly, defect formation and potential applications, *Journal of Inorganic and Organometallic Polymers and Materials.* **17**(3), 483–508 (2007).
2. H. Qi and T. Hegmann, Impact of nanoscale particles and carbon nanotubes on current and future generations of liquid crystal displays, *J. Mater. Chem.* **18**(28), 3288–3294 (2008).
3. H. K. Bisoyi and S. Kumar, Liquid-crystal nanoscience: an emerging avenue of soft self-assembly, *Chem. Soc. Rev.* **40**(1), 306–319 (2011).
4. U. Shivakumar, J. Mirzaei, X. Feng, A. Sharma, P. Moreira, and T. Hegmann, Nanoparticles: complex and multifaceted additives for liquid crystals, *Liq. Cryst.* **38**(11-12), 1495–1514 (2011).
5. J. Mirzaei, M. Reznikov, and T. Hegmann, Quantum dots as liquid crystal dopants, *J. Mater. Chem.* **22**(42), 22350–22365 (2012).
6. O. Stamatoiu, J. Mirzaei, X. Feng, and T. Hegmann, Nanoparticles in liquid crystals and liquid crystalline nanoparticles, *Topics Current Chemistry.* **318**, 331–393 (2012).
7. S. Kaur, S. P. Singh, A. M. Biradar, A. Choudhary, and K. Sreenivas, Enhanced electro-optical properties in gold nanoparticles doped ferroelectric liquid crystals, *Appl. Phys. Lett.* **91**(2), 023120 (2007).
8. J. Prakash, A. Choudhary, A. Kumar, D. S. Mehta, and A. M. Biradar, Nonvolatile memory effect based on gold nanoparticles doped ferroelectric liquid crystal, *Appl. Phys. Lett.* **93**(11), 112904 (2008).
9. T. Joshi, A. Kumar, J. Prakash, and A. M. Biradar, Low power operation of ferroelectric liquid crystal system dispersed with zinc oxide nanoparticles, *Appl. Phys. Lett.* **96**(25), 253109 (2010).
10. H. H. Liang, Y. Z. Xiao, F. J. Hsh, C. C. Wu, and J. Y. Lee, Enhancing the electro-optical properties of ferroelectric liquid crystals by doping ferroelectric nanoparticles, *Liq. Cryst.* **37**(3), 255–261 (2010).
11. A. Kumar and A. M. Biradar, Effect of cadmium telluride quantum dots on the dielectric and electro-optical properties of ferroelectric liquid crystals, *Phys. Rev. E.* **83**(4), 041708 (2011).
12. A. Lapanik, A. Rudzki, B. Kinkead, H. Qi, T. Hegmann, and W. Haase, Electrooptical and dielectric properties of alkylthiol-capped gold nanoparticle-

ferroelectric liquid crystal nanocomposites: influence of chain length and tethered liquid crystal functional groups, *Soft Matter.* **8**(33), 8722–8728 (2012).

13. B. Rozic, M. Jagodic, S. Gyergyek, M. Drofenik, S. Kralj, Z. Jaglicic, and Z. Kutnjak, Mixtures of magnetic nanoparticles and the ferroelectric liquid crystal: New soft magnetoelectrics, *Ferroelectrics.* **431**, 150–153 (2012).

14. D. P. Singh, S. K. Gupta, K. K. Pandey, S. P. Yadav, M. C. Varia, and R. Manohar, Ferroelectric liquid crystal matrix dispersed with cu doped zno nanoparticles, *J. Non-Cryst. Solids.* **363**, 178–186 (2013).

15. D. P. Singh, S. K. Gupta, A. Srivastava, and R. Manohar, The phenomenon of induced photoluminescence in ferroelectric mesophase, *J. Lumin.* **139**, 60–63 (2013).

16. R. K. Shukla, X. Feng, S. Umadevi, T. Hegmann, and W. Haase, Influence of different amount of functionalized bulky gold nanorods dopant on the electrooptical, dielectric and optical properties of the FLC host, *Chem. Phys. Lett.* **599**, 80–85 (2014).

17. H. Qi and T. Hegmann, Formation of periodic stripe patterns in nematic liquid crystals doped with functionalized gold nanoparticles, *J. Mater. Chem.* **16**(43), 4197–4205 (2006).

18. H. Qi, J. O'ÄôNeil, and T. Hegmann, Chirality transfer in nematic liquid crystals doped with (s)-naproxen-functionalized gold nanoclusters: an induced circular dichroism study, *J. Mater. Chem.* **18**(4), 374–380 (2008).

19. A. Sharma, T. Mori, H.-C. Lee, M. Worden, E. Bidwell, and T. Hegmann, Detecting, visualizing, and measuring gold nanoparticle chirality using helical pitch measurements in nematic liquid crystal phases, *ACS Nano.* **8**(12), 11966–11976 (2014).

20. J. Mirzaei, M. Urbanski, H. S. Kitzerow, and T. Hegmann, Hydrophobic gold nanoparticles via silane conjugation: chemically and thermally robust nanoparticles as dopants for nematic liquid crystals, *Philosophical Transactions of the Royal Society a-Mathematical Physical and Engineering Sciences.* **371**(1988) (2013).

21. S. B. Chernyshuk, B. I. Lev, and H. Yokoyama, Paranematic interaction between nanoparticles of ordinary shape, *Physical review. E, Statistical, nonlinear, and soft matter physics.* **71**(6 Pt 1), 062701 (2005).

22. M. Urbanski, J. Mirzaei, T. Hegmann, and H. S. Kitzerow, Nanoparticle doping in nematic liquid crystals: Distinction between surface and bulk effects by numerical simulations, *ChemPhysChem.* **15**(7), 1395–1404 (2014).

23. G. L. Nealon, R. Greget, C. Dominguez, Z. T. Nagy, D. Guillon, J.-L. Gallani, and B. Donnio, Liquid-crystalline nanoparticles: Hybrid design and mesophase structures, *Beilstein J. Org. Chem.* **8**, 349–370 (2012).

24. H. Qi, B. Kinkead, V. M. Marx, H. R. Zhang, and T. Hegmann, Miscibility and alignment effects of mixed monolayer cyanobiphenyl liquid-crystal-capped gold nanoparticles in nematic cyanobiphenyl liquid crystal hosts, *ChemPhysChem.* **10**(8), 1211–1218 (2009).

25. D. Coursault, J. Grand, B. Zappone, H. Ayeb, G. Levi, N. Felidj, and E. Lacaze, Linear self-assembly of nanoparticles within liquid crystal defect arrays,

Adv. Mater. **24**(11), 1461–1465 (2012).

26. M. Urbanski, Nanoparticle doping in nematic liquid crystals, *Ph.D. thesis (University of Paderborn)*. pp. urn:nbn:de:hbz:466:2-10850 (2013).

27. W. Lewandowski, M. Wojcik, and E. Gorecka, Metal nanoparticles with liquid-crystalline ligands: Controlling nanoparticle superlattice structure and properties, *ChemPhysChem.* **15**(7), 1283–1295 (2014).

28. M. Draper, I. M. Saez, S. J. Cowling, P. Gai, B. Heinrich, B. Donnio, D. Guillon, and J. W. Goodby, Self-assembly and shape morphology of liquid-crystalline gold metamaterials, *Adv. Funct. Mater.* **21**(7), 1260–1278 (2011).

29. J. Mirzaei, M. Urbanski, H. S. Kitzerow, and T. Hegmann, Synthesis of liquid crystal silane-functionalized gold nanoparticles and their effects on the optical and electrooptic properties of a structurally related nematic liquid crystal, *ChemPhysChem.* **15**(7), 1381–1394 (2014).

30. H. Qi, B. Kinkead, and T. Hegmann, Unprecedented dual alignment mode and freedericksz transition in planar nematic liquid crystal cells doped with gold nanoclusters, *Adv. Funct. Mater.* **18**(2), 212–221 (2008).

31. B. Kinkead and T. Hegmann, Effects of size, capping agent, and concentration of cdse and cdte quantum dots doped into a nematic liquid crystal on the optical and electro-optic properties of the final colloidal liquid crystal mixture, *J. Mater. Chem.* **20**(3), 448–458 (2010).

32. C. Gautier and T. Burgi, Chiral gold nanoparticles, *ChemPhysChem.* **10**(3), 483–492 (2009).

33. Z. Y. Fan and A. O. Govorov, Plasmonic circular dichroism of chiral metal nanoparticle assemblies, *Nano. Lett.* **10**(7), 2580–2587 (2010).

34. A. O. Govorov, Z. Y. Fan, P. Hernandez, J. M. Slocik, and R. R. Naik, Theory of circular dichroism of nanomaterials comprising chiral molecules and nanocrystals: Plasmon enhancement, dipole interactions, and dielectric effects, *Nano. Lett.* **10**(4), 1374–1382 (2010).

35. A. Guerrero-Martinez, J. L. Alonso-Gomez, B. Auguie, M. M. Cid, and L. M. Liz-Marzan, From individual to collective chirality in metal nanoparticles, *Nano Today.* **6**(4), 381–400 (2011).

36. L. B. Wang, L. G. Xu, H. Kuang, C. L. Xu, and N. A. Kotov, Dynamic nanoparticle assemblies, *Accounts Chem. Res.* **45**(11), 1916–1926 (2012).

37. S. Campidelli, T. Brandmüller, A. Hirsch, I. M. Saez, J. W. Goodby, and R. Deschenaux, An optically-active liquid-crystalline hexa-adduct of [60] fullerene which displays supramolecular helical organization, *Chem. Commun.* (41), 4282–4284 (2006).

38. W. Ma, H. Kuang, L. B. Wang, L. G. Xu, W. S. Chang, H. N. Zhang, M. Z. Sun, Y. Y. Zhu, Y. Zhao, L. Q. Liu, C. L. Xu, S. Link, and N. A. Kotov, Chiral plasmonics of self-assembled nanorod dimers, *Scientific Reports.* **3**, 1934 (2013).

39. L. G. Xu, W. Ma, L. B. Wang, C. L. Xu, H. Kuang, and N. A. Kotov, Nanoparticle assemblies: dimensional transformation of nanomaterials and scalability, *Chem. Soc. Rev.* **42**(7), 3114–3126 (2013).

40. S. Knoppe and T. Burgi, Chirality in thiolate-protected gold clusters, *Accounts Chem. Res.* **47**(4), 1318–1326 (2014).

41. H. Qi and T. Hegmann, Postsynthesis racemization and place exchange reactions. another step to unravel the origin of chirality for chiral ligand-capped gold nanoparticles, *J. Am. Chem. Soc.* **130**(43), 14201–14206 (2008).

42. A. L. Rodarte, Z. S. Nuno, B. H. Cao, R. J. Pandolfi, M. T. Quint, S. Ghosh, J. E. Hein, and L. S. Hirst, Tuning quantum-dot organization in liquid crystals for robust photonic applications, *ChemPhysChem.* **15**(7), 1413–1421 (2014).

43. L. Cseh and G. H. Mehl, The design and investigation of room temperature thermotropic nematic gold nanoparticles, *J. Am. Chem. Soc.* **128**(41), 13376–13377 (2006).

44. L. Cseh and G. H. Mehl, Structure-property relationships in nematic gold nanoparticles, *J. Mater. Chem.* **17**(4), 311–315 (2007).

45. X. B. Zeng, F. Liu, A. G. Fowler, G. Ungar, L. Cseh, G. H. Mehl, and J. E. Macdonald, 3D ordered gold strings by coating nanoparticles with mesogens, *Adv. Mater.* **21**(17), 1746–1750 (2009).

46. S. Umadevi, X. Feng, and T. Hegmann, Large area self-assembly of nematic liquid-crystal-functionalized gold nanorods, *Adv. Funct. Mater.* **23**(11), 1393–1403 (2013).

47. S. Khatua, P. Manna, W. S. Chang, A. Tcherniak, E. Friedlander, E. R. Zubarev, and S. Link, Plasmonic nanoparticles-liquid crystal composites, *J. Phys. Chem. C.* **114**(16), 7251–7257 (2010).

48. J. Mirzaei, M. Urbanski, K. Yu, H. S. Kitzerow, and T. Hegmann, Nanocomposites of a nematic liquid crystal doped with magic-sized cdse quantum dots, *J. Mater. Chem.* **21**(34), 12710–12716 (2011).

49. M. Urbanski, B. Kinkead, T. Hegmann, and H. S. Kitzerow, Director field of birefringent stripes in liquid crystal/nanoparticle dispersions, *Liq. Cryst.* **37**(9), 1151–1156 (2010).

50. M. Urbanski, B. Kinkead, H. Qi, T. Hegmann, and H. S. Kitzerow, Electroconvection in nematic liquid crystals via nanoparticle doping, *Nanoscale.* **2**(7), 1118–1121 (2010).

51. H. Qi and T. Hegmann, Multiple alignment modes for nematic liquid crystals doped with alkylthiol-capped gold nanoparticles, *ACS Appl. Mater. Interf.* **1**(8), 1731–1738 (2009).

52. M. Reznikov, A. Sharma, and T. Hegmann, Ink-jet printed nanoparticle alignment layers: Easy design and fabrication of patterned alignment layers for nematic liquid crystals, *Particle & Particle Systems Characterization.* **31**(2), 257–265 (2014).

53. Y. Joseph, I. Besnard, M. Rosenberger, B. Guse, H. G. Nothofer, J. M. Wessels, U. Wild, A. Knop-Gericke, D. S. Su, R. Schlogl, A. Yasuda, and T. Vossmeyer, Self-assembled gold nanoparticle/alkanedithiol films: Preparation, electron microscopy, XPS-analysis, charge transport, and vapor-sensing properties, *J. Phys. Chem. B.* **107**(30), 7406–7413 (2003).

54. L. M. Lopatina and J. V. Selinger, Theory of ferroelectric nanoparticles in nematic liquid crystals, *Phys. Rev. Lett.* **102**(19) (2009).

55. H. Duran, B. Gazdecki, A. Yamashita, and T. Kyu, Effect of carbon nanotubes on phase transitions of nematic liquid crystals, *Liq. Cryst.* **32**(7),

815–821 (2005).

56. M. Wojcik, W. Lewandowski, J. Matraszek, J. Mieczkowski, J. Borysiuk, D. Pociecha, and E. Gorecka, Liquid-crystalline phases made of gold nanoparticles, *Angew. Chem. (Int. Ed.).* **48**(28), 5167–5169 (2009).

57. M. Wojcik, M. Kolpaczynska, D. Pociecha, J. Mieczkowski, and E. Gorecka, Multidimensional structures made by gold nanoparticles with shape-adaptive grafting layers, *Soft Matter.* **6**(21), 5397–5400 (2010).

58. M. M. Wojcik, M. Gora, J. Mieczkowski, J. Romiszewski, E. Gorecka, and D. Pociecha, Temperature-controlled liquid crystalline polymorphism of gold nanoparticles, *Soft Matter.* **7**(22), 10561–10564 (2011).

59. D. F. Gardner, J. S. Evans, and I. I. Smalyukh, Towards reconfigurable optical metamaterials: colloidal nanoparticle self-assembly and self-alignment in liquid crystals, *Mol. Cryst. Liq. Cryst.* **545**(1), 3/[1227]–21/[1245] (2011).

60. C. H. Yu, C. P. Schubert, C. Welch, B. J. Tang, M.-G. Tamba, and G. H. Mehl, Design, synthesis, and characterization of mesogenic amine-capped nematic gold nanoparticles with surface-enhanced plasmonic resonances, *J. Am. Chem. Soc.* **134**(11), 5076–5079 (2012).

61. X. Mang, X. Zeng, B. Tang, F. Liu, G. Ungar, R. Zhang, L. Cseh, and G. H. Mehl, Control of anisotropic self-assembly of gold nanoparticles coated with mesogens, *J. Mater. Chem.* **22**, 11101–11106 (2012).

62. J. Dintinger, B.-J. Tang, X. Zeng, F. Liu, T. Kienzler, H. Mehl, Georg, G. Ungar, C. Rockstuhl, and T. Scharf, A self-organized anisotropic liquid-crystal plasmonic metamaterial, *Adv. Mater.* **25**(14), 1999–2004 (2013).

63. H. S. Kitzerow. Photonic micro and nanostructures, metamaterials. In eds. J. W. Goodby, P. J. Collings, T. Kato, C. Tschierske, H. Gleeson, and P. Raynes, *Handbook of Liquid Crystals*, pp. 373–426. Wiley Online Library (2014).

Chapter 15

Inorganic nanotubes and nanorods in liquid crystals

Irena Drevenšek-Olenik

University of Ljubljana, Faculty of Mathematics and Physics,
Jadranska 19, SI 1000 Ljubljana, Slovenia,
J. Stefan Institute, Jamova 39, SI 1000 Ljubljana, Slovenia
irena.drevensek@ijs.si

Research efforts that focus on possible improvement of the physical properties of thermotropic liquid crystals by addition of inorganic 1D nanoparticles (inorganic nanotubes, nanorods, etc.) are reviewed. The emphasis is on modification of electro-optic switching characteristics relevant for display-related applications. In most cases the dopants generate a decrease of the threshold voltage for electrooptic switching and also a decrease of the corresponding switching times. We discuss various possible reasons for the observed effects and point out specific characteristics related to 1D nature of the dopants. We also describe investigations of inclusion of 1D nanoparticles into photo-polymerizable nematic liquid crystalline materials. Photo-polymerization in the aligned nematic phase provides a convenient way to fabricate solid polymer films with strongly anisotropic angular distribution of the nanoparticles. Investigations of structural and optical properties of some selected systems are surveyed.

Contents

1. Introduction

At first glance, one might expect that inclusion of rod-shaped nanoparticles into conventional liquid crystals (LCs) composed of rodlike molecules (calamatic LCs) should be a very straightforward harmonizing process, as both subsystems have a natural tendency to organize into orientationally ordered structures. In reality, however, the process of mixing is often quite problematic, because the building blocks of the two components typically have considerably different sizes and exhibit a rather poor chemical compatibility. Various mechanisms aimed to overcome these problems and to obtain satisfactory mixing properties have been systematically investigated for carbon nanotubes (CNTs) (see other chapters of this book), while investigations of other types of nanotube- and nanorod-forming particles are at present still very scattered, because different research groups have access to different kinds of one-dimensional (1-D) nanomaterials and are interested in different physical properties and applications perspectives of the resulting mixtures. This chapter focuses on investigations related to insertion of inorganic 1-D nanoparticles into various LC materials. Particles made of ferroelectric and ferromagnetic materials are excluded from the description, as they are considered in a separate chapter.

Most of the inorganic 1-D nanoparticle-LC mixtures investigated up till now have involved thermotropic LCs doped with rod-shaped particles with diameters d in the range of 1-100 nm and lengths L from 10 nm to 10 μm. Such mixtures mostly belong to the category of the LC colloidal suspensions in which the diameter of the particles is large compared to the surface anchoring extrapolation length $\xi = K/W$ (10 nm $< \xi <$ 10 μm) of the nematic phase, where K is the Frank elastic constant of the LC phase and W is surface anchoring energy at the LC-particle interface.[1] This type of dopant particles in general causes a substantial distortion of the director field in the vicinity of their surface and due to the associated increase of the elastic free energy of the LC medium they have a strong tendency to flocculate.[2,3] The intriguing properties of LC colloidal suspensions are extensively described in several recent review papers.[4–15] In these reviews the emphasis is on nanodopants of spherical (granular) shape and/or on CNTs, while descriptions related to nanotubes and nanorods from inorganic compounds are scarce.

2. Inorganic nanotubes and nanorods

2.1. *Historical development*

The discovery of CNTs in 1991[16] invigorated scientific interest in all kinds of one-dimensional (1-D) nanostructures. Due to their many functional properties, CNTs were found to be very promising as additives to different organic materials leading to enhancement of mechanical, thermal, electrical and optical properties of the resulting composites. Fabrication of high quality composites, however, requires very pure starting material and good particle dispersion, which even nowadays still poses considerable difficulties for CNTs. For these reasons the synthesis of competitive tubular assemblies, in particular inorganic nanotubes and nanorods, found increasing interest. With the discovery of fullerene-like nanoparticles and nanotube structures made of tungsten disulfide (WS_2) in 1992[17] and shortly afterwards also of molybdenum disulfide (MoS_2),[18–20] it was realized that carbon represents only one example of a wide class of layered materials that can form 1-D morphologies. In the following years, fabrication of an extensive plethora of different kinds of synthetic inorganic 1-D nanoparticles was reported.

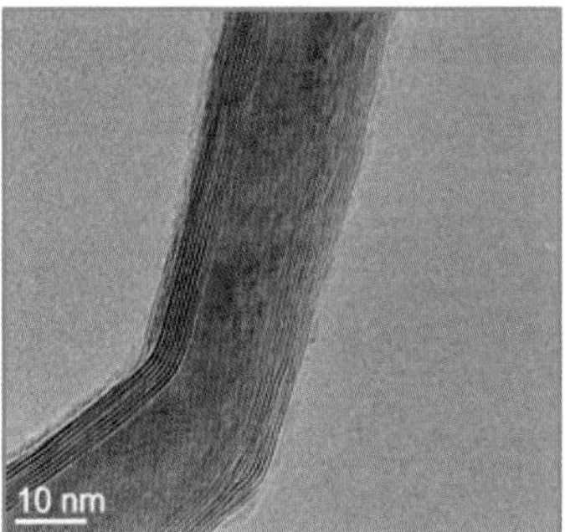

Fig. 1.   High-resolution transmission electron microscopy (HR-TEM) image of multi-walled MoS_2 nanotube (courtesy of A. Kovic, J. Stefan Institute, Ljubljana, Slovenia).

2.2. *Types of inorganic nanotubes and nanorods*

Nanotubes of transition metal chalcogenide materials (denoted as TMC, where TM denotes transition metals like Mo, W, Nb, etc.; and C denotes chalcogens like S, Se, etc.), can be synthesised by different strategies, e.g. by chemical vapour deposition, use of solid templates, chalcogenization etc.[21,22] They can be multi-walled or single-walled. Their production in macroscopic amounts allowed systematic studies of their properties and possible applications.[23] Using SEM and AFM tips as a probe, in-situ tensile and buckling experiments were carried-out on individual tubes.[24] The observed tensile strength with Young's modulus in the TPa range was found to be exceedingly high in comparison to conventional high strength materials.[25] Optical spectroscopy of MS_2 nanotubes revealed their semiconducting nature.[26] Intercalation of lithium (Li) and hydrogen (H) into nanotube structures was investigated in view of their energy storage capabilities and promising values of the discharge capacity were revealed.[27] Recently the production of MS_2 nanotubes was scaled-up to the commercial level,[28] which makes these materials now available for widespread research as well as industrial activities.

Another interesting type of 1-D nanoparticle-forming materials are transition metal chalcogen halogenides, described by the formula $TM_6C_yH_z$ (TMCH), where H denotes halogen, which is most usually iodine (I). Their composition is given by $8.2 < (y + z) < 10$.[29–31] It has been demonstrated that, conversely to CNT and TMC nanotubes, TMCH nanotubes and nanowires exhibit one-type electric conductivity behaviour, are dispersible in common solvents and tend to debundle in solution.[32,33] This makes them ideal candidates for conductive fillers for various kinds of composite systems. They display also many other fascinating physical and chemical properties that make them promising for applications such as wear resistant materials, lubricants, pressure, temperature and chemical sensors or indicators.[34–37] The properties of TMCH nanotubes and nanowires are sensitive to the stoichiometry of the material, which could be controlled by adjusting the synthesis conditions.[38] Therefore tailoring material properties for selected applications is feasible as well as essential for possible commercialization of composites incorporating this type of 1-D nanoparticles.

Conventional ceramics compounds, such as titanium-oxide (TiO_2) and zinc-oxide (ZnO), can form 1-D nanostructures too.[39,40] These nanostructures belong to a broad family of metal-oxide (MOx) nanotubes and nanorods that involves also materials like vanadium oxide (VOx), copper oxide (CuO), indium oxide (In_2O_3), manganese dioxide (MnO_2), aluminium oxide (Al_2O_3), and silica (SiO_2).[41,42] Their unique characteristics are broad structural versatility and flexibility. Various exchange reactions, intercalations and surface modifications can be performed such that the 1-D morphology of the starting structure remains well preserved. Due to this

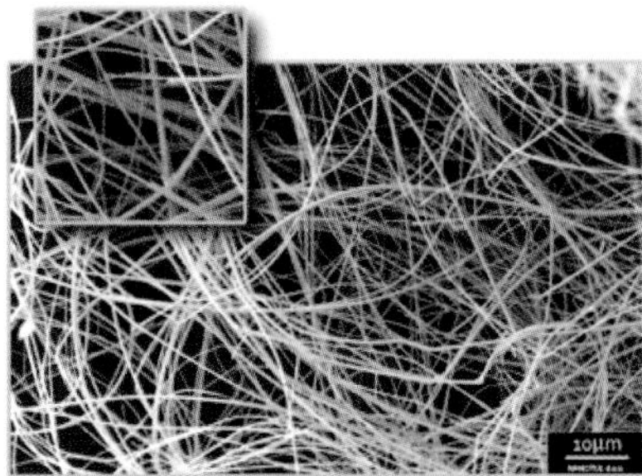

Fig. 2. Scanning electron microscopy (SEM) image of $Mo_6S_2I_8$ nanotubes (courtesy of M. Remškar, Nanotul d.o.o., Slovenia).

property, MOx nanotubes and nanowires are known for their outstanding sensing, sensitizing and catalytic effects.[43–45]

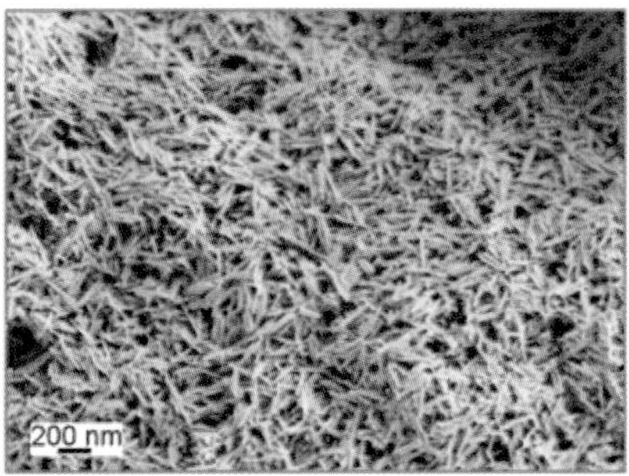

Fig. 3. Scanning electron microscopy (SEM) image of MnO_2 nanorods (courtesy of P. Umek, J. Stefan Institute, Ljubljana, Slovenia).

Another class of nanotube-forming materials are nitrides, such as boron nitride (BN), gallium nitride (GaN), carbon nitride (CN), boron-carbon nitride (BCN), etc. These nanotubes are structurally analogous to CNTs, so they are mechanically robust and exhibit good chemical and thermal stability. BN nanotubes are electrically insulating (band gap 5 eV), however, their thermal conductivity is similar to the thermal conductivity of CNTs.[46,47] GaN nanotubes are electrically semiconducting and consequently possess interesting optical properties, such as photoluminescence.[48,49] CN nanotubes are electrically conductive and are commended for their biocompatibility.[50,51] BCN nanotubes, depending on their composition, display intermediate properties between the BN and the CN nanotubes.[52] Interesting filler material are also Molybdenum nitride (MoN) nanowires, which were recently found to exhibit superconducting properties.[53] They are composed from the hexagonal δ_3 phase of MoN and exhibit superconducting critical temperature T_c of 11 K.

A very important family of 1-D nanoparticles are metallic nanowires. They can be fabricated from practically all conventional metals, such as nonmagnetic silver (Ag), copper (Cu), gold (Au), zinc (Zn), and molybdenum (Mo), as well as from magnetic iron (Fe), nickel (Ni) and cobalt (Co), and also from various metallic alloys.[54–57] The electronic transport properties of metallic nanowires strongly depend on the wire diameter.[58] For diameters much larger than the carrier mean free path of the bulk medium, the wires behave similar to the bulk material. For diameters similar or smaller than the career mean free path, interface-related effects become important. At very small diameters, quantum confinement of the carriers plays a dominant role. The most apparent application of metallic nanowires is in interconnects for nanoelectronic circuits. Other possible uses are for thermoelectric devices, magnetic data storage units, and chemical and biochemical sensing devices.[59]

Besides the 1-D nanoparticles classes described above, there exist numerous other inorganic nanotube- and nanorod- structures, such as structures from semiconducting, mixed-phase or metal-doped materials. One should also not overlook the rich group of naturally formed 1-D (fibrillar) structures that are found in various mineral depositions.[60,61] Another very broad category are hybrid 1-D systems, such as core-shell nanotubes, nanotube peapods, decorated nanotubes and nanowires, polymer-grafted nanotubes and nanowires etc. Currently, there seems to be practically no limits for fabrication of new kinds of 1-D nanosize objects and new synthetic achievements are reported almost every day.[62]

Finally, it should be noted, that at suitable conditions spherical particles immersed in the uniaxial LC phase can form chain-like aggregates that effectually behave as 1-D inclusions.[63–65] The interesting aspect of this kind of systems is that the length of the chains can be controlled *in-situ* by application of external stimuli, for instance magnetic field.[66] This provides a very convenient method to tune the interaction properties between the dopant and the host medium.

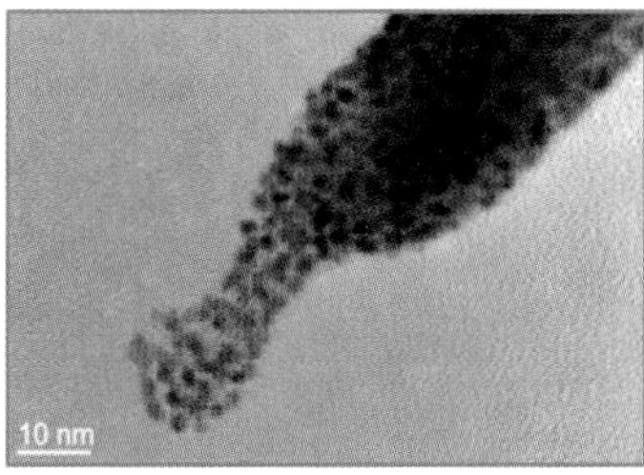

Fig. 4. Transmission electron microscopy (TEM) image of a bundle of MoSI nanowires decorated with platinum (Pt) nanoparticles (courtesy of A. Kovic, J. Stefan Institute, Ljubljana, Slovenia).

3. Introducing nanotubes and nanorods into the LC host

As described in Chap. 3, already in simple isotropic fluids the aggregation properties of rod-shaped particles are very different from the aggregation properties of the spherical particles. The difference becomes even more profound in the nematic phase, in which additional torque originating from directional interactions with the surrounding fluid comes into play.[67] Determination of the strength of this torque is still an open experimental problem.

One of the primary experimental challenges related to the introduction of any kind of nanoparticles into liquid crystals is to obtain good nanoparticle dispersion and in the same time preserve the LC order of the host medium.[4,68,69] The effect of dopants on the LC order can be most simply tested by monitoring the shifts of the transition temperatures between different LC phases. Most commonly the nematic-isotropic (N-I) phase transition temperature T_{NI} is probed. Addition of 1-D nanoparticles can cause both: an increase or a decrease of the LC order and consequently of the T_{NI}.[70–74] A change $T_{\mathrm{NI}} \approx 0$ is in general supposed to indicate a very good compatibility between both components, but in practice, unfortunately, it often means that the dopant has precipitated from the suspension.[75] When being at least partially dispersed, most of the 1-D nanodopants induce a down-shift of T_{NI}. As a down-shift can also result from various impurities present in the mixture, such as remaining solvent molecules, cross-checking experiments have to be performed to resolve different contributions.

Figure 5 shows results of the analysis of the T_{NI} in the mixtures of 4-cyano-4'-pentylbiphenyl (5CB) with two semiconducting dopants: MnO_2 nanorods (see Fig. 3) and WS_2 nanotubes, both at the concentration of

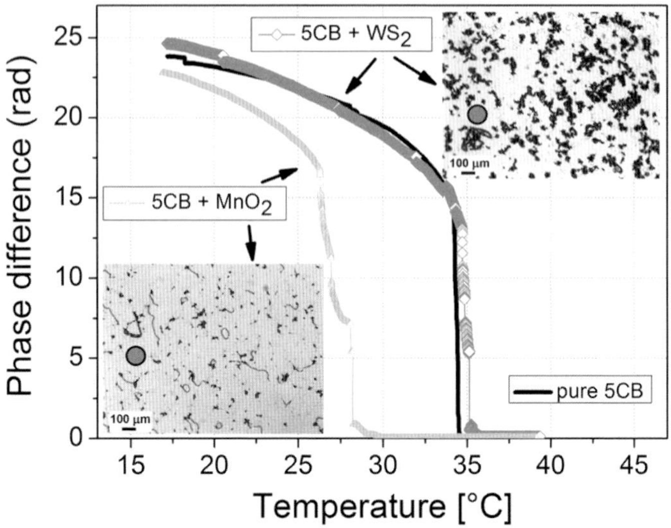

Fig. 5.   Temperature dependence of the optical phase difference in mixtures of 5CB with MnO$_2$ nanorods (triangles) and WS$_2$ nanotubes (diamonds). The concentration of the dopants was 0.5 wt-%. The black solid line represents data for pure 5CB. The insets show optical polarization microscopy images of the samples in the nematic phase. The circles here indicate typical laser spot size in optical measurements. Reproduced with permission from Ref. 76, copyright Willey-VCH, 2013).

0.5 wt-%.[76]   The former had diameters in the range $d = 20 - 30$ nm and lengths $L = 100 - 700$ nm and the latter had $d = 80 - 120$ nm and $L \sim 10$ μm.   No surface functionalization of the dopants was performed. The compounds were mixed via a common solvent (isopropanol) and after evaporation of the solvent and subsequent ultrasonication the mixture was introduced into standard 12 μm thick glass cells with alignment layers for planar LC orientation.   Optical retardation (phase difference) $\Delta\phi$ between the extraordinary and ordinary ray at a wavelength of 633 nm was measured.   The drop of $\Delta\phi$ from $\Delta\phi > 0$ to $\Delta\phi = 0$ signifies the phase transition.   The results show that MnO$_2$ nanorods cause a significant decrease of the T_{NI}, while WS$_2$ nanotubes cause a small increase of the T_{NI}.

While optical techniques can avoid regions in the vicinity of the agglomerates, which typically behave very different from the regions in-between them,[77] this is not possible for calorimetric (DSC) and many other techniques (XRD, SAXS, NMR, dielectric spectroscopy etc.) standardly used to probe the LC order.[78]   These techniques hence always reveal a cumulative response of the LC-nanoparticle mixture including the agglomerates. To solve the agglomeration problem, various physical procedures have been developed to keep the dispersion stable for at least several hours, which is usually enough to perform the measurements. Since most of the inorganic nanoparticles are quite well dispersible in the isotropic phase of the LC medium, one of the frequently used methods is to prepare the mixture at $T > T_{NI}$ and then quickly reduce (quench) the temperature to $T \ll T_{NI}$.[79] Another possibility is permanent stirring of the mixture during slow cooling from $T > T_{NI}$ to $T < T_{NI}$, which is sometimes repeated in several cooling/heating cycles.[80] The third method is to introduce a dry nanoparticle powder directly into the nematic phase and homogenize the mixture by a powerful ultrasound source.[81] All these methods can be subsequently combined also by centrifugation to remove residual aggregates.[82]

To obtain long-term dispersion stability, chemical modification (functionalization) of the nanotube/nanorod surfaces is performed. The choice of optimal surface coating depends on size and chemical composition of the particles as well as on chemical composition and type of the LC host. For inorganic dopants good results are achieved by a soft organic coating that is setting a relatively week boundary condition for the LC molecules.[83,84] The soft shell can be grafted with an outer layer of mesogenic molecules to further improve the compatibility.[85–87] Inorganic surfaces in general prefer planar anchoring of the LC molecules.[88] Consequently, functionalization with different surfactants is typically used to alter the surface anchoring condition from planar to homeotropic.[89,90] Very intriguing properties are obtained with surface coatings based on photosensitive groups, which offer a possibility to modify surface anchoring properties by optical illumination.[79,91]

One of the elegant methods to preserve nanoparticle dispersion in the LC host, is to 'fix' the dispersed mixture by polymerization.[92,93] The level of polymerization can be either partial (polymer-stabilised suspension (PSS)) or complete (polymerized LC). Figure 6a shows a SEM image of 0.1 wt-% MoS_2 nanotubes (see also Fig. 1) incorporated into a fully polymerized commercial photoreactive LC material (RM257, Merck Ltd.).[94] The nanotubes had diameters of around 50 nm and lengths up to several micrometers. The nanotube dry powder was introduced directly into the LC material and dispersed by ultrasonic homogenization. The mixture was then placed in a standard glass cell with rubbed polyimide surface alignment layers and photo-polymerization reaction was performed. During the individual processes of homogenization and photo-polymerization, the material was kept

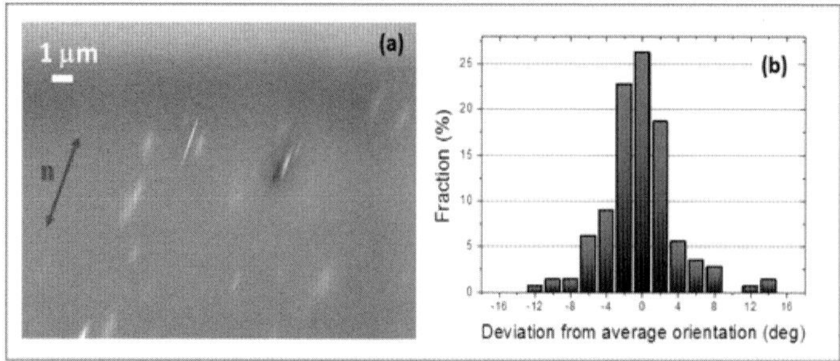

Fig. 6. (a) SEM image (COMPO mode) of MoS_2 nanotubes (0.1 wt-%) incorporated into photopolymerized LC material. Bright objects are nanotube bundles. (b) Statistical analsis of the angular distribution of the bundles with respect to the direction of nematic director **n**. (With permission from Ref. 94, copyright American Chemical Society, 2014).

in its nematic phase $(T = 80°C)$. Afterwards, it was slowly cooled to room temperature. The resulting solid polymer film showed good dispersion and an excellent level of nanotube alignment with an in-plane orientational order parameter $S_p = \langle \cos(2\varphi) \rangle = 0.97$, where φ is the angle between the average direction of the nanotubes in the image plane and the direction of a specific nanotube and brackets denote averaging (Fig. 6b). The described strategy can be used to fabricate polymeric composites for applications in which strong and controllable anisotropy of a selected physical property plays a distinctive role, such as for instance directionally selective flexible strain-gauge sensors or polarization-sensitive optical couplers.

4. Effect on electro-optical response

The majority of applications of liquid crystals in commercial devices are based on the very strong electro-optical response of the LC phases, which is a consequence of a unique combination of the soft elasticity with a large anisotropy of dielectric and optical properties.[95] But, as this response is collective on the molecular-scale level, it is usually relatively slow (ms range). Consequently, one of the primary motivations to introduce nanodopants into the LC materials is to speed up the electrical response. Another challenge is to reduce the operational voltage magnitude and thus the power consumption of the devices. These goals can be attained either by modifying the mechanical (viscoelastic) or by changing the electrical properties.

4.1. *Viscoelastic properties*

Viscoelastic properties of LCs are conveniently probed by dynamic light scattering (DLS).[96] This nonperturbative method gives information on the ratios of elastic constants to effective viscosities for different eigenmodes of thermally-induced fluctuations of the LC director field $\mathbf{n}(\mathbf{r})$, where $\mathbf{n}$ is preferential orientation of the LC molecules (director). The inverse relaxation times of the two low-frequency eigenmodes of the nematic phase are given as:[97,98]

$$\frac{1}{\tau_\alpha} = \frac{K_{\alpha\alpha}q_\perp^2 + K_{33}q_\parallel^2}{\eta_\alpha^{\mathrm{eff}}(\mathbf{q})} \tag{1}$$

where $\alpha = 1, 2$ and K_{ii} denotes Frank elastic constants and indices $i = 1, 2$ and 3 denote splay, twist and bend deformations, respectively. The effective viscosities of both eigenmodes depend on the orientation of the scattering wave vector $\mathbf{q}$ with respect to the nematic director $\mathbf{n}$, where the symbol $\perp$ denotes a component perpendicular and the symbol $\parallel$ a component parallel to $\mathbf{n}$.[99]

Figure 7 shows the temperature dependence of inverse relaxation times of thermally-induced fluctuations measured in the nematic phase of 4-octyl-4'-cianobiphenyl (8CB) doped with different concentrations of MoS_2 nanotubes ($c = 0.05 - 0.2$ wt-%).[99] Nanotubes with relatively small dimensions ($d \sim 5$ nm, $L \sim 20$ nm) were used. The associated scattering arrangements were such that the values of $K_{33}/\eta_2^{\mathrm{eff}}$ and $K_{11}/\eta_1^{\mathrm{eff}}$ were resolved. The results show that both viscoelastic ratios decrease with increasing concentration of the nanotubes. They also reveal a decrease of the nematic-isotropic transition temperature T_{NI} and of the nematic - smectic A transition tem-

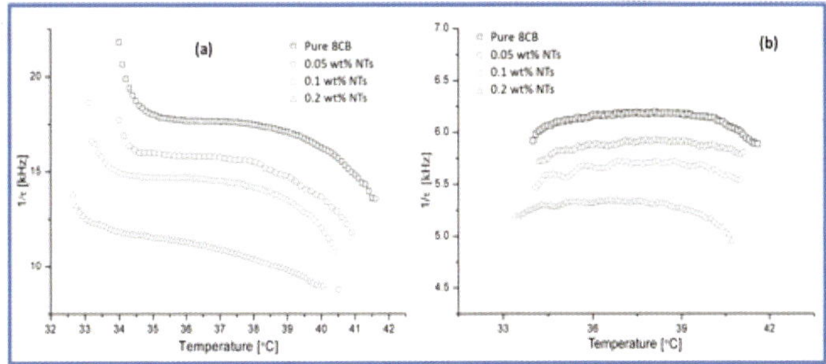

Fig. 7. Temperature dependence of inverse relaxation times for (a) bend-type and (b) splay-type orientational fluctuations. Measurements were performed at a scattering angle of 50°. (With permission from Ref. 99, copyright Taylor & Francis Group, 2005).

perature T_{NA} by increasing nanotube concentration. In the vicinity of T_{NA} ($T \sim 33°\mathrm{C}$) the ratio of $K_{33}/\eta_2^{\mathrm{eff}}$ (Fig. 7a) also exhibits a typical divergent behaviour.[100]

To obtain separate data on elastic constants and viscosity coefficients, a combination of different experimental techniques is required. By combining dielectric and electrooptical measurements, Tripathi *et al.* found that addition of zinc-oxide (ZnO) nanorods ($d = 12 - 15$ nm, $L = 40 - 80$ nm, $c = 0.5 - 1.5$ wt-%) to the standard nematic LC material N-(4-methoxybenzylidene)-4-butylaniline (MBBA) causes a significant increase of the elastic constant K_{11} as well as of the rotational viscosity coefficient γ.[80] Also in this system the observed modifications were larger for larger concentrations of the dopant. Similar effects were observed for ZnO nanorods added to 5CB[101] and for gold (Au) nanowires introduced into 8CB.[102] On the contrary, Sawai *et al.* detected a decrease of both K_{11} and K_{33}, induced by addition of gold nanowires to 5CB,[103] while Nayek *et al.* detected a decrease of K_{11} and an increase of K_{33} for cadmium sulfide (CdS) nanorods incorporated into a commercial nematic blend ZLI1636 (Merck Ltd.).[104] Consequently, because the reports on viscoelastic properties of inorganic nanotube/nanorod mixtures with LCs are still relatively rare and systematic studies are lacking, the present status of knowledge is far from providing any verified material engineering stategies.

4.2. *Electrical properties*

The complex dielectric permittivity of the LC phases is profoundly anisotropic and strongly frequency dependent. To resolve the details of various dielectric relaxation processes, capacitance measurements of standard aligned LC cells need to be accomplished in a broad frequency range.[105] Nevertheless, to obtain a first rough idea on the effect of a selected dopant on the material response to external voltage, it is usually sufficient to analyse the Frederiks reorientational transition at a fixed frequency. The threshold voltage U_{th} for the most typical splay-type reorientation in a planarly aligned cell can be written as:[106]

$$U_{\mathrm{th}} = \pi \sqrt{\frac{K_{11}}{\epsilon_0 \epsilon_a}} \qquad (2)$$

where $\epsilon_a = \epsilon_{||} - \epsilon_\perp$ corresponds to low-frequency dielectric anisotropy associated with effective dielectric constants of the suspension.[107] For particles that significantly affect the LC orientational order, also modification of the K_{11} with respect to the pure LC material should be considered.

The Frederiks transition can be detected by various methods. Figure 8 shows results of measurements of transmitted optical intensity I_t through a LC cell placed between two crossed polarizers oriented at 45° with respect to the alignment axis.[108] The measurements were performed with a He-Ne laser beam (λ =633 nm) focused to a spot size of about 100 μm. The investigated material was a commercial nematic LC mixture TL203 (Merck Ltd.) doped with $Mo_6S_4I_6$ nanotubes ($d \sim 50$ nm, $L \sim 5$ μm, 0.1 wt-%). The gap of the glass cell was set by spacers of a thickness of 50 μm. The transition was induced by a 1 kHz square waveform voltage with the amplitude U. Due to variation of the thickness of the LC layer in the cell, the optical phase retardation $\Delta\phi$ and the associated transmitted intensity at $U = 0$ exhibit different values in different sample regions. The results presented in Fig. 8 correspond to the two limiting cases associated with minimal and maximal transmitted intensities. The transmitted intensity is constant for $U < U_{th}$ because of a homogeneous orientation of the LC director field, and oscillates for $U > U_{th}$ because of an increasing reorientation angle of the LC molecules that produces a decreasing retardation. Each oscillation period of $I_t(U)$ corresponds to the modification of $\Delta\phi$ by 2π. The amplitude of oscillations decreases by increasing voltage due to averaging of the signal

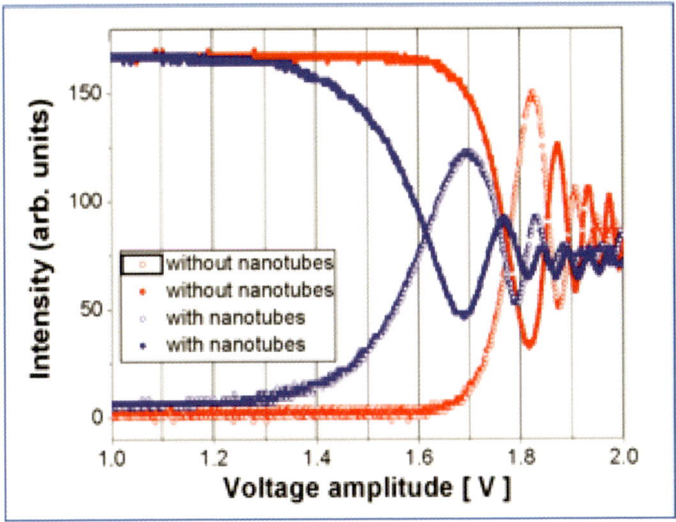

Fig. 8. Voltage dependence of transmitted optical intensity for pure TL203 (Merck Ltd.)(red symbols) and for mixture of TL203 with 0.1 wt-% MoSI nanotubes (blue symbols). (Reproduced with permission from Ref. 108, copyright Sensors & Transducers, 2011).

over the inhomogeneities in the illuminated region of the sample, which is more crucial at larger voltages. The obtained results show, that addition of nanotubes causes a drop U_{th} from $U_{th} \sim 1.6$ V to $U_{th} \sim 1.2$ V.

DLS measurements performed on the same samples showed only minor modification of the ratio $K_1/\eta_1^{\mathrm{eff}}$, so it was suggested that the observed decrease of U_{th} is a consequence of the increased dielectric anisotropy ϵ_a of the mixture. However, a theoretical analysis based on the Maxwell-Garnett effective medium theory predicts that an increase of ϵ_a for the investigated mixture should be negligible.[107] Consequently, the observed decrease of U_{th}[108] does not seem to be primarily related to the nanotube-induced modification of ϵ_a, but to modifications of the entire reorientation process associated with the Frederiks transition. The nanotube bundles and especially the nanotube agglomerates produce strong local distortions of the director field, which can serve as the 'seed points' causing a significant molecular reorientation already at voltages considerably below U_{th}. The nanotubes can also segregate on the confining glass surfaces and modify their alignment properties.[14] Some separate investigations have actually shown that a controlled deposition of inorganic rod-shaped particles onto glass substrates can be used to tune the surface anchoring condition.[89,109,110]

A decrease of U_{th} due to addition of inorganic nanotubes and nanorods to various nematic LCs was observed in many other studies too.[76,84,102–104,111,112] The effect is most often attributed to the enlarged dielectric anisotropy of the mixture, which is ascribed to different cooperative phenomena, such as an increase of the overall nematic orientational order[102] or appearance of an additional dielectric relaxation mode.[104] It is also quite usual, that nanodopants reduce the concentration of free ions in the mixture, which as well leads to an effectively lower value of U_{th}.[5] Besides this, the reduced concentration of free ions also helps improving the voltage holding properties of the LC cells.[113] However, there exist also reports that claim a considerable increase of U_{th} induced by doping with rod-shaped inorganic nanoparticles.[101] As an extreme case, Tripathi *et al.* observed an increase of U_{th} by a factor of 10 for MBBA doped with 1.5 wt% ZnO nanorods.[80] The increase was attributed to copper ions (8% Cu^{2+}) present in the dopant that cause an increase of the charge density near the interface. The ions also modify the electrical conductivity σ of the system.

Strong modifications of σ are generally observed for metallic nanodopants.[114] Sridevi *et al.* studied 8CB doped with gold nanorods ($c = 2$ wt-%) and found an increase of both $\sigma_{||}$ and $\sigma_{\perp}$, by more than two orders of magnitude, while the anisotropy of the conductivity $\sigma_a = \sigma_{||} - \sigma_{\perp}$

remained nearly the same.[102] While a decrease of U_{th} is in general supposed to be very advantageous, because it reduces power consumption of the LC devices, an increase of the conductivity is counterproductive and rises electrical power dissipation.

From the descriptions given above it is evident that the observed value of U_{th} in the particular mixture is affected by many different parameters that are often interrelated to each other. Consequently it can happen that addition of nanoparticles on the one hand produces a desired decrease of the U_{th}, but on the other hand some other properties exhibit unfavourable changes. So, to obtain broader understanding of various processes affecting the Frederiks transition, investigations should be extended to analyse the effect of external voltage also on other properties besides U_{th}.

4.3. *Switching dynamics*

The nematic director field $\mathbf{n}(\mathbf{r})$ of the LC layer sandwiched between two flat solid surfaces is typically switched between two configurations. One of these two configurations is established by the torque caused by application of an external electric field (field-on-configuration) and another one by the torque originating from the interfacial interaction at the confining surfaces (field-off-configuration). Rod-shaped nanodopants present in the LC host are directionally trapped within the director field $\mathbf{n}(\mathbf{r})$ and consequently they reorient during the switching process accordingly to the associated modifications of $\mathbf{n}(\mathbf{r})$.[115,116] As will be described in the following section, this LC-driven nanoparticle reorientation can be directly utilised for some applications exploiting the specific properties of the nanodopant. But, because the presence the dopant causes also modification of the visco-elastic and electrical properties of the LC medium, it can indirectly influence also the switching process itself.

Switching dynamics can be investigated by monitoring temporal variation of optical retardation $\Delta\phi(t)$ in the LC cell after switching on and removal of the external voltage. Figure 9 shows the results obtained for the splay-type reorienation of $\mathbf{n}(\mathbf{r})$ in a previously described system of MnO_2 nanorods and WS_2 nanotubes in 5CB (see also Fig. 5).[76] A 1 kHz square waveform carrier voltage with selected RMS amplitude was connected to the ITO electrodes and amplitude modulated (100% modulation depth) with modulation frequency of 0.1 Hz. The switching on process associated with $U > U_{th}$ involves competition between field-induced torque and the torque of the surface anchoring forces, which in general makes the reorien-

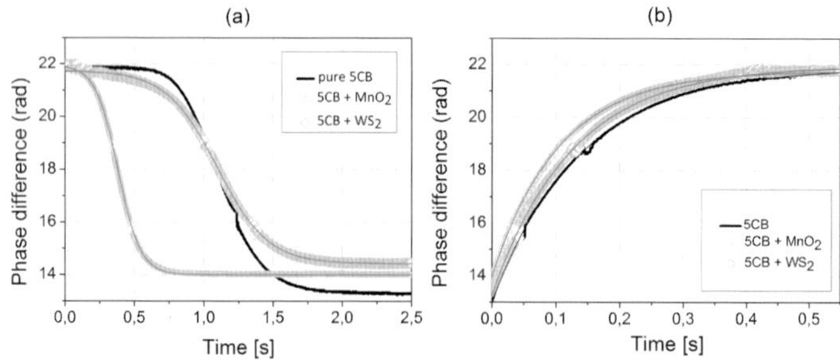

Fig. 9. Time dependence of optical retardation after (a) switching on and (b) switching off the external voltage (amplitude of 1 V). Solid lines are fits to the response functions described by Eqs. 3 and (4). Reproduced with permission from Ref. 76, copyright Willey-VCH, 2013).

tation kinetics quite complicated. However, for voltages slightly above U_{th} the deviation of $\mathbf{n}(\mathbf{r})$ from the initial planar orientation is relatively small and the following approximate relation can be used:[117,118]

$$\Delta\phi(t) = B_1 - B_2/(1 + Ce^{-\frac{2t}{\tau_{on}}}), \quad \frac{1}{\tau_{on}} = \frac{\epsilon_0\epsilon_a}{\gamma_1^* D^2}\left(U^2 - U_{th}^2\right) \tag{3}$$

where D is the thickness of the LC layer and γ_1^* is the effective viscosity that is close to the rotational viscosity coefficient γ_1.[96] The constants B_1, B_2 and C are related to the initial and final tilt angles of the director with respect to the substrates.[118] Results obtained after switching on a voltage $U = 1$ V are shown in Fig. 9a. There is a very good agreement between the experimental data and fitting curves according to Eq. (3). Besides the parameter τ_{on}, which is associated with the maximal slope of the response function, an important parameter governing the dynamics of the reorientation process is also the initial phase retardation $\Delta\phi_0 = \Delta\phi(t = 0) = B_1 - \frac{B_2}{C+1}$, which is related to deviations from the perfect planar LC alignment at $U = 0$.[118] The value of $\Delta\phi_0$ is minimal and hence the alignment is most perfect in pure 5CB, which is the reason that switching on process in pure 5CB starts with the longest initial plateau region. Sample doped with MnO_2 nanorods exhibits a value of $\Delta\phi_0$ by nearly a factor of 20 larger than for pure 5CB and consequently reorients with the shortest initial delay.

The dynamic response following removal of the external voltage (switching-off-process, Fig. 9b) corresponds to a simple exponential relaxation given as:[117]

$$\Delta\phi(t) = A_1 - A_2 e^{-t/\tau_{off}}, \quad \frac{1}{\tau_{off}} = \frac{K_{11}}{\gamma_1^*}\left(\frac{\pi}{D}\right)^2 \tag{4}$$

One can notice that relaxation is faster in doped samples than in pure 5CB. As the rotational viscosity coefficient γ_1 usually increases due to the additives, the observed increase of the relaxation rate $(1/\tau_{\text{off}})$ is attributed to the increase of the effective elastic constant K_{11} induced by the dopants.

The results demonstrate that addition MnO_2 nanorods to 5CB produces a significant decrease of both τ_{on} and τ_{off}, so that the total switching time defined as $\tau = \tau_{\text{on}} + \tau_{\text{on}}$ at $U = 1$ V decreases from $\tau = 0.43$ s observed in pure 5CB to $\tau = 0.27$ s for 5CB doped with 0.5 wt-% MnO_2 nanorods. Besides the increase of K_{11}, the effect is believed to be mainly associated with the increase of the dielectric anisotropy ϵ_a of the mixture. The origin of the increase of ϵ_a in this system is not yet clarified. A considerable decrease of the total switching time was observed also for other investigated inorganic nanotube/nanorod – nematic LC mixtures.[80,84,101,112,119] The most profound effect is reported for incorporation of 1.5 wt-% ZnO nanorods in MBBA, which resulted in a decrease of the total response time τ by nearly one order of magnitude (from 90 ms to 10 ms at $U = 6$ V).[80]

Despite the fact that inorganic 1-D nanodopants can significantly speed-up the conventional switching process of the nematic LC structure, it is quite improbable that they can 'push' the response time from the millisecond down to the microsecond region. So, to attain the microsecond range, ferroelectric liquid crystals (FLCs) are usually used as the host medium. Ferroelectricity most typically appears in the smectic C phase composed of chiral LC molecules (SmC* phase).[120] Due to spontaneous electric polarization present in the SmC* phase, the nature of the switching process in FLCs is very different from the switching process in the nematic LCs. Podgornov *et al.* and recently Shukla *et al.* investigated incorporation of 0.1-0.5 wt% gold nanorods on the switching dynamics of some commercial FLC mixtures and generally observed a decrease of the switching time τ. The maximum observed modification was from $\tau = 40$ μs to $\tau = 20$ μs.[121,122] The effect was attributed to the dopant-induced increase of the local electric field in the smectic layers, which takes place via shunting of the electrical double layer near the interfaces. A reduced switching time was observed also in FLC materials doped with 0.1-0.3 wt-% semiconducting CdS nanorods and was attributed to increased spontaneous polarization of the SmC* phase.[123] Besides the switching time τ, also many other properties of FLCs were found to exhibit substantial changes due to addition of inorganic nanotubes and nanorods.[114,124,125]

5. Some specific new properties and applications

5.1. *LC-mediated plasmonic properties*

Rod-shaped metallic nanoparticles exhibit large anisotropy of optical absorption and scattering properties, which is a consequence of the large difference between the resonant properties of the longitudinal and the transversal (with respect to the geometrical axis of the particle) surface plasmon oscillations.[126–128] However, to be able to exploit this anisotropy in various optical devices, the particles need to be directionally aligned on the macroscopic scale. This can be conveniently realized by their incorporation into the LC host medium, which besides alignment provides also a possibility to modify the alignment direction by application of an external electric field or other external stimuli. Potential applications of this effect are tuneable plasmonic polarizers, colour filters, shutters, reflectors etc.

Investigations of plasmonic properties of metallic nanorod–LC systems focus mainly on gold nanorods (GNRs), because here methods for fabrication and surface functionalization are well developed and because surface plasmon resonances appear in the spectral region of visible and near infrared light, which is convenient to be analysed.[129,130] Early studies considered standard nematic LC cells with GNRs covering one of the two planar substrate layers. Interaction with the aligned nematic phase induced directional alignment of the nanorods and reorientation of the surrounding LC medium resulted in considerable modifications of the extinction spectrum of the medium.[131] An interesting effect of nonreciprocal behaviour with respect to the propagation direction of the optical beam was also noticed.[132] The first example of a successful alignment of GNRs in a bulk of the nematic LC phase was reported in 2007 for a surfactant-based lyotropic LC host material.[133] The alignment resulted in a strongly polarization-sensitive extinction spectrum of the medium, due to which the colour of the sample observed in transmission optical microscopy varied by changing the direction of the incident optical polarization. Modification of the GNR alignment and consequently of the spectral properties of the mixture by shearing and by application of an external magnetic field was also demonstrated.[133] The samples were stable for several days. A similar GNR alignment effect, but with the alignment direction perpendicular to the nematic director field $\mathbf{n}(\mathbf{r})$, was later realized also for a lytropic LC phase composed of discoidal micellar units.[83] Incorporation of a chiral additive to the LC host produced a helicoidal arrangement of the GNRs. Analogous helicoidal assembling was recently demonstrated also for GNRs dispersed in the cholesteric phase of cellulose nanocrystals.[134–136]

By structural investigations based on small-angle X-ray scattering Thomas *et al.* demonstrated that with suitable surface functionalization of the GNRs it is possible to obtain their alignment also in the conventional thermotropic LCs, such as 5CB and E7 mixture (Merck Ltd.).[137] It was also shown that the alignment can be disrupted and reconfigured by an external electric field. The group of Smalyukh has recently extended these investigations to systematically characterize the optical properties of the GNR-thermotropic LC mixtures.

Figure 10 shows results obtained for GNRs with diameter $d \sim 20$ nm and length $L \sim 50$ nm incorporated in 5CB.[138] Longitudinal and the transversal surface plasmon resonances (SPRs) for this system appear at 690 nm and at 520 nm, respectively. The mixture was placed into the standard planarly aligned LC cell. Figure 10a shows the dependence of the transmission of the cell for linearly polarized white light as a function of the external voltage amplitude U. The polarization direction (marked in the image as **P**) was parallel to the direction of the nematic director **n** at $U=0$. For $U < U_{th}$ the transmission is constant, while for $U > U_{th}$ it increases with increasing voltage. This happens because the GNRs together with the nematic director field **n(r)** reorient from the parallel to the perpendicular orientation with respect to the polarization direction **P** and consequently the optical extinction due to the longitudinal SPR decreases.[139] The insets in Fig. 10a show the visual appearance of the sample in transmitted light for $U < U_{th}$ and $U > U_{th}$. The sample changes its colour from green to red. Figure 10b shows the associated extinction spectra at $U = 0$ and $U = 8$ V,

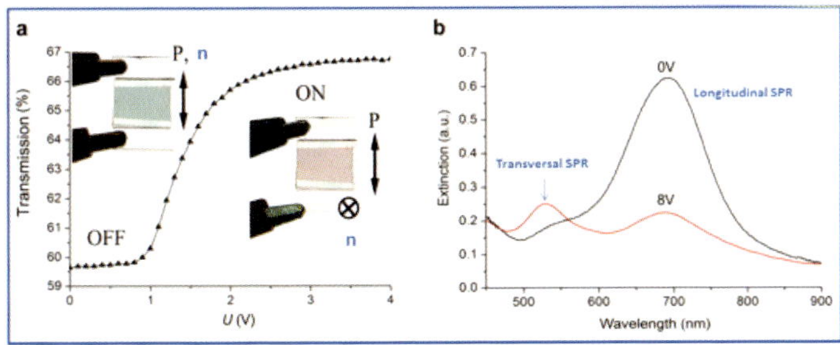

Fig. 10. Electric switching of a plasmonic guest-host LC system with GNRs. (a) Transmission of linearly polarized light versus applied voltage, (b) extinction spectra for **P** along the substrate rubbing direction for $U = 0$ and $U = 8$ V. (Reproduced with permission from Ref. 138, copyright American Chemical Society, 2014).

which proves that the extinction in the red part of the spectrum is indeed significantly reduced at $U = 8$ V.

The above described dependence of the colour of transmitted light on the angle between the polarization of the incident light $\mathbf{P}$ and the nematic director $\mathbf{n}$ can be used to inscribe switchable coloured patterns into the composite structure. This can be achieved, for instance, by using patterned photoalignment layers instead of the standard unidirectionally rubbed substrates.[82,138,140] Such patterns are visible for $U < U_{th}$ and become invisible for $U > U_{th}$. The effect can be used in display applications and also for smart windows, opto-optical modulation devices etc.

Incorporation of GNRs into other LC phases and systems can lead to many additional interesting plasmonic properties. For example, Wong *et al.* found that addition of 0.06 wt-% GNRs to the LC blue phase (BP) causes an expansion of the BP temperature range. Besides this it generates a considerable red shift of the Bragg reflection peak.[141] Mixtures of GNRs and other metallic nanorods with FLCs are expected to result in switchable plasmonic systems with microsecond response, while incorporation of metallic nanorods into polymeric and elastomeric LC materials opens up various possibilities for mechanical and optical tuning of the plasmonic properties.[142–144] Consequently, the field of metallic nanorod-LC colloidal systems will for sure further expand in the near future.

5.2. *LC-mediated photoluminescent properties*

The above described operational principles for LC materials doped with metallic nanorods can be exploited also for semiconducting nanorods. Instead of absorption the main property of interest in this case is photoluminescence. Optical excitation and optical emission of single nanorods are strongly polarization dependent, indicating that electric dipole is induced predominantly along the long axis of the rods.[145] A macroscopic assembly of aligned nanorods is therefore expected to emit optical radiation with a high degree of polarization.

Wu *et al.* investigated incorporation of cadmium sulphide (CdS) nanorods ($d \sim 5$ nm, $L \sim 40$ nm, $c < 0.1$ wt-%) in the commercial nematic LC mixture E7 (Merck Ltd).[81] The nanorods were deposited on one of the glass substrates and after this a standard planarly aligned LC cell was assembled. Supersonic treatment was employed to induce transfer of the nanorods from the surface into the LC medium. Then the cell was illuminated with an UV laser beam at 374 nm. Figure 11a shows the resulting

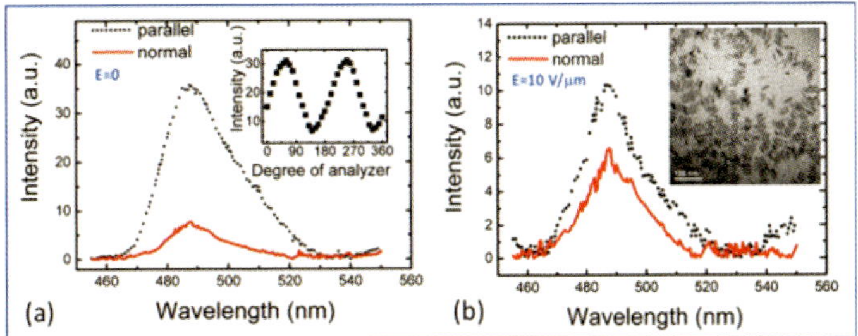

Fig. 11. Polarization dependence of photoluminescence spectra obtained for (a) $E = 0$ and (b) $E = 10$ MV/m. Luminiscence intensity polarized in direction paralel and perpendicular (normal) with respect to the rubbing direction was measured. The inset in (b) shows TEM image of the nanorods (Reproduced with permission from Ref. 81, copyright American Chemical Society, 2007).

photoluminescence spectra detected for optical analyser orientations parallel and perpendicular with respect to the rubbing direction (defining the direction of **n**) of the substrates. The corresponding polarization ratio is defined as:

$$\rho = \frac{I_{||} - I_{\perp}}{I_{||} + I_{\perp}} \tag{5}$$

where I_{II} and $I_{\perp}$ denote luminescence intensities for polarization parallel and perpendicular to **n**, respectively. The observed value $\rho = 0.63$ is very high in comparison with other previously reported methods for nanorods alignment. Figure 11b shows photoluminescence spectra obtained when an electric voltage with amplitude $U \gg U_{th}$ was applied to the cell. The voltage induces reorientation of the nematic director field **n(r)** and consequently also of the incorporated CdS nanorods from direction parallel to the rubbing direction to direction perpendicular to it. As a result, the polarization ratio decreases to $\rho \sim 0.2$.

The same group repeated experiments with cadmium selenide (CdSe) nanorods, but the samples were assembled such that nanorods were mixed with the LC host before filling-in the glass cell.[146] Also in this way the polarization state of the photoluminescence from the semiconducting nanorod-LC system can be effectively controlled by an external electric field. Recently, the experiments were extended to doping E7 with a mixture of CdSe nanorods and CdSe quantum dots and the results show that in such multi component photoluminescent systems external voltage can be used to manipulate not only the polarization state, but also the colour of the emitted light.[147]

Danilov *et al.* investigated CdSe and ZnS nanorods of similar sizes introduced into a conventional nematic mixture as well as into a gel-forming nematic LC system with acrylate additives.[148,149] In both cases relatively large concentrations of nanorods were used, but good alignment was obtained anyway. In a recent study, the same group used 5CB-methyl methacrylate (MMA) mixture as a host material and demonstrated external field-induced modulation of luminescence intensity with modulation depth of 40% and response times on the scale of several seconds.[150] Acharya *et al.* studied ultrasmall zinc sulphide (ZnS) nanorods ($d \sim 1.3$ nm, $L \sim 4$ nm) as an additive to the nematic LC mixture ZLI-4792 (Merck Ltd.).[112] The mixture was placed in-between two polarizers and for $U = 10$ V the transmitted intensity exhibited a 'giant' polarization anisotropy of 0.93 with maximum intensity in direction perpendicular to the ordered nanorods.[151] When the field was turned off, the polarization ratio reduced to 0.2.

Introduction of semiconducting nanorods into more complex LC phases brings additional interesting features. For example, Roy *et al.* observed a red-shift and a substantial enhancement of the photoluminescence intensity for a combination of CdS nanorods with an antiferroelectric LC material.[152] Besides using FLC and AFLC hosts, there is also lot of other possibilities for composing interesting luminecent systems based on LC-nanorod suspensions, for instance incorporation into polymer-dispersed LC structures or use of patterned LC assemblies.[140]

6. Conclusions and future perspectives

Despite of a strong boost of interest for inorganic nanotubes and nanorods acting as additives to LC materials, which took place during the last decade, this field is at the moment still in a relatively preliminary stage. Most of the studies are focused on doping-induced modifications of the properties of the nematic phase, while investigations related to properties of other phases and phase transitions are quite scarce. In most cases the research is stimulated by exploring a specific system in purpose to obtain improved properties with regard to some specific application, while attaining fundamental understanding of the observed effects is usually less vital. Examples of appealing fundamental open problems are, for instance, how size and concentration of the rod-shaped nanoparticles exhibiting spontaneous tendency to form an achiral assembly influence the periodicity of the chiral LC phases or how smectic ordering affects the translational and rotational motion of the particles. The present research efforts are also strongly dominated by experimental investigations, while theoretical considerations are very rare and often also far too general.

Considering doping-induced modifications of mechanical properties of the nematic phase, i.e. elastic constants and viscosity coefficients, the present state of knowledge is very scattered and sometimes even self-contradictory, so there is still a long way towards understanding of the associated phenomena. Investigations of effects of dopants on density and thermal properties of the mixtures are at the moment practically completely absent. The same is true also for investigations of various ionic and charge-transfer effects. Thorough analyses of response of the mixtures to external electric field and other external stimuli implemented within a broad frequency range are also very rare. All these properties have to be systematically investigated in the future.

Investigations of modifications of optical properties were so far limited mainly to the standard electro-optical switching. However, it is known that doping of LCs can strongly affect also their nonlinear optical response, in particular the optical Kerr effect.[153] In relation to this, Petti *et al.* have recently performed a couple of studies that revealed strong modifications of photorefractive and thermo-optical properties of 5CB induced by addition of CdSe/CdS nanorods.[154,155] Results of their investigations are definitely a challenging base for further research on this topic. Besides the optical Kerr effect, also electronic optical nonlinearities, such as optical second-harmonic generation (SHG), might become very intriguing, for instance in a system of strongly SHG-active nanorods incorporated into switchable LC configurations.

In accordance with generally observed strong growth of research activities on various kinds of nanocomposite systems, the field of inorganic nanotube/nanorod-LC colloidal suspensions will surely expand also in the future. It is expected that dispersibility problems, which are at the moment still one of the central issues when it comes to materials control and reproducibility, will soon be overcome and consequently the efforts will shift to searching for most optimal combinations to obtain mixtures with specific tailored properties. However, any predictions about which of those properties will one day result in new commercially successful LC-based devices are at the moment still very speculative.

Acknowledgments

The author acknowledges financial support from the Slovenian Research Program P1-0192 "Light and matter".

References

1. O. Lavrentovich, B. Lev, A. Trokhymchuk, *Condensed Matter Physics* (2010).
2. O. Guzmán, E. B. Kim, S. Grollau, N. L. Abbott, J. J. de Pablo, Defect structure around two colloids in a liquid crystal, *Phys. Rev. Lett.* **91**(23), 235507 (2003).
3. D. L. Cheung, M. P. Allen, Forces between cylindrical nanoparticles in a liquid crystal, *Langmuir* **24**(4), 1411–1417 (2008).
4. H. Stark, Physics of colloidal dispersions in nematic liquid crystals, *Phys. Rep.* **351**(6), 387–474 (2001).
5. Y. A. Garbovskiy, A. V. Glushchenko, In eds. R. Camly and R. Stamps, *Solid State Physics, Vol. 62*, pp. 1–74, Elsevier, Amsterdam (2011).
6. I. Muševič, Forces in nematic liquid crystals: from nanoscale interfacial forces to long-range forces in nematic colloids, *Liq. Cryst.* **36**(6-7), 639–647 (2009).
7. U. Shivakumar, J. Mirzaei, X. Feng, A. Sharma, P. Moreira, T. Hegmann, Nanoparticles: complex and multifaceted additives for liquid crystals, *Liq. Cryst.* **38**(11-12), 1495–1514 (2011).
8. C. Zakri, Carbon nanotubes and liquid crystalline phases, *Liq. Cryst. Today* **16**(1), 1–11 (2007).
9. J. P. F. Lagerwall, G. Scalia, Carbon nanotubes in liquid crystals, *J. Mater. Chem.* **18**(25), 2890–2898 (2008).
10. H. Qi, T. Hegmann, Impact of nanoscale particles and carbon nanotubes on current and future generations of liquid crystal displays, *J. Mater. Chem.* **18**(28), 3288–3294 (2008).
11. C. Blanc, D. Coursault, E. Lacaze, Ordering nano- and microparticles assemblies with liquid crystals, *Liquid Crystals Reviews*, pp. 83–109 (2013).
12. T. Hegmann, H. Qi, V. Marx, Nanoparticles in liquid crystals: Synthesis, self-assembly, defect formation and potential applications, *J. Inorg. Organomet. Polym. & Mater.* **17**(3), 483–508 (2007).
13. H. K. Bisoyi, S. Kumar, Liquid-crystal nanoscience: an emerging avenue of soft self-assembly, *Chem. Soc. Rev.* **40**(1), 306–319 (2011).
14. O. Stamatoiu, J. Mirzaei, X. Feng, T. Hegmann, Nanoparticles in liquid crystals and liquid crystalline nanoparticles, *Top. Curr. Chem.* **318**, 331–393 (2012).
15. S. Umadevi, G. Venkatchalam, T. Hegmann, Nanoparticles as additives and building blocks for liquid crystal phases, In eds. J. W. Goodby, P. J. Collings, T. Kato, C. Tschierske, H. Gleeson, and P. Raynes, *Handbook of Liquid Crystals - 2nd edition, vol. 6*, pp. 27–76, Wiley-VCH, Weinheim (2013).

16. S. Iijima, Helical microtubules of graphitic carbon, *Nature* **354**(6348), 56–58 (1991).

17. R. Tenne, L. Margulis, M. Genut, G. Hodes, Polyhedral and cylindrical structures of tungsten disulphide, *Nature* **360**(6403), 444–446 (1992).

18. L. Margulis, G. Saltra, R. Tenne, M. Tallanker, Nested fullerene-like structures, *Nature* **365**(6442), 113–114 (1993).

19. Y. Feldman, E. Wasserman, D. J. Srolovitz, R. Tenne, High-rate, gasphase growth of MoS2 nested inorganic fullerenes and nanotubes, *Science* **267**(5195), 222–225 (1995).

20. M. Remskar, Z. Skraba, F. Cleton, R. Sanjines, F. Levy, MoS2 as microtubes, *Appl. Phys. Lett.* **69**(3), 351–353 (1996).

21. R. Tenne, Fullerene-like materials and nanotubes from inorganic compounds with a layered (2-D) structure, *Colloid Surf. A-Physicochem. Eng. Asp.* **208**(1), 83–92 (2002).

22. M. Remskar, Inorganic nanotubes, *Adv. Mater.* **16**(17), 1497–1504 (2004).

23. A. Zak, L. Sallacan-Ecker, A. Margolin, M. Genut, R. Tenne, Insight into the growth mechanism of WS2 nanotubes in the scaled-up fluidized-bed reactor, *Nano* **4**(02), 91–98 (2009).

24. M. S. Wang, I. Kaplan-Ashiri, X. L. Wei, R. Rosentsveig, H. D. Wagner, R. Tenne, L. M. Peng, In situ TEM measurements of the mechanical properties and behavior of WS2 nanotubes, *Nano Research* **1**, 22–31 (2008).

25. A. Kis, D. Mihailovic, M. Remskar, A. Mrzel, A. Jesih, I. Piwonski, A. J. Kulik, W. Benoît, L. Forro, Shear and Young's moduli of MoS2 nanotube ropes, *Adv. Mater.* **15**(9), 733–736 (2003).

26. G. L. Frey, R. Tenne, M. J. Matthews, M. S. Dresselhaus, G. Dresselhaus, Optical properties of MS2 (M=Mo, W) inorganic fullerene-like and nanotube material optical absorption and resonance Raman measurements, *J. Mater. Res.* **13**(9), 2412–2417 (1998).

27. H. T. Wang, Z. Y. Lu, S. C. Xu, D. S. Kong, J. J. Cha, G. Y. Zheng, P. C. Hsu, K. Yan, D. Bradshaw, F. B. Prinz, Y. Cui, Electrochemical tuning of vertically aligned MoS2 nanofilms and its application in improving hydrogen evolution reaction, *P. Natl. Acad. Sci.* **110**(49), 19701–19706 (2013).

28. A. Zak, L. Sallacan Ecker, R. Efrati, L. Drangai, N. Fleischer, R. Tenne, Large-scale synthesis of WS2 multiwall nanotubes and their dispersion, an update, *Sensors & Transducers* **12**, 1–10 (2011).

29. M. Remskar, A. Mrzel, Z. Skraba, A. Jesih, M. Ceh, J. Demsar, P. Stadelmann, F. Lévy, D. Mihailovic, Self-assembly of subnanometer-diameter single-wall MoS2 nanotubes, *Science* **292**(5516), 479–481 (2001).

30. D. Vrbani, M. Remskar, A. Jesih, A. Mrzel, P. Umek, M. Ponikvar, B. Jancar, A. Meden, B. Novosel, S. Pejovnik, P. Venturini, J. C. Coleman, D. Mihailovic, Air-stable monodispersed Mo6S3I6 nanowires, *Nanotechnology* **15**(5), 635–638 (2004).

31. D. Mihailovic, Physical and functional properties of transition metal chalcohalide polymers, *Prog. Mater. Sci.* **54**(3), 309–350 (2009).

32. M. Uplaznik, B. Bercic, J. Strle, M. I. Ploscaru, D. Dvorsek, P. Kusar,

M. Devetak, D. Vengust, B. Podobnik, D. D. Mihailovic, Conductivity of single Mo6S9-xIx molecular nanowire bundles, *Nanotechnology* **17**(20), 5142 (2006).

33. M. Uplaznik, B. Bercic, M. Remskar, D. Mihailovic, Quantum charge transport in Mo6S3I6 molecular wire circuits, *Phys. Rev. B* **80**(8), 085402 (2009).

34. V. Nemani, M. Zumer, B. Zajec, J. Pahor, M. Remskar, A. Mrzel, P. Panjan, D. Mihailovic, Field-emission properties of molybdenum disulfide nanotubes, *Appl. Phys. Lett.* **82**(25), 4573–4575 (2003).

35. D. Mihailovic, Z. Jaglicic, D. Arcon, A. Mrzel, A. Zorko, M. Remskar, V. V. Kabanov, R. Dominko, M. Gaberscek, C. J. Gomez-Garcia, J. M. Martinez-Agudo, E. Coronado, Unusual magnetic state in lithium-doped MoS2 nanotubes, *Phys. Rev. Lett.* **90**(14), 146401 (2003).

36. A. Zimina, S. Eisebitt, M. Freiwald, S. Cramm, W. Eberhardt, A. Mrzel, D. Mihailovic, Electronic structure of subnanometer diameter MoS2-I-x nanotubes, *Nano. Lett.* **4**(9), 1749–1753 (2004).

37. T. Yang, S. Okano, S. Berber, D. Tománek, Interplay between structure and magnetism in Mo12S9I9 nanowires, *Phys. Rev. Lett.* **96**(12), 125502 (2006).

38. A. Meden, A. Kodre, J. Padeznik Gomilsek, I. Arcon, I. Vilfan, D. Vrbanic, A. Mrzel, D. Mihailovic, Atomic and electronic structure of Mo6S9-xIx nanowires, *Nanotechnology* **16**(9), 1578 (2005).

39. P. Hoyer, Formation of a titanium dioxide nanotube array, *Langmuir* **12**(6), 1411–1413 (1996).

40. J. J. Wu, S. C. Liu, C. T. Wu, K. H. Chen, L. C. Chen, Heterostructures of ZnO-Zn coaxial nanocables and ZnO nanotubes, *Appl. Phys. Lett.* **81**(7), 1312–1314 (2002).

41. G. R. Patzke, F. Krumeich, R. Nesper, Oxidic nanotubes and nanorods: anisotropic modules for a future nanotechnology, *Angew. Chem. (Int. Ed.)* **41**(14), 2446–2461 (2002).

42. P. Umek, R. C. Korosec, A. Gloter, U. Pirnat, The control of the diameter and length of MnO2 nanorods by regulation of reaction parameters and their thermogravimetric properties, *Mater. Res. Bull.* **46**(2), 278–284 (2011).

43. E. Comini, G. Faglia, G. Sberveglieri, Z. Pan, Z. L. Wang, Stable and highly sensitive gas sensors based on semiconducting oxide nanobelts, *Appl. Phys. Lett.* **81**, 1869–1871 (2002).

44. E. Comini, C. Baratto, G. Faglia, M. Ferroni, A. Ponzoni, D. Zappa, G. Sberveglieri, Metal oxide nanowire chemical and biochemical sensors, *J. Mater. Res.* **28**(21), 2911–2931 (2013).

45. C. W. Lai, J. C. Juan, W. B. Ko, S. Bee Abd Hamid, An overview: recent development of titanium oxide nanotubes as photocatalyst for dye degradation, *International Journal of Photoenergy* **2014**, 524135 (2014).

46. N. G. Chopra, R. J. Luyken, K. Cherrey, V. H. Crespi, M. L. Cohen, S. G. Louie, A. Zettl, Boron nitride nanotubes, *Science* **269**(5226), 966967 (1995).

47. D. Golberg, Y. Bando, Y. Huang, T. Terao, M. Mitome, C. Tang, C. Zhi, Boron nitride nanotubes and nanosheets, *ACS Nano* **4**(6), 2979–2993 (2010).

48. J. Y. Li, X. L. Chen, Z. Y. Qiao, Y. G. Cao, H. Li, Synthesis of GaN nanotubes, *J. Mater. Sci. Lett.* **20**(21), 1987–1988 (2001).

49. J. Goldberger, R. He, Y. Zhang, S. Lee, H. Yan, H. J. Choi, P. Yang, Single-crystal gallium nitride nanotubes, *Nature* **422**(6932), 599–602 (2003).

50. Y. Miyamoto, M. L. Cohen, S. G. Louie, Theoretical investigation of graphitic carbon nitride and possible tubule forms, *Solid State Commun.* **102**(8), 605–608 (1997).

51. X. Lu, H. Wang, S. Zhang, D. Cui, Q. Wang, Synthesis, characterization and electrocatalytic properties of carbon nitride nanotubes for methanol electrooxidation, *Solid State Sciences* **11**(2), 428–432 (2009).

52. C. Y. Zhi, X. D. Bai, E. G. Wang, Boron carbonitride nanotubes, *J. Nanosci. Nanotechnol.* **4**(1-2), 35–51 (2004).

53. J. Buh, A. Kovic, A. Mrzel, Z. Jaglicic, A. Jesih, D. Mihailovic, Template synthesis of single-phase delta(3)-MoN superconducting nanowires, *Nanotechnology* **25**(2), 025601 (2014).

54. J. C. Hutleen, K. B. Jirage, C. R. Martin, Introducing chemical transport selectivity into gold nanotubule membrane, *J. Am. Chem. Soc.* **120**, 6603–6604 (1998).

55. G. Tourillon, L. Pontonnier, J. P. Levy, V. Langlais, Electrochemically synthesized Co and Fe nanowires and nanotubes, *Electrochemical and Solid-State Letters* **3**(1), 20–23 (2000).

56. C. C. Han, M. Y. Bai, J. T. Lee, A new and easy method for making Ni and Cu microtubules and their regularly assembled structures, *Chem. Mater.* **13**(11), 4260–4268 (2001).

57. C. Yang, H. Gu, W. Lin, M. M. Yuen, C. P. Wong, M. Xiong, B. Gao, Silver nanowires: from scalable synthesis to recyclable foldable electronics, *Adv. Mater.* **23**(27), 3052–3056 (2011).

58. Z. B. Zhang, X. Z. Sun, M. S. Dresselhaus, J. Y. Ying, J. Heremans, Electronic transport properties of single-crystal bismuth nanowire arrays, *Phys. Rev. B* **61**(7), 4850 (2000).

59. M. S. Dresselhaus, Y. M. Lin, O. Rabin, M. R. Black, J. Kong, G. Dresselhaus, Nanowires, In *Springer Handbook of Nanotechnology*, pp. 119–167, Springer, 2010.

60. P. J. F. Harris, *Carbon nanotubes and related structures: new materials for the twenty-first century*, Cambridge, UK (1999).

61. V. A. Davis, Liquid crystalline assembly of nanocylinders, *J. Mater. Res.* **26**(2), 140–153 (2011).

62. C. N. R. Rao, A. Govindaraj, Nanotubes and nanowires, RSC nanoscience & nanotechnology series (2005).

63. I. Musevic, M. Skarabot, U. Tkalec, M. Ravnik, S. Zumer, Two-dimensional nematic colloidal crystals self-assembled by topological defects, *Science* **313**(5789), 954–958 (2006).

64. M. Ravnik, M. Skarabot, S. Zumer, U. Tkalec, I. Poberaj, D. Babic, N. Osterman, I. Musevic, Entangled nematic colloidal dimers and wires, *Phys. Rev. Lett.* **99**(24), 247801 (2007).

65. F. Mondiot, R. Botet, P. Snabre, O. Mondain-Monval, J. C. Loudet, Col-

loidal aggregation and dynamics in anisotropic fluids, *Proc. Natl. Acad. Sci. USA* **111**(16), 5831–5836 (2014).

66. S. Kredentser, O. Buluy, P. Davidson, I. Dozov, S. Malynych, V. Reshetnyak, K. Slyusarenko, Y. Reznikov, Strong orientational coupling in two-component suspensions of rod-like nanoparticles, *Soft Matter* **9**(20), 5061–5066 (2013).

67. P. E. Kornilovitch, Van der waals interaction in uniaxial anisotropic media, *J. Phys.: Condens. Matter* **25**(3), 035102 (2013).

68. S. V. Burylov, Y. L. Raikher, Orientation of a solid particle embedded in a monodomain nematic liquid crystal, *Phys. Rev. E* **50**(1), 358–367 (1994).

69. M. A. Osipov, M. V. Gorkunov, Molecular theory of phase separation in nematic liquid crystals doped with spherical nanoparticles, *ChemPhysChem* **15**(7), 1496–1501 (2014).

70. D. Andrienko, M. P. Allen, G. Skacej, S. Zumer, Defect structures and torque on an elongated colloidal particle immersed in a liquid crystal host, *Phys. Rev. E.* **65**(4), 041702 (2002).

71. F. R. Hung, O. Guzmán, B. T. Gettelfinger, N. L. Abbott, J. J. De Pablo, Anisotropic nanoparticles immersed in a nematic liquid crystal: Defect structures and potentials of mean force, *Phys. Rev. E.* **74**(1), 011711 (2006).

72. R. Basu, G. S. Iannacchione, Orientational coupling enhancement in a carbon nanotube dispersed liquid crystal, *Phys. Rev. E.* **81**(5), 051705 (2010).

73. H. Duran, B. Gazdecki, A. Yamashita, T. Kyu, Effect of carbon nanotubes on phase transitions of nematic liquid crystals, *Liq. Cryst.* **32**(7), 815–821 (2005).

74. A. Matsuyama, Phase separations in mixtures of a liquid crystal and a nanocolloidal particle, *J. Chem. Phys.* **131**(20), 204904 (2009).

75. P. Poulin, V. A. Raghunathan, P. Richetti, D. J. Roux, On the dispersion of latex particles in a nematic solution. I. Experimental evidence and simple model, *J. Phys. II* **4**(9), 1557–1569 (1994).

76. D. Rajh, S. Shelestiuk, A. Mertelj, A. Mrzel, P. Umek, S. Irusta, A. Zak, I. Drevensek-Olenik, Effect of inorganic 1D nanoparticles on electrooptic properties of 5CB liquid crystal, *physica status solidi (a)* **210**(11), 2328–2334 (2013).

77. V. V. Ponevchinsky, A. I. Goncharuk, V. I. Vasilsev, N. I. Lebovka, M. S. Soskin, Cluster self-organization of nanotubes in a nematic phase: The percolation behavior and appearance of optical singularities, *JETP letters* **91**(5), 241–244 (2010).

78. S. K. Prasad, K. L. Sandhya, G. G. Nair, U. S. Hiremath, C. V. Yelamaggad, S. Sampath, Electrical conductivity and dielectric constant measurements of liquid crystal-gold nanoparticle composites, *Liq. Cryst.* **33**(10), 1121–1125 (2006).

79. B. Senyuk, D. Glugla, I. I. Smalyukh, Rotational and translational diffusion of anisotropic gold nanoparticles in liquid crystals controlled by varying surface anchoring, *Phys. Rev. E.* **88**(6), 062507 (2013).

80. P. K. Tripathi, A. K. Misra, S. Manohar, S. K. Gupta, R. Manohar, Improved dielectric and electro-optical parameters of ZnO nano-particle (8%

Cu2+) doped nematic liquid crystal, *J. Mol. Struct.* **1035**, 371–377 (2013).

81. K. J. Wu, K. C. Chu, C. Y. Chao, Y. F. Chen, C. W. Lai, C. C. Kang, C. Y. Chen, P. T. Chou, CdS nanorods imbedded in liquid crystal cells for smart optoelectronic devices, *Nano. Lett.* **7**, 1908–1913 (2007).

82. Q. Liu, J. Tang, Y. Zhang, A. Martinez, S. Wang, S. He, T. J. White, I. I. Smalyukh, Shape-dependent dispersion and alignment of nonaggregating plasmonic gold nanoparticles in lyotropic and thermotropic liquid crystals, *Phys. Rev. E.* **89**(5), 052505 (2014).

83. Q. Liu, B. Senyuk, J. Tang, T. Lee, J. Qian, S. He, I. I. Smalyukh, Plasmonic complex fluids of nematiclike and helicoidal self-assemblies of gold nanorods with a negative order parameter, *Phys. Rev. Lett.* **109**(8), 088301 (2012).

84. S. Kundu, J. P. Hill, G. J. Richards, K. Ariga, A. H. Khan, U. Thupakula, S. Acharya, *ACS App. Mater. Interfaces* **2**(19), 2759–2766 (2010).

85. M. Zorn, S. Meuer, M. N. Tahir, Y. Khalavka, C. Sönnichsen, W. Tremel, R. Zentel, Liquid crystalline phases from polymer functionalised semiconducting nanorods, *J. Mater. Chem.* **18**(25), 3050–3058 (2008).

86. H. Qi, B. Kinkead, V. M. Marx, H. R. Zhang, T. Hegmann, Miscibility and alignment effects of mixed monolayer cyanobiphenyl liquid-crystal-capped gold nanoparticles in nematic cyanobiphenyl liquid crystal hosts, *ChemPhysChem* **10**(8), 1211–1218 (2009).

87. S. Kubo, R. Taguchi, S. Hadano, M. Naria, O. Watanabe, T. Iyoda, M. Nakagawa, Surface-assisted unidirectional orientation of ZnO nanorods hybridized with nematic liquid crystals, *ACS Appl. Mater. Interfaces* **6**(2), 811–818 (2014).

88. C. Lapointe, A. Hultgren, D. M. Silevitch, E. J. Felton, D. H. Reich, R. L. Leheny, Elastic torque and the levitation of metal wires by a nematic liquid crystal, *Science* **303**(5658), 652–655 (2004).

89. M. D. Lynch, D. L. Patrick, Controlling the orientation of micron-sized rod-shaped SiC particles with nematic liquid crystal solvents, *Chem. Mater.* **16**(5), 762–767 (2004).

90. S. Torgova, E. Pozhidaev, A. Lobanov, M. Minchenko, B. Khlebtsov, Nanocomposites consisting of gold nanorods and nematic liquid crystals: Optical properties, *Mol. Cryst. Liq. Cryst.* **525**, 176–183 (2010).

91. S. Prathap Chandran, F. Mondiot, O. Mondain-Monval, J. C. Loudet, Photonic control of surface anchoring on solid colloids dispersed in liquid crystals, *Langmuir* **27**(24), 15185–15198 (2011).

92. M. V. Gorkunov, G. A. Shandryuk, A. M. Shatalova, I. Yu. Kutergina, A. S. Merekalov, Y. V. Kudryavtsev, R. V. Talroze, M. A. Osipov, Phase separation effects and the nematic-isotropic transition in polymer and low molecular weight liquid crystals doped with nanoparticles, *Soft Matter* **9**(13), 3578–3588 (2013).

93. R. Cervini, G. P. Simon, M. Ginic-Markovic, J. G. Matisons, C. Huynh, S. Hawkins, Aligned silane-treated MWCNT/liquid crystal polymer films, *Nanotechnology* **19**(17), 175602 (2008).

94. B. Tasic, A. Mrzel, M. Huskic, X. Zhang, I. Drevensek-Olenik, Alignment of MoS2 nanotubes in a photopolymerizable liquid-crystalline material, *J.*

Phys. Chem. C. **118**(45), 26396–26401 (2014).

95. B. Bahadur, *Liquid crystals—Applications and Uses*, Vol. 3, World Scientific, Singapore (1992).

96. W. H. de Jeu, *Physical properties of Liquid Crystalline Materials*, Gordon & Breach Science Pub. (1980).

97. Orsay Liquid Crystal Group, Quasielastic Rayleigh scattering in nematic liquid crystals, *Phys. Rev. Lett.* **22**, 1361–1363 (1969).

98. Orsay Liquid Crystal Group, Dynamics of Fluctuations in Nematic Liquid Crystals *J. Chem. Phys.* **51**(2), 816–822 (1969).

99. M. Avsec, A. Mertelj, I. Drevensek-Olenik, A. Mrzel, M. Copic, Viscoelastic properties of nematic-MoS2 nanotubes mixtures, *Mol. Cryst. Liq. Cryst.* **435**, 823 (2005).

100. M. E. Lewis, I. Khan, H. Vithana, A. Baldwin, D. L. Johnson, M. E. Neubert, Light scattering near the nematic-smectic-A liquid-crystal phase-transition, *Phys. Rev. A* **38**(7), 3702–3709 (1988).

101. R. Manohar, S. P. Yadav, A. K. Srivastava, A. K. Misra, K. K. Pandey, P. K. Sharma, A. C. Pandey, Zinc oxide (1% Cu) nanoparticle in nematic liquid crystal: Dielectric and electro-optical study, *Jap. J. Appl. Phys.* **48**(10), 101501 (2009).

102. S. Sridevi, S. K. Prasad, G. G. Nair, V. D'Britto, B. L. V. Prasad, Enhancement of anisotropic conductivity, elastic, and dielectric constants in a liquid crystal-gold nanorod system, *Appl. Phys. Lett.* **97**(15), 151913 (2010).

103. H. Sawai, T. Matsuura, H. Kakiuchi, T. Ohgi, Y. Shiraishi, N. Toshima, Preparation and electrooptic properties of liquid crystal devices doped with cucurbituril-protected gold nanowires, *Chem. Lett.* **41**(10), 1160–1162 (2012).

104. P. Nayek, S. Karan, S. Kundu, S. H. Lee, S. D. Gupta, S. K. Roy, S. K. Roy, Effect of cadmium sulfide nanorod content on Freedericksz threshold voltage, splay and bend elastic constants in liquid-crystal nanocomposites, *J. Phys. D-Appl. Phys.* **45**(23), 235303 (2012).

105. J. W. Goodby, P. J. Collins, T. Kato, C. Tschierske, H. Gleeson, P. Raynes, *Handbook of Liquid Crystals, 8 Volume Set*, Wiley-VCH (2014).

106. P. G. de Gennes, *The Physics of Liquid Crystals*, Clarendon Press, Oxford, UK (1974).

107. S. M. Shelestiuk, V. Yu. Reshetnyak, T. J. Sluckin, Frederiks transition in ferroelectric liquid-crystal nanosuspensions, *Phys. Rev. E.* **83**(4), 041705 (2011).

108. J. Milavec, A. Mrzel, I. Drevenšek-Olenik, M. Pevnyi, V. Reshetnyak, Effect of Mo6SxI10-x nanotubes addition on electrooptical properties of polymer-dispersed liquid crystals, *Sensors & Transducers* **12**, 18–25 (2011).

109. M. Z. Chen, W. S. Chen, S. C. Jeng, S. H. Yang, Y. F. Chung, Liquid crystal alignment on zinc oxide nanowire arrays for LCDs applications, *Opt. Express* **21**(24), 29277–29282 (2013).

110. Y. J. Lim, Y. E. Choi, S. W. Kang, D. Y. Kim, S. H. Lee, Y. B. Hahn, Vertical alignment of liquid crystals with zinc oxide nanorods, *Nanotechnology* **24**(34), 345702 (2013).

111. Y. Williams, K. Chan, J. H. Park, I. C. Khoo, B. Lewis, T. E. Mallouk, Electro-optical and nonlinear optical properties of semiconductor nanorod doped liquid crystals, *Proc. SPIE* **5936**, 593613 (2005).

112. S. Acharya, S. Kundu, J. P. Hill, G. J. Richards, K. Ariga, Nanorod-driven orientational control of liquid crystal for polarization-tailored electro-optic devices, *Adv. Mater.* **21**(9), 989–993 (2009).

113. C.-Y. Tang, S.-M. Huang, W. Lee, Electrical properties of nematic liquid crystals doped with anatase-TiO2 nanoparticles, *J. Phys. D-Appl. Phys.* **44**, 355102 (2011).

114. A. Choudhary, G. Singh, A. M. Biradar, Advances in gold nanoparticle-liquid crystal composites, *Nanoscale* **6**(14), 7743–7756 (2014).

115. M. D. Lynch, L. Patrick, Organizing carbon nanotubes with liquid crystals, *Nano. Lett.* **2**(11), 1197–1201 (2002).

116. Y. Tao, Y. H. Tam, Dynamics of ZnO nanowires immersed in in-plane switching liquid crystal cells, *Appl. Phys. Lett.* **103**, 203102 (2013).

117. P. Pieranski, F. Brochard, E. Guyon, Static and dynamic behaviour of a nematic liquid-crystal in a magnetic-field, 2. Dynamics, *J. Physique* **34**(1), 35–48 (1973).

118. R. B. Alaverdyan, L. S. Aslanyan, V. V. Margaryan, E. A. Santrosyan, Yu. S. Chilingaryan, Dynamics of Freedericksz transition in the oscillating electric field, *Mol. Cryst. Liq. Cryst.* **453**, 15–27 (2008).

119. S. Kundu, J. P. Hill, G. J. Richards, K. Ariga, A. H. Khan, U. Thupakula, S. Acharya, Crystallographic phase induced electro-optic properties of nanorod blend nematic liquid crystal, *J. Nanosci. Nanotechnol.* **11**(9), 7729–7734 (2011).

120. I. Musevic, R. Blinc, B. Zeks, *The Physics of Ferroelectric and Antiferroelectric Liquid Crystals*, World Scientific, Singapore (2000).

121. F. V. Podgornov, A. V. Ryzhkova, W. Haase, Influence of gold nanorods size on electro-optical and dielectric properties of ferroelectric liquid crystals, *Appl. Phys. Lett.* **97**(21), 212903 (2010).

122. R. K. Shukla, X. Feng, S. Umadevi, T. Hegmann, W. Haase, Influence of different amount of functionalized bulky gold nanorods dopant on the electrooptical, dielectric and optical properties of the FLC host, *Chem. Phys. Lett.* **599**, 80–85 (2014).

123. P. Malik, A. Chaudhary, R. Mehra, K. K. Raina, Electrooptic and dielectric studies in cadmium sulphide nanorods/ferroelectric liquid crystal mixtures, *Adv. Cond. Matter. Phys.* **2012**, 853160 (2012).

124. K. Pal, U. N. Maiti, T. P. Majumder, S. C. Debnath, S. Ghosh, S. K. Roy, J. M. Oton, Switching of ferroelectric liquid crystal doped with cetyltrimethylammonium bromide-assisted CdS nanostructures, *Nanotechnology* **24**(12), 125702 (2013).

125. R. Manohar, A. K. Srivastava, P. K. Tripathi, D. P. Singh, Dielectric and electro-optical study of ZnO nano rods doped ferroelectric liquid crystals, *J. Mater. Sci.* **46**(18), 5969–5976 (2011).

126. S. Link, M. A. El-Sayed, Optical properties and ultrafast dynamics of metallic nanocrystals, *Annu. Rev. Phys. Chem.* **54**, 331–366 (2003).

127. E. Hutter, J. H. Fendler, Exploitation of localized surface plasmon resonance, *Adv. Mater.* **16**(19), 1685–1706 (2004).

128. K. S. Lee, M. A. El-sayed, Gold and silver nanoparticles in sensing and imaging: Sensitivity of plasmon response to size, shape, and metal composition, *J. Phys. Chem. B* **110**(39), 19220–19225 (2006).

129. C. J. Murphy, T. K. San, A. M. Gole, C. J. Orendorff, J. X. Gao, L. Gou, S. E. Hunyadi, T. Li, Anisotropic metal nanoparticles: Synthesis, assembly, and optical applications, *J. Phys. Chem. B.* **109**(29), 13857–13870 (2006).

130. S. E. Lohse, C. J. Murphy, The quest for shape control: A history of gold nanorod synthesis, *Chem. Mater.* **25**(8), 1250–1261 (2013).

131. K. C. Chu, C. Y. Chao, Y. F. Chen, Y. C. Wu, C. C. Chen, Electrically controlled surface plasmon resonance frequency of gold nanorods, *Appl. Phys. Lett.* **89**(10), 103107 (2006).

132. P. R. Evans, G. A. Wurtz, W. R. Hendren, R. ATkinson, W. Dickson, A. V. Zayats, R. J. Pollard, Electrically switchable nonreciprocal transmission of plasmonic nanorods with liquid crystal, *Appl. Phys. Lett.* **91**, 043101 (2007).

133. Q. Liu, Y. Cui, D. Gardner, X. Li, S. He, I. I. Smalyukh, Self-alignment of plasmonic gold nanorods in reconfigurable anisotropic fluids for tunable bulk metamaterial applications, *Nano. Lett.* **10**(4), 1347–1353 (2010).

134. J. P. F. Lagerwall, C. Schütz, M. Salajkova, J. Noh, J. H. Park, G. Scalia, L. Bergstrom, Cellulose nanocrystal-based materials: from liquid crystal self-assembly and glass formation to multifunctional thin films, *NPG Asia Materials* **6**(1), e80 (2014).

135. Q. Liu, M. G. Campbell, J. S. Evans, I. I. Smalyukh, Orientationally ordered colloidal co-dispersions of gold nanorods and cellulose nanocrystals, *Adv. Mater.* **26**(42), 7178–7184 (2014).

136. M. G. Campbell, Q. Liu, A. Sanders, J. S. Evans, I. I. Smalyukh, Preparation of nanocomposite plasmonic films made from cellulose nanocrystals or mesoporous silica decorated with unidirectionally aligned gold nanorods, *Materials* **7**(4), 3021–3033 (2014).

137. M. R. Thomas, S. Klein, R. J. Greasty, S. Mann, A. W. Perriman, R. M. Richardson, Nematic director-induced switching of assemblies of hexagonally packed gold nanorods, *Adv. Mater.* **24**(32), 4424–4429 (2012).

138. Q. Liu, Y. Yuan, I. I. Smalyukh, Electrically and optically tunable plasmonic guest-host liquid crystals with long-range ordered nanoparticles, *Nano. Lett.* **14**(7), 4071–4077 (2014).

139. S. D. Peroukidis, V. Yannopapas, A. G. Vanakaras, S. Droulias, D. J. Photinos, Plasmonic response of ordered arrays of gold nanorods immersed within a nematic liquid crystal, *Liq. Cryst.* **41**(10), 1430–1435 (2014).

140. B. W. Lee, N. A. Clark, Alignment of liquid crystals with patterned isotropic surfaces, *Science* **291**(30 March), 2576–2580 (2001).

141. J. M. Wong, J. Y. Hwang, L. C. Chien, Electrically reconfigurable and thermally sensitive optical properties of gold nanorods dispersed liquid crystal blue phase, *Soft Matter* **7**(18), 7956–7959 (2011).

142. C. Xue, K. Gutierrez-Cuevas, M. Gao, A. Urbas, Q. Li, Photomodulated

self-assembly of hydrophobic thiol monolayer-protected gold nanorods and their alignment in thermotropic liquid crystal, *J. Phys. Chem. C* **117**(41), 21603–21608 (2013).

143. C. Ohm, M. Brehmer, R. Zentel, Applications of liquid crystalline elastomers, *Adv. Polym. Sci.* **250**, 49–93 (2012).

144. M. Devetak, B. Zupancic, A. Lebar, P. Umek, B. Zalar, V. Domenici, G. Ambrozic, M. Zigon, M. Copic, I. Drevensek-Olenik, Micropatterning of light-sensitive liquid-crystal elastomers, *Phys. Rev. E* **80**(5), 050701 (2009).

145. X. Chen, A. Nazzal, D. Goorskey, M. Xiao, *Phys. Rev. B* **64**, 245304 (2001).

146. T. J. Lin, C. C. Chen, S. Cheng, Y. F. Chen, Liquid crystal cells with built-in CdSe nanotubes for chromogenic smart emission devices, *Opt. Express* **16**(2), 671–678 (2008).

147. H. S. Chen, C. W. Chen, C. H. Wang, F. C. Chu, C. Y. Chao, C. C. Kang, P. T. Chou, Y. F. Chen, Color-tunable light-emitting device based on the mixture of CdSe nanorods and dots embedded in liquid-crystal cells, *J. Phys. Chem. C.* **114**(17), 7995–7998 (2010).

148. V. V. Danilov, M. V. Artem'ev, A. V. Baranov, G. M. Ermolaeva, N. A. Utkina, A. I. Khrebtov, Fluorescence of semiconductor nanorods in liquid-crystal composites, *Opt. Spectrosc.* **105**(2), 306–309 (2008).

149. V. V. Danilov, M. V. Artem'ev, A. V. Baranov, A. O. Orlova, M. V. Mukhina, A. I. Khrebtov, Liquid-crystal composites with controlled photoluminescence of CdSe/ZnS semiconductor quantum rods, *Opt. Spectrosc.* **110**(6), 897–902 (2011).

150. M. V. Mukhina, V. V. Danilov, A. O. Orlova, M. V. Fedorov, M. V. Artemyev, A. V. Baranov, Electrically controlled polarized photoluminescence of CdSe/ZnS nanorods embedded in a liquid crystal template, *Nanotechnology* **23**(32), 325201 (2012).

151. S. Acharya, A. B. Panda, S. frima, Y. Golan, Polarization properties and switchable assembly of ultranarrow ZnSe nanorods, *Adv. Mater.* **19**(8), 1105–1108 (2007).

152. J. S. Roy, T. P. Majumder, R. Dabrowski, Enhanced photoluminescence in CdS nanorods doped with antiferroelectric liquid crystals, *J. Lumin.* **148**, 330–333 (2014).

153. L. Lucchetti, M. Gentili, F. Simoni, Colossal optical nonlinearity induced by a low frequency external electric field in dye-doped liquid crystals, *Opt. Express* **14**(6), 2236–2241 (2006).

154. L. Petti, M. Rippa, A. Fiore, L. Manna, P. Mormile, Dynamic orientational photorefractive gratings observed in CdSe/CdS nanorods imbedded in liquid crystal cells, *Opt. Mater.* **32**(9), 1060–1065 (2010).

155. L. Petti, M. Rippa, A. Fiore, L. Manna, P. Mormile, Optically induced light modulation in an hybrid nanocomposite system of inorganic CdSe/CdS nanorods and nematic liquid crystals, *Opt. Mater.* **32**(9), 1011–1016 (2010).

Chapter 16

Liquid crystals from mesogens containing gold nanoparticles

Wiktor Lewandowski and Ewa Gorecka*

University of Warsaw, Department of Chemistry, Warsaw, Poland
**gorecka@chem.uw.edu.pl*

Long-range ordered structures made of nanoparticles are perspective materials for future optical, electronic and sensing technologies. Conspicuous physicochemical features of nanoparticle aggregates originate from distant-dependent collective interactions, therefore lately a lot of attention was put to the development of assembly strategies allowing control over nanoparticle spatial distribution. In this chapter we will focus on the assembly process based on using thermotropic liquid-crystalline molecules as surface nanoparticle ligands. First, we discuss architectural parameters that influence structure and thermal properties of the aggregates. Then, we show that this approach enables formation of assemblies with metamaterial characteristic, gives access to dynamic materials with light-, magneto- and thermo-responsive behavior and allows formation of aggregates with unique structures, which all make this strategy an attractive object of research.

Contents

1. Introduction

The self-assembly (SA) of nanoparticles (NPs) into ordered structures with controlled inter-particle spacing is of great practical importance in various fields of science and engineering.[1,2] NPs form a variety of structures if the surface of a particle is grafted with appropriate ligands which introduce specific interactions and thus allow us to control the SA process. A number of particle surface ligands used for SA encompass charged molecules,[3] biological structures such as DNA ligands,[4,5] large chemical compounds such as polymers,[6,7] small inorganic ions[8,9] and many more.[10] Within the last 15 years a new path was explored which is based on the utilization of liquid crystals (LCs) as nanoparticle surface ligands. This strategy capitalizes on the inherent tendency of LCs to form anisotropic structures and it will be the main focus of this chapter. Throughout the text we will refer to NPs covered with LCs as 'liquid-crystalline nanoparticles' (LC-NPs) or 'hybrid nanoparticles', while the term 'LC-based strategy' will refer to the synthesis of these materials. Since some ligands themselves do not form liquid-crystalline phases but small modification of their molecular structure leads to mesogenic properties, such compounds will be referred as 'promesogenic'.

In this chapter we will briefly discuss developments in the field of liquid-crystalline NPs from the perspective of different architectures of ligands attached to the surface of metallic nanoparticles and show how it translates to obtaining materials with internal long-range order. We will also underline the importance of the LC-based nanoparticle self-assembly strategy by showing how it can be used to prepare otherwise hardly accessible systems with metamaterial characteristics, light-, magneto- and thermo-responsive behavior. We will mainly focus on metallic nanoparticles due to their interesting collective plasmonic properties and discuss contribution to the field of plasmonics. It should be noted, that advances in the field of LC-NPs have been previously reviewed in a series of publications,[11–19] however since the number of reports in the field is constantly growing here we account for the latest achievements. It should be noted, that besides metal nanoparticles also the assembly of quantum dots[20,21] and iron oxide nanoparticles[22–25] was achieved using the LC-ligands approach, however these will not be discussed in detail here.

The review outlined here is complementary to the knowledge presented in other chapters of this section of the book and the Reader should be specifically aware of the discrimination of self-assembly of nanoparticles by covering them with (pro)mesogenic ligands (as discussed here) and by embedding nanoparticles into a liquid-crystalline host. One striking difference is the fraction of the metal volume of the material which for the systems discussed here is at least few percent whereas doping results usually in more 'dilute' (in regard of the metal/oxide volume fraction) systems.

2. Techniques for synthesis and examination of nanoparticles coated with liquid crystalline molecules

Throughout the last two decades a plethora of methods have been developed to prepare nanoparticles with predesigned size, shape and constitution[26-28] and the acquired knowledge allows for precise control of the properties of as obtained nanocrystals. One of the challenges is to introduce functional ligands at nanoparticle surface. These strategies rely on the use of proper ligand molecules during synthesis of nanoparticles,[29,30] ligand exchange reactions after nanoparticles were obtained[31,32] or performing chemical reactions at functional groups of ligands covering a nanoparticle.[33] All of these methods have been applied to obtain liquid-crystalline nanoparticles and will be discussed when considering individual examples in the following subchapters.

The most frequently method used for preparation of LC-NPs is based on ligand-exchange reaction. In this approach metal NPs are first obtained capitalizing on the wealth of available methods (most frequently Brust–Schiffrin method) and then, in a consecutive step, (pro)mesogenic molecules are introduced to the surface of NPs. By varying conditions of the exchange reaction one can achieve a relatively good control of the rate of the mixed organic coating layer composition. Another strategy, that is introduction of the (pro)mesogenic molecules at the NPs synthesis step yields materials covered exclusively with LC-ligands. A summary of the different strategies is given in Fig. 1. An important part of the preparation scheme is to make sure that no unbound ligands are present in the system, as this could influence the self-assembly process. To evaluate the purity of the sample, but also to assess its composition, a variety of methods are used. In ^{1}H NMR spectroscopy purity is verified by broadening of signals characteristic to molecules bound to nanoparticle surface, i.e. no sharp peaks related to free ligands should be observed. On the other hand, thermogravimetric measurements (TGA) allow estimation of the number of ligands and give insight into the organic coating composition; for this purpose also X-ray photoelectron spectroscopy can be used. The information about size of metal core is

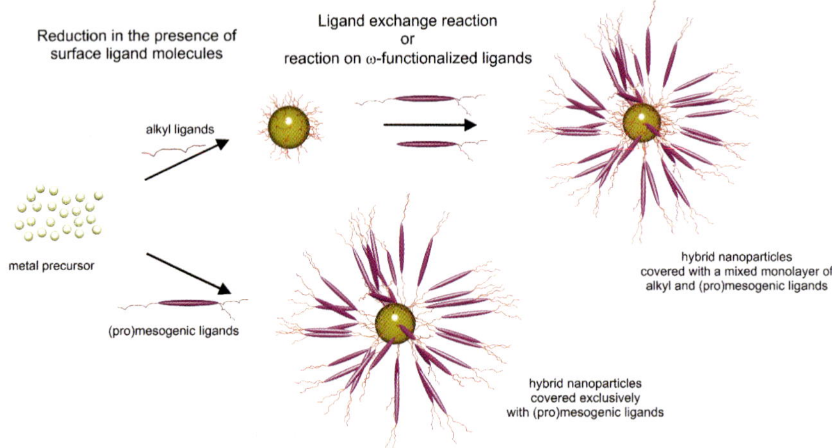

Fig. 1. Basic strategies for liquid-crystalline nanoparticle synthesis. (Pro)mesogenic ligands can be introduced to NPs surface either in the direct synthesis step (bottom) or using two step procedure (up). In the latter, alkane coated nanoparticles are obtained in the first step and then LC-ligands are introduced via a consecutive reaction (ligand exchange or reaction with a functionalized ligand). Reprinted with permission from [14]. Copyright 2014 John Wiley and Sons.

often obtained by analyzing transmission electron microscopy (TEM) pictures or from the small-angle x-ray scattering (SAXS) experiment, in which LC-NPs are suspended in a liquid solvent and the dependence of intensity of scattered beam vs. wave vector q is analyzed.

To assess self-assembly properties of nanoparticles usually a combination of techniques is used. The most popular and informative are TEM and X-ray techniques: small angle X-ray diffraction (SAXRD) and grazing incidence scattering (GISAXS). Also the differential scanning calorimetry (DSC) and polarized IR spectroscopy (FT-IR) are used. For the purpose of assessing functionality of the material UV-Vis measurements can be applied.

3. Design rules for LC-NPs systems

The future applications of LC-NPs systems are largely dependent on the ability to achieve specific, pre-designed properties of the materials. Therefore, a lot of attention was put on establishing 'design rules' of LC-NPs. One of the most evident factors is the structure of the (pro)mesogenic ligands. Molecules having:

- rod-like
- bent-core
- discotic and
- dendrimeric

architectures were screened for inducing liquid-crystalline phases made of hybrid NPs.

We will discuss developments of LC-NPs research following this division, however, also including other crucial structural parameters of the hybrid NPs, such as:

- attachment geometry of ligands to the nanoparticle surface (lateral vs. side-on)
- bulkiness of the terminal alkyl chains of ligands
- length of the flexible spacer between ligands core and nanoparticle surface
- length of the alkyl co-ligands for hybrid NPs with mixed organic coating layers
- branching of dendrimeric ligands.

An important feature of the ligands is that they comprise a docking moiety pending at a flexible chain which allows to attach the (pro)mesogen to the surface of nanocrystals. Since most of the work was done using gold nanoparticles, the mercapto-functional group was the most frequently applied, as it strongly bounds to gold.[34,35] However, when introduction of the ligand was performed using chemical reactions at functional groups of ligands covering nanoparticle (pro)mesogens with amine, alkyne and trimethoxysilane end groups were used.[36–40]

It is important to note that mesogenic properties of ligands are not a prerequisite for formation of LC phase by NPs.[41–43] In most cases the small ($\sim$2-3 nm diameter) gold NPs were tested, however few examples of using larger Au[36,38–40,44,45] or Ag[45,46] nanocrystals are also known. By varying nanocrystals and (pro)mesogenic ligands one can also assure interesting functional behavior of the materials, giving access to materials exhibiting e.g.:

- plasmonic anisotropy,
- dynamic reconfiguration of the aggregate and
- dynamically controlled metamaterial properties.

3.1. *Rod-like ligands with lateral attachment*

The most extensive research was devoted to mesogenic ligands with 'rod-like' shape. Several different types of rod-like molecules have been tested. They comprise between 1-4 aromatic rings (usually 3-4) including biphenyl, stilbene and diazobenzene moieties, which are common building-blocks for liquid crystals.[47–49]

Initial studies in the area of LC-NPs were performed at the beginning of the XXIst century. The first example of LC-NPs was given by Kanayama *et al.*[50] The authors prepared hybrid nanoparticles, covered exclusively with rod-like mesogen. They modified a well known Brust–Schiffrin protocol, by using 10-[(trans-(4-pentylcyclohex-yl)phenoxy)]decane-1-thiol as a capping ligand instead of dodecanethiol that was originally applied. The authors obtained 3 nm diameter gold nanoparticles covered exclusively with LC ligands (sample **I**, Table 1). The DSC measurements evidenced a double-melting behavior of the material indicating formation of a liquid-crystalline phase made of nanoparticles. It was shown that the clearing point for NPs with mesogenic ligands is much higher than for free ligands, confirming successful preparation of a new type of material. Though details of the phase structure were not investigated, this first example of LC-based self-assembly approach was the outset to a new field of interest.

Four years later In *et al.*[51] reported spontaneous formation of one dimensional arrangement of small spherical, $(2.7 \pm 0.5$ nm diameter) Au nanoparticles covered with cyanobiphenyl derivative (material **II**). This work set the future standards for LC-nanoparticles analysis; formation of the ordered assembly was evidenced using small-angle XRD and TEM measurements. The TEM micrographs of a thermally annealed sample evidenced formation of rows of nanoparticles with the gap distance of about 5.8 nm, much larger than the metal core diameter. Finally, SAXRD revealed two broad peaks (with d spacing 6.3 and 2.9 nm) which were attributed to inter-array and in-array NP spacing. The periodicities determined by x-ray method were in good agreement with the values obtained from TEM measurements.

Soon, another set of NPs grafted with cyanobiphenyl derivatives were described by Goodby *et al.*[52] These authors synthesized small ($\sim$2.4 nm) diameter gold nanoparticles covered with phosphine ligands, that were later fully exchanged by cyanobiphenyl mesogens (materials **IIIa– IIIe**). The DSC measurements of hybrid materials revealed three thermal events in the temperature scans, indicating phase transitions between LC phases, but the structure of LC phases was not investigated. It is worth to note here that phase assignment to smectic phase indicated in the articles cited throughout this chapter often relies on the observation of birefringence for samples with lamellar order of particles, however not always proofs for long-range orientational order of ligands are given.

Table 1. Summary of the phase behavior of the hybrid NPs with **rodlike and dimeric rod-like polycatenar** ligands discussed in the text. An asterisk (*) indicates data based on SAXRD. Cr, N, Lam, Sm, Col_h, Iso stand for crystal, nematic, lamellar, smectic, columnar hexagonal and isotropic phase, respectively. LC and dec stand for an unidentified mesophase and decomposition, respectively. Meta. stands for a metastable mixture.

NP type	NP diameter [nm]	Ligand structure	Phase transition temperatures [°C]	Sample nb.	Ref.
Au	3	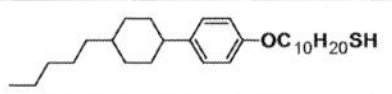 $OC_{10}H_{20}SH$	Cr 74 LC 114 Iso	**I**	50
Au	2.7 ± 0.5	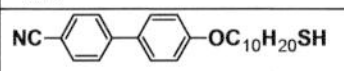 NC— —$OC_{10}H_{20}SH$	Cr 110 LC 130 Iso	**II**	51
Au	2.4	NC— —$OC_nH_{2n}SH$, n = 8-12	n=8, Meta.: Sm/N (89.7, 106.6; 149.9)	**IIIa**	52
			n=9, Meta.: Sm/N (85.3; 100.8; 151.6)	**IIIb**	
			n=10, Meta.: Sm/N (82.1; 99.2; 151.9)	**IIIc**	
			n=11, Meta.: Sm/N (79.8; 92.1; 149.7)	**IIId**	
			n=12, Meta.: Sm/N (85.1; 100.8; 150.5)	**IIIe**	
Au	2 ± 0.4	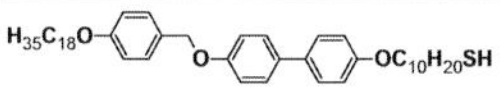 $H_{35}C_{18}O$— —$OC_{10}H_{20}SH$	C6: Sm	**IVa**	53
			C8: Sm	**IVb**	
			C12: Sm	**IVc**	
			C18: Sm	**IVd**	
Au	2 ± 0.4	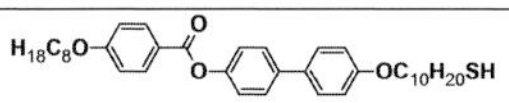 $H_{18}C_8O$— —$OC_{10}H_{20}SH$	C6: Sm	**Va**	53
			C8: Sm	**Vb**	
			C12: Sm	**Vc**	
			C18: Sm	**Vd**	
Au	~ 2.2	$H_{33}C_{16}O$—(Cl)— —$C_5H_{10}SH$	C4: Sm 190 (dec)	**VIa**	42
			C8: Sm 160 Iso	**VIb**	
			C12: no LC	**VIc**	
Au	~ 2.2	$H_{33}C_{16}O$—(Cl)— —$C_{10}H_{20}SH$	C4: Sm 150 Iso	**VIIa**	42
			C8: Sm 110 Iso	**VIIb**	
			C12: Sm 110 Iso	**VIIc**	

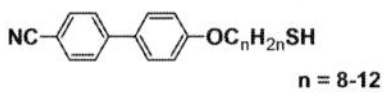

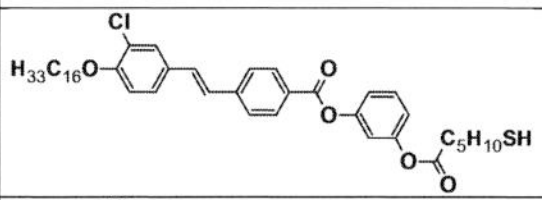

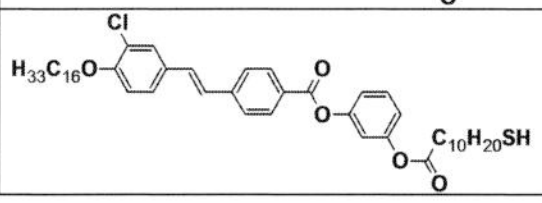

Table 1. (*Continued*)

NP type	NP diameter [nm]	Ligand structure	Phase transition temperatures [°C]	Sample nb.	Ref.
Au	~2.2	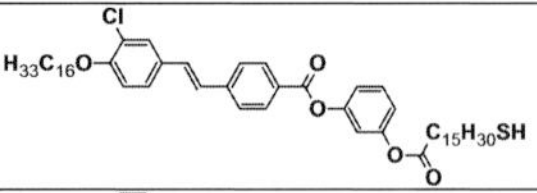	C4: 130 Iso C8: 110 Iso C12: 93 Iso	**VIIIa** **VIIIb** **VIIIc**	42
Au	1.5 ± 0.2	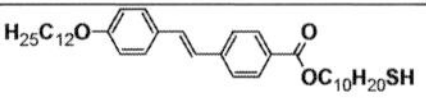	Sm 160 C Iso	**IX**	54
Ag	2.4 ± 0.3	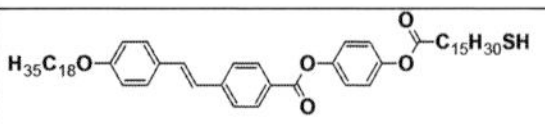	Sm 170 (dec)	**X**	45
Au	2 ± 0.5	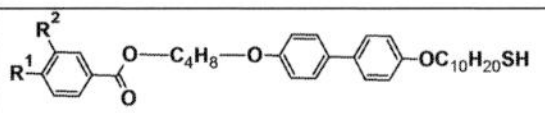 XIa $R^1=R^2=OC_{10}H_{21}$ XIb $R^2=OC_{10}H_{21}$ $R^1=H$	Sm 120 Iso Sm 140 Iso	**XIa** **XIb**	55
Au	2 ± 0.5	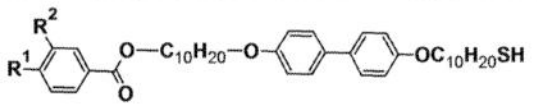 XIIa $R^1=R^2=OC_8H_{17}$ XIIc $R^2=OC_{10}H_{21}$ $R^1=H$ XIIb $R^2=OC_8H_{17}$ $R^1=H$	Sm 120 Iso Sm 120 Iso	**XIIa** **XIIb**	55
Au	C0: 1.94 ± 0.32 C6: 1.91 ± 0.31 C12: 2.01 ± 0.32	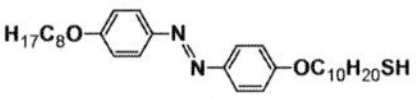	C0: Lam 162.8 Iso* C6: Col_h 154.4 Iso* C12: Col_h 139.6 Iso*	**XIIIa** **XIIIb** **XIIIc**	56
Au	2.09 ± 0.41	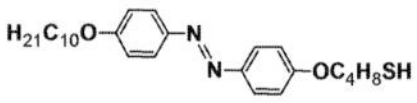	C0: Lam 169.8 Iso* C6: Col 162.8 Iso* C12: Col 163.1 Iso*	**XIVa** **XIVb** **XIVc**	56
Au	1.5 ± 0.2	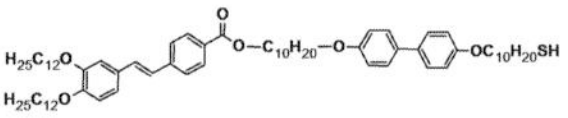	Sm 165 Iso	**XV**	54
Au	1.5 ± 0.2	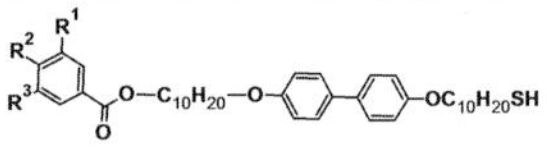 XVIa $R^1=R^2=R^3=OC_{12}H_{25}$ XVIb $R^1=R^2=OC_{12}H_{25}$ $R^3=H$ XVIc $R^1=OC_{12}H_{25}$ $R^2=R^3=H$	Sm 85 Iso Sm 125 Iso no LC	**XVIa** **XVIb** **XVIc**	54

In the early 2000s also two publications related to formation of LC-phases made of anisotropic TiO_2[57] and ferrite[25] nanoparticles covered with mesogens were published. Briefly, it was shown that anisotropy of the core of nanoparticles supported nematic ordering of these materials.

Our group was one of a few to perform systematic studies for establishing designing rules for LC-NPs. First, M. Wojcik *et al.*[53] identified the influence of alkane co-ligand length on the formation of a long-range order for LC-NPs using SAXRD method as a complementary technique to the previously used TEM and POM methods. The X-ray pattern for sample (**IVa**, Fig. 2) aligned by shearing allowed to obtain a detailed view of the NPs assembly. A series of commensurate sharp reflections corresponding to layer periodicity ($\sim$10 nm) in the direction perpendicular to the shearing direction and a diffused signal parallel ($\sim$3 nm) to it were observed. This pattern is characteristic of a lamellar structure, meaning that the observed periodicities correspond to inter-layer and in-layer distances between metal centers, respectively. Interestingly, LC-nanoparticles covered with the same mesogenic molecule but different length n-alkylthiols (**IVa-IVd**) had the same inter-layer spacing, while the measured in-layer distance increased with increasing alkylthiol length. Apparently, due to the flexibility of the spacer unit (pro)mesogenic ligands attached to the metal surface could rearrange in space, they are collected mainly above and below metal sphere, forming organic sublayers separating layers made of metal centers. Spacing between the metal cores inside the layer was mainly determined by n-alkylthiol length (materials **IV, V**). It was therefore deduced, that particle-to-particle distance can be controlled via proper choice of n-alkyl co-ligands.

By expanding the knowledge from the above mentioned results also the combined influence of alkylthiol length and length of the alkyl spacer of the promesogenic ligand for stilbene-moiety comprising molecules was

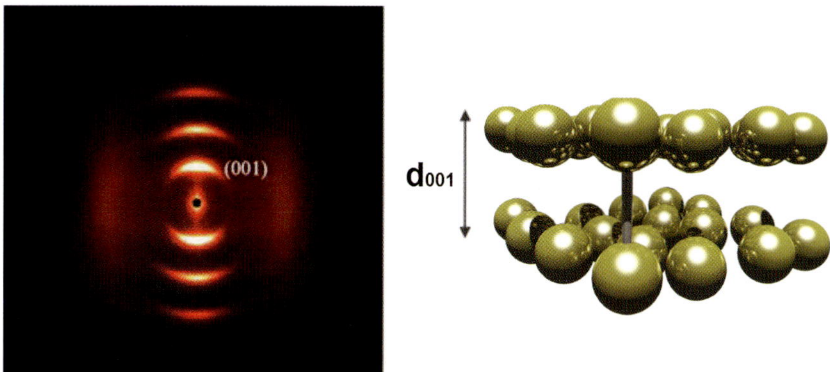

Fig. 2. Small angle XRD pattern of lamellar phase made of LC-NPs (material **IVa**) and schematic picture of the phase, with inter-layer spacing $d_{001} \sim 8.4$ nm. Adapted by permission of The Royal Society of Chemistry [53].

investigated.[42] Similarly to previous results[53] small ($\sim$ 2.2 nm) diameter gold nanoparticles covered with different n-alkylthiols (C4, C8 and C12) were first prepared and then ligand exchange reaction was performed, using three types of mesogenic molecules, leading to 9 types of hybrid materials (materials **VI**, **VII**, **VIII**) with ratio of mesogenic to alkyl ligands ca. 1:1 (based on NMR and TGA data). The SAXRD analysis of monodomain samples in combination with TEM measurements allowed to determine the internal structure of these materials, revealing for most of these materials long-range ordered lamellar structures and for others 3D superlattices with base-centered orthorhombic unit cells. Two major conclusions were drawn from this work, which are summarized in Fig. 3. The first was based on the observation that the longer the mesogenic molecule spacer the more

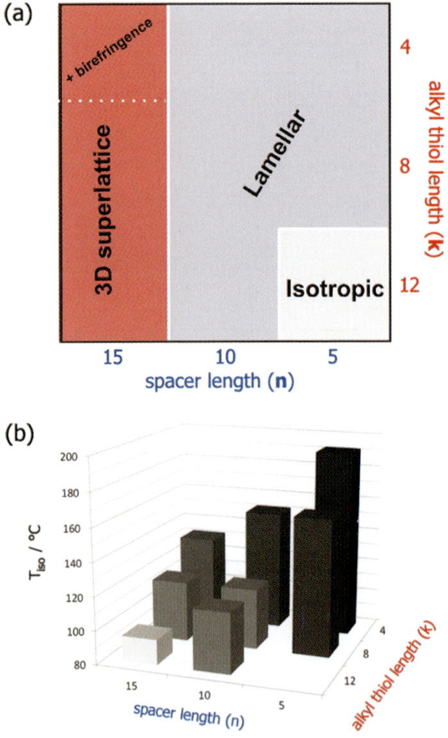

Fig. 3. Types of structure formed by self-assembled hybrid nanoparticles (a) and the lattice melting temperature (b) as a function of the structural parameters of the surface ligands, n and k (materials **VI**, **VII**, **VIII**). Reprinted with permission from [42]. Copyright 2013 American Chemical Society.

ordered assemblies of the NPs are observed. This relationship can be further strengthened by shortening the length of alkyl co-ligands. Therefore, the flexibility of the mesogenic molecule seems to be one of the key parameters controlling the degree of order within the materials. Secondly, a systematic variation of clearing temperature, evidenced reversed correlation between phase transition temperature and separation between the metallic particles.

The ability of (pro)mesogenic ligands to form anisotropic arrangements were confirmed for LC-NPs with stilbene mesogenic ligands. It is worth to notice that often structures formed by NPs do not show the birefringence or their birefringence is very low. Notably, Wolska *et al.*[54] experimentally proved that the birefringence originates from weak orientational arrangement of ligands in the organic sublayer (Fig. 4). Polarized IR spectroscopy of a thermally aligned annealed sample (material **IX**) showed that the orientational order parameter for mesogenic core groups is $S \sim 0.1$. Moreover, the birefringence of the material is recovered after cooling the material from isotropic phase.

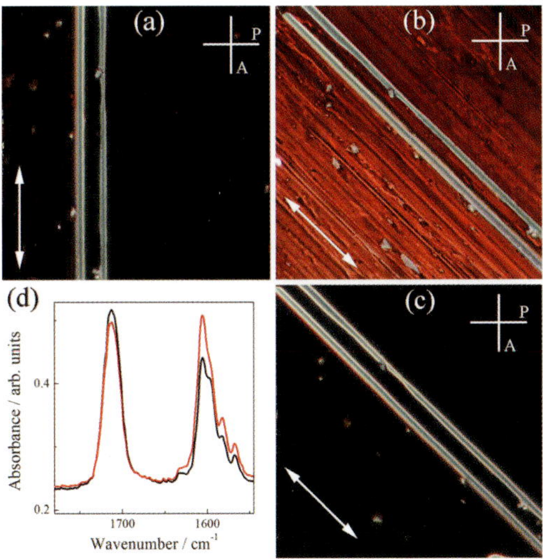

Fig. 4.   Sheared material **IX** at 70°C observed under crossed polarizers, with the shearing direction along (a) and inclined (b) from the polarizer direction shows optical birefringence. (c) After melting the sample above 160°C the birefringence is lost. (d) Polarized IR spectra showing absorption bands related to phenyl ring stretching (at 1605 cm⁻¹) and carbonyl group stretching (at 1710 cm⁻¹) recorded for light polarized along (red) and perpendicular (black) to the rubbing direction, showing weak orientational order of mesogenic units. Reproduced by permission of The Royal Society of Chemistry [54].

We have also shown that anisotropic arrangement of stilbene (pro)mesogenic ligands can translate to functional anisotropy[45] of the material. In the first report showing applicability of the approach to a metallic nanoparticle different than gold we have prepared silver nanoparticles (4.4 ± 0.3 nm diameter) using a modified Wang method[58] in which instead of dodecylamine ligands hexanethiol molecules were used. Then, in a ligand exchange reaction, a portion ($\sim 58\%$) of the n-alkanethiols at the surface of Ag NPs was substituted by mesogenic molecule. For hybrid Ag NPs (material **Xa**) thermal annealing of the sample revealed a set of narrow Bragg peaks. Shearing of the material at elevated temperature ($\sim 150°$C) enabled preparation of a monodomain sample for which SAXRD studies were performed. It was deduced that a layer structure is formed (inter-layer distance ca. 13.1 nm and particle-to-particle distance ~ 6.6 nm).

Further insight into the sample was gained by polarized IR spectroscopy, which evidenced that for these materials mesogenic molecules are preferentially aligned along the layers (perpendicular to the layer normal) made of metal particles. The lamellar phase was thermally stable until decomposition of material at $\sim 160°$C. Notably, polarized UV-Vis showed a 20 nm redshift of plasmon peak maxima when polarization of the incident light was changed from perpendicular to parallel to the average direction of mesogenic ligand main axes (Fig. 7a). It corresponds to the difference between extraordinary and ordinary refractive indices of about 0.14. Therefore it was deduced that alignment of the LC ligands as well as anisotropic arrangement of Ag particles are responsible for the observed plasmon angular dependence.

Recently,[55] it was shown for hybrid nanoparticles with stilbene rod-like mesogenic ligands that it is possible to control the structure of the LC-NPs not only at the level of individual nanoparticles but also orientation of the whole aggregate. Hybrid gold nanoparticles (with diameter 2 ± 0.5 nm, material **XI, XII**) covered with a mixed organic layer comprising decanethiol and mesogenic ligands (molar ratio 1:1) were prepared using Brust–Schiffrin and ligand exchange protocols. The SAXRD evidenced lamellar structures for all samples, however the orientation of layers was dependent on sample history, i.e. on the temperature at which shearing is preformed (Fig. 5). When the sample is sheared at low temperature ($\sim 40°$C) the layer normal was along shearing direction leadicating formation of a 'transverse mode of alignment'[59] for which the layer normal is parallel to the shearing direction but perpendicular to the shearing gradient. However, when alignment procedure was performed at higher temperature ($\sim 80°$C) the direction of

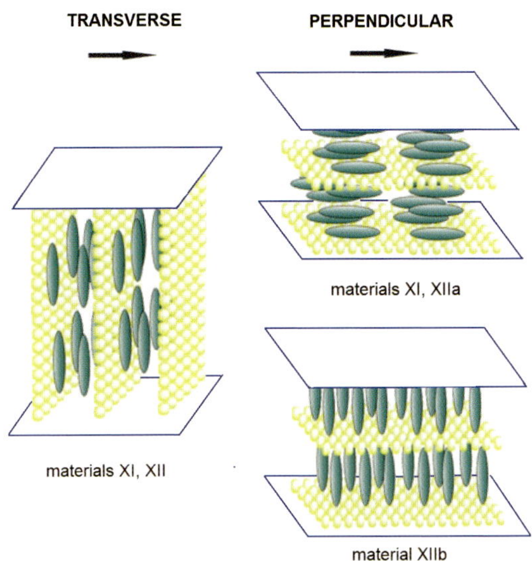

Fig. 5.　Scheme of nanoparticles orientation in space in respect to the shearing direction in transverse and perpendicular modes. Blue ellipses represent mesogenic ligands. Black arrow indicates the shearing direction. Shearing gradient is perpendicular to the glass plates (white with blue outline), thus is perpendicular to the shearing direction. Adapted by permission of The Royal Society of Chemistry [55].

layer normal was perpendicular ('perpendicular mode of alignment'[60]) to the shearing direction and the shearing gradient. In all cases except for the material **XIIb** the orientation of the long axes of the mesogenic molecules is parallel to the nanocrystal layers (Fig. 5). Moreover, shearing at intermediate temperature (60°C) did not allow to observe spatial orientation of layers. These results reveal strongly temperature dependent material viscosity.

Also rod-like, photosensitive azobenzene derivatives were used to drive the assembly of nanoparticles. Chen *et al.*[56] prepared a series of hybrid NPs which were either exclusively or partially covered with azobenzene mesogenic ligands (materials **XIII** and **XIV**), following Brust–Schiffrin synthesis with the sole use of mesogenic capping agents or by ligand exchange using hexane- or dodecanethiol capped gold nanoparticles (1:1 ratio). TEM was used to estimate sizes of metallic cores which were ca. 2 nm diameter (before heating, see Table 5 for details). Thermal properties of NPs were first investigated by DSC revealing phase transitions which were ascribed to appearance of liquid-crystalline phases with clearing point between 140 and 170°C. The DSC also allowed the authors to discuss the stability of the materials. For LC-NPs covered exclusively with mesogenic ligands (**XIIIa** and **XIVa**) second heating and first cooling were markedly different from the first heating cycle; the subsequent heating/cooling cycles were reproducible. It was concluded that thermolysis process was occurring since TGA did not indicate decomposition below 260°C, while NMR revealed presence of disulfide byproducts in the mixture after heating cycle. Conversely, hybrid NPs with mixed organic coating exhibited higher stability and reproducibility of DSC thermograms with only partial thermolysis.

Self-assembly of NPs was further investigated by combined SAXRD and WAXRD studies, indicating appearance of non-crystalline aggregates with nanometer scale order. For the materials **XIIIa** and **XIVa** SAXRD measurements indicated a lamellar structure. For **XIIIa** it was shown that above 165°C only one, diffusive scattering signal was present. On consecutive cooling scan lamellar structure was not recovered. On the other hand, for the samples **XIIIb,c** Bragg reflections position indicated formation of 2D hexagonal structure that could be reversely melted.

Finally, it was shown that the density of organic layer of (pro)mesogenic ligands can be the decisive factor for final arrangements of NPs.[54] For hybrid nanoparticles covered with relatively low number of dimeric ligands (25-35% of mesogenic thiols; materials **XV**, **XVI**) SAXRD measurements indicated formation of a lamellar structure, in analogy to the monomeric material **IX**. However, for these structures the mesogenic ligands were mainly bundled on one side of the metallic core, resulting in arrangement where organic layers were intersected by bilayer of metal spheres. The fact that an unusual arrangement of nanoparticles is observed can be interpreted in the view of the low density of organic material covering metallic nanoclusters. Formation of lamellar structure requires packing of metallic spheres which would ensure effective filling of space with organic material typically leading to density of the organic layer ~ 1 gcm^{-3}. Since the volume of organic coating is larger than in the case of alkyl ligands contribution of this factor is relatively large. It means also that it should be possible to control nanoparticle assembly by controlling the fraction of mesogenic ligands in the organic coating layer.[36]

Another factor that was found to influence strongly ordering of nanoparticles was the branching of the ligands. For rod-like mesogens increasing the number of tails often induces modulation of layers or introduce hexagonal columnar structure. In one of these studies a series of branched molecules

Table 2. Summary of the phase behavior of the hybrid NPs with branched rodlike ligands discussed in the text. Sm, ModSm, Col, Iso stand for smectic, modulated smectic, columnar and isotropic phase, respectively.

NP type	NP diameter [nm]	Ligand structure	Phase transition temperatures [°C]	Sample nb.	Ref.
Au	2 ± 0.2	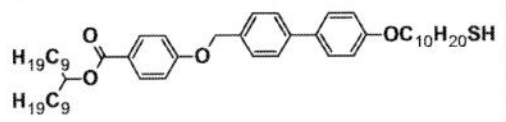 $H_{19}C_9$, $H_{19}C_9$ branched ester — benzoate — O — biphenyl — $OC_{10}H_{20}SH$	Sm 110 Iso	**XVII**	61
Au	2 ± 0.2	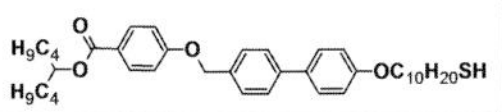 H_9C_4, H_9C_4 branched ester — benzoate — O — biphenyl — $OC_{10}H_{20}SH$	Col 150	**XVIII**	61
Au	2 ± 0.4	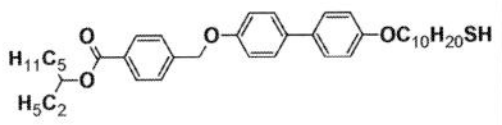 $H_{11}C_5$, H_5C_2 branched ester — benzoate — O — biphenyl — $OC_{10}H_{20}SH$	C6: Sm C8: ModSm C10: Col C12: Col C18: -	**XIXa** **XIXb** **XIXc** **XIXd** **XIXe**	53, 61
Au	2 ± 0.4	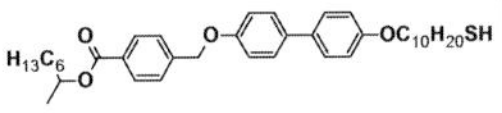 $H_{13}C_6$ branched ester — benzoate — O — biphenyl — $OC_{10}H_{20}SH$	C6: Sm C8: Sm C12: Col C18: -	**XXa** **XXb** **XXc** **XXd**	53

were prepared (Table 2) and attached to the small gold NPs.[61] The Au NPs (2 ± 0.2 nm) were prepared using Brust–Schiffrin and ligand exchange protocols; mesogenic molecules constituted between 33 and 50% of the organic coating layer of nanoparticles, while the second ligand was dodecanethiol. Within these limits SAXRD measurements evidenced that the material **XVII** formed a lamellar structure, while for **XVIII** and **XIXd** several incommensurate signals were observed from more complex 3D structure. Mechanical shearing at 80°C allowed to achieve a monodomain structure and the collected Bragg diffractogram was indexed assuming a body-centered orthorhombic unit cell with dimensions $a \sim 8.3$, $b \sim 4.8$, $c \sim 6.7$ nm. Later the effect of alkanethiols on SA was studied[53] (hybrid materials **XIX** and **XX**), resulting in the columnar, smectic and modulated smectic phase formation as identified via SAXRD measurements. The arrangement type was dependent on the length of alkanethiol ligands. The tendency has been explained based on the architectural parameters of the obtained hybrid materials, i.e. the length of the alkanethiols which determines spacing between nanoparticles and the volume of mesogenic ligands attached to an individual nanoparticle.

3.2. *Rod-like ligands with side-on attachment*

A very successful example of class of mesogens used for driving the assembly of nanoparticles are rod-like molecules that are attached to the surface of nanoparticles in a side-on geometry. Initial studies on this type of materials were presented by Cseh and Mehl.[62] The preliminary studies were conducted for 1.6±0.4 nm diameter gold nanoparticles covered with a mixed layer of organic compounds – hexanethiol and mesogenic thiol in the ratio 1:1 (as determined with ^{1}H NMR), the NPs were prepared by a two-step process involving ligand-exchange reaction. The obtained structure (material **XXI**) was examined with DSC and POM measurements. Two thermal events taking place at -3 and 43.8°C were ascribed to glass transition and clearing, respectively.

In a consequent study, mesogen with four aromatic rings was used to drive the assembly of nanoparticles into liquid-crystalline phases, underlining the importance of alkane co-ligands length on assembly of LC-NPs.[63] Two types of hybrid materials 1.7 ± 0.4 and 2.0 ± 0.4 nm diameter gold nanoparticles with a mixed ligand shell (alkylthiol to mesogenic ligands ratio $\sim$2:1) were prepared (materials **XXIIa,b**) following the earlier procedure.[62] The DSC scans have shown two phase transitions for both structures, while POM observation evidenced marbled or *Schlieren* textures. Since the material was miscible with the ligands, the authors have drawn preliminary conclusion that the nanoparticles form a nematic phase. Importantly, authors noted that alkanethiols ligand length enabled control over structure transition temperatures by controlling freedom of movement of the mesogenic groups as well as plastifying effect. Later, using more precise GISAXS and TEM methods authors ruled out the initial phase assignment[64] and concluded that the material with dodecanethiol co-ligands (**XXIIIb**) forms rhombohedral lattice with space group R3m and the unit cell parameters: $a \sim 8.00$ nm and $c \sim 3.54$ nm. In this phase nanoparticles are arranged into columns that are packed into triangular lattice with three non-equivalent columns in one unit cell. These findings were supported by TEM images showing nanoparticle assembly with inter-particle spacings corresponding to those derived from GISAXS. The authors were also able to determine the influence of n-alkylthiol co-ligand length on the self-assembly properties of LC-NPs.[65] For this purpose three types of hybrid nanoparticles were prepared: covered with mesogen exclusively (**XXIVa**) and with a mixed organic coating (hexane- and dodecanethiol co-ligands, **XXIVb** and **c**, respectively). For the material **XXIVa** in between 30 and 105°C sharp Bragg peaks were observed in SAXRD and GISAXS experiments which were indexed assuming a 3D hexagonal lattice with the space group P6/mmm. Above 105°C the peaks disappeared which indicated formation of an isotropic liquid. Reconstructed electron density map showed that metallic spheres were positioned at the corners of the 3D hexagonal unit cell with inter-particle distances along a and c axes almost the same.

Moreover, the authors concluded that the absence of birefringence of the sample means that the mesogenic ligands have no preferred global orientation. In the case of material **XXIVb** SAXRD experiments revealed three sharp Bragg reflections corresponding to a simple 2D hexagonal lattice. Besides them, a broad peak is observed along the shearing direction, reflecting that NPs have no long-range correlation along the column axis. Additionally, the sample showed non-zero birefringence and optical texture characteristic to a nematic phase due to small volume fraction (ca. 5%) of gold embedded between mesogens having orientational order. In the case of material **XXIVc** GISAXS indicated formation of a face-centered cubic (FCC) lattice. Based on the above results the authors concluded that hybrid NPs with rod-like mesogens attached in side-on geometry preferably form strings that are arranged into hexagonal lattice with different orientation of the mesogens around the metallic nanoparticles (Fig. 6).

In order to drive the assembly of larger (ca. 10 nm diameter) nanoparticles (material **XXV**) with well-defined plasmonic properties the larger,

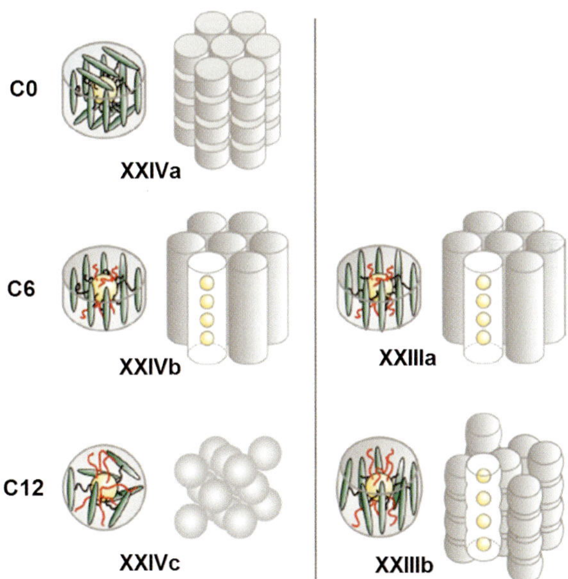

Fig. 6. Schematic illustration of the different arrangements of ligands and co-ligands around a nanoparticle depending on the relative amount of alkylthiols co-ligands (red, C6 or C12, C0 without alkylthiols), and the type of mesogenic ligand (green), and of the different resulting types of ordered self-assembly for materials **XXIII** and **XXIV**. Reproduced from [65] with permission from The Royal Society of Chemistry.

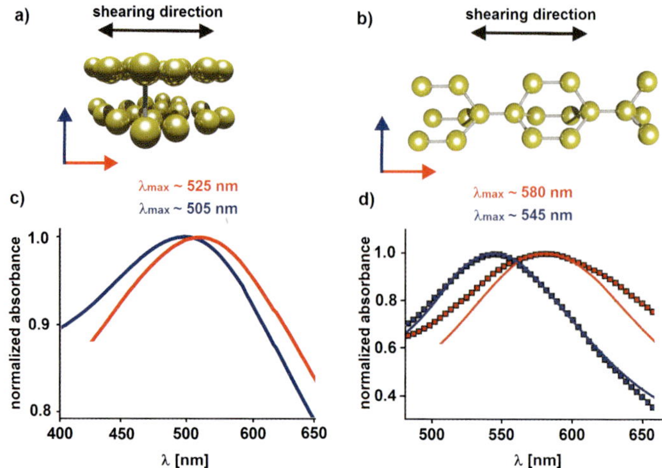

Fig. 7. Scheme of nanoparticle spatial organization in (**a**) layered of material **X** and (**b**) P63/mmc phases of material **XXVI**; director of mesogenic ligands is aligned along the shearing direction; direction of light polarization used in UV/Vis measurements parallel and perpendicular to the shearing direction is shown in red and blue colors, respectively. c), d) UV/Vis absorption measurements of phases shown in (a) and (b), respectively, using polarized light; blue and red curves correspond to the measurements done using light polarized in directions indicated by arrows in (a) and (b). (a, b) Reprinted with permission from [14]. Copyright 2014 John Wiley and Sons. (c) Reproduced from [45] with permission from The Royal Society of Chemistry. (d) Adapted with permission from [44]. Copyright 2013 John Wiley and Sons.

four-ring, mesogenic ligand was used.[40] Dec-9-enylamine-functionalized Au NPs were synthesized and then hydrosilylation of terminal olefin groups mediated by Karstedt's catalyst was performed to attach disiloxane derivative of the mesogen. The UV-Vis measurements confirmed plasmonic behavior of the system with clear absorption band maxima at ca. 520 nm. Based on DSC and POM studies nematic phase was found for these hybrid NPs, however it was not possible to prepare an oriented sample. Despite this, from the applicative point of view it was important that the use of a long spacer that includes a siloxane group helped to lower the viscosity of the material.

Later, it was shown that by using plasmonic NPs formation of an anisotropic plasmonic metamaterial is possible.[44] Using the three-ring ligands and following earlier procedures[62] hybrid nanoparticles were prepared (material **XXVI**) with particles having metal core diameter ~ 3 nm. The DSC study of the material evidenced a thermal event at 73.6°C which was attributed to a clearing transition. The material was highly viscous therefore mechanical shearing could be used to prepare the aligned sample. POM observation confirmed that optical axis is oriented along the shearing direction. GISAXS measurements evidenced $P6_3/mmc$ structure of nanoparticles. Interestingly, in this arrangement the gap distance between the NPs (surface-to-surface) was only 1.0–1.2 nm, which contributes to profound optical properties of the material. Polarization dependent absorption measurements revealed a shift of plasmonic band maxima form 540 to 590 nm when the angle between shearing direction and polarizer was changed from 90 to 0°. This unusually large shift was assumed to originate from two factors: orientational order of mesogenic ligands, that affects refractive index as well as anisotropic NP-NP interactions inside the structure.

Table 3. Summary of the phase behavior of the hybrid NPs with **side-on attached rodlike** ligands discussed in the text. Cr, N, Col_h, Col_r, Iso, FCC stand for crystal, nematic, columnar hexagonal, columnar rectangular, isotropic and face centered cubic phase, respectively. g stands for glass.

NP type	NP diameter [nm]	Ligand structure	Phase transition temperatures [°C]	Sample nb.	Ref.
Au	1.6 ± 0.4	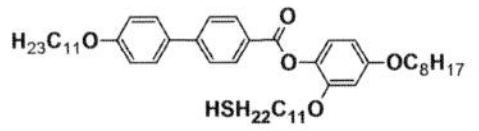 $H_{23}C_{11}O$–〈biphenyl-benzoate〉–OC_8H_{17}; $HSH_{22}C_{11}O$	g 3 N 43.8 Iso	**XXI**	62
Au	C6: 1.7 ± 0.4 C12: 2.0 ± 0.4	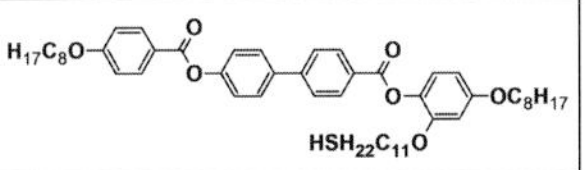 $H_{17}C_8O$–〈benzoate-biphenyl-benzoate〉–OC_8H_{17}; $HSH_{22}C_{11}O$	C6: Cr 73.1 N 118.7 Iso C12: Cr 45.7 N 126 Iso	**XXIIa** **XXIIb**	63
Au	C6: 1.7 ± 0.4 C12: 2.0 ± 0.4	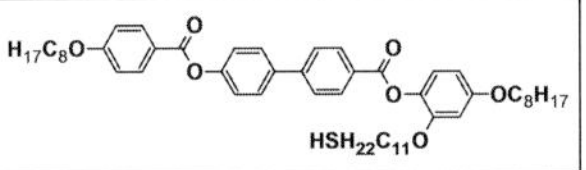 $H_{17}C_8O$–〈benzoate-biphenyl-benzoate〉–OC_8H_{17}; $HSH_{22}C_{11}O$	C6: Col_r 80 Col_h 118.7 Iso C12: R3m 126 Iso	**XXIIIa** **XXIIIb**	64
Au	C0: 1.79 C6: 1.62 C12: 2.27	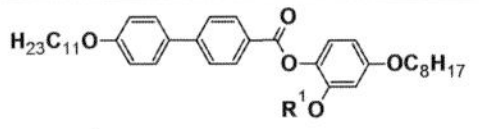 $H_{23}C_{11}O$–〈biphenyl-benzoate〉–OC_8H_{17}; R^1O; **XXIVa** $R^1 = C_5H_{10}SH$; **XXIVb, XXIVc** $R^1 = C_{11}H_{22}SH$	C0: 30 P6/mmm 105 Iso C6: N 45 Iso C12: FCC	**XXIVa** **XXIVb** **XXIVc**	65
Au	9.98 ± 2.2	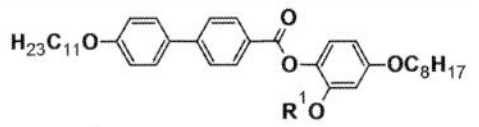 $H_{23}C_{11}O$–〈biphenyl-benzoate〉–OC_8H_{17}; R^1O; **XXIVa** $R^1 = C_5H_{10}SH$; **XXIVb, XXIVc** $R^1 = C_{11}H_{22}SH$	Cr 37.5 N 94.5 Iso	**XXV**	40
Au	~ 3	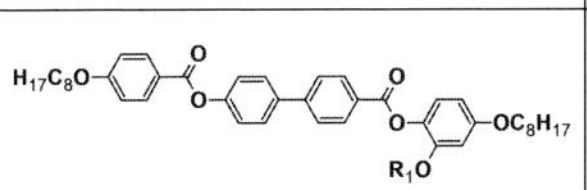 $H_{17}C_8O$–〈benzoate-biphenyl-benzoate〉–OC_8H_{17}; R_1O; $R^1 = C_{11}H_{22}Si(CH_3)_2OSi(CH_3)_2C_{10}H_{20}NH_2$	N 73.6 Iso (P6$_3$/mmc after vapor annealing)	**XXVI**	44

3.3. *Bent-core and dendritic ligands*

Besides the linear ligands also other geometry ligands were used to drive the NPs assembly. The bent-core mesogens attract a lot of attention due to their ability to form polar liquid crystals, thus it was an obvious idea to use them as ligands to graft nanoparticles.[61,66] Unfortunately, so far none of these hybrid materials self-assembled into long-range ordered structures in this state. This may be due to relatively high transition temperatures preventing observation of thermodynamically stable anisotropic structures below decomposition temperature.

It should be noted, that up-to this point we have considered the use of various small mesogenic molecules for LC-NPs preparation. One of the limitations of this approach is that a finite number of mesogenic units can be introduced to the nanoparticle surface, thus volume of the organic coating layer is limited. To solve this problem dendrimeric molecules were applied since by tailoring generation they can introduce different numbers of mesogenic subunits per one anchoring place at the surface of nanoparticle. Therefore, they give access to LC-NPs structures with versatile volume of organic coating which is not available when small mesogenic molecules are used. The first report concerning LC-NPs with dendritic ligands was presented by Terazzi *et al.*[41] Gold nanoparticles of size 2.1 ± 0.5 nm were prepared following a Brust–Schiffrin method using dodecanethiol ligands. A portion (ca. 42%) of the molecules at the Au NPs surface was then exchanged to a promesogenic, dendritic compound, yielding material **XXIX**. The dendritic molecule was designed as to exhibit cone-like conformation favoring interactions between the particles (assured by rigid core of the molecule) and fluidity (assured by alkyl chains at the periphery of the molecule). The DSC measurements reproducibly showed a single broad enantiotropic phase transition at $-12.2°$C, which was ascribed to the melting of the material. Up to $200°$C no additional thermal events were evidenced. The SAXRD measurements evidenced short range positional order of NPs between -10 and $60°$C while at higher temperatures (60 and $120°$C) a cubic lattice space group Im3m was assigned to the structure. Phase assignment to cubic structure was further supported by the lack of birefringence of the sample.

Another example of dendritic compounds for LC-NPs preparation was shown by Deschenaux *et al.*[37] Interestingly, these molecules were introduced to NPs surface using reaction on ω-substituted ligands of AuNPs. In detail, NPs were first prepared using the Brust–Schiffrin protocol and then a ligand-exchange reaction was used to introduce ω-bromo substituted thiol molecules to the NPs surface. The ω-bromo moiety was then partially replaced with an azide group. Consequently, Huisgen 1,3-dipolar cycloaddition was used to react functionalized nanoparticles with one of the two alkyne dendrimers. Based on ^{1}H NMR, IR and TGA number of the various ligands in the organic coating layer was calculated. POM was used to investigate self-assembly properties of the hybrid materials (**XXIXa,b**) testing monotropic liquid-crystalline behavior. Based on the observation of small focal-conic fan textures smectic-A phase was assigned to the aggregates.

The influence of radial density profile of organic corona on LC-NPs assembly was studied by Kanie, Ungar *et al.*[36] The authors attached amine-functionalized (pro)mesogenic ligands to the nanoparticles (6.8 ± 0.7 nm) via reaction with free carboxylic moieties pending at the ends of alkyl surface ligands. First-, second-, and third-generation phenethyl ether-type dendrons were used. The DSC measurements revealed two thermal events taking place at 0 and $220°$C as well as 9 and $220°$C, respectively. However, SAXRD measurements evidenced formation of long-range ordered structure only for one of these materials, showing the importance of dendron generation and grafting density on LC NPs assembly. From 30 to $130°$C two signals were observed, from 2D hexagonal lattice. At higher temperatures (150-$170°$C) the observed XRD pattern was consistent with a simple cubic (SC) structure. Notably, it is the first observation of simple cubic symmetry for spherical NPs. It can be assumed that it originates from fluidity of dendrimers which allowed complete filling of the empty space in between the hard spheres defined as metallic core together the inner (alkyl) organic corona.

4. Dynamic reconfiguration of nanoparticle aggregates

One of the most desirable features of next generation materials is stimuli responsiveness, which enables predictable changes of materials properties. A broad range of applications is foreseen for such smart materials making them an attractive object of research. In the case of nanoparticle-based systems adaptive behavior has been already shown applicable in preparing drug delivery vehicles and biosensors. However, in these examples dynamic behavior is limited to solvated environments. Thus, it does not allow to precisely manipulate inter-particle spacing and collective interactions of nanoparticles. In clear contrast to these methods the approach based on liquid-crystalline ligands enables stimuli responsive behavior of densely

Table 4. Summary of the phase behavior of the hybrid NPs with **side-on attached rodlike ligands discussed in the text**. Cr, N, SmA, SC, Cub, Iso stand for crystal, nematic, smectic A, simple cubic and cubic phase, respectively. HS, g, dec stand for a 2D hexagonal superlattice, glass and decomposition, respectively. G1 and G2 relate to dendron generation 1 and 2.

NP type	NP diameter [nm]	Ligand structure	Phase transition temperature [°C]	Sample nb.	Ref.
Au	2.1 ± 0.5	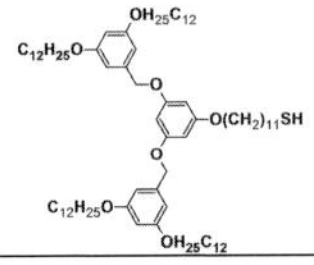 (chemical structure: $C_{12}H_{25}O$, $OH_{25}C_{12}$, $O(CH_2)_{11}SH$)	Cr 12.2 Iso 70–80 Cub 180 (dec)	**XXVIII**	41
Au	1.5 ± 0.5	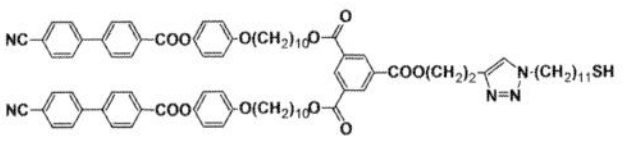 (chemical structure: NC–…–COO–…–$O(CH_2)_{10}O$–…–$COO(CH_2)_2$–…–N-$(CH_2)_{11}SH$, $N{=}N$)	G1: 90 SmA 145 G2: 90 SmA 165	**XXIXa** **XXIXb**	37
Au	6.8 ± 0.7	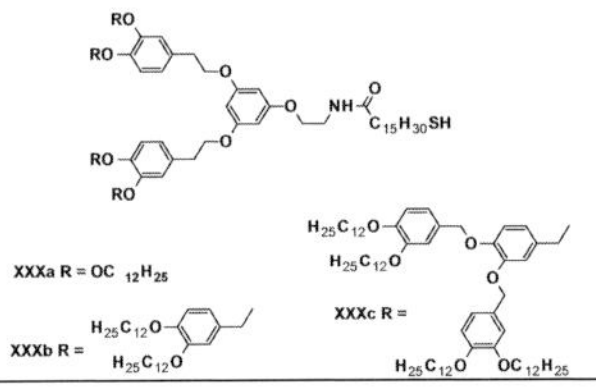 (chemical structure: RO, NH, $C_{15}H_{30}SH$; $H_{25}C_{12}O$, $OC_{12}H_{25}$; **XXXa** R = $OC_{12}H_{25}$, **XXXb** R =, **XXXc** R =)	0 HS 130 SC 220	**XXXa** **XXXb** **XXXc**	36
Fe_2O_3		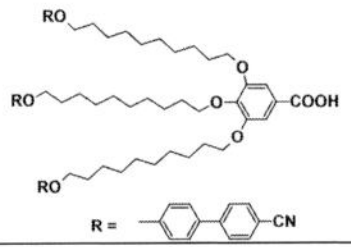 (chemical structure: RO, $COOH$, R = …–CN)	g 40–60 N 180.2 Iso	**XXXI**	23
Fe_2O_3		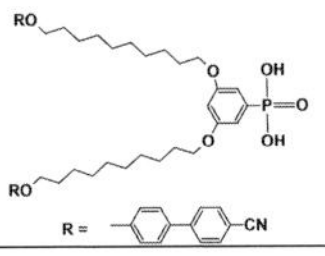 (chemical structure: RO, OH, $P{=}O$, OH, R = …–CN)	g 30–50 N 174.2 Iso	**XXXII**	23

packed nanoparticle aggregates, which opens the way to many budding applications.

Dynamic control over mesogenic nanoparticle aggregates reported to date was achieved using various thermo-, light- and magneto- stimuli. The exerted changes are especially interesting if they influence nearest-neighbor spacing between particles or their orientation, since in both cases the switching of physicochemical properties can be envisaged.

Temperature responsiveness of the described materials stems from the use of thermotropic (pro)mesogenic ligands to drive the assembly of nanoparticles into aggregates. The range of temperatures in which phase transitions of mesogenic nanoparticle assemblies are found is wide, ranging from ca. 50 to 180°C, and depends on hybrid NPs design (as discussed in the section on designing rules for LC-NPs). The upper temperature limit is set by decomposition point of nanoparticles which is usually ca. 160°C for systems based on Au NPs, but can be higher for example in the case of ferrite[25] or TiO_2[57] NPs. As expected based on knowledge of thermotropic liquid crystals variation of temperature enabled observation of two types of switching:

- long-to-short range order transition (clearing) and
- switching between different long-range ordered phases.

To date, the lowest reported isotropization temperature is 43.8°C, observed for the nematic to isotropic phase transition of small gold nanoparticles.[62] The clearing temperature is heavily dependent on hybrid nanoparticle design as can be seen from the Tables 1-3. Unfortunately, usually the change of inter-particle spacing corresponding to clearing event was not discussed, therefore only limited data is available.[61] For the sample **XVIII** it was measured that within lamellar structure in-plane spacing between NPs (nearest-neighbor distance) was ca. 3 nm. In the isotropic phase the average distance between particles increases to 5.4 nm. Taking the size of the nanoparticles into account the distance variation may be translated to change of the gap between surfaces of particles from 1 to 2.4 nm. The change of nearest neighbor distance between nanoparticles that can be induced by clearing can be used to prepare switchable metamaterials as recently presented.[67] It was shown that the silver nanoparticles (4.7 ± 0.5 nm diameter) with organic shell comprising dodecanethiol and mesogenic ligands (material **XXXIII**) self-assembled into a lamellar structure with nearest-neighbor distance of 6.1 nm. Above 95°C the reconfiguration of the assembly takes place and above this temperature particles have an isotropic distribution with mean inter-particle distance of 7.4 nm. The change of spacing results in blueshift of plasmonic band maxima by 20 nm and this process is reversible. Notably, ellipsometry evidenced epsilon-near-zero (ENZ) properties of the material **XXXIII**, while theoretical modeling has further shown that the ENZ properties are thermally switchable.

The first example of switching behavior of long-to-long range order type exhibited by LC-coated nanoparticles was given in the work of Kanie and Sugimoto.[57] These authors prepared TiO_2 nanoparticles with highly anisotropic shape—width up to 30 nm and aspect ratio above 10—and covered them with mesogenic ligand (material **XXXIV**). Combined DSC and POM studies evidenced nematic ordering of nanoparticles between 73 and 118°C, above which optical birefringence of the material disappeared. However, further heating of the sample resulted in the reappearance of a *Schlieren* texture. This was ascribed by the authors to presumably nematic to nematic transition, which, as deduced from XRD measurements, was accompanied by changes of inter-particle (center-to-center) spacing from 33.2 to 33.6 nm.

In some cases it was shown that by varying temperature it is possible to control periodicities of the assembly, without influencing its symmetry.[45] Using X-ray method it was shown for the material **XXXV** that temperature allowed for controlling structural parameters of a modulated lamellar phase. The modulation period changed profoundly with varying temperature and it was concluded that the observed changes were due to the variation of the averaged inter-particle distance within the layer. Ungar *et al.*[64] achieved temperature switching between two different types with long-range ordered phases. For 1.7 ± 0.4 nm diameter gold nanoparticles covered with hexanethiol and mesogenic ligands (ratio 6:4, respectively) **XXIIIa** the 2D rectangular lattice of c2mm symmetry transformers to 2D hexagonal, p6mm symmetry structure at $\sim 80°C$ and the phase transition was accompanied by shortening of the unit cell dimension along a direction from 7.44 to 7.10 nm, but almost without influence on the nearest-neighbor distance inside the columns (0.02 nm difference).

Recently NP-based systems with more complex polymorphism was studied by Wojcik *et al.*[43] TEM studies of a thermally annealed sample (material **XXXVI**) revealed layered structure made of metallic particles at room temperature. Formation of a lamellar phase was confirmed also with XRD measurements, revealing interlayer distance 8.4 nm, and intralayer distance of ~ 3.0 nm. Upon heating, the layers undulate and above 152°C transition to a rectangular columnar phase with unit cell dimensions along a and b axes 6.74 (nearest-neighbor spacing) and 15.57 nm, respectively, was evidenced. Further heating results in a hexagonal columnar phase (at 158°C) with inter-particle spacing of 7.12 nm. This phase was stable up to 162°C at which clearing occurred. This study is a proof of principle that it is possible to achieve multiple long-to-long range ordered phases for single LC-NPs system.

Magnetic field responsive LC-NPs were prepared by Hegmann *et al.*[39] In this report gold nanorods with 28.6 ± 2 nm length and 6.5 ± 1.5 nm width were prepared. Ligand exchange reaction of the native ligand (cetyltrimethylammonium bromide) to mercaptotrimethoxysilane and then reaction with LC silane was used to introduce mesogenic ligands to the surface of nanoparticles. As prepared material (**XXXVII**) exhibited only short-range order, however addition of a very small portion of free LC-ligand molecules (1% mass) caused formation of large-area self-assembled structures with correlation length of up to hundreds of nm as shown by TEM. Two types of structures were observed in TEM measurements: end-to-end connected chains of rods aligned in a parallel fashion as well as smectic-like structures. Dynamic rearrangement of the material, i.e. changing the orientation of nanorods from parallel to normal to the substrate was possible with a hand-held magnet. The achieved tunability confirms that LC-approach allows also for dynamic reorientation of the assembly.

Also, light-responsive LC-NPs with ligands comprising azobenzene units were found. The idea of introducing such molecules to nanoparticle surface to control nanoparticle spacing in the neat state was introduced in the literature in the early 2000's.[68] Later, it was shown that photoswitching of the azo ligands from *trans* to *cis* conformation can be used to control magnetic properties of nanoparticles assemblies.[69,70] Furthermore, azobenzene derivatives were used to obtain LC-phases as discusses above.[56] However, only lately it was shown that the structure of liquid-crystalline NPs can be influenced with light.[46] The hybrid gold and silver NPs were prepared using a two-step approach that was previously discussed.[45,61] In all cases, besides promesogenic compounds, hexanethiol co-ligand was present in the organic coating layer, with ca. 1:1 ratio of alkane to promesogenic ligands for all samples. Monodomain samples were prepared by mechanical shearing at ca. 70°C and investigated with SAXRD. Lamellar and columnar phases were identified (see Table 5 for details) and phase assignment was further confirmed with TEM analysis. The most important observation was that mesophases of hybrid nanoparticles were photoresponsive (**XXXVIII–XLII**). When illuminated with UV light, the Bragg reflections disappeared and a single diffusive signal (**XXXVIII– XLI**) evidencing transition to isotropic phase appeared. This process was fully reversible, when UV light was turned off the lamellar structure was restored. A different behavior was observed for the sample with two different (pro)mesogenic ligands (**XLII**). In this case photoisomerization with UV-light caused shortening of inter-layer spacing, however long-range order was still present. Again, this tunability was reversible.

In summary it can be said that in comparison to other methods for controlling inter-particle spacing the method based on (pro)mesogenic ligands allows for relatively large variability. It is a reasonable compromise

Table 5. Summary of the phase behavior of dynamically controlled hybrid NPs with **azobenzene** ligands discussed in the text. Lam, Sm, ModSm, Col, Col_h, Col_r, Iso stand for lamellar, smectic, modulated smectic, columnar, columnar hexagonal, columnar rectangular and isotropic phase, respectively. dec stands for decomposition. N^a and N^b represent two different nematic phases.

NP type	NP diameter [nm]	Ligand structure	Phase transition temperature [°C]	Sample nb.	Ref.
Ag	4.7 ± 0.5	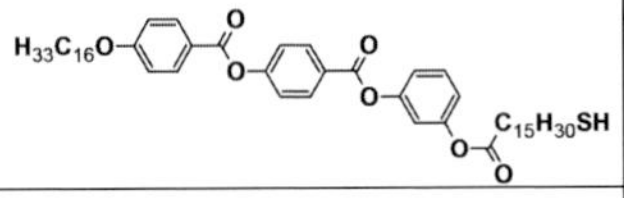 $H_{33}C_{16}O$— ... —$C_{15}H_{30}SH$	Lm 85 Iso	**XXXIII**	67
TiO_2	nano needles	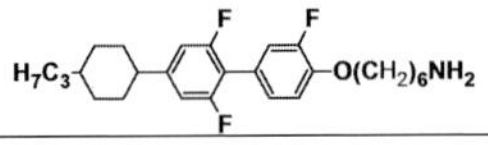 H_7C_3— ... —$O(CH_2)_6NH_2$ (F, F, F)	73 N^a 118 N^b	**XXXIV**	57
Au	4.4 ± 0.3	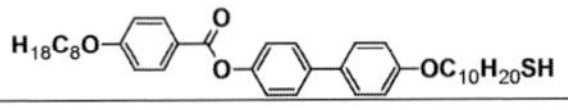 $H_{18}C_8O$— ... —$OC_{10}H_{20}SH$	ModSm 180 (dec)	**XXXV**	45
Au	2 - 3	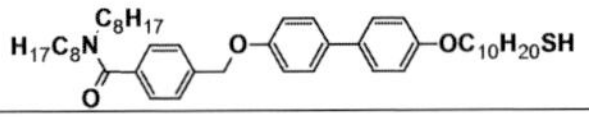 $H_{17}C_8N$ (C_8H_{17})— ... —$OC_{10}H_{20}SH$	Sm 148 Col_r 152 Col_h 158 Iso	**XXXVI**	43
Au nano rods	28.6 ± 2 length 6.5 ± 1.5 width	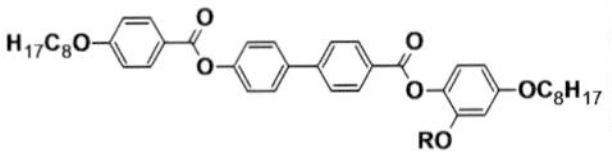 $H_{17}C_8O$— ... —OC_8H_{17} RO— R = $C_{11}H_{22}Si(OCH_3)_2OSi(OCH_3)_2C_3H_6SH$	chain-like and Lam structures	**XXXVII**	39
Au	2.5 ± 0.4	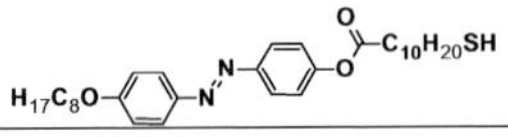 $H_{17}C_8O$— ... N=N ... —$C_{10}H_{20}SH$	Lam 160 Iso	**XXXVIII**	46
Au	2.5 ± 0.4	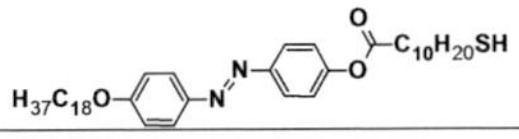 $H_{37}C_{18}O$— ... N=N ... —$C_{10}H_{20}SH$	Lam 160 Iso	**XXXIX**	46
		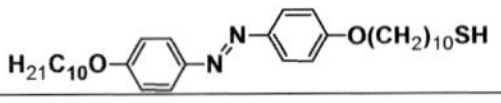 $H_{21}C_{10}O$— ... N=N ... —$O(CH_2)_{10}SH$	Lam 165 Iso	**XL**	46
Au Ag	2.5 ± 0.4 4.2 ± 0.3	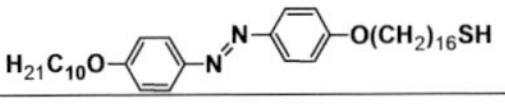 $H_{21}C_{10}O$— ... N=N ... —$O(CH_2)_{16}SH$	Col 155 Iso Lam 157 Iso	**XLIa** **XLIb**	46
Au	2.5 ± 0.4	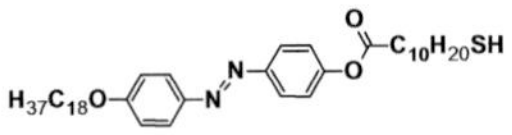 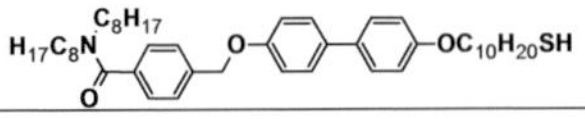 $H_{37}C_{18}O$— ... N=N ... —$C_{10}H_{20}SH$ $H_{17}C_8N$ (C_8H_{17})— ... —$OC_{10}H_{20}SH$	Lam 165 Iso	**XLII**	46

between achieving strong collective interactions as in the case of small inorganic ligands (those allow to achieve only static self-assembly) and dynamic self-assembly methods that rely on solvated environments (in the dissolved state collective interactions are not observed).

5. Summary

It should be stressed that in the case of metal particles grafted with organic layer there is a lot of flexibility for designing new hybrids. We can play with metal size and shape, with chemical structure of co-ligands attached to metal surface, but also the relative ratio of organic ligands in the grafting layer.

The driving mechanism for self-organization of LC-NPs is the tendency for spatial self-segregation of organic and metallic parts of NPs. Thus, not only chemical structure of ligands, but in many cases also the way ligands are attached to the surface is important for the system to display long-range ordered structures. It is crucial that the ligands are attached to the metal surface by long flexible spacer to allow them easy redistribution around the metal core. Most of the research was performed for rod-like mesogenic ligands attached either laterally or terminally to the metal surface. Notably, for lateral attachment it seems that the string-like arrangement of NPs is favored and such strings easily form variety of columnar structures, while for terminally attached rod-like ligands strong tendency toward lamellar structures is observed. Only for some of these systems textures typical for the LC with non-zero birefringence were observed. When considering birefringence, it was proven that it results from orientational order of mesogens, however most LC-NPs systems show zero birefringence. Thus, apparently orientational or positional order in the organic layer is not crucial for NPs to display long range organization.

For most of the studied materials the organic grafting layer was composed of a mixture of mesogenic and n-alkyl ligands. Both are important from the point of view of self-assembly process. The length of n-alkyl chains influence the inter-particle distance in the strings or the layers as well as influence thermal stability of the superstructures. Playing with relative concentration of mesogenic ligands *vs.* alkyl ligands in the grafting layer of NPs the distance between layers (or columns) can be tuned as the system adapts to proper (common for organic matter) density in organic sublayer separating metal cores. For large concentration of ligands the layers (columns) are separated by a double layer of organic material, while for low number of ligands organic coronas of nanoparticles interdigitate decreasing distance between layers/columns. The large advantage of NPs forming liquid-like structure is their tunability to external factor; so far, thermo-, magneto- and photo-tunability was studied. Since the external stimuli can result in reconfiguration of NPs arrangement, thus switching distance between particles, plasmon frequency shift should be observed. This phenomenon was confirmed for temperature variation.

Photo-tunability on the other hand was obtained by introducing the photochromic molecules (azo-dyes) into organic corona of NPs, resulting in reversible melting or change of layer spacing for such systems. Finally, although LC-based strategy did not allow to achieve metamaterials with negative refractive index in the visible range yet, an ambitious goal of this research is still to be obtained, already for some materials near-zero-epsilon property was demonstrated. It can be thus said that further research is needed in the field of liquid-crystalline nanoparticles self-assembly to go from a laboratory to industry, however the fast development seen over the last few years promises great perspectives for future technologies.

References

1. B. Prasad, C. Sorensen, and K. J. Klabunde, Gold nanoparticle superlattices, *Chem. Soc. Rev.* **37**(9), 1871–1883 (2008).
2. D. V. Talapin, J.-S. Lee, M. V. Kovalenko, and E. V. Shevchenko, Prospects of colloidal nanocrystals for electronic and optoelectronic applications, *Chem. Rev.* **110**(1), 389–458 (2009).
3. A. Kalsin, M. Fialkowski, M. Paszewski, S. Smoukov, K. Bishop, and B. Grzybowski, Electrostatic self-assembly of binary nanoparticle crystals with a diamond-like lattice, *Science.* **312**, 420 (2006).
4. R. J. Macfarlane, B. Lee, M. R. Jones, N. Harris, G. C. Schatz, and C. A. Mirkin, Nanoparticle superlattice engineering with DNA, *Science.* **334**(6053), 204–208 (2011).
5. S. J. Tan, M. J. Campolongo, D. Luo, and W. Cheng, Building plasmonic nanostructures with DNA, *Nat. Nanotechnol.* **6**(5), 268–276 (2011).
6. S. Ehlert, S. M. Taheri, D. Pirner, M. Drechsler, H.-W. Schmidt, and S. Fo rster, Polymer ligand exchange to control stabilization and compatibilization of nanocrystals, *ACS Nano.* **8**(6), 6114–6122 (2014).
7. B. Li, D.-M. Smilgies, A. D. Price, D. L. Huber, P. G. Clem, and H. Fan, Poly (n-isopropylacrylamide) surfactant-functionalized responsive silver nanoparticles and superlattices, *ACS Nano.* **8**(5), 4799–4804 (2014).
8. A. Dong, Y. Jiao, and D. J. Milliron, Electronically coupled nanocrystal superlattice films by in situ ligand exchange at the liquidñair interface, *ACS Nano.* **7**(12), 10978–10984 (2013).
9. W.-K. Koh, S. R. Saudari, A. T. Fafarman, C. R. Kagan, and C. B. Murray, Thiocyanate-capped pbs nanocubes: ambipolar transport enables quantum dot based circuits on a flexible substrate, *Nano. Lett.* **11**, 4764–4767 (2011).
10. M. Grzelczak, J. Vermant, E. M. Furst, and L. M. Liz-Marzán, Directed self-assembly of nanoparticles, *ACS Nano.* **4**(7), 3591–3605 (2010).

11. H. K. Bisoyi and S. Kumar, Liquid-crystal nanoscience: an emerging avenue of soft self-assembly, *Chem. Soc. Rev.* **40**(1), 306–319 (2011).

12. C. Blanc, D. Coursault, and E. Lacaze, Ordering nano- and microparticles assemblies with liquid crystals, *Liq. Cryst. Rev.* pp. 1–27 (2013).

13. T. Hegmann, H. Qi, and V. Marx, Nanoparticles in liquid crystals: Synthesis, self-assembly, defect formation and potential applications, *J. Inorg. Organometal. Polym. Mater.* **17**(3), 483–508 (2007).

14. W. Lewandowski, M. Wojcik, and E. Gorecka, Metal nanoparticles with liquid-crystalline ligands: Controlling nanoparticle superlattice structure and properties, *ChemPhysChem.* **15**(7), 1283–1295 (2014).

15. Q. Li, Nanoscience with liquid crystals, *Cham: Springer* (2014).

16. G. L. Nealon, R. Greget, C. Dominguez, Z. T. Nagy, D. Guillon, J.-L. Gallani, and B. Donnio, Liquid-crystalline nanoparticles: Hybrid design and mesophase structures, *Beilstein J. Org. Chem.* **8**, 349–370 (2012).

17. H. Qi and T. Hegmann, Liquid crystal-gold nanoparticle composites, *Liq. Cryst. Today.* **20**(4), 102–114 (2011).

18. S. Saliba, C. Mingotaud, L. Kahn, Myrtil, and J.-D. Marty, Liquid crystalline thermotropic and lyotropic nanohybrids, *Nanoscale.* **5**(15), 6641–6661 (2013).

19. O. Stamatoiu, J. Mirzaei, X. Feng, and T. Hegmann, Nanoparticles in liquid crystals and liquid crystalline nanoparticles, *Topics Current Chemistry.* **318**, 331–393 (2012).

20. S. Saliba, Y. Coppel, P. Davidson, C. Mingotaud, B. Chaudret, M. L. Kahn, and J.-D. Marty, Liquid crystal based on hybrid zinc oxide nanoparticles, *J. Mater. Chem.* **21**(19), 6821–6823 (2011).

21. S. Saliba, Y. Coppel, C. Mingotaud, J. D. Marty, and M. L. Kahn, Zno/liquid crystalline nanohybrids: From properties in solution to anisotropic growth, *Chem. Eur. J.* **18**(26), 8084–8091 (2012).

22. S. W. Buathong, D. Ung, T. J. Daou, C. Ulhaq-Bouillet, G. Pourroy, D. Guillon, L. Ivanova, I. Bernhardt, S. Bégin-Colin, and B. Donnio, Thermal, magnetic, and luminescent properties of dendronized ferrite nanoparticles, *J. Phys. Chem. C.* **113**(28), 12201–12212 (2009).

23. A. Demortière, S. Buathong, B. P. Pichon, P. Panissod, D. Guillon, S. Bégin Colin, and B. Donnio, Nematic like organization of magnetic mesogen hybridized nanoparticles, *Small.* **6**(12), 1341–1346 (2010).

24. S. Fleutot, G. L. Nealon, M. Pauly, B. P. Pichon, C. Leuvrey, M. Drillon, J.-L. Gallani, D. Guillon, B. Donnio, and S. Begin-Colin, Spacing-dependent dipolar interactions in dendronized magnetic iron oxide nanoparticle 2D arrays and powders, *Nanoscale.* **5**(4), 1507–1516 (2013).

25. K. Kanie and A. Muramatsu, Organic-inorganic hybrid liquid crystals: Thermotropic mesophases formed by hybridization of liquid-crystalline phosphates and monodispersed alpha-fe2O3 particles, *J. Am. Chem. Soc.* **127**(33), 11578–11579 (2005).

26. M. Grzelczak, J. Pérez-Juste, P. Mulvaney, and L. M. Liz-Marzán, Shape control in gold nanoparticle synthesis, *Chem. Soc. Rev.* **37**(9), 1783–1791 (2008).

27. J. H. Han, S. Lee, and J. Cheon, Synthesis and structural transformations

of colloidal 2D layered metal chalcogenide nanocrystals, *Chem. Soc. Rev.* **42** (7), 2581–2591 (2013).

28. H. You, S. Yang, B. Ding, and H. Yang, Synthesis of colloidal metal and metal alloy nanoparticles for electrochemical energy applications, *Chem. Soc. Rev.* **42**(7), 2880–2904 (2013).

29. M. Brust, M. Walker, D. Bethell, D. J. Schiffrin, and R. Whyman, Synthesis of thiol-derivatised gold nanoparticles in a two-phase liquid-liquid system, *J. Chem. Soc., Chem. Commun.* (7), 801–802 (1994).

30. R. H. Terrill, T. A. Postlethwaite, C.-H. Chen, C.-D. Poon, A. Terzis, A. Chen, J. E. Hutchison, M. R. Clark, and G. Wignall, Monolayers in three dimensions: NMR, SAXS, thermal, and electron hopping studies of alkanethiol stabilized gold clusters, *J. Am. Chem. Soc.* **117**(50), 12537–12548 (1995).

31. M. J. Hostetler, S. J. Green, J. J. Stokes, and R. W. Murray, Monolayers in three dimensions: synthesis and electrochemistry of ω-functionalized alkanethiolate-stabilized gold cluster compounds, *J. Am. Chem. Soc.* **118** (17), 4212–4213 (1996).

32. M. J. Hostetler, A. C. Templeton, and R. W. Murray, Dynamics of place-exchange reactions on monolayer-protected gold cluster molecules, *Langmuir.* **15**(11), 3782–3789 (1999).

33. A. C. Templeton, M. J. Hostetler, C. T. Kraft, and R. W. Murray, Reactivity of monolayer-protected gold cluster molecules: steric effects, *J. Am. Chem. Soc.* **120**(8), 1906–1911 (1998).

34. M. J. Hostetler, J. E. Wingate, C.-J. Zhong, J. E. Harris, R. W. Vachet, M. R. Clark, J. D. Londono, S. J. Green, J. J. Stokes, G. D. Wignall, G. Glish, M. D. Porter, N. D. Evans, and R. W. Murray, Alkanethiolate gold cluster molecules with core diameters from 1.5 to 5.2 nm: core and monolayer properties as a function of core size, *Langmuir.* **14**(1), 17–30 (1998).

35. J. C. Love, L. A. Estroff, J. K. Kriebel, R. G. Nuzzo, and G. M. Whitesides, Self-assembled monolayers of thiolates on metals as a form of nanotechnology, *Chem. Rev.* **105**(4), 1103–1170 (2005).

36. K. Kanie, M. Matsubara, X. Zeng, F. Liu, G. Ungar, H. Nakamura, and A. Muramatsu, Simple cubic packing of gold nanoparticles through rational design of their dendrimeric corona, *J. Am. Chem. Soc.* **134**(2), 808–811 (2012).

37. S. Mischler, S. Guerra, and R. Deschenaux, Design of liquid-crystalline gold nanoparticles by click chemistry, *Chem. Commun.* **48**(16), 2183–2185 (2012).

38. S. Umadevi, X. Feng, and T. Hegmann, Bent-core and nematic liquid crystal functionalized gold nanorods, *Ferroelectrics.* **431**, 164–175 (2012).

39. S. Umadevi, X. Feng, and T. Hegmann, Large area self-assembly of nematic liquid-crystal-functionalized gold nanorods, *Adv. Funct. Mater.* **23**(11), 1393–1403 (2013).

40. C. H. Yu, C. P. J. Schubert, C. Welch, B. J. Tang, M.-G. Tamba, and G. H. Mehl, Design, synthesis, and characterization of mesogenic amine-capped nematic gold nanoparticles with surface-enhanced plasmonic resonances, *J. Am. Chem. Soc.* **134**(11), 5076–5079 (2012).

41. B. Donnio, P. Garcia-Vazquez, J.-L. Gallani, D. Guillon, and E. Terazzi, Dendronized ferromagnetic gold nanoparticles self-organized in a thermotropic cubic phase, *Adv. Mater.* **19**(21), 3534–3539 (2007).

42. W. Lewandowski, K. Jatczak, D. Pociecha, and J. Mieczkowski, Control of gold nanoparticle superlattice properties via mesogenic ligand architecture, *Langmuir.* **29**(10), 3404–3410 (2013).

43. M. M. Wojcik, M. Gora, J. Mieczkowski, J. Romiszewski, E. Gorecka, and D. Pociecha, Temperature-controlled liquid crystalline polymorphism of gold nanoparticles, *Soft Matter.* **7**(22), 10561–10564 (2011).

44. J. Dintinger, B.-J. Tang, X. Zeng, F. Liu, T. Kienzler, G. H. Mehl, G. Ungar, C. Rockstuhl, and T. Scharf, A self-organized anisotropic liquid-crystal plasmonic metamaterial, *Adv. Mater.* **25**(14), 1999–2004 (2013).

45. W. Lewandowski, D. Constantin, K. Walicka, D. Pociecha, J. Mieczkowski, and E. Gorecka, Smectic mesophases of functionalized silver and gold nanoparticles with anisotropic plasmonic properties, *Chem. Commun.* **49**(71), 7845–7847 (2013).

46. A. Zep, M. M. Wojcik, W. Lewandowski, K. Sitkowska, A. Prominski, J. Mieczkowski, D. Pociecha, and E. Gorecka, Phototunable liquid-crystalline phases made of nanoparticles, *Angew. Chem. (Int. Ed.).* **53**(50), 13725–13728 (2014).

47. T. Ikeda and O. Tsutsumi, Optical switching and image storage by means of azobenzene liquid-crystal films, *Science.* **268**(5219), 1873–1875 (1995).

48. G. Vertogen and W. H. De Jeu, *Thermotropic liquid crystals, fundamentals.* Springer-Verlag, Berlin (1988).

49. W. Young, A. Aviram, and R. Cox, Stilbene derivatives. new class of room temperature nematic liquids, *J. Am. Chem. Soc.* **94**(11), 3976–3981 (1972).

50. N. Kanayama, O. Tsutsumi, A. Kanazawa, and T. Ikeda, Distinct thermodynamic behaviour of a mesomorphic gold nanoparticle covered with a liquid-crystalline compound, *Chem. Commun.* (24), 2640–2641 (2001).

51. I. In, Y. Jun, Y. Kim, and S. Kim, Spontaneous one dimensional arrangement of spherical au nanoparticles with liquid crystal ligands, *Chem. Commun.* (6), 800–801 (2005).

52. M. Draper, I. M. Saez, S. J. Cowling, P. Gai, B. Heinrich, B. Donnio, D. Guillon, and J. W. Goodby, Self-assembly and shape morphology of liquid-crystalline gold metamaterials, *Adv. Funct. Mater.* **21**(7), 1260–1278 (2011).

53. M. Wojcik, M. Kolpaczynska, D. Pociecha, J. Mieczkowski, and E. Gorecka, Multidimensional structures made by gold nanoparticles with shape-adaptive grafting layers, *Soft Matter.* **6**(21), 5397–5400 (2010).

54. J. M. Wolska, D. Pociecha, J. Mieczkowski, and E. Gorecka, Gold nanoparticles with flexible mesogenic grafting layers, *Soft Matter.* **9**(11), 3005–3008 (2013).

55. J. M. Wolska, D. Pociecha, J. Mieczkowski, and E. Gorecka, Control of sample alignment mode for hybrid lamellar systems based on gold nanoparticles, *Chem. Commun.* **50**(59), 7975–7978 (2014).

56. J. Duan, M. Wang, H. Bian, Y. Zhou, J. Ma, C. Liu, and D. Chen, Azobenzene mesogen-passivated gold nanoparticles: Controlled preparation, self-

organized superstructures, thermal behavior and photoisomerization, *Mater. Chem. Phys.* **148**(3), 1013–1021 (2014).

57. K. Kanie and T. Sugimoto, Organic-inorganic hybrid liquid crystals: Hybridization of calamitic liquid-crystalline amines with monodispersed anisotropic tio2 nanoparticles, *J. Am. Chem. Soc.* **125**(35), 10518–10519 (2003).

58. Y. Chen and X. Wang, Novel phase-transfer preparation of monodisperse silver and gold nanoparticles at room temperature, *Mater. Lett.* **62**(16), 2215–2218 (2008).

59. C. M. Bates, M. J. Maher, D. W. Janes, C. J. Ellison, and C. G. Willson, Block copolymer lithography, *Macromolecules.* **47**(1), 2–12 (2014).

60. O. O. Mykhaylyk, A. J. Parnell, A. Pryke, and J. P. A. Fairclough, Direct imaging of the orientational dynamics of block copolymer lamellar phase subjected to shear flow, *Macromolecules.* **45**(12), 5260–5272 (2012).

61. M. Wojcik, W. Lewandowski, J. Matraszek, J. Mieczkowski, J. Borysiuk, D. Pociecha, and E. Gorecka, Liquid-crystalline phases made of gold nanoparticles, *Angew. Chem. (Int. Ed.).* **48**(28), 5167–5169 (2009).

62. L. Cseh and G. H. Mehl, The design and investigation of room temperature thermotropic nematic gold nanoparticles, *J. Am. Chem. Soc.* **128**(41), 13376–13377 (2006).

63. L. Cseh and G. H. Mehl, Structure-property relationships in nematic gold nanoparticles, *J. Mater. Chem.* **17**(4), 311–315 (2007).

64. X. Zeng, F. Liu, A. G. Fowler, G. Ungar, L. Cseh, G. H. Mehl, and J. E. Macdonald, 3D ordered gold strings by coating nanoparticles with mesogens, *Adv. Mater.* **21**(17), 1746–1750 (2009).

65. X. Mang, X. Zeng, B. Tang, F. Liu, G. Ungar, R. Zhang, L. Cseh, and G. H. Mehl, Control of anisotropic self-assembly of gold nanoparticles coated with mesogens, *J. Mater. Chem.* **22**(22), 11101–11106 (2012).

66. V. M. Marx, H. Girgis, P. A. Heiney, and T. Hegmann, Bent-core liquid crystal (LC) decorated gold nanoclusters: synthesis, self-assembly, and effects in mixtures with bent-core LC hosts, *J. Mater. Chem.* **18**(25), 2983–2994 (2008).

67. W. Lewandowski, M. Fruhnert, J. Mieczkowski, C. Rockstuhl, and E. Gorecka, Dynamically self-assembled silver nanoparticles as a thermally tunable metamaterial, *Nat. Commun.* **6**, 6590 (2015).

68. J. Zhang, J. Whitesell, and M. Fox, Photoreactivity of self-assembled monolayers of azobenzene or stilbene derivatives capped on colloidal gold clusters, *Chem. Mater.* **13**(7), 2323–2331 (2001).

69. R. Mikami, M. Taguchi, K. Yamada, K. Suzuki, O. Sato, and Y. Einaga, Reversible photo-switching of the magnetization of iron oxide nanoparticles at room temperature, *Angew. Chem. (Int. Ed.).* **43**(45), 6135–6139 (2004).

70. M. Suda, M. Nakagawa, T. Iyoda, and Y. Einaga, Reversible photoswitching of ferromagnetic fept nanoparticles at room temperature, *J. Am. Chem. Soc.* **129**(17), 5538–5543 (2007).

Chapter 17

Carbon nanotubes in thermotropic low molar mass liquid crystals

Stefan Schymura[a], Ji Hyun Park[b], Ingo Dierking[c] and Giusy Scalia[b]

[a] Helmholtz-Zentrum Dresden - Rossendorf e.V., Forschungsstelle Leipzig, Institut für Ressourcenökologie, 04318 Leipzig, Germany
[b] University of Luxembourg, Physics & Materials Science Research Unit, 1511 Luxembourg, Luxembourg
[c] School of Physics and Astronomy, University of Manchester, Oxford Road, Manchester M13 9PL, United Kingdom
s.schymura@hzdr.de, jihyun.park@uni.lu, giusy@solcanta.com, ingo.dierking@manchester.ac.uk

Carbon nanotubes constitute a highly anisotropic form of carbon with outstanding mechanical, thermal and electrical properties. Their dispersion and organization are important but challenging and this chapter describes the advantages of using thermotropic liquid crystals as host for nanotube dispersion and ordering. The self organization of LCs is an attractive way to manipulate nanoparticles such as carbon nanotubes or graphene flakes. Compared to standard carbon nanotube composites (e.g. with disordered polymer hosts) the introduction of the nanotubes into an LC allows not only the transfer of the outstanding nanotube properties to the macroscopic phase, providing strength and conductivity, but these properties also become anisotropic, following the transfer of the orientational order from the LC to the CNTs.

The responsiveness of liquid crystals to external stimuli is also a very attractive feature for dynamically and reversibly tuning the properties of the composites. In fact the application of weak electric or magnetic fields induces a change in molecular orientation of the LC bringing along the carbon nanotubes and this translates into a substantial variation in conductivity.

CNTs have also been used as dopant for enhancing the LC display performance reporting increases in response time and decrease in switching threshold due to an increase of dielectric anisotropy, or variation of other properties, or a reduction of charges by an ion-trapping effect. However, the reports in the literature give contradictory results and there are still questions to answer for a full understanding of the mechanism.

603

The enormous variety of molecules that form liquid crystalline phases provides additional strength and potential to the liquid-crystal-based route towards nanotube alignment and realization of novel functional systems.

Contents

1. Introduction

Carbon nanotubes (CNTs) are crystalline allotropes of carbon with atoms hexagonally arranged in curved lattices forming hollow cylinders of diameters in the nanometer scale and aspect ratios of very high value that can easily go up to 10^8, thus being excellent examples of 1-dimensional materials.[1] They can have walls formed by just one layer, the Single-Wall CNTs (SWCNTs), or be formed by several concentric cylinders, the Multi-Wall CNTs (MWCNTs). Even if CNTs can be found in nature, their existence was brought to the general attention by Iijima in 1991.[2] After their discovery, carbon nanotubes have attracted great interest not only for their truly 1-dimensional nature but also for the variety of possible applications. One obvious proposal was as replacement of carbon fibers, used for decades as fillers in composites, due to their superior mechanical properties, but many other applications appeared possible thanks to several outstanding properties. CNTs have very high Young's modulus, ~ 1.25 TPa for SWCNTs and 0.27–0.95 TPa for MWCNTs, thermal conductivity of ~ 6600 W/mK (SWCNT), 3000 W/mK (MWCNT).[3–6] SWCNTs have also excellent electrical properties with a charge mobility of $\sim 10,000$ cm^{2}V^{-1}s^{-1}, 10 times higher than silicon, and they can carry an electrical current density in the order of 10^9 A/cm^2 that is 10^3 times greater than a typical metal such as copper.[7,8] SWCNTs typically have diameters of 0.4–3.0 nm while MWCNTs, since they are composed of several walls, have larger diameters than SWCNTs with values that can be higher than 100 nm.

A common way to explain the structure of CNTs is simply to describe them as a result of the rolling-up of graphene, which is one layer of graphite, hence a 2-dimensional carbon allotrope. In fact the nanotube walls are structurally similar to graphene, having each carbon atom covalently bonded to three neighbor carbon atoms, with sp^2 hybridization. As a result of the atomic structural arrangement, CNTs can have Young's modulus and tensile strength higher than steel. SWCNTs can be metallic or semi-conductive depending on how a strip virtually cut from the graphene sheet is rolled up and specifically by the orientation of the graphene lattice (referred as helicity or often as the chirality), defined by the length of the chiral vector $\mathbf{C} = n\mathbf{a}_1 + m\mathbf{a}_2$ as shown in Fig. 1. The couple of indices (n, m) identifies the type of tube and determines its properties, metallic or semiconducting, and these correspond to different energy profiles in the density of states as shown in the left and right images of Fig. 2, respectively. The graphs are also useful for assessing the optical properties, estimating the values of the photon energies for the various transitions. The so-called armchair CNTs have $n = m$ and are always metallic while the zig-zag have $n = 0$ or $m = 0$, and chiral CNTs have the other (n, m) values obtaining metallic or semiconducting characteristics. In contrast, multi-walled CNTs are mainly metallic but with properties affected by the proximity of the walls. In general the extreme values of the properties of SWCNTs are not matched by MWCNTs.

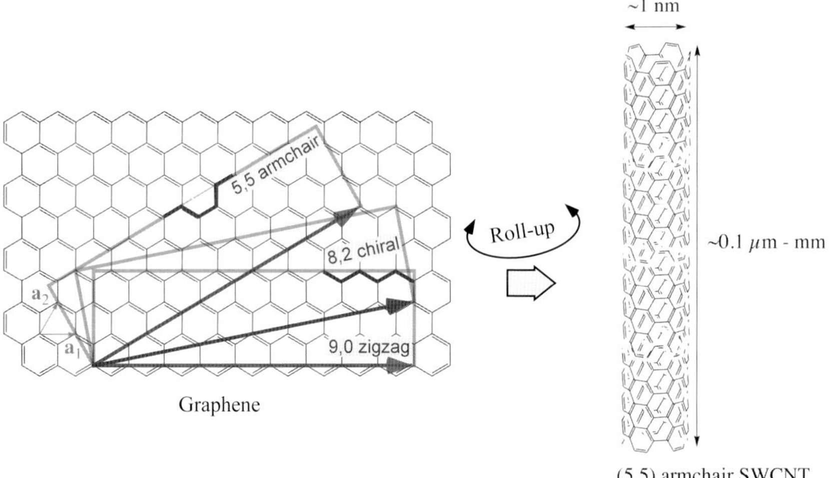

Fig. 1. Scheme of strips from graphene derived along different chiral vectors (given by the black arrows on the left image) thus (n, m) and the virtual rolling up for forming CNTs (the right image).

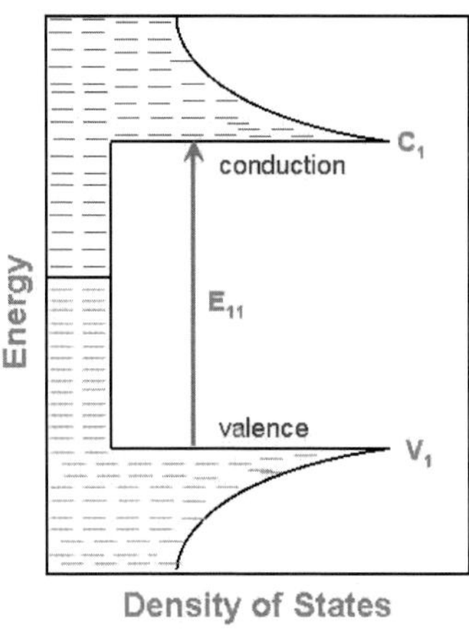

Metallic SWNT

v$_1$ → c$_1$ corresponds to the "first van Hove" optical transition

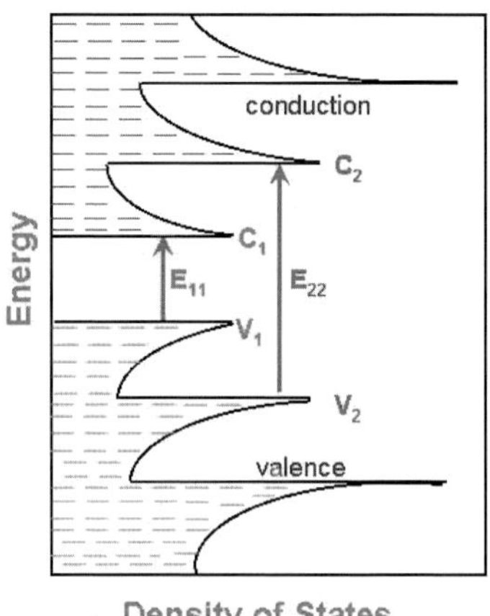

Semiconducting SWNT

v$_2$ → c$_2$ corresponds to the "second van Hove" optical transition

Fig. 2. The electronic energy profiles reveal the electronic nature of SWCNTs if metallic (left image) or semiconductive (right). Source: Materialscientist at English Wikipedia (licensed under the Creative Commons Attribution-Share Alike 3.0 Unported license).

CNTs can be synthesized in large quantities with various methods such as arc-discharge, laser ablation and especially chemical vapor deposition (CVD). In general the synthesis is based on the evaporation of carbon or a carbon-containing precursor and the reassembly into the tubular structure of CNTs. The SWCNTs produced by the high pressure carbon monoxide (HiPco) process are commonly used for their fairly good properties and high purity, thus there is large amount of literature available. Production methods and fractionation routes[9] aim at reducing the inhomogeneity of SWCNT samples and to obtain tubes with more targeted and similar properties. This is expected to remarkably improve applications.

Apart from the inhomogeneity of CNT samples two other problems hinder several more sophisticated applications of CNTs: the long-term separation of CNTs into isolated tubes rather than the common aggregates, and the control of their orientation. Naturally CNTs attract each other by van der Waals forces forming ordered bundles which can further aggregate into disordered assemblies. Dispersing nanotubes is not an easy task but it is relevant to address for using them effectively. Small weights of CNT powder contain an extremely large number of tubes. Already small concentrations, if they are uniformly dispersed in a host, result in enhanced properties, provided that they are uniformly distributed. The presence of aggregates does not only bring nonuniformity but also negative effects on the properties, as well as the need of a higher loading in order to observe macroscopic effects. For example, the effect of good dispersion is apparent in the change of rheological properties of a suspension of CNTs that above the threshold concentration from very fluid becomes a viscous gel once the debundling becomes effective leading to rigidity percolation between the isolated tubes. All this highlights the importance of CNT individualization steps when mixing nanotubes with hosts and this applies also in our specific case, with liquid crystals. The most successful approaches rely on the use of surfactants as described in other chapters. However, also some thermotropic liquid crystals have shown surprisingly good performance considering the nature of the system and this will be described in the following paragraph.

As discussed in several reviews,[10–15] the LC-unique feature of fluidity and orientational order makes LC/CNT composites interesting beyond the possibility of the LC used as a good dispersion medium. This is because it can serve to solve the second problem in CNT applications, the control of the CNT orientation, which has been shown to be relevant in applications.[3] CNTs dispersed in LCs generally adopt the same alignment direction as their host. This even opens up the possibility of active control of the CNT orientation as LCs are readily switched by e.g. electric or magnetic fields. Another aspect that got the attention is that the CNT doping of LCs may also have a benefit from the guests, the CNTs enhancing the LC properties with respect to their display performance.

As a general remark, it is worth to point out that some of the findings of the research on LC-CNT dispersions can be extended to other types of carbon nanoparticles, like graphene flakes or also small fullerenes like C_{60}. However, the latter are distinct in certain aspects, such as the very good dispersability in thermotropic nematic LCs.

2. Dispersion of CNTs in thermotropic LCs

The seemingly simple task of dispersing CNTs in thermotropic LCs is in actuality a quite challenging endeavor both from a procedural and a substance-focused viewpoint. At first glance, a typical thermotropic LC seems to be an ideal candidate as CNT-solvent, following a *simila similibus solvuntur* (lat.: like dissolves like) approach, being aprotic, structurally relatively non-polar, yet highly polarizable and with the possibility of $\pi - \pi$

stacking interactions between their typical biphenyl core structure and the CNT-wall. However, in this rule of thumb the problems one faces when dispersing nanotubes in any solvent are already coded. The mixing of two substances is governed by the Gibbs free energy of mixing $\Delta_{mix}G$ which is connected to the enthalpy change $\Delta_{mix}H$ and entropy change $\Delta_{mix}S$ of the mixing process at the temperature T:

$$\Delta_{mix}G = \Delta_{mix}H - T\Delta_{mix}S \tag{1}$$

"Like dissolves like" means that the inter-substance interactions are similar to the intra-substance interactions of the to-be-mixed materials, hence the enthalpy of mixing is close to zero. The mixing process is driven by the entropical contribution which is typically in favor of mixing as a mixed system consists of more disorder/randomness. It has a higher probability as it is realized by more microstates than a demixed system. It is here that the CNTs become a special case. In a reasoning following the Flory-Huggins-theory for polymer solutions the mixing entropy is particularly low in the case of CNT dispersion.[16] A polymer solution has lower entropy of mixing in comparison to a monomer solution since the bonding together of the monomers in the polymer reduces the degree of freedom in the monomer arrangement. This effect is even more pronounced for long, stiff "polymers" such as CNTs. In Fig. 3 the difference in degree of freedom is visualized showing 5 monomers and some possible configurations in a 2-dimensional space defined by a 5 × 5 lattice. Even if the monomers (on the left) and the CNT, represented by the five monomers linked together, (on the right) occupy the same total surface, the number of possible spatial configurations

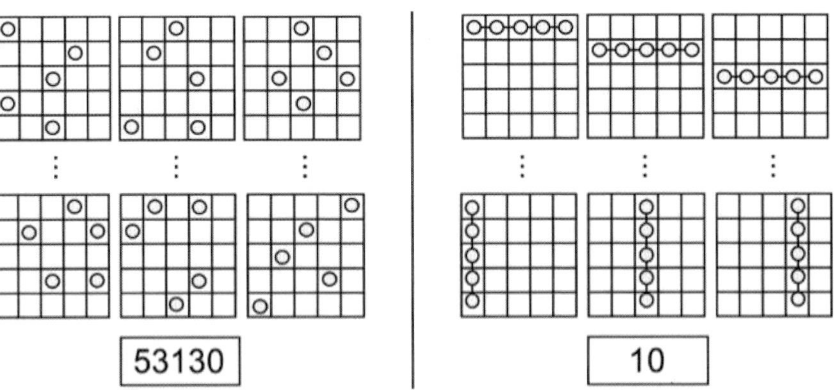

Fig. 3.   Number of possible arrangements of five 'monomers' in a 5 × 5 'solvent' lattice (left) and a long stiff 'polymer', i.e. a CNT (right).

accessible to the nanotubes are hugely inferior to the arrangements of the monomers as indicated in the insets.

In addition, the already low entropy is even further decreased by the effect of strong, patterned adsorption of solvent molecules on the CNTs.[17,18] In a fashion similar to the hydrophobic effect, which entropically keeps oil and water from mixing[19] (at least such small "oils" as pentane and hexane should mix with water were it only for enthalpic reasons), adsorption onto the CNT wall (an "icy" cage of water around alkyl chains in case of oil in water) results in a considerable loss in rotational and translational freedom of the adsorbed molecules. The effect becomes more prominent the more CNT surface area gets exposed to the solvent in a dispersion process. This is where the LC adds another step of complexity onto our simple "like dissolves like" problem: as orientational order is the natural state of a nematic LC the entropy penalty one has to pay for CNT dispersion is less pronounced than in an isotropic solvent.[20,21]

In accordance with the considerations outlined above, Schymura *et al.*[20,21] find that, initially, a coarse dispersion of CNTs is easily achieved in various thermotropic LCs by simple stirring, as indeed "like dissolves like". The stirring experiments reveal an exceptionally fast visible debundling of CNT aggregates that could not be reproduced using standard CNT dispersion media, such as 1-Methyl-2-pyrrolidone (NMP) or aqueous solutions of sodium dodecylbenzenesulfonate (SDBS). Disordered CNT aggregates induce distortions in the LC director orientation, hence the reduction of the size of aggregates in a suspension in an LC becomes an energetically favorable condition, from the point of view of minimizing the LC distortions. However, since the entropic burden due to strong, patterned adsorption increases during the debundling process, such a mixing through stirring only yields a very coarse dispersion, only appearing homogeneous by simple visual inspection, settling fast upon centrifugation. The nanotubes are kept together in bundles by strong van der Waals forces. As commonly done for dispersing CNTs, higher quality dispersions can be achieved with ultrasonic treatments (with stirring as a possible exceptionally gentle first step for reducing the time of ultrasonication that can induce defects in the nanotubes).

While the stirring experiments did not reveal any significant differences between typical thermotropic LCs (only a viscosity dependence of the stirring time till visible homogeneity (by eye) was found), distinct variations between the stability of ultrasonically produced high-quality dispersions in the different LCs employed was observed, as shown in Fig. 4. These differ-

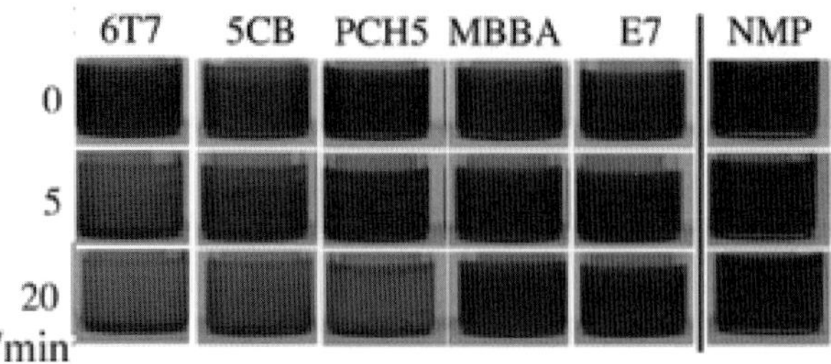

Fig. 4.   Dispersion stability after centrifugation of CNT dispersions, realized using 30 min. of ultrasonication, in various nematics and in a standard organic solvent, NMP, for comparison. Copyright (2010) Wiley. Used with permission from Ref. 20.

ences could not be explained in terms of molecular dipole moment or relative electrical permittivity, which factor into the enthalpic contributions due to their role for CNT/LC interaction forces. Rather, the contribution of a patterned adsorption can explain the bad performance of some LC molecular structures. Two liquid crystals showed distinctively better performance than the others, namely N-(4-Methoxybenzylidene)-4-butylaniline (MBBA) and E7, a mixture of several cyanobiphenyls. These experiments highlight the role of the chemical structure of the LC host for the dispersion quality of CNT suspensions. A strategy for improving, in general terms, the miscibility is to coat the nanotubes with e.g. polymers that would counteract aggregation and have affinity with the host.[22] Higher concentrations could then be achieved but the properties of nanotubes can be strongly affected by the coating.

Overall, it proved to be important to maintain the LC host in its nematic phase, as a heating into the isotropic phase during or after the dispersion process promotes aggregation. A set-up that can be used for counteracting the heating effect during sonication is shown in Fig. 5. The sample is placed in a cooling water bath while the tip-sonication is performed. The nematic–isotropic transition makes the strong adsorption effect observable as the transition occurs last around CNT aggregates.[23] This can be related to the prediction that nanotubes can influence also the type of nematic–isotropic phase transition of the LC, that from first order can become continuous for variations of a coupling parameter that depends on the effective tube diameter.[24,25] In practice, this might be considered the bundle diameter, which would increase with aggregation.

The study of the aggregate formation in liquid can be done by using image analysis methods, basically transforming the images in black and

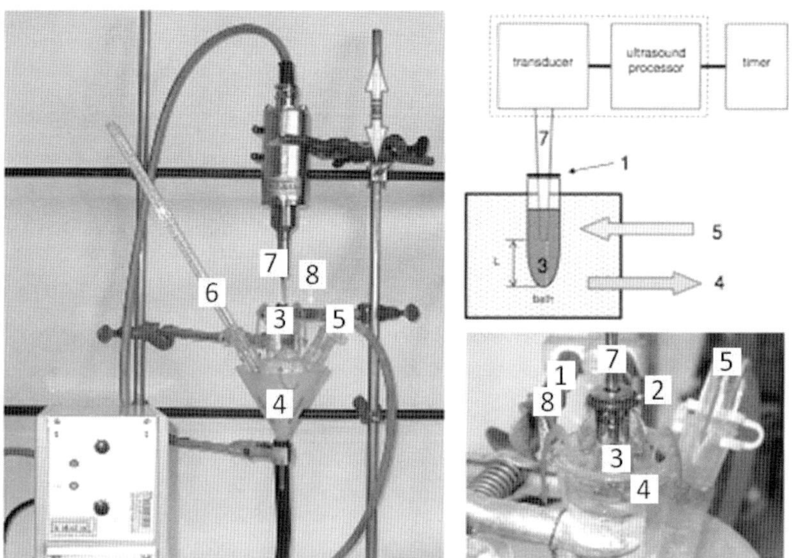

Fig. 5.   Example of a sonication setup for dispersing CNTs in LCs. The numbers in the images correspond to: 1 washer, 2 O-ring, 3 sample vial in bath, 4 cooling water out, 5 cooling water in, 6 thermometer, 7 sonotrode, 8 sample holder (timer not shown). Courtesy of Martin Kühnast, Martin-Luther University Halle-Wittenberg, Germany.

white and evaluating the number of pixels covering the aggregate area.[20,26] The analysis is obviously considering the aggregates in two dimensions but it is anyhow useful for estimating the formation of percolation networks as function of the concentration but also the average dimension of the aggregates, useful for more quantitative comparisons of the dispersion ability of different LC hosts.

The dispersion of nanotubes is generally easier in the nematic phase than in higher ordered phases, in which the dispersion can be very difficult. In fact, the fluid state is often above room temperature and thus the complete dispersion process needs to be performed at higher temperature. One must either work strictly within a specific temperature range throughout all the stages, for keeping the host in the desired phase, or one may heat above the clearing temperature for working in the isotropic phase, with the likelihood of CNT aggregation when cooling into the liquid crystal phase. In general, the tendency to segregate the nanotubes outside of the LC regions, with consequent aggregate formation, is more pronounced for higher ordered phases since small perturbations of the molecular order result in the expulsion of the source of the disorder. In other words, even small CNT aggregates are pushed together, which results in the formation of larger and larger aggregates in a sort of amplifying loop. Thus the dispersion of pristine CNTs either in discotics or in smectic LCs usually yields poor results. In order to add CNTs and also to ensure a low concentration, the nanotubes are often pre-dispersed in solvents to be evaporated after mixing with higher order LC like ferroelectrics.[27] This approach has also been used with nematics,[28] but particular care has to be taken to check if residuals of solvent remain since they can interfere with the LC properties. Another approach followed in the literature is to use another LC, that can be a better dispersant than the main host, like a nematic that would blend with the targeted AFLC host.[29,30]

In this chapter we do not cover the case of cholesteric (chiral nematic) LCs as host for CNT dispersion. We refer the reader interested in this topic to the work of the group around Longin Lisetski. They have published several papers on the topic, discussing dispersion,[31,32] aggregation[33] as well as the effect on the optical properties.[34] Schymura also did a preliminary study, comparing dispersion of different carbon nanoparticles in a short-pitch cholesteric mixture.[21]

3. Electrical switching of LC-CNT composites

Two main purposes have driven the first studies on CNT-LC composites. On the one hand the LC is used to disperse and control the orientation of the CNTs, on the other hand the CNTs are used to influence the properties of the LC. In the case of CNTs doped into a macroscopically aligned LC, the nanotubes, if dispersed well, align along the director of the LC.[28,35,36] Any other orientation or the presence of large aggregates would induce elastic distortions in the director field, making the orientation of the tube along the director the energetically preferred situation. The most unambiguous ways to confirm the alignment of the CNTs is to directly infer the orientational information from the nanotubes using e.g. polarized Raman spectroscopy (see Chapter 7), but indirect information can be obtained by the observation of anisotropic features of the compound such as conductivity or the relative permittivity. Bare nanotubes tend to align with their long axis parallel to the LC director in nematics due to surface interaction, but suitable surface treatments of CNTs have been used to change the alignment direction.[37,38]

Several authors have reported beneficial effects of CNT doping on the display performance of thermotropic LCs, such as faster switching times and lower switching voltage/Frederiks threshold.[39-43] This is attributed to either a higher dielectric anisotropy of the composite or an ion trapping effect reducing the free ions in the composite, therefore increasing the effective cell voltage at a given applied external voltage, due to a decreased ionic screening effect. The LC host and the nanotubes have different dielectric constants and the original idea was that nanotubes, being metallic or semiconducting, have an extremely high value of the permittivity that would give higher dielectric anisotropy in the composite. The increase would directly affect the Frederiks threshold voltage, decreasing it as seen in Chap. 2, Eq. (12). Of course the effect of doping can alter also other properties of the LC host such as viscosity or elastic constants, and the effects are expected to depend strongly on the concentration of CNTs, as well as on the type and purity. The experimental investigations are typically carried out at very low nanotube concentrations, aiming at avoiding aggregation and a too dramatic change of the LC properties to conditions far away from the display requirements.

However, a certain degree of dielectric compensation or screening is expected from the host molecules which would reduce or even compensate the expected high dielectric value. Theoretical predictions of the behavior of the composite, described with different permittivities of the host and of the anisotropic inclusions, can be done using approaches based on the Maxwell-Garnett theory. This can derive the electrical response of the system macroscopically but for a full picture also simulations on the interfacial interactions are relevant in the analysis of the system behavior. Simulation of the anchoring of trifluorophenyl-2 (TFP2) liquid crystal on the surface of a carbon nanotube using density functional theory predicted strong anchoring on the nanotube surface and at the same time that a permanent dipole moment is generated onto the nanotube.[44] According to the authors this effect can be responsible for reported improvements of the switching behavior. The interaction between LC molecules and CNT surface depends strongly on the actual structures of the two components that clearly affect the type of anchoring. For the theory describing inclusions in LCs we refer the reader to Chapters 3 and 4.

The experimental results of the CNT-LC switching behavior appear sketchy, sometimes contradictory and the improvements not straightforward to achieve. It is worth to point out that most often characterization data on the used CNTs and/or dispersion quality are lacking. The overall picture and the reasons for the different behaviors remain so far unclear. The lack of CNT characterization data and of information on dispersion quality in many studies prevents drawing clear cut conclusions at the moment.

Schymura and Scalia found no decrease in Frederiks threshold when studying various CNT-LC composites, and they could not observe a significant increase in dielectric anisotropy for mixtures of E7 LC and various types of CNTs produced with different methods (Fig. 6).[45] Increasing the nanotube concentration does not improve the switching process and high local concentrations can even hinder the reorientation. Scalia *et al.*[46] could show by Raman measurements of LC bands during switching that in the

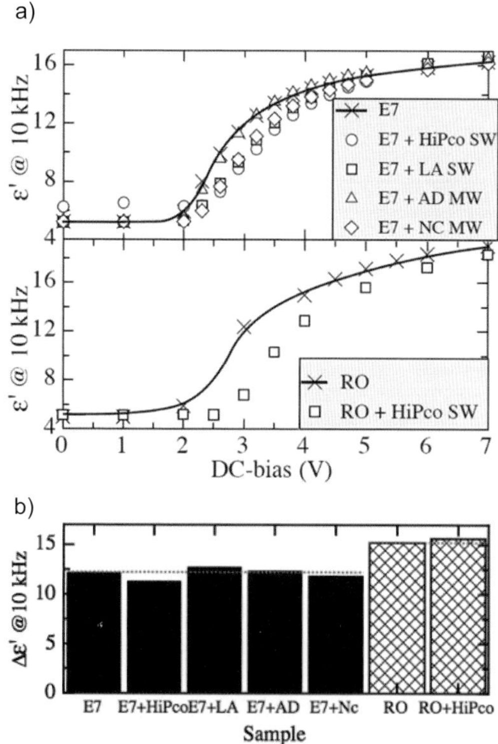

Fig. 6. (a) Behavior of the relative permittivity for different D.C. voltage applied to various CNT-LC composites and (b) dielectric anisotropy of these composites. SW and MW stand for Single-Wall and Multi-Wall, respectively. The following abbreviations indicate CNT synthesis method or manufacturer: LA=Laser Ablation (kindly supplied by B. Hornbostel); AD=Arc Discharge (kindly supplied by M. Haluska); NC=Nanocyl (manufacturer). Copyright (2013) The Royal Society. Reused with original author's permission from Ref. 45.

presence of large CNT aggregates the switching behavior of the LC is affected rather negatively, the switching voltage increasing significantly, see Fig. 7. The presence of carbon nanotubes in the liquid crystal offers additional surface for the anchoring and for high nanotube concentration so LC molecules are strongly confined between the voids of the network resulting in reduced response to electric fields.

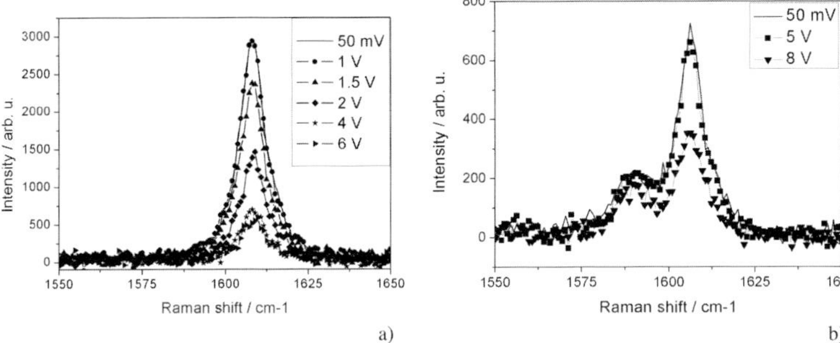

Fig. 7. LC reorientation without nanotubes (a) and in presence of a large SWCNT aggregate (b) measured by polarized Raman spectroscopy following the change in peak intensity of Raman bands increasing applied field for pure E7 LC is shown. In (b) the reorientation of LCs in presence of a large SWCNT aggregate is strongly inhibited as an effect of the interaction between LC and SWCNTs. Copyright (2007) Wiley. Used with permission from Ref. 46.

The electrical properties of CNT-LC dispersions are also monitored with AC fields of varying frequency, useful to identify possible different contributions to the response and to measure composite parameters during the LC reorientation, typically obtained by applying additional DC voltage to the probing AC fields. The response can be modeled by using circuital elements within certain frequency region.[47] Moreover, the CNT doping, at high CNT loads, was shown to potentially increase the low frequency conductivity likely due to the occurrence of percolation, see Fig. 8.

CNT dispersions which show no or only a small increase in conductivity at zero DC bias voltage (Fig. 8a) exhibit a jump in conductivity upon application of a DC field perpendicular to the original planar orientation (Fig. 8b), indicating the formation of CNT networks possibly percolating. Only at very minute CNT concentration the composites behave as does the pure LC. The corresponding threshold between 3.6 and 9.4 μg/mL is particularly low in comparison with other reported data.[48] As a liquid host comparison, Lima *et al.* achieved percolation only at 25 μg/mL under continuous sonication in chloroform.[49]

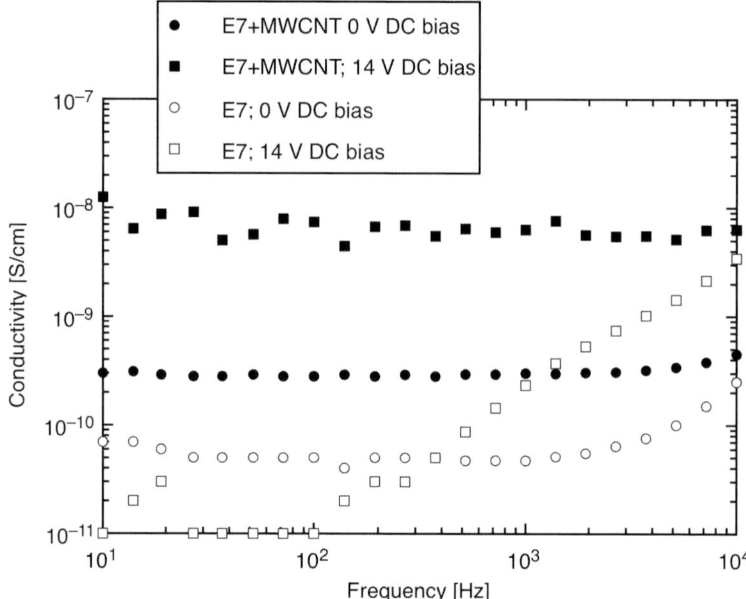

Fig. 8. Conductivity of LC/CNT composite of MWCNT (Arc Discharge, courtesy of M. Haluska) in E7 in the planar state at 0 V DC, and switched from planar alignment to homeotropic alignment at 14 V DC bias.

4. Magnetic switching of LC-CNT composites

As previously described, nanotubes can be oriented via elastic interactions with the self-organized director field of the host liquid crystal.[28] The LC can be reoriented by application of weak electric fields, inducing a Frederiks transition from planar to homeotropic for a positive value of the LC dielectric anisotropy $\Delta\epsilon > 0$, which results in the transition from a state with no or very small conductivity to a state with high conductivity. Likewise, it can be switched from homeotropic (conductive) to planar (non-conductive) alignment using host materials with $\Delta\epsilon < 0$.[50] Similarly, modulation of the conductivity can be achieved by switching the LC with magnetic fields,[51] thanks to the magnetic susceptibility anisotropy $(\Delta\chi)$ of the liquid crystal, which is mostly positive $(\Delta\chi > 0)$. This process is schematically illustrated in Fig. 9a.

Figure 9b shows the comparison of the response between the neat liquid crystal and the nanotube doped LC by means of the conductivity at a measuring voltage of 0.2 V, below the electric Frederiks threshold voltage, at

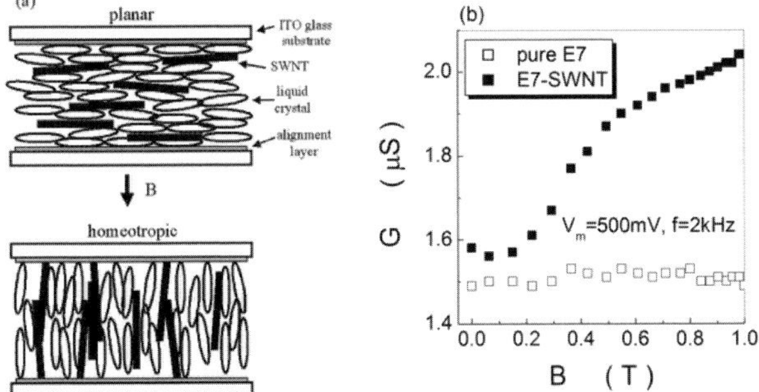

Fig. 9.　(a) Schematic representation of the planar to homeotropic transition of the nanotubes dispersed in a nematic liquid crystal with positive magnetic susceptibility. (b) The conductivity of the neat liquid crystal (open squares) does not change during the transition, while the nanotube doped material exhibits an increasing conductivity as the threshold field is exceeded. Copyright (2005) American Institute of Physics. Used with permission from Ref. 51.

a frequency of 2 kHz. For the non-doped sample the conductivity remains practically constant at a low value for increasing magnetic field strength, while for the nanotube doped liquid crystal the conductivity strongly increases as the magnetic Frederiks threshold field is passed. Further, we notice that the magnetic threshold field B_{th} is independent of the measuring voltage and frequency (Fig. 10a), but inversely proportional to the cell gap (Fig. 10b), as expected since the threshold value is given by:

$$B_{th} = \frac{\pi}{d}\sqrt{\frac{K_{11}}{\epsilon_0 \Delta\chi}} \tag{2}$$

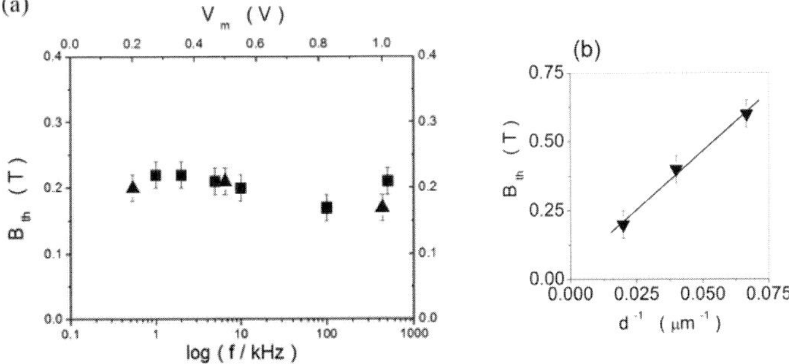

Fig. 10.　(a) The threshold magnetic field is independent of the measuring voltage (triangles) and the measuring frequency (squares). (b) The magnetic threshold field is inversely proportional to the sandwich cell gap.

where K_{11} is the splay elastic constant, $\Delta\chi$ is the magnetic susceptibility anisotropy and d is the cell gap.

The response to a changing applied magnetic field can be measured dynamically, as illustrated in Fig. 11, where it should be noted that this only represents a proof-of-principle investigation without any cell and material optimization whatsoever.

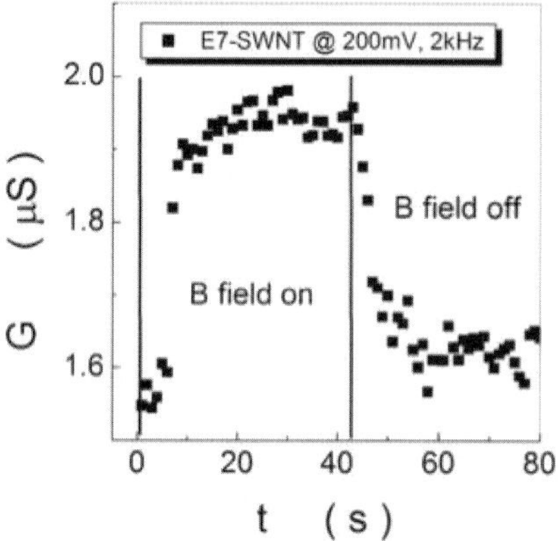

Fig. 11. Conductivity response to a changing magnetic field, demonstrating a magnetically steered electric on-off switch. Copyright (2005) American Institute of Physics. Used with permission from Ref. 51.

5. Nanotube effects on properties of ferroelectric liquid crystals

Up to now we have only discussed the properties and effects of nanotubes on nematic liquid crystals, i.e. those with purely orientational order, the ones that are most commonly employed in display devices. However, there is a class of liquid crystals, the ferroelectric liquid crystals (FLCs),[52,53] that is interesting for its very fast response to electric fields. These chiral LCs have orientational order of the director but they also exhibit a one dimensional positional order, with the director tilted with respect to the smectic layer normal. In thin films they show ferroelectricity thus the appearance of a spontaneous polarization P_S.[54,55]

The director switching process of FLCs is, in contrast to nematics, dependent on the polarity of the applied electric field, and a reorientation between two stable states with polarization "up" and "down", respectively, is observed, which corresponds to two orientations of the director, $+\theta$ and

$-\theta$, and thus to two optical states for proper polarizers-cell arrangement. During the director reorientation the latter switches along the so called tilt-cone as in Fig. 5 in Chap. 2. The switching process of a ferroelectric liquid crystal is about 1000 times faster than that of a nematic, and it is electric field driven, with equal response times, for the switching "on" as well as the switching "off" process. The response time τ, generally measured for a change in optical transmission from 10% to 90%, is given by:

$$\tau = \frac{\gamma_{eff}}{EP_S} \tag{3}$$

where γ_{eff} is an effective rotational viscosity, E the applied electric field amplitude, and P_S the spontaneous polarization.

At first, it should be noted that the addition of nanotubes to a ferroelectric liquid crystal can substantially depress the phase transition temperature from the paraelectric to the ferroelectric phase, SmA*-SmC*.[27] While the transition temperatures between isotropic and nematic, as well as nematic to smectic-A are often more or less independent of nanotube content, the transition from smectic-A* to smectic-C* can be lowered by 10 K and more for nanotube concentrations as small as 0.05% by weight. It is therefore advisable to investigate the properties of the doped systems as a function of reduced temperature $T - T_C$, where T_C is the phase transition temperature from SmA* to SmC*. This can then help to provide a clearer picture of the actual influence of nanotubes as a function of concentration.

The two fundamental parameters of a ferroelectric liquid crystal are the tilt angle, θ, and the spontaneous polarization, P_S. When multiwall carbon nanotubes are added to an FLC, it was found that the tilt angle decreases approximately linearly with increasing nanotube concentration (Fig. 12a).[27,56] It is anticipated that this behavior can be attributed to the nanotubes being oriented along the smectic layer normal of the high temperature SmA* phase. When lowering the temperature into SmC*, molecules stay anchored at the nanotube bundles, and elastic interaction decreases the effective tilt angle. At the same time the spontaneous polarization slightly increases with increasing nanotube concentration (Fig. 12b). This may be due to an interaction between the molecular dipole moments of the FLC and the induced dipole moment of the nanotubes, enhancing the polarization. In the classic Landau theory,[57] tilt angle and spontaneous polarization are linearly dependent, described by a bilinear coupling coefficient C, with $P_S \propto \epsilon_0 \chi_0 C \theta$, where ϵ_0 is the vacuum permittivity and χ_0 is the dielectric susceptibility. It is found that the linear coupling between tilt and polarization increases with increasing nanotube concentration, until

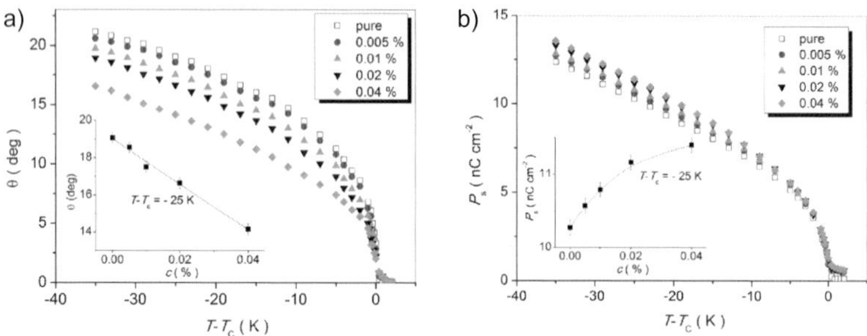

Fig. 12. (a) Tilt angle and (b) spontaneous polarization as a function of reduced temperature for various concentrations of multiwall nanotubes dispersed in a ferroelectric liquid crystal. Copyright (2014) EDP Sciences. Used with permission from Ref. 27.

saturation for larger concentrations.[27]

Related to the spontaneous polarization and an applied electric field is the response time, τ, Eq. (3), which is of fundamental importance for the application of FLCs in devices. For neat ferroelectric liquid crystals, the response time is generally found to decrease with increasing temperature, due to a reduced effective rotational viscosity. This behavior is also observed for nanotube doped FLCs, while the response times at constant temperature increase for increasing nanotube concentration (Fig. 13a). This can be attributed to an increase in rotational viscosity with increasing nanotube concentration, because the increase in spontaneous polarization would lead to an opposing effect. The rotational viscosity thus decreases with increasing temperature, as expected, and increases with increasing nanotube concentration at a given temperature (Fig. 13b). The latter behavior is

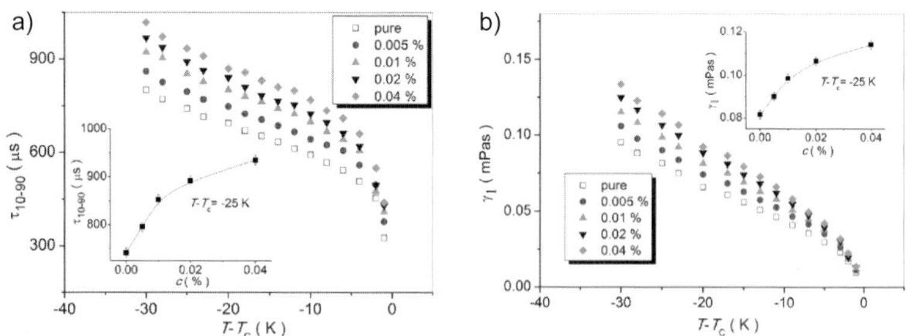

Fig. 13. Reduced temperature dependence of (a) the response time and (b) the rotational viscosity for several different concentrations of multiwall nanotubes dispersed in a ferroelectric liquid crystal. Copyright (2014) EDP Sciences. Used with permission from Ref. 27.

intuitively caused by the interaction between the liquid crystal molecules and the graphitic surface of the dispersed nanotube bundles. Other reports are found in literature,[56,58,59] which indicate a decreasing viscosity and response time. This is explained via a screening of the spontaneous polarization by the induced polarization of the nanotubes.

Dielectric spectroscopy of ferroelectric liquid crystals generally reveals two collective relaxation processes, the soft mode at higher frequencies, which is related to tilt angle fluctuations, and the Goldstone mode at lower frequencies, which is due to director fluctuations on the tilt cone.[60] The soft mode is strongly temperature dependent, and can only be observed around the vicinity of the SmA* to SmC* transition. It is thus likely that an observed relaxation in a FLC-nanotube system is related to the Goldstone mode. The results reported in literature are inconclusive, where both an increase[27,61,62] and a decrease[56,59,63] in dielectric strength were observed for increasing nanotube concentration. Nevertheless, in the case of an increasing spontaneous polarization an increase in dielectric strength is the reasonably expected behavior, as indeed found, see Fig. 14. The Goldstone mode dielectric strength strongly depends on spontaneous polarization and tilt angle, with $\Delta\epsilon \propto (P_S/\theta)^2$, which here increases with increasing nanotube concentration. The relaxation frequency f_R at the same time shifts to lower frequencies for increasing nanotube concentration. The latter trend can be motivated from the fact that the relaxation frequency is inversely proportional to the rotational viscosity, $f_R \propto 1/\gamma$.

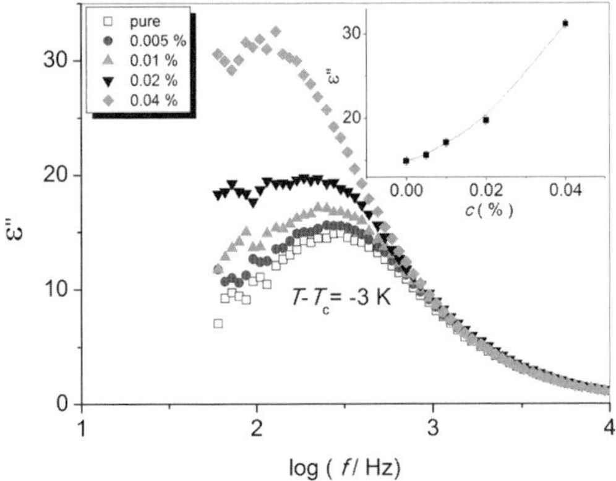

Fig. 14. Goldstone mode relaxation of a ferroelectric liquid crystal doped by various concentrations of multiwall nanotubes. Copyright (2014) EDP Sciences. Used with permission from Ref. 27.

6. Applications of LC-nanotube dispersions

Liquid crystals are successfully used in displays thanks to the excellent electro-optical performance. Relatively small fields can change the optical state by reorienting the molecules from a steady state orientation determined by suitable surface treatments. One of the proposed uses of liquid crystal – nanotube dispersions is for the enhancement of the electrooptic properties of nematic displays and similar devices, following the reports on the decrease of the reorientational threshold voltage as described in Sec. 3, useful in reducing the power consumption of display devices. Besides the fact that other reports do not confirm the improvement it is clear that even in case the conditions for the beneficial effect of doping are identified, the CNT-LC dispersion has to fulfill stability requirements. Moreover, the quality of the nanotubes used for doping has to reach high purity standards to avoid the addition of unwanted contaminants that can deteriorate the long term performance of displays. The quality of dispersion and the concentration of nanotubes are also relevant parameters since the threshold voltage is found to increase with increasing nanotube concentration,[64] which implies that any device would need to be addressed at higher voltages, somewhat diminishing the enhancement gained before.

Another possible use of carbon nanotubes in displays is as aligning layer. One of the most popular ways to achieve uniform planar alignment is to apply a unidirectionally rubbed thin polymer layer, often polyimide, deposited on a substrate via spin-coating. Interestingly, also CNTs, deposited on surfaces with unidirectional alignment, are able to impose uniform planar alignment on liquid crystals.[65] Carbon nanotubes are compatible with flexible substrates and can form transparent and conductive layers as replacement for Indium Tin Oxide.[66] They can thus be used for applying electric fields to switch the LC and therefore, at the same time, change the transmission of light. Thus they are attractive for the integration with LC devices adding functionalities.[67,68] Suspended sheets of aligned CNTs can be produced from forests[69] and act also as polarizers that could be included in optical systems with LCs. After switching the composites, domains are observed not to relax to the original state and the use as a memory effect has been proposed.[70]

Recently, a new display mode was introduced using the Blue Phase (BP).[71] These are fast switching screens which do not need any alignment technology because the BP is optically isotropic resulting in a naturally dark state between crossed polarizers. The bright state is induced by electric field application based on the Kerr effect to produce a change in birefringence. One big problem of this very promising technology was the narrow temperature range of the existence of the BP. The BPs are frustrated defect phases of chiral materials between the isotropic and the chiral nematic, or cholesteric, phase with defects arranged in a cubic lattice. Several different techniques have been proposed to achieve broad Blue Phases, with one of the most successful being polymer stabilization,[72,73] but also the addition of nanoparticles,[73–75] the use of twist inversion compounds,[73] doping with bent-core mesogens,[73,76] or the addition of short chain polymers.[77] Most of these methods have one aspect in common, they rely on guest materials filling the defects of the Blue Phase, and thus reducing the free energy and widening the phase. Since nanotubes have a similar diameter as the defect cores, and at the same time are flexible enough to penetrate between different unit cells, they could be promising dopants to widen BPs. Investigations so far have shown a slight increase of Blue Phase width,[73] but by far not to an extent desirable for applications.

Ions in liquid crystals deteriorate the performance reducing the effective voltage applied and the impurities are not only present from the start but they can increase during operation. Among the different strategies proposed for purification there is also the use of nanomaterials due to their large surface area, as reviewed in Ref. 75, even if reports so far give contradictory results. In this framework carbon nanotubes can be attractive for catching ions even generated during the operation, useful for prolonging the device lifetime.

We have previously shown that the reorientation of liquid crystals by electric or magnetic fields from planar to homeotropic configuration or vice versa produces a large change in conductivity when doping with nanotubes.[28,50,51] Not only the switching out of the cell plane is attractive but also the in plane switching of the composite, proposed for new architectures for computing.[78] After reorientation the increase in conductivity can be seen as an electrical readout with response triggered by fields with strength above a certain threshold applicable e.g. for sensing applications. The dynamic change of the optical properties makes it attractive to use them in combination with the optical properties of CNTs like saturable absorber.[79] The molecular reorientation can also be induced by the electric field of light and the optical reorientational threshold can be reduced dramatically by doping, the so-called Janossy effect.[80] Photorefractive effects have been also reported in nematic LCs doped with CNTs.[81,82]

Among the advantages of using LCs for CNT composites are the easy integrability in devices, the recovery of initial state also after deformation and other advantages that make LC successful in displays. LCs are very responsive materials and this means that a selected response of the composite can be modulated by many different external stimuli for example mechanical or chemicals or thermal inputs transduced into electrical outputs. The properties of CNTs have long been explored in polymer composites and the advantages are expected to apply also for polymer LC hosts. Also, the fact that the host has LC properties results in enhanced anisotropic properties due to an aligning effect of the dispersed nanotubes.[83,84] These aspects are connected to the discussions in Chap. 18, on elastomeric composites.

The applications of CNT-LC composites can in general find an interest in various contexts where the nanotube properties are the key asset and the anisotropy of the properties would enhance the final results. Anisotropic composites are increasingly attractive thanks to the commercial availability nowadays of SWCNTs with metallic or semiconductive characteristics and the improvements in fractionation methods for the selection of nanotubes with different band-gaps. An interesting system is constituted by CNTs with various types of molecules encapsulated, used for changing the CNT properties, even if reports exist of negligible effects.[85] Typically, encapsulation of CNTs is done with fullerenes but also dyes have been introduced.[86,87] The LC constitutes an aligning field for the encapsulated CNTs, providing directionality for e.g. the optical response of the embedded species. Finally, we believe that there are also other attractive uses worth to be exploited using, for example, the current generated by a difference in temperature or vice versa (thermoelectric effect) in combination with the intriguing properties of liquid crystals, polar and non polar, combining fluidity with order, able to easily change optical state but also to waveguide light.

References

1. R. Saito, M. S. Dresselhaus, and G. Dresselhaus, *Physical properties of carbon nanotubes*. Imperial College Press, UK (1998).
2. S. Iijima, Helical microtubules of graphitic carbon, *Nature*. **354**(6348), 56–58 (1991).
3. R. H. Baughman, A. A. Zakhidov, and W. A. de Heer, Carbon nanotubes - the route toward applications, *Science*. **297**(5582), 787–792 (2002).
4. S. Berber, Y.-K. Kwon, and D. Tomanek, Unusually high thermal conductivity of carbon nanotubes, *Phys. Rev. Lett.* **84**(20), 4613 (2000).
5. M. Meo and M. Rossi, Prediction of Young's modulus of single wall carbon

nanotubes by molecular-mechanics based finite element modelling, *Compos. Sci. Technol.* **66**(11), 1597–1605 (2006).

6. M.-F. Yu, O. Lourie, M. J. Dyer, K. Moloni, T. F. Kelly, and R. S. Ruoff, Strength and breaking mechanism of multiwalled carbon nanotubes under tensile load, *Science.* **287**(5453), 637–640 (2000).

7. S. Hong and S. Myung, A flexible approach to mobility, *Nature Nanotech.* **2**, 207–208 (2007).

8. S. Kang, C. Kocabas, T. Ozel, M. Shim, N. Pimparkar, M. Alam, S. Rotkin, and J. Rogers, High-performance electronics using dense, perfectly aligned arrays of single-walled carbon nanotubes, *Nat. Nanotechnol.* **2**(4), 230–236 (2007).

9. M. Arnold, S. Stupp, and M. Hersam, Enrichment of single-walled carbon nanotubes by diameter in density gradients, *Nano. Lett.* **5**(4), 713–718 (2005).

10. J. P. F. Lagerwall and G. Scalia, Carbon nanotubes in liquid crystals, *J. Mater. Chem.* **18**(25), 2890–2898 (2008).

11. M. Rahman and W. Lee, Scientific duo of carbon nanotubes and nematic liquid crystals, *J. Phys. D-Appl. Phys.* **42**(6), 063001 (2009).

12. G. Scalia, Alignment of carbon nanotubes in thermotropic and lyotropic liquid crystals, *ChemPhysChem.* **11**(2), 333–340 (2010).

13. G. Scalia. Liquid crystals of carbon nanotubes and carbon nanotubes in liquid crystals. In ed. Q. Li, *Liquid Crystals Beyond Display Applications.* John Wiley & Sons (2012).

14. J. Lagerwall and G. Scalia. Carbon nanotubes in liquid crystals. In eds. J. W. Goodby, P. J. Collings, T. Kato, C. Tschierske, H. Gleeson, and P. Raynes, *Handbook of Liquid Crystals, Volume 6.* Wiley-VCH, Weinheim (2014).

15. L. Lisetski, M. Soskin, and N. Lebovka. Carbon nanotubes in liquid crystals: Fundamental properties and applications. pp. 243–297. Springer International Publishing, Cham (2015).

16. S. Bergin, Z. Sun, D. Rickard, P. Streich, J. Hamilton, and J. Coleman, Multicomponent solubility parameters for single-walled carbon nanotube-solvent mixtures, *ACS Nano.* **3**(8), 2340–2350 (2009).

17. D. M. Walba, F. Stevens, D. C. Parks, N. A. Clark, and M. D. Wand, Near-atomic resolution imaging of ferroelectric liquid-crystal molecules on graphite by stm, *Science.* **267**(5201), 1144–1147 (1995).

18. F. Balavoine, P. Schultz, C. Richard, V. Mallouh, T. Ebbesen, and C. Mioskowski, Helical crystallization of proteins on carbon nanotubes: A first step towards the development of new biosensors, *Angew. Chem. (Int. Ed.).* **38**(13-14), 1912–1915 (1999).

19. T. Silverstein, The real reason why oil and water don't mix, *J. Chem. Educ.* **75**(1), 116 (1998).

20. S. Schymura, M. Kühnast, V. Lutz, S. Jagiella, U. Dettlaff-Weglikowska, S. Roth, F. Giesselmann, C. Tschierske, G. Scalia, and J. Lagerwall, Towards efficient dispersion of carbon nanotubes in thermotropic liquid crystals, *Adv. Funct. Mater.* **20**(19), 3350–3357 (2010).

21. S. Schymura. *Liquid Crystalline Carbon Nanotube Suspensions: From Unique Challenges to Unique Properties.* PhD thesis, Martin-Luther-Universität

Halle-Wittenberg, Halle, Germany (2013).

22. Y. Ji, Y. Y. Huang, and M. Terentjev, Eugene, Dissolving and aligning carbon nanotubes in thermotropic liquid crystals, *Langmuir.* **27**(21), 13254–13260 (2011).

23. G. Scalia, J. P. F. Lagerwall, M. Haluska, U. Dettlaff-Weglikowska, F. Giesselmann, and S. Roth, Effect of phenyl rings in liquid crystal molecules on swcnts studied by raman spectroscopy, *Phys. Stat. Sol. (b).* **243**(13), 3238–3241 (2006).

24. P. van der Schoot, V. Popa-Nita, and S. Kralj, Alignment of carbon nanotubes in nematic liquid crystals, *J. Phys. Chem. B.* **112**(15), 4512–4518 (2008).

25. V. Popa-Nita and S. Kralj, Liquid crystal-carbon nanotubes mixtures, *J. Chem. Phys.* **132**(2), 024902 (2010).

26. A. Goncharuk, N. Lebovka, L. Lisetski, and S. Minenko, Aggregation, percolation and phase transitions in nematic liquid crystal EBBA doped with carbon nanotubes, *J. Phys. D: Appl. Phys.* **42**(16), 165411 (2009).

27. M. Yakemseva, I. Dierking, N. Kapernaum, N. Usoltseva, and F. Giesselmann, Dispersions of multi-wall carbon nanotubes in ferroelectric liquid crystals, *Eur. Phys. J. E.* **37**(2) (2014).

28. I. Dierking, G. Scalia, P. Morales, and D. Leclere, Aligning and reorienting carbon nanotubes with nematic liquid crystals, *Adv. Mater.* **16**(11), 865–869 (2004).

29. J. P. F. Lagerwall, R. Dabrowski, and G. Scalia, Antiferroelectric liquid crystals with induced intermediate polar phases and the effects of doping with carbon nanotubes, *J. Non-Cryst. Solids.* **353**(47-51), 4411–4417 (2007).

30. L.-C. Chien, D. J. Broer, H. Kikuchi, and N. V. Tabiryan, eds., *Nanotube networks in liquid crystals.* SPIE (2016).

31. L. N. Lisetski, S. S. Minenko, A. V. Zhukov, P. P. Shtifanyuk, and N. I. Lebovka, Dispersions of carbon nanotubes in cholesteric liquid crystals, *Mol. Cryst. Liq. Cryst.* **510**, 43–50 (2009).

32. A. Samoilov, S. Minenko, L. Lisetski, N. Lebovka, M. S. Soskin, and S. I. Torgova, Dispersions of carbon nanotubes in cholesteric liquid crystals with photoactive components, *Funct. Mater.* **21**(4), 373–378 (2014).

33. L. Lisetski, S. Minenko, A. Fedoryako, N. I. Lebovka, and M. Soskin, Dispersions of carbon nanotubes in cholesteric liquid crystals: features of aggregate formation, *Funct. Mater.* **20**(2), 153–157 (2013).

34. N. I. Lebovka, L. N. Lisetski, M. I. Nesterenko, V. D. Panikarskaya, N. A. Kasian, S. S. Minenko, and M. S. Soskin, Anomalous selective reflection in cholesteryl oleyl carbonate – nematic 5CB mixtures and effects of their doping by single-walled carbon nanotubes, *Liq. Cryst.* **40**(7), 968–975 (2013).

35. M. Lynch and D. Patrick, Organizing carbon nanotubes with liquid crystals, *Nano. Lett.* **2**(11), 1197–1201 (2002).

36. G. Scalia, M. Haluska, U. Dettlaff-Weglikowska, F. Giesselmann, and S. Roth, Polarized raman spectroscopy study of SWCNT orientational order in an aligning liquid crystalline matrix, *AIP Conf. Proc.* **786**, 114–117 (2005).

37. H. Agha and Y. Galerne, Interactions of carbon nanotubes in a nematic liquid

crystal. II. experiment, *Phys. Rev. E.* **93**(4) (2016).

38. Y. Galerne, Interactions of carbon nanotubes in a nematic liquid crystal. I. theory., *Phys. Rev. E.* **93**(4-1), 042702 (2016).

39. I. S. Baik, S. Y. Jeon, S. H. Lee, K. A. Park, S. H. Jeong, K. H. An, and Y. H. Lee, Electrical-field effect on carbon nanotubes in a twisted nematic liquid crystal cell, *Appl. Phys. Lett.* **87**(26), 263110 (2005).

40. H. Y. Chen, W. Lee, and N. A. Clark, Faster electro-optical response characteristics of a carbon-nanotube-nematic suspension, *Appl. Phys. Lett.* **90**(3), 033510 (2007).

41. H. Chen and W. Lee, Suppression of field screening in nematic liquid crystals by carbon nanotubes, *Appl. Phys. Lett.* **88**(22), 222105 (2006).

42. J. Kumar, V. Manjuladevi, R. Gupta, and S. Kumar, Fast response in TN liquid-crystal cells: effect of functionalised carbon nanotubes, *Liq. Cryst.* **43**(4), 488–496 (2015).

43. W. Lee, C. Wang, and Y. Shih, Effects of carbon nanosolids on the electro-optical properties of a twisted nematic liquid-crystal host, *Appl. Phys. Lett.* **85**(4), 513–515 (2004).

44. K. Park, S. Lee, S. Lee, and Y. Lee, Anchoring a liquid crystal molecule on a single-walled carbon nanotube, *J. Phys. Chem. C.* **111**(4), 1620–1624 (2007).

45. S. Schymura and G. Scalia, On the effect of carbon nanotubes on properties of liquid crystals., *Philos. Transact. A Math. Phys. Eng. Sci.* **371**(1988), 20120261 (2013).

46. G. Scalia, J. P. F. Lagerwall, S. Schymura, M. Haluska, F. Giesselmann, and S. Roth, Carbon nanotubes in liquid crystals as versatile functional materials, *Phys. Stat. Sol. (b).* **244**(11), 4212–4217 (2007).

47. A. Garcia-Garcia, R. Vergaz, J. Algorri, M. Geday, and J. Oton, The peculiar electrical response of liquid crystal-carbon nanotube systems as seen by impedance spectroscopy, *J. Phys. D: Appl. Phys.* **48**(37), 375302 (2015).

48. M. Monti, M. Natali, L. Torre, and J. M. Kenny, The alignment of single walled carbon nanotubes in an epoxy resin by applying a DC electric field, *Carbon.* **50**(7), 2453–2464 (2012).

49. M. Lima, M. Andrade, V. Skakalova, C. Bergmann, and S. Roth, Dynamic percolation of carbon nanotubes in liquid medium, *J. Mater. Chem.* **17**(46), 4846–4853 (2007).

50. I. Dierking, G. Scalia, and P. Morales, Liquid crystal-carbon nanotube dispersions, *J. Appl. Phys.* **97**, 044309 (2005).

51. I. Dierking and S. San, Magnetically steered liquid crystal-nanotube switch, *Appl. Phys. Lett.* **87**(23), 233507 (2005).

52. S. T. Lagerwall, *Ferroelectric and antiferroelectric liquid crystals.* Wiley-VCH, Weinheim (1999).

53. I. Musevic, R. Blinc, and B. Zeks, *The physics of ferroelectric and antiferroelectric liquid crystals.* World Scientific, Singapore (2000).

54. R. B. Meyer, L. Liebert, L. Strzelecki, and P. Keller, Ferroelectric liquid crystals, *J. Phys. (Paris) Lett.* **36**(3), L69–71 (1975).

55. N. A. Clark and S. T. Lagerwall, Submicrosecond bistable electro-optic switching in liquid crystals, *Appl. Phys. Lett.* **36**(11), 899–901 (1980).

56. P. Malik, A. Chaudhary, R. Mehra, and K. Raina, Electro-optic, thermo-optic and dielectric responses of multiwalled carbon nanotube doped ferroelectric liquid crystal thin films, *J. Mol. Liq.* **165**, 7–11 (2012).

57. T. Carlsson, B. Zeks, A. Levstik, C. Filipic, I. Levstik, and R. Blinc, Generalized landau model of ferroelectric liquid crystals, *Phys. Rev. A.* **36**(3), 1484 (1987).

58. J. Prakash, A. Choudhary, D. Mehta, and A. Biradar, Effect of carbon nanotubes on response time of ferroelectric liquid crystals, *Phys. Rev. E.* **80**(1), 012701 (2009).

59. F. V. Podgornov, A. M. Suvorova, A. V. Lapanik, and W. Haase, Electrooptic and dielectric properties of ferroelectric liquid crystal/single walled carbon nanotubes dispersions confined in thin cells, *Chem. Phys. Lett.* **479**(4), 206–210 (2009).

60. F. Gouda, K. Skarp, and S. Lagerwall, Dielectric studies of the soft mode and goldstone mode in ferroelectric liquid crystals, *Ferroelectrics.* **113**(1-4), 165–206 (1991).

61. R. K. Shukla, K. Raina, V. Hamplova, M. Kaspar, and A. Bubnov, Dielectric behaviour of the composite system: multiwall carbon nanotubes dispersed in ferroelectric liquid crystal, *Phase Transitions.* **84**(9-10), 850–857 (2011).

62. S. K. Gupta, A. Kumar, A. K. Srivastava, and R. Manohar, Modification in dielectric properties of SWCNT doped ferroelectric liquid crystals, *J. Non-Cryst. Solids.* **357**(7), 1822–1826 (2011).

63. P. Arora, A. Mikulko, F. Podgornov, and W. Haase, Dielectric and electro-optic properties of new ferroelectric liquid crystalline mixture doped with carbon nanotubes, *Mol. Cryst. Liq. Cryst.* **502**(1), 1–8 (2009).

64. C. Huang, C. Hu, H. Pan, and K. Lo, Electrooptical responses of carbon nanotube-doped liquid crystal devices, *Jpn. J. Appl. Phys.* **44**(11), 8077–8081 (2005).

65. J. Russell, S. Oh, I. LaRue, O. Zhou, and E. Samulski, Alignment of nematic liquid crystals using carbon nanotube films, *Thin Solid Films.* **509**(1-2), 53–57 (2006).

66. E. Artukovic, M. Kaempgen, D. Hecht, S. Roth, and G. Grüner, Transparent and flexible carbon nanotube transistors, *Nano. Lett.* **5**(4), 757–760 (2005).

67. K. Won, R. Rajasekharan, P. Hands, Q. Dai, and T. Wilkinson, Adaptive lenticular lens array using a hybrid liquid crystal–carbon nanotube nanophotonic device, *Opt. Eng.* **50**(5), 054002 (2011).

68. A. A. Khan, G. D. M. Dabera, H. Butt, M. M. Qasim, G. A. Amaratunga, S. R. P. Silva, and T. D. Wilkinson, Tunable scattering from liquid crystal devices using carbon nanotubes network electrodes, *Nanoscale.* **7**(1), 330–336 (2015).

69. M. Zhang, S. Fang, A. A. Zakhidov, S. B. Lee, A. E. Aliev, C. D. Williams, K. R. Atkinson, and R. H. Baughman, Strong, transparent, multifunctional, carbon nanotube sheets, *Science.* **309**, 1215–1219 (2005).

70. R. Basu and G. Iannacchione, Carbon nanotube dispersed liquid crystal: A nano electromechanical system, *Appl. Phys. Lett.* **93**(18), 183105 (2008).

71. H. Kikuchi, H. Higuchi, Y. Hasaba, and T. Iwata, *SID07 Digest,.* **38**, 1737

(2007).

72. H. Kikuchi, M. Yokota, Y. Hisakado, H. Yang, and T. Kajiyama, Polymer-stabilized liquid crystal blue phases, *Nat. Mater.* **1**(1), 64–68 (2002).

73. I. Dierking, W. Blenkhorn, E. Credland, W. Drake, R. Kociuruba, B. Kayser, and T. Michael, Stabilising liquid crystalline blue phases, *Soft Matter.* **8**(16), 4355–4362 (2012).

74. E. Karatairi, B. Rozic, Z. Kutnjak, V. Tzitzios, G. Nounesis, G. Cordoyiannis, J. Thoen, C. Glorieux, and S. Kralj, Nanoparticle-induced widening of the temperature range of liquid-crystalline blue phases, *Phys. Rev. E.* **81**, 041703 (2010).

75. Y. Garbovskiy and I. Glushchenko, Nano-objects and ions in liquid crystals: ion trapping effect and related phenomena, *Crystals.* **5**(4), 501–533 (2015).

76. M. Nakata, Y. Takanishi, J. Watanabe, and H. Takezoe, Blue phases induced by doping chiral nematic liquid crystals with nonchiral molecules, *Phys. Rev. E.* **68**(4), 041710 (2003).

77. N. Kasch, I. Dierking, and M. Turner, Stabilization of the liquid crystalline blue phase by the addition of short-chain polystyrene, *Soft Matter.* **9**(19), 4789–4793 (2013).

78. M. Massey, D. Volpati, F. Qaiser, A. Kotsialos, C. Pearson, D. Zeze, and M. Petty, Alignment of liquid crystal/carbon nanotube dispersions for application in unconventional computing., *AIP Conf. Proc.* **1648**, 280009 (2015).

79. F. Wang, D. Popa, Z. Sun, T. Hasan, F. Torrisi, and A. C. Ferrari, Characterization of dynamic nonlinear absorption of carbon nanotube saturable absorber, *Conference on Lasers and Electro-Optics.* p. JWA96 (2010).

80. I. Janossy, Molecular interpretation of the absorption-induced optical reorientation of nematic liquid crystals, *Phys. Rev. E.* **49**(4), 2957 (1994).

81. I. Khoo, J. Ding, Y. Zhang, K. Chen, and A. Diaz, Supra-nonlinear photorefractive response of single-walled carbon nanotube-and c60-doped nematic liquid crystal, *Appl. Phys. Lett.* **82** (2003).

82. *Supra-photorefractivity in C60 and carbon-nanotubes-doped nematic liquid crystals*, vol. Optical Science and Technology, SPIE's 48th Annual Meeting. International Society for Optics and Photonics (2003).

83. B. Smith, Z. Benes, D. Luzzi, J. Fischer, D. Walters, M. Casavant, J. Schmidt, and R. Smalley, Structural anisotropy of magnetically aligned single wall carbon nanotube films, *Appl. Phys. Lett.* **77**(5), 663–665 (2000).

84. J. E. Fischer, W. Zhou, J. Vavro, C. Llaguno, C. Guthy, R. Haggenmueller, M. J. Casavant, D. E. Walters, and R. E. Smalley, Magnetically aligned single wall carbon nanotube films: Preferred orientation and anisotropic transport properties, *J. Appl. Phys.* **93**(4), 2157–2163 (2003).

85. N. Tschirner, K. Brose, J. Maultzsch, K. Yanagi, H. Kataura, and C. Thomsen, The influence of incorporated β carotene on the vibrational properties of single wall carbon nanotubes, *Phys. Stat. Solidi (b).* **247**(11–12), 2734–2737 (2010).

86. M. Tange, T. Okazaki, Z. Liu, K. Suenaga, and S. Iijima, Room-temperature y-type emission of perylenes by encapsulation within single-walled carbon nanotubes, *Nanoscale.* **8**(15), 7834–7839 (2016).

87. K. Yanagi, K. Iakoubovskii, S. Kazaoui, N. Minami, Y. Maniwa, Y. Miyata, and H. Kataura, Light-harvesting function of β-carotene inside carbon nanotubes, *Phys. Rev. B.* **74**(15), 155420 (2006).

Chapter 18

Carbon nanotubes dispersed in liquid crystal elastomers

Yang Yang and Yan Ji

Department of Chemistry, Tsinghua University, Beijing, China, 100084
jiyan@mail.tsinghua.edu.cn

Liquid crystal elastomers (LCEs), as the name indicates, unite the anisotropic order of liquid crystals and rubber elasticity of elastomers into polymer networks. One of the most notable features of LCEs is that properly aligned LCEs exhibit dramatic and reversible shape deformation (e.g. elongation-contraction) in response to various stimuli. In recent years, carbon nanotubes (CNTs) were introduced into LCEs. Besides enabling remote and spatial control of the actuation via light and electronic field, CNTs are also utilized to align mesogens as well as to improve the mechanical and electronic property of the composites. Some potential applications of CNT-LCE nanocomposites have been demonstrated. This chapter describes the preparation of CNT dispersed LCEs, new physical properties resulted from CNTs, their actuation and their proposed applications.

Contents

1. Introduction

Liquid crystalline elastomers (LCEs) are lightly crosslinked polymer networks with mesogenic groups chemically bonded to polymer chains.[1] According to alignment patterns of mesogens, LCEs are distributed into nematic LCEs, smectic LCEs and cholesteric LCEs. And based on the location of mesogens, LCEs are categorized into main-chain LCEs and side-chain LCEs. Similar to low molecular liquid crystals, the rigid mesogens integrated in the crosslinked networks have spontaneous orientational order. If all the mesogens are uniaxially aligned throughout the material and topologically fixed by crosslinked networks, these LCEs are termed as monodomain LCEs. When each domain of LCEs takes random orientation, these networks are known as polydomain LCEs. The monodomain LCEs are especially attractive for they are able to transfer external stimuli into dramatic shape deformation, which was firstly theoretically predicted by De Gennes *et al.*[2,3] and experimentally verified by Finkelmann and co-workers.[4] With more than two decades' research, LCEs with diverse chemical compositions and structures have been developed. The potential applications have been extended to a wide range of areas including muscle mimics, valves in microfluidic systems, tunable lasing media, etc.[5–10] Several excellent books and reviews have been published on LCEs.[1,11–14]

The underlying mechanism of actuation relates to the liquid crystal (LC)-isotropic phase transition. As illustrated in Fig. 1a, with the side-chain nematic LCE as an example, the mesogens of monodomain LCEs are more or less uniformly oriented in the LC phase. Due to the strong coupling between mesogens and the polymer network, the polymer chains also exhibit an anisotropic chain conformation. Upon external stimuli, the LC phase is changed into isotropic phase. Along with the mesogens disordering, the polymer chains turn into spherical chain conformation. The change between anisotropic conformation and isotropic conformation results in a shape change of the material. In polydomain samples, we cannot observe the overall shape change of the bulk material because the direction of shape deformation in each domain is random. But in the monodomain samples, all the areas show the same type of shape change (such as contraction or extension in the same direction), leading to a macroscopic change in bulk material. Despite some differences in details, this actuation mechanism also works for main-chain LCEs and LCEs with other mesophases. As shown in Fig. 1b, when a monodomain main-chain LCE film undergoes a LC-isotropic phase transition by heating, the material contracts; while

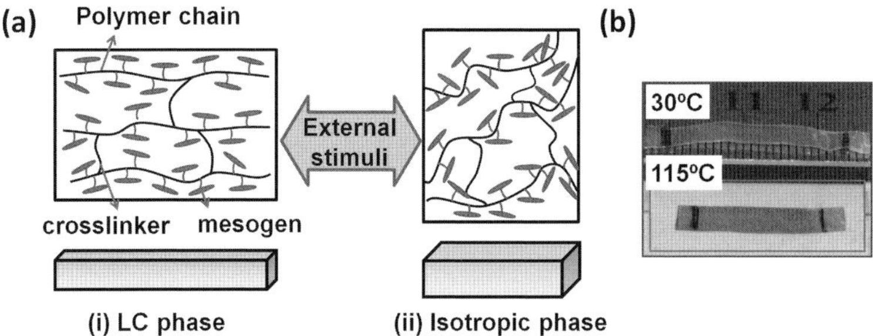

Fig. 1. (a) Reversible shape deformation of LCE between LC phase and isotropic phase. (b) The change of length of a main-chain monodomain LCE film between the LC phase (30°C) and the isotropic phase (115°C). Reprinted with permission.[15] Copyright (2013), Nature Publishing Group.

cooling the film to go through the isotropic-LC phase transition, mesogens realign, leading the LCE film to recover to its original shape. This order change is reversible because it is controlled by thermodynamic equilibrium while the directionality is controlled by the crosslinks. The performance of actuation can be measured by calculating the elongation ratio $(L - L_0)/L_0$ or extension ratio (L/L_0) (L is the length of material in the LC phase, and L_0 is the length of material in the isotropic phase). The larger ratio, the better actuation. Usually, main-chain LCEs are expected to possess better actuation than side-chain LCEs. Besides contraction-extension, another popular motion of LCEs is bending. When we mention LCEs in this chapter, we refer to monodomain LCEs from now on unless we explicitly mention otherwise.

Various stimuli can be used to trigger the LC-isotropic transition. Heat is the most widely used stimulus. It works very well in labs. However, for real-world applications, direct heating not only is not possible in many circumstances (e.g. when LCEs are used in electronic devices), but also lacks remote and spatial control of the actuation. Moreover, it needs considerable time for direct heating to reach a certain temperature. Cooling down at a very high speed also represents a big problem. In such a context, light and electric field are far more desirable as they can be switched on and off rapidly. LCEs incorporating light-sensitive isomerizable chromophores have been extensively investigated.[5,16,17] Typically those LCEs bend on irradiation of UV light. Motors,[5] grippers,[18] artificial cilia[9] and so on have been beautifully fabricated based on such kind of LCEs. In consideration of safety issues, however, infrared and visible light are preferred to harmful UV light. Ferroelectric mesogens provide an effective way to achieve LCEs sensitive to electric field, but the actuation magnitudes are very small.[19,20] Inserting winding wires into LCEs may initiate the LC-isotropic phase by resistive joule heating upon the application of electrical field.[21] But the mechanical incompatibility between stiff wires and the elastic LCEs represents a critical issue. Alternatively, nanoparticles sensitive to external stimuli came into the picture. The incorporation of nanoparticles leads to not only the enhancement of the mechanical, electrical and thermal properties of LCE materials, but also makes it possible to manipulate the actuation in a non-contact way. For example, magnetic iron oxide nanoparticles enable LCE to contract upon the application of magnetic field, for the magnetic nanoparticles can convert electromagnetic energy into local heat and induce the LC-isotropic phase transition.[22] In another case, embedding gold nanoparticles into LCEs resulted in improved actuator strain rate and response rate to heat.[23]

Of all the nanoparticles dispersed into LCEs, carbon nanotubes (CNTs) are of particular interest. As mentioned in previous chapters, both multi-walled CNTs (MWCNTs) and single-walled CNTs (SWCNTs) possess excellent thermal, electrical, optical and mechanical properties.[24] Their nanometer-scale diameters and one-dimensional lengths ranging from centimeters to microns bring forth to a high aspect ratio and large surface area.[25] In addition, CNTs have remarkable thermal and chemical stability. CNTs have been introduced into various polymers to enhance the thermal, electric and mechanical properties (such as strength and toughness) of polymer matrix.[26,27] As CNTs can absorb light of almost all wavelengths[28] and subsequently convert the optical energy into thermal energy,[29,30] CNTs may be perceived as nano-scale heat supply sources to trigger photo-response of matrixes. As demonstrated by Koerner *et al.* with the shape-memory polyurethanes, the addition of CNTs offers polyurethane the sensitivity to infrared light.[31] Doping LCEs with CNTs started about a decade ago.[32–34] Not only CNTs enable light and electric field controllable mechanical actuation, but also mesogens can be aligned by the CNTs. Here we summarize the recent progresses in this area, focusing on the preparation of CNT-LCE, the new physical properties of LCEs due to the involvement of CNTs, their response to light and electric field as well as research on their potential applications. Some LC networks have glass transitions above room temperature. Strictly speaking, they are not LC elastomers. But as they have similar actuation as LCEs which are elastic at room temperature, their CNT nanocomposites are also included here.

2. Fabrication of CNT-LCE nanocomposites

There are two most popular methods to prepare LCEs. The first one is two-step crosslinking procedure, which was first developed by Finkelmann *et al.* with polysiloxane side-chain LCEs.[4,35] The starting materials including a linear polyhydrosiloxane chain are dissolved into a limited amount of solvent. As the reaction goes by, the mixture forms a partially crosslinked gel with certain mechanical strength. By mechanical force, the gel is stretched to uniformly align mesogens and unfold the polymer chains. The stretched gel is dried while a second-stage crosslinking reaction continues under load, resulting in a fully-crosslinked monodomain LCE sample where the orientation is permanently locked. The second popular way is to first align the mesogens by alignment layers, electric field or magnetic field before any crosslinking or polymerization. Typically the reaction starts with low-molecular-weight acrylate liquid crystalline monomers which can be polymerized by light after they are aligned first. This approach makes it possible to prepare monodomain LCEs with little defects. Some new techniques are developed over the years based on this method. For example, its combination with ink-printing makes it possible to make large scale artificial cilia and other mini actuators.[9] Recently, we brought forth a new method to prepare monodomain LCEs using polydomain LCEs with exchangeable links.[15] The alignment can be done by stretching such polydomain LCEs at high temperature. Due to the presence of exchangeable links, the polymer topology reorganizes and the aligned structure can be preserved to form monodomain LCEs.

So far, the majority of CNT-LCE nanocomposites reported was fabricated by the traditional two-step crosslinking method. A common practice is to disperse CNTs in solutions first and then add them to the reaction mixture as one component before the reaction starts. Compared with the preparation of neat LCEs without CNTs, a few details need to be revised due to the addition of CNTs. For example, in the first crosslinking step, the popular method is to use centrifuge to get a flat gel-like film. The centrifugation speed needs to be slower than that used for the preparation of neat LCEs because CNTs are easy to precipitate into the bottom layer of the film. To avoid the precipitation of CNTs, Li *et al.* used a casting method instead of centrifugation. As sketched in Scheme 1, they put the reaction mixture including SWCNTs into a rectangular polytetrafluoroethylene mold. After the reaction mixture gelled, the weakly crosslinked LCE film was peeled off the mold and a second step crosslinking was continued while the film was under load.[36]

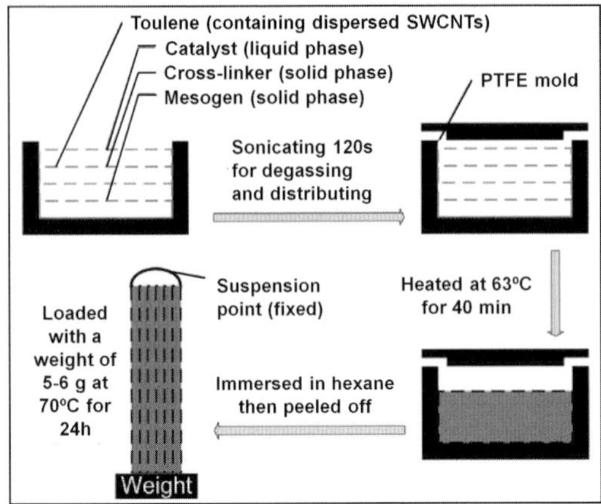

Scheme 1. Fabrication process of SWCNT-LCE nanocomposite films. Reprinted with permission.[36] Copyright (2011), The Royal Society of Chemistry.

To prepare CNT-LCEs via two-step crosslinking method, one of the most important issues is to disperse CNTs evenly into LCEs, for the property of CNT-LCE nanocomposites depends strongly on the dispersion quality of CNTs. Due to the high aspect ratio and strong Van de Waal force between CNTs, CNTs have a tendency to aggregate and are poorly compatible with most solvents.[37,38] They are more difficult than most other nanoparticles to be evenly dispersed into polymers.[39–41] Extensive research efforts have been paid to conquer this challenge.[38,42,43] To get a homogenous dispersion of CNTs in LCEs turns out to be even harder, for there is another basic requirement: the addition of CNTs must not destroy the integrity of the liquid crystalline order. Since the mechanical actuation is directly related to the LC-isotropic transition, it is ideal that the original thermal properties of the neat LCEs are not damaged by the introduction of CNTs. This represents a substantial obstacle in developing CNT-LCE nanocomposites.

To solve this problem, mechanical stirring was the very first solution.[34] Because mechanical shearing did not substantially decrease CNTs' large specific surface area, more often than not, CNTs aggregated again after being left to stand for a period of time or during the crosslinking process. Several hours of shearing were necessary to homogenize the reaction mixture.[34] Later, ultrasonication became a better choice. Courty firstly dispersed CNTs in toluene by sonication and mechanical stirrer for at least 24 hours.[32] Then this CNT solution was transferred into reacting mixture and mechanically stirred for another 4-6 hours. Finally, the catalyst for crosslinking was added to start the reaction so as to make LCEs by the traditional two-step crosslinking method. Even though ultrasonication is more powerful, only a very small amount of CNTs can be dispersed evenly in LCEs. Moreover, this method does not work well for SWCNTs, which are generally more difficult than MWCNTs to be dispersed. For an example, Li *et al.* fabricated CNT-LCE nanocomposites by mixing SWCNTs into the reaction mixture solution under ultrasonication for 2 min before crosslinking the mixture to obtain a crosslinked nematic side-chain LCE network.[36] CNT agglomerated severely during the crosslinking procedure. The resultant CNT-LCE nanocomposites were in fact macroscopically phase separated, which could be obviously spotted in the final nanocomposites.

To obtain a high loading of CNTs with good dispersion quality, dispersants were utilized. There are various methods that can help de-bundle CNTs.[40,41] Non-covalent functionalization of CNTs includes using surfactants, biomacromolecules, as well as polymers. It does not influence CNTs' intrinsic physical properties.[44] For the covalent functionalization, CNTs can normally modified with functional groups (such as -COOH and -OH).[45,46] Despite of a wide range of dispersants available, few are fit for dispersing CNTs into LCE matrix, for the dispersants themselves may cause the disruption of LC orders. To disperse SWCNTs into LCE, Yang *et al.* used a rigid conjugated polymer, poly(p-phenyleneethynylene) (PPE, Fig. 2a),[47] to modify SWCNTs' surface while preserving their intrinsic properties by $\pi - \pi$ interaction instead of polymer wrapping. 0.1-0.2 wt% SWCNTs can be dispersed homogeneously into acrylate based LCE matrix by this method.[48] To better avoid the disruption of LC order of polysiloxane based LCEs, Ji *et al.* designed and synthesized a liquid crystalline dispersant PyMC (Fig. 2b).[43] This dispersant contains two pyrene end groups and siloxane moieties. Compared to ordinary dispersants, such dispersant has better compatibility with the LCE matrix based on polysiloxane chains. Both pyrene groups and the rigid mesogens interact with CNTs by aromatic stacking. PyMC can efficiently disperse CNTs in not only organic solvents (such as chloroform) (Fig. 2c) but also in LCE matrixes. A high CNT loading up to 3 wt% can be achieved as well. We recently found that a kind of polymer of intrinsic microporosity[49] called PIM-1 (Fig. 2d) was an excellent dispersant. A homogenous solution with 1 mg PIM-1 and 1 mg MWCNT in 4 ml chloroform can be obtained by sonication for 30 min. This homogenous solution can be used to disperse CNTs into epoxy[50] and epoxy type LCEs.[51]

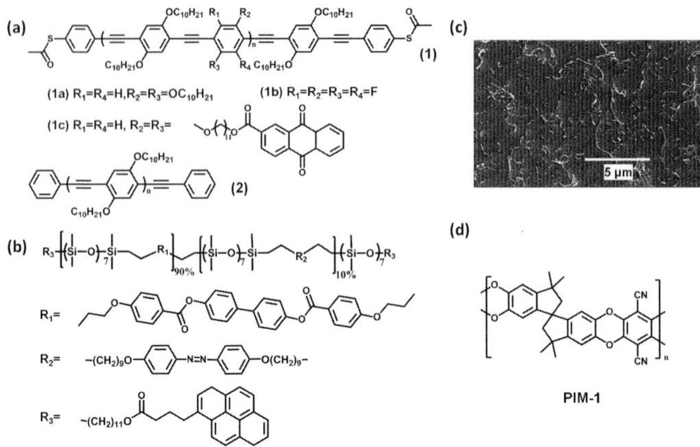

Fig. 2. (a) The structure of PPE. Reprinted with permission.[47] Copyright (2012), American Chemical Society. (b) The structure of PyMC.[43] (c) SEM image of well-separated CNTs dispersed by PyMC. Reprinted with permission.[43] Copyright (2010), WILEY-VCH. (d) The structure of PIM-1.

While the majority of CNT-LCEs are flat films, Camargo *et al.* developed a technique based on stamping to prepare three dimensional CNT-LCE structures.[52] A punch mould with pins and a die mould with matched holes (see Scheme 2a) were used. After the reaction mixture formed a lightly crosslinked gel by the traditional two-step method, the gel film was sandwiched between punch mould and die mould. While pressing the punch mould into die mould, areas around the pins were stretched. A second-step crosslinking was carried out while keeping a constant stress on this sandwiched set-up. After peeled away from the moulds, a film with dome-shape blisters (Scheme 2b) was obtained.

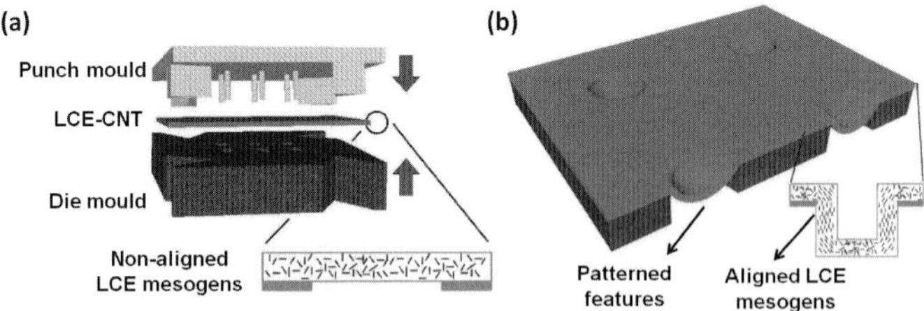

Scheme 2. Preparation of 3-dimensional blisters: structuring and stretching sequence. (a) Mould alignment and gearing and LCE-CNT stretching. (b) Punch releasing and LCE mesogen alignment (mesogens are drawn as lines to illustrate). Reprinted with permission.[52] Copyright (2011), WILEY-VCH.

Recently Wang *et al.* introduced a novel strategy to prepare CNT-LCE nanocomposites using aligned CNT array.[53] As shown in Fig. 3, CNT array was grown on a silicon matrix by chemical vapor deposition. The mixture of liquid crystalline monomers, crosslinker and photoinitiator were melted and then injected into the CNT array. Further photopolymerization of the monomers gave out a crosslinked polymer with CNT array inside.[53] This method not only efficiently avoided the CNT aggregation, but also greatly improved the mechanical and electric properties of the LCEs. Using hydrogen bonding to physically crosslink liquid crystalline polymers, Ozawa *et al.* prepared uniaxially aligned CNT dispersed LC network by drawing fibers from the melt nanocomposite.[54] To help dispersing CNTs into the polymer, they covalently modified CNTs by introducing carboxyl acid groups onto SWCNTs.

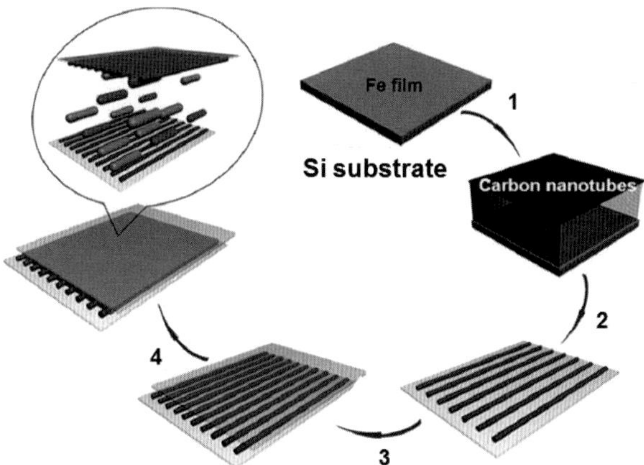

Fig. 3. Preparation of an oriented CLCP/CNT nanocomposite film in four steps: (1) growth of a CNT array by chemical vapor deposition; (2) formation and stabilization of the CNT sheet on a glass substrate; (3) preparation of the LC cell by using two CNT-sheet-covered glass slides; and (4) injection of the molten mixture including the monomers, crosslinker, and photoinitiator into the LC cell. Reprinted with permission.[53] Copyright (2012), WILEY-VCH.

3. New properties due to the addition of CNTs

3.1. *Mechanical properties*

With the presence of CNTs, a general observation on the change of LCEs is the stiffening of the matrix.[34] The more CNTs, the darker the color, as well as the stiffer the sample. According to Courty *et al.*, the Young modulus of LCEs with 0.02 wt% MWCNTs was almost 1.5 times that of the neat LCEs (see Fig. 4a).[32] It is easy to understand this observation when considering that the Young modulus of CNTs is about 1 TPa. The reinforcement of mechanical properties was also noticed in the LCEs dispersed with SWCNTs. Li *et al.* found that the tensile fracture strength of CNT-LCE nanocomposite was much higher than that of the neat LCEs.[36] The enhancement of mechanical property by SWCNTs was utilized on purpose by Ozawa *et al.* to improve the mechanical stability of hydrogen bonded azobenzene LC polymers.[54] At a concentration of 0.1% SWCNTs, the tensile stress was 1.6 times larger than that of samples without SWCNTs. However, higher concentration of SWCNTs makes the composite much brittle. This was also reflected by the decrease of strain-at-break with the increase of SWC-NTs. When highly aligned CNT arrays were used for the preparation of CNT-LCE nanocomposites, the strengthening of mechanical property was even more remarkable (Fig. 4b). The tensile strength reached above 1 GPa while the neat matrix was only 16 MPa.[55]

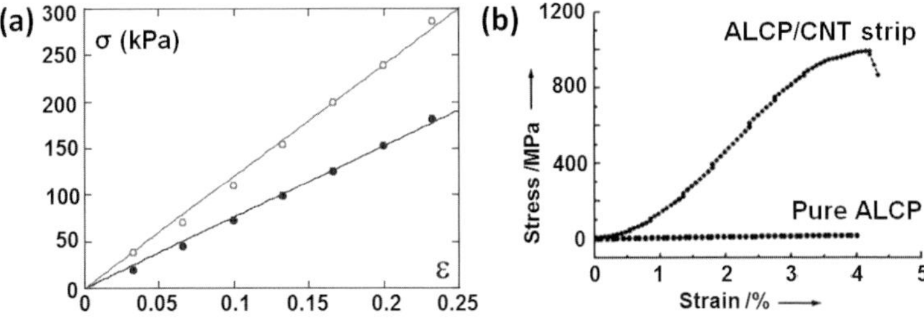

Fig. 4. (a) Equilibrium stress-strain variation on uniaxial extension $\epsilon = \Delta L/L$ along the director (and CNT alignment) axis, for the pure network (•) and the 0.02% CNT composite (◦). The solid lines of linear fit provide the Young (extension) modulus $Y_0 \approx$ 0.76 MPa and $Y_{CNT} \approx$ 1.2 MPa for the two systems.[32] (b) Stress-strain curves of pure azobenzene liquid crystalline polymer network (ALCP) and ALCP/CNT composite strips. Reprinted with permission.[55] Copyright (2012), WILEY-VCH.

3.2. *Electric properties*

One attractive perspective on creating CNT-LCEs dwells in the improvement of electrical conductivity. For most CNT-LCE nanocomposites, they are not conductive. The major reason is the low concentration of CNTs. On one hand, efficient charge transport demands the formation of a continuous (percolated) network of interconnected tubes inside LCE matrix, which requires high concentration of CNTs. On the other hand, maintaining LC integrity and the mechanical actuation prefers as few CNTs as possible. Moreover, sometimes the CNTs are "wrapped" by polymeric dispersants, which prevents CNTs from effective contact. However, the dielectric property can be improved with the addition of relatively high concentration of CNTs, for CNTs possess very huge anisotropic dielectric-constants. As investigated by Ji *et al.* with CNT-LCEs prepared by the assistance of PyMC, all the nanocomposites behaves like traditional capacitors even though the CNT concentration reached 3 wt% (Fig. 5a).[43] The addition of 0.1 wt% CNTs had little effect on the dielectric properties. When the concentration was increased to 1 wt%, there was a distinct decrease of the low-frequency resistivity.

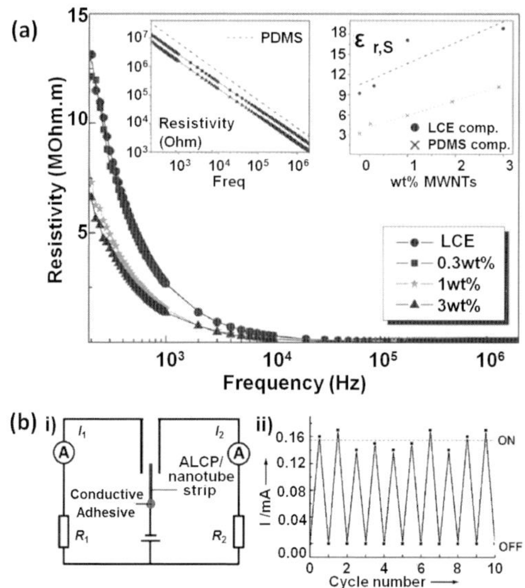

Fig. 5. (a) Complex resistivity against frequency for the CNT-LCE composites of different CNT loading. The left insert compares the scaling behavior on a log-log scale with that of a neat PDMS. The right insert shows the large improvement in the extrapolated effective dielectric constants when CNTs are added to the LCE matrix. Reprinted with permission.[43] Copyright (2010), WILEY-VCH. (b) Application of the electrically conductive ALCP/nanotube composite strip for a remote electric switch. (i) Illustration of the experimental setup. (ii) The reversible switch between connection and disconnection for the left electric circuit in (i). Reprinted with permission.[55] Copyright (2012), WILEY-VCH.

An effective route to get conducting CNT nanocomposites is to employ highly aligned CNT array. As demonstrated by Sun *et al.*, the azobenzene based liquid crystalline network formed within CNT array had a conductivity of above 350 S/cm.[55] Since the azobenzene groups are responsive to UV light and the azobenzene groups are aligned by the CNT array, the conductivity can be changed with the irradiation of light. The conductivity of UV irradiated nanocomposites where azobenzene groups were in the *cis* state was about 2% higher than that of the nanocomposites where the majority of azobenzene groups were in the *trans* state. It was explained that the distance between nanotubes decreased slightly upon *trans-cis* transition with the irradiation of UV light. Such change was totally reversible and there was little change on the conductivity even after 100 cycles. Such kind of material can be used as an electric switch to disconnect or connect a circuit upon the irradiation of light (Fig. 5b).

3.3. *Anisotropic optical properties*

As pointed out by Courty *et al.*, CNTs can be aligned during the stretching process when preparing CNT-LCE nanocomposites by the two-step crosslinking method.[32] According to scanning electron microscopy (SEM), they found that CNTs were more or less parallel to the stretching direction. Because CNTs absorb light of a wide range of wavelengths, the orientation of CNTs results in some additional anisotropic optical properties. As demonstrated by Ji *et al.* by transmission time-domain spectroscopy, the absorption of light at terahertz frequency range increased with the increased loading of CNTs (Fig. 6).[43] When the CNT concentration was high enough, the anisotropic absorption became salient. The absorption coefficient of parallel polarization was much larger than that in the perpendicular direction. Correspondingly, the refractive index of parallel direction was higher than that of the perpendicular direction. The anisotropic absorption was also reported in azobenzene liquid crystalline networks prepared with CNT array, but those absorption resulted from the azobenzene groups instead of CNTs.[53,55]

4. Mechanical actuation

4.1. *Thermo-mechanical actuation*

Even though much attention has been paid to avoid impairing the properties of LCEs, adding CNTs into LCEs sometimes weakens the thermo-

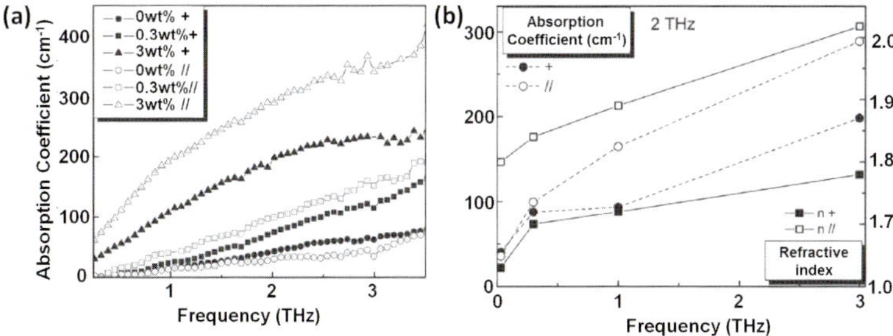

Fig. 6. (a) THz time-domain spectroscopy: absorption coefficient spectra of a blank, 0.3 and 3 wt% CNT composites when the THz polarization is parallel, //, and perpendicular, +, to the direction of LCEs. (b) The absorption coefficient and the refractive index of samples with different CNT concentrations at 2 THz. Reprinted with permission.[43] Copyright (2010), WILEY-VCH.

actuation. As shown in Fig. 7a, the extension ratio was reduced when 0.02 % MWCNT is introduced into LCEs without any dispersants.[32] There are three possible reasons accounting for such weakening effect. Firstly, CNTs are impurities after all. They may have a negative effect on the formation of liquid crystalline order. Secondly, CNTs are rigid, which may increase the stiffness of the LCEs and restrain the LCE matrix from free deformation. Thirdly, the CNTs are highly anisotropic. If some CNTs are aligned in the LCEs during the stretching step of the two-step crosslinking method, they may prevent the composite from fully contraction along the alignment direction.[32] However, such weakening effect can be relieved by improving

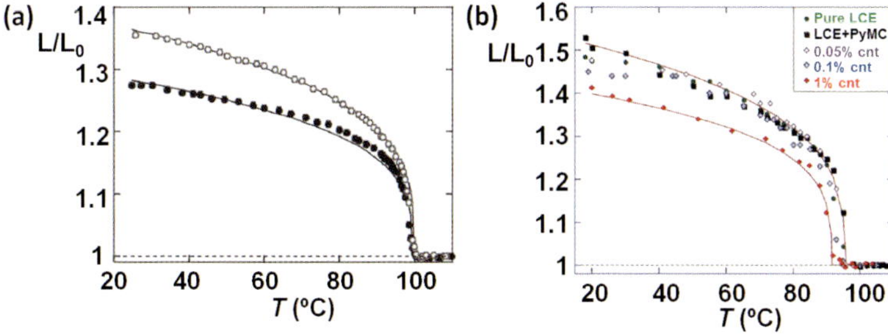

Fig. 7. (a) The thermal actuations of pure LCE (○) and CNT-LCE with 0.02 wt% CNT (●).[32] (b) The extension ratio of LCE with different concentrations of CNT between isotropic phase and LC phase. Reprinted with permission.[56] Copyright (2012), The Royal Society of Chemistry.

the dispersion quality of CNTs. When PyMC was used as an dispersant, the thermo-actuation of the samples was almost the same to that of neat LCEs even when the CNT concentration reached 1 wt%.[43] But when the CNT concentration was even higher (3 wt%), the weakening effect became obvious. The elongation ratio was reduced by 70%. This dependence of the weakening effect on the CNT concentration was also proved by Marshall's well (see Fig. 7b).[56]

4.2. *Photo-mechanical actuation*

Light-driven actuation is one of the most inviting features of CNT-LCE nanocomposites. As shown in Fig. 8, the CNT-LCE stripe contracted upon the irradiation of light, while it returned to its initial state 10 s after the light was turned off. It is generally recognized that such actuation is attributed to the photo-thermal effect of CNTs. As we have previously mentioned that CNTs, especially SWCNT,[57] have strong absorption of light over a wide-range of wavelengths. They are able to efficiently convert the optical energy into thermal energy. When they are embedded into LCEs, they may act like micro-heaters upon the irradiation of light. The temperature of the nanocomposite increases immediately. It can reach above the LC phase transition temperature (T_i) within several seconds if proper inten-

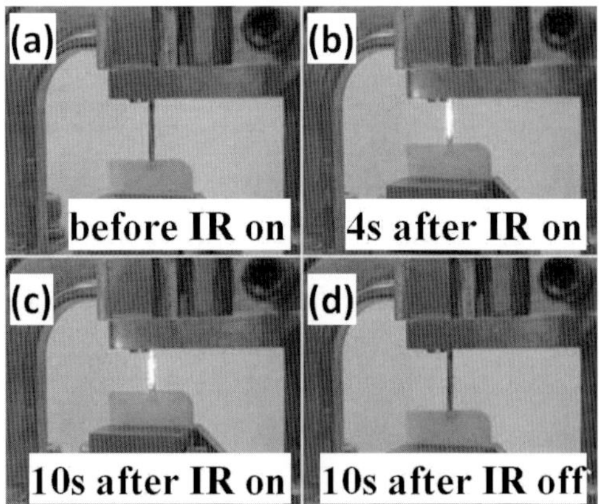

Fig. 8. IR-actuation frames of a 0.2 wt% SWCNT-LCE nanocomposite film subjected to 16 min of curing and 160% hot-drawing. (a) The SWCNT-LCE nanocomposite film before the IR beam was turned on. (b) The film after the IR beam was turned on for four seconds. (c) The film after it had fully contracted after the IR was turned on for 10 seconds. (d) The film after it had returned to its original length with the IR beam turned off. Reprinted with permission.[48] Copyright (2008), WILEY-VCH.

sity of light is used. As a result, the actuation of CNT-LCE material occurs. When the light is turned off, the temperature drops very quickly, leading to the recovery of the original shape. Besides photo-thermal effect, there is another possible mechanism that may contribute to the observed actuation: the alignment of CNTs. Ahir *et al.* believed that the actuation was directly related to the uniaxial orientation of the nanotubes even though photothermal effect also played an important role.[34,58] Since the speed of the light actuation is very fast, Yang *et al.* suggested that a SWCNT network existed in their system and such network provided a thermal conduction pathway for the delivery of heat to the whole matrix.[48] No matter whether a network of nanotubes presents or not, it is for sure that the high thermal conductivity of CNTs benefits the heat transport in the composites.

Besides contraction-extension, bending-unbending of CNT-LCE nanocompoiste is also possible. Bending can be realized by focusing light to some area of a cantilever made of CNT-LCEs. The bending kinetics investigated by Torras *et al.* showed that the cantilever bended due to the temperature gradient and the resultant inhomogeneous strain distribution inside the sample (Fig. 9a).[59] Bending can also be achieved by bilayers made from SWCNT-LCE and silicone elastomer. As shown in Fig. 9b, when exposed to IR light, the CNT-LCE film tends to contract. However, as it is bonded to silicone by glue, the CNT-LCE film cannot contract freely. Instead, the whole bilayer film bends toward light.[60] There is an unusual bending mechanism when CNT array is used to make azobenzene liquid crystalline polymer composites.[55] Normally, to get the bending-unbending of azobenzene liquid crystalline networks, UV and visible light have to be used alternatively. And the sample normally bends towards light. However, the sample prepared by highly aligned CNT array can be actuated by UV light alone. As shown in Fig. 9c, when UV light was delivered at one side of the sample, the sample bent away from the light instead of towards the light. And when the other side was irradiated by UV light again, the sample bent backwards. Even though the actual mechanism of bending and unbending is still the isomerization of azobenzene groups, such usual bending effect relates to involvement of CNTs. The CNT array induces a homeotropic alignment of azobenzene groups, as shown in Fig. 9d. As UV penetration is limited to the very top of the material, only the surface layer contracts under UV. Due to the homeotropic alignment, the sample bends away from the light.

Many factors affect the photo-actuation of CNT-LCEs. Generally speaking, the actuation improves as light intensity increases. This is demon-

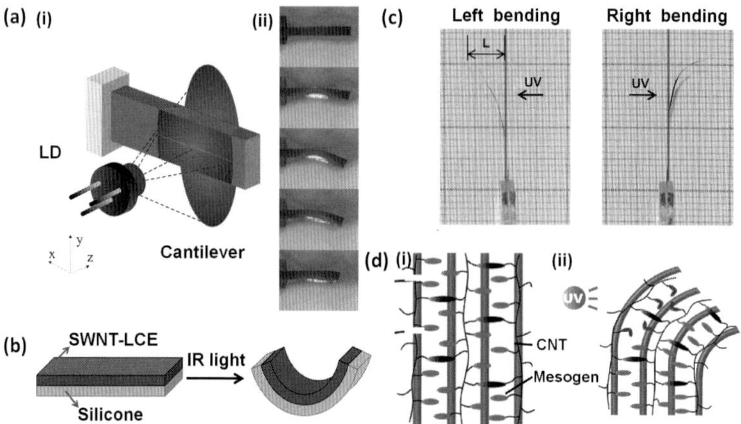

Fig. 9. Bending-unbending of CNT-LCE nanocomposites.(a) (i) Schematic bending of a cantilever; (ii) top view images of the cantilever (Y axis). The images were obtained at 0, 2, 4, 8 and 14 s after the light was switched on. The cantilever on the photos was 4 mm long and 0.5 mm thick. After irradiation, it is 3.2 mm long—contraction 1.25—and 0.6 mm thick—expansion 1.2—. Reprinted with permission.[59] Copyright (2011), AIP Publishing LLC. (b) Scheme of a SWCNT-LCE composite/silicone bilayer film undergoing bending upon IR irradiation. Reprinted with permission.[60] Copyright (2013), WILEY-VCH. (c) Photomechanical bending of ALCP/CNT away from UV light.[55] (d) (i) Illustration of an ALCP/CNT composite; (ii) Illustration of the deformation of the ALCP/CNT composite under UV light. Reprinted with permission.[55] Copyright (2012), WILEY-VCH.

strated by Marshall *et al.* as well.[56] They used a 670 nm monochromatic light to study the dependence on light intensity by dynamometry. The lengths of CNT-LCEs were fixed, the actuation stresses were measured. As shown in Fig. 10a, the actuation stress increases as the intensity rises from 30, 50, 67 to 87 mW/cm^2. As for the effect of wavelength, existing reports on CNT-LCE photo-actuation are triggered by light range from IR to visible wavelength. Marshall *et al.* also tested the effect of wavelength on this photo-actuation measured by actuation stresses as well. According to their result, generated actuation stresses were 2.0 KPa, 2.3 KPa, 1.9 KPa when the wavelengths were 670 nm, 785 nm, 980 nm respectively.[56] It seemed that those three wavelengths are of no significant impact on the actuation. However, Li *et al.* found that lower light intensity was needed if white light instead of infrared light was used.[36] CNT concentration is another parameter that has important influence on the photo-actuation. As found by Marshall *et al.*,[56] the magnitude of this rapid light-actuation of MWCNT-LCE increases along with the increasing CNT concentration

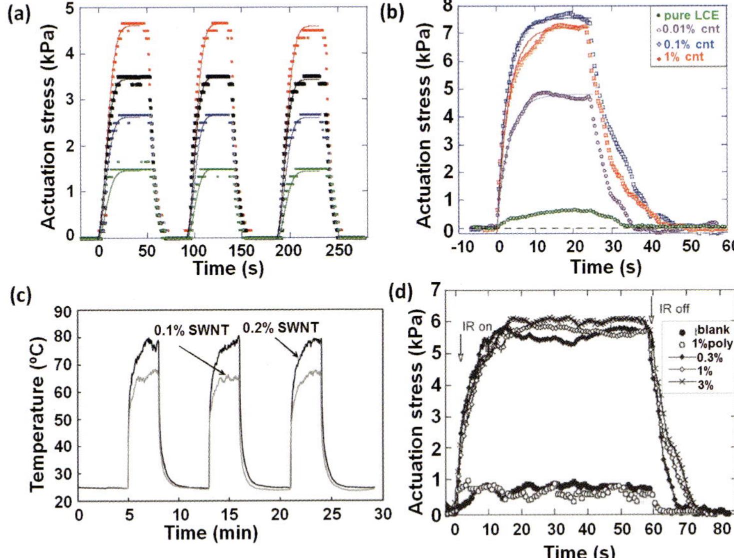

Fig. 10. (a) Comparison of the actuation response at different incident light intensity: 0.1% CNT composite at ca. 30, 50, 67 and 87 mW/cm^2 for the increasing curves. The plot also demonstrates the repeatability of actuation. Reprinted with permission.[56] Copyright (2012), The Royal Society of Chemistry. (b) Actuation of LCE samples with different concentrations of added CNTs; these indicate that the actuation strength is non-monotonic, with an optimal CNT concentration below 1%. Reprinted with permission.[56] Copyright (2012), The Royal Society of Chemistry. (c) The temperature responses to an IR stimulus in SWCNT-LCE nanocomposite films with 0.1 and 0.2 wt% PPE-SWCNT loading-levels. Reprinted with permission.[48] Copyright (2008), WILEY-VCH. (d) Infrared photo-induced actuation in constant-strain geometry, for the samples labeled on the plot. Reprinted with permission.[43] Copyright (2010), WILEY-VCH.

until it reaches a critical value of 0.1 wt% CNT (Fig. 10b). This is easy to understand, for the more CNTs, the more light energy is converted into heat quickly. As confirmed by Yang *et al.*, the highest temperature induced by 0.2% SWCNT was higher than that resulting from the absorption of light by 0.1% SWCNT (Fig. 10c).[48] However, Ji *et al.* found that CNT-LCEs with CNT contents of 0.3, 1 and 3 wt% generated almost the same actuation stresses (Fig. 10d). The authors thought that it was because CNTs absorbed IR light efficiently and converted to heat in all cases, and well-dispersed CNTs did not affect LCEs' motion for their compatibility.[43]

4.3. *Electro-mechanical actuation*

In 2003, Courty *et al.* reported, for the first time, the electro-mechanical effect of LCE-CNT nanocomposites by embedding MWCNTs into a nematic LCE.[32] The proposed mechanism is related to the alignment of CNTs. Since the film was prepared by the traditional two-step method, CNTs were aligned to some extend during the stretching step. When the CNT-LCE film was exposed to an electric field perpendicular to the aligning direction of CNTs, CNTs in the materials produced large torque to rotate to the direction parallel to the imposed electric field. As this force was transferred to the LCE network, mechanical actuation of LCE occurred (Fig. 11a). Such effect was also observed with LCEs of 0.0085 wt% CNTs. This actuation stress (σ) increased as CNT concentration increased. In contrast, such actuation was not observed in neat LCEs. The mechanical actuation also relied on the electric field. As seen in Fig. 11b, when CNT-LCEs exposed to stronger electric fields, maximum actuation stress (σ_{max}) increased.

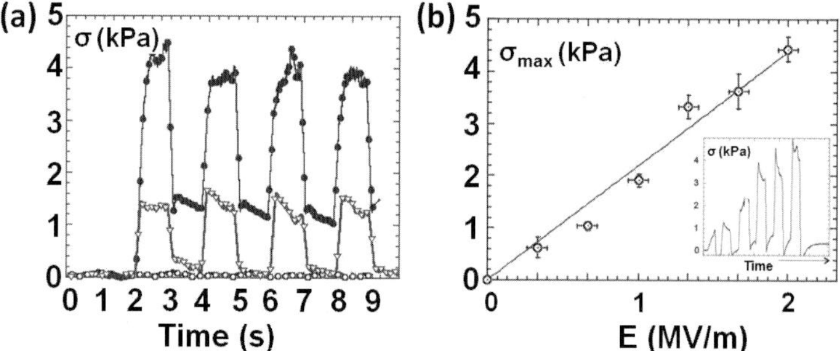

Fig. 11. (a) Generated actuation stress (σ) of CNT-LCEs with different CNT concentrations when subjected to an electric field $(E \approx 1.9 \text{ MV/m})$ in "field-on" and "field-off" cycles. As CNT concentration increased, LCE responded more evidently. (Concentration: 0 % (○), 0.0085 % (∇) and 0.02 % (●)). (b) Generated maximum actuation stress (σ_{max}) on different field strength of CNT-LCE with 0.02 wt% CNT loading. The inset showed the elapsed time dependence, with each cycle at increasing constant field E. Reprinted with permission.[32] Copyright (2003), IOPscience.

4.4. *Potential applications of CNT-LCEs*

In the past few years, some research efforts have been paid to motivate CNT-LCE nanocomposites towards real-world application. Most of the devices constructed so far are based on the photo-actuation of CNT-LCEs. Refreshable tactile devices have been explored within the framework of an FP7 European project. Using the processing method developed by Camargo *et al.* which has been mentioned above, dome-shaped blisters with monodomain regions on the walls were produced on the polydomain LCE-CNT films (Fig. 12a). The blisters exhibited localised actuation by local irradiation as illustrated in Fig. 12b.[52] When exposed to light, the blister contracted and recovered to its original height when the light was off. This up-down actuation by light is similar to the tactile display. They also implemented batch fabrication an preliminary tests on this kind of refreshable tactile devices.[61] Those micro-actuators exhibited no performance degradation after repeated up-down movement for hundreds of times (Fig. 12c), making them very promising candidates for indefatigable apparatuses.[62]

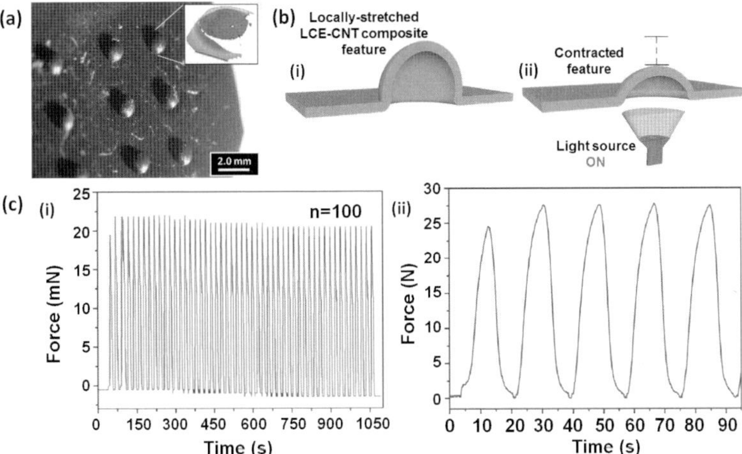

Fig. 12. (a) Optical stereoscopic picture of blister pattern on a polydomain CNT-LCE strip. Inset: 3D topographic confocal image of one feature. Colours represent the topography level of the dot (the dot height is about 400 μm).[52] (b) Actuation scheme of dome-shape. (i) Ambientstate, light source is off. (ii) Actuated state: feature contracts when the light is on. Reprinted with permission.[52] Copyright (2011), WILEY-VCH. (c) (i) Cyclic actuation of the actuator for n=100 cycles. Notice that the behavior of the pin remains almost constant during the entire test. (ii) Details of the shapes of the force peaks measured during four cycles-magnification of the graph in (i). Reprinted with permission.[62] Copyright (2014), Elsevier B. V.

CNT-LCEs stand a good chance of being used as robotic components. Employing SWCNT-LCE/silicone bilayer structure mentioned in Sec. 2,

Kohlmeyer *et al.* demonstrated such possibility.[60] A Venus flytrap-inspired gripper was made to mimic robotic arms (Fig. 13a). The gripper exhibited reversible and repeatable closing-opening in response to NIR light. With proper design, grippers could pick up and transfer objects by controlled-light. They also made an inchworm walker device out of the SWCNT-LCE/silicone bilayer films and two PC films with different shapes (Figs. 13b and 13c). The inch worm device could climb a ratcheted wood (Fig. 13d) in response to on-off NIR light cycles (Fig. 13e).

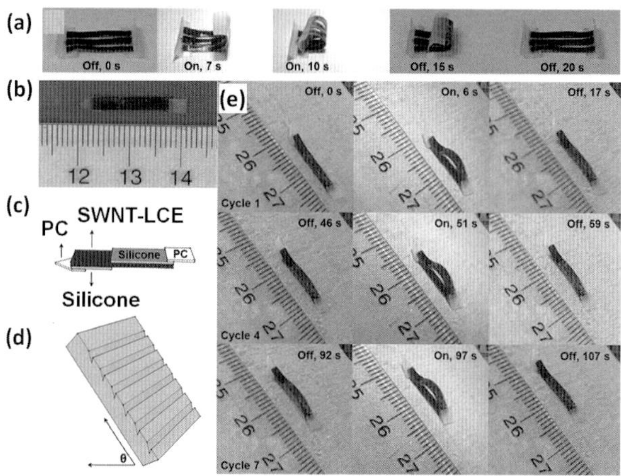

Fig. 13. (a) Reversible closing-opening of a Venus flytrap-inspired gripper in response to light. The structure has two curved PC films that are connected by three SWCNT-LCE/silicone bilayer hinges.[60] (b) Photograph and (c) scheme of an inchworm walker device. (d) Scheme of a ratcheted wood substrate. (e) The inchworm walker crawling up the wood substrate at a 50° incline in response to on and off cycles of light. The SWCNT loading is 0.1 wt% for all samples. Reprinted with permission.[60] Copyright (2013), WILEY-VCH.

As for the response of CNT-LCEs to white light, the researchers came up with the idea to fabricate artificial heliotropism out of CNT-LCEs.[63] To enhance the mechanical properties of CNT-LCEs, they were incorporated with polyurethane (PU) fiber network.[63] Because high intensity of white was necessary to trigger the actuation of CNT-LCE nanocomposite, a set of light concentrator and heat collector was designed to help the device to response to natural sunlight. As shown in Fig. 14, those CNT-LCE films contracted when exposed to sunlight while those unexposed to sunlight remained the original height. Therefore, the solar cell panel supported the

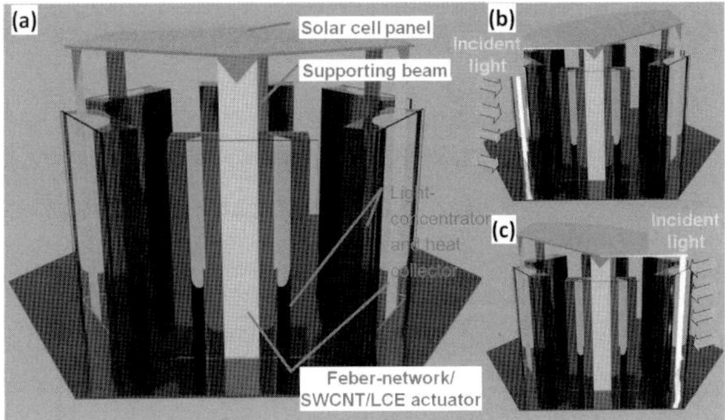

Fig. 14. Concept of the artificial heliotropism. (a) 3D schematic of the system. (b, c) 3D schematic of the heliotropic behavior. The actuator (s) facing the sun contracts, tilting the solar cell towards the sunlight. Reprinted with permission.[63] Copyright (2012), WILEY-VCH.

CNT-LCE films tilted towards sunlight, which increased the photocurrent output of the solar cells.

5. Conclusion

In the past decade, we have witnessed significant advances in CNT-LCE nanocomposites. In terms of preparation of CNT-LCE nanocomposites, the dispersion quality has been improved and relatively high loading of CNTs in LCE has been achieved. In spite of the difficulty to prepare actuators with three dimensional configurations, dome-shape blisters have been design and fabricated. The extraordinary mechanical, electrical and optical properties of CNTs have endowed LCEs new properties that are not observed in neat LCEs. The thermal-mechanical actuation of LCEs is largely maintained in the presence of CNTs. More importantly, remote control on the actuation by light and electric field has been demonstrated. Some factors that influence the actuation have been examined. The excellent photo-mechanical actuation has been exploited to make useful devices out of CNT-LCEs. Moreover, in addition to aligning mesogens, CNT array provides a novel approach to prepare nanocomposites with outstanding mechanical and electronic properties. However, this area is far from maturity. For example, the light intensity for photo-mechanical actuation is still too high to use the ordinary sunlight directly while the electromechanical actuation demands a strong electric field. Even though several prototype devices of CNT-LCE nanocomposites have been reported, there is still a long way to go for their real-world application, which needs the collaborative input from experts in multi-discipline.

References

1. M. Warner, E. M. Terentjev, *Liquid crystal elastomers*, Oxford university Press (2007).
2. P. G. De Gennes, M. Hébert, R. Kant, *Artificial muscles based on nematic gels*, Macromol. Symp., Wiley Online Library, 39–49 (1997).
3. P.-G. d. Gennes, Un muscle artificiel semi-rapide. *Comptes Rendus de l'Académie des Sciences-Series IIB-Mechanics-Physics-Chemistry-Astronomy*, **324**, 343–348 (1997).
4. J. Küpfer, H. Finkelmann, Liquid crystal elastomers: influence of the orientational distribution of the crosslinks on the phase behaviour and reorientation processes, *Macromol. Chem. Phys.*, **195**, 1353–1367 (1994).
5. M. Yamada, M. Kondo, J. I. Mamiya, Y. Yu, M. Kinoshita, C. J. Barrett, T. Ikeda, Photomobile polymer materials: towards light-driven plastic motors, *Angew. Chem. Int. Ed.*, **47**, 4986–4988 (2008).
6. M. Camacho-Lopez, H. Finkelmann, P. Palffy-Muhoray, M. Shelley, Fast liquid-crystal elastomer swims into the dark, *Nat. Mater.*, **3**, 307–310 (2004).
7. Y. Yu, M. Nakano, T. Ikeda, Photomechanics: directed bending of a polymer film by light, *Nature*, **425**, 145–145 (2003).
8. A. Buguin, M. Li, P. Silberzan, B. Ladoux, P. Keller, Micro-actuators: When artificial muscles made of nematic liquid crystal elastomers meet soft lithography. *J. Am. Chem. Soc.*, **128**, 1088–1089 (2006).
9. C. L. van Oosten, C. W. Bastiaansen, D. J. Broer, Printed artificial cilia from liquid-crystal network actuators modularly driven by light, *Nat. Mater.*, **8**, 677–682 (2009).
10. A. Garcia-Márquez, A. Demortière, B. Heinrich, D. Guillon, S. Bégin-Colin, B. Donnio, Iron oxide nanoparticle-containing main-chain liquid crystalline elastomer: towards soft magnetoactive networks, *J. Mater. Chem.*, **21**, 8994–8996 (2011).
11. W. H. de Jeu, editor, Liquid crystal elastomers: materials and applications preface, Springer (2012).
12. C. Ohm, M. Brehmer, R. Zentel, Liquid crystalline elastomers as actuators and sensors, *Adv. Mater.*, **22**, 3366–3387 (2010).
13. Y. Ji, J. E. Marshall, E. M. Terentjev, Nanoparticle-liquid crystalline elastomer composites, *Polymers*, **4**, 316–340 (2012).
14. H. Jiang, C. Li, X. Huang, Actuators based on liquid crystalline elastomer materials, *Nanoscale*, **5**, 5225–5240 (2013).
15. Z. Pei, Y. Yang, Q. Chen, E. M. Terentjev, Y. Wei, Y. Ji, Mouldable liquid-crystalline elastomer actuators with exchangeable covalent bonds, *Nat. Mater.*, **13**, 36–41 (2013).
16. R. Yin, W. Xu, M. Kondo, C. Yen, J. Mamiya, T. Ikeda, Y. Yu, Can sunlight

drive the photoinduced bending of polymer films? *J. Mater. Chem.*, **19**, 3141–3143 (2009).

17. M. Yamada, M. Kondo, R. Miyasato, Y. Naka, J. Mamiya, M. Kinoshita, A. Shishido, Y. Yu, C. J. Barrett, T. Ikeda, Photomobile polymer materials-various three—dimensional movements, *J. Mater. Chem.*, **19**, 60–62 (2008).

18. A. Sánchez-Ferrer, T. Fischl, M. Stubenrauch, H. Wurmus, M. Hoffmann, H. Finkelmann, Photo-crosslinked side-chain liquid-crystalline elastomers for microsystems, *Macromol. Chem. Phys.*, **210**, 1671–1677 (2009).

19. W. Lehmann, H. Skupin, C. Tolksdorf, E. Gebhard, R. Zentel, P. Krüger, M. Lösche, F. Kremer, Giant lateral electrostriction in ferroelectric liquid-crystalline elastomers, *Nature*, **410**, 447–450 (2001).

20. P. Heinze, H. Finkelmann, Shear deformation and ferroelectricity in chiral SmC* main-chain elastomers, *Macromolecules*, **43**, 6655–6665 (2010).

21. Y. Huang, J. Biggins, Y. Ji, E. Terentjev, Mechanical bistability in liquid crystal elastomer-wire composite actuators, *J. Appl. Phys.*, **107**, 083515 (2010).

22. A. Kaiser, M. Winkler, S. Krause, H. Finkelmann, A. M. Schmidt, Magnetoactive liquid crystal elastomer nanocomposites, *J. Mater. Chem.*, **19**, 538–543 (2009).

23. R. Montazami, C. M. Spillmann, J. Naciri, B. R. Ratna, Enhanced thermo-mechanical properties of a nematic liquid crystal elastomer doped with gold nanoparticles, *Sensor Actuat A-Phys*, **178**, 175–178 (2012).

24. P. M. Ajayan, J. M. Tour, Materials science: nanotube composites, *Nature*, **447**, 1066–1068 (2007).

25. R. Saito, G. Dresselhaus, M. S. Dresselhaus, Physical properties of carbon nanotubes, ed., Imperial College Press (1998).

26. P. Harris, Carbon nanotube composites, *Int. Mater. Rev.*, **49**, 31–43 (2004).

27. H. Peng, X. Sun, Highly aligned carbon nanotube/polymer composites with much improved electrical conductivities, *Chem. Phys. Lett.*, **471**, 103–105 (2009).

28. K. Mizuno, J. Ishii, H. Kishida, Y. Hayamizu, S. Yasuda, D. N. Futaba, M. Yumura, K. Hata, A black body absorber from vertically aligned single-walled carbon nanotubes, *P. Natl. Acad. Sci. USA*, **106**, 6044–6047 (2009).

29. P. Ajayan, M. Terrones, A. De la Guardia, V. Huc, N. Grobert, B. Wei, H. Lezec, G. Ramanath, T. Ebbesen, Nanotubes in a flash–ignition and re-construction, *Science*, **296**, 705–705 (2002).

30. D. Okawa, S. J. Pastine, A. Zettl, J. M. Fréchet, Surface tension mediated conversion of light to work, *J. Am. Chem. Soc.*, **131**, 5396–5398 (2009).

31. H. Koerner, G. Price, N. A. Pearce, M. Alexander, R. A. Vaia, Remotely actuated polymer nanocomposites—stress-recovery of carbon-nanotube-filled thermoplastic elastomers, *Nat. Mater.*, **3**, 115–120 (2004).

32. S. Courty, J. Mine, A. Tajbakhsh, E. Terentjev, Nematic elastomers with aligned carbon nanotubes: New electromechanical actuators, *Europhys. Lett.*, **64**, 654–660 (2003).

33. S. V. Ahir, E. M. Terentjev, Photomechanical actuation in polymer-nanotube composites, *Nat. Mater.*, **4**, 491–495 (2005).

34. S. Ahir, A. Squires, A. Tajbakhsh, E. Terentjev, Infrared actuation in aligned polymer-nanotube composites, *Physical Review B*, **73**, 085420 (2006).

35. H. Finkelmann, H. J. Kock, G. Rehage, Investigations on liquid crystalline polysiloxanes 3. Liquid crystalline elastomers-a new type of liquid crystalline material, *Makromol. Rapid Commun.*, **2**, 317–322 (1981).

36. C. Li, Y. Liu, C. Lo, H. Jiang, Reversible white-light actuation of carbon nanotube incorporated liquid crystalline elastomer nanocomposites, *Soft Matter*, **7**, 7511–7516 (2011).

37. L. Vaisman, H. D. Wagner, G. Marom, The role of surfactants in dispersion of carbon nanotubes, *Adv. Colloid Interface Sci.*, **128**, 37–46 (2006).

38. J. Zou, L. Liu, H. Chen, S. I. Khondaker, R. D. McCullough, Q. Huo, L. Zhai, Dispersion of pristine carbon nanotubes using conjugated block copolymers, *Adv. Mater.*, **20**, 2055–2060 (2008).

39. Y. Ji, Y. Y. Huang, A. R. Tajbakhsh, E. M. Terentjev, Polysiloxane surfactants for the dispersion of carbon nanotubes in nonpolar organic solvents, *Langmuir*, **25**, 12325–12331 (2009).

40. Z. Spitalsky, D. Tasis, K. Papagelis, C. Galiotis, Carbon nanotube-polymer composites: chemistry, processing, mechanical and electrical properties, *Prog. Polym. Sci.*, **35**, 357–401 (2010).

41. N. G. Sahoo, S. Rana, J. W. Cho, L. Li, S. H. Chan, Polymer nanocomposites based on functionalized carbon nanotubes, *Prog. Polym. Sci.*, **35**, 837–867 (2010).

42. S. Manivannan, I. O. Jeong, J. H. Ryu, C. S. Lee, K. S. Kim, J. Jang, K. C. Park, Dispersion of single-walled carbon nanotubes in aqueous and organic solvents through a polymer wrapping functionalization, *J. Mater. Sci.-Mater. EL*, **20**, 223–229 (2009).

43. Y. Ji, Y. Y. Huang, R. Rungsawang, E. M. Terentjev, Dispersion and alignment of carbon nanotubes in liquid crystalline polymers and elastomers, *Adv. Mater.*, **22**, 3436–3440 (2010).

44. S. Bandow, A. Rao, K. Williams, A. Thess, R. Smalley, P. Eklund, Purification of single-wall carbon nanotubes by microfiltration, *J. Phys. Chem. B*, **101**, 8839–8842 (1997).

45. X. Zhang, T. Sreekumar, T. Liu, S. Kumar, Properties and structure of nitric acid oxidized single wall carbon nanotube films, *J. Phys. Chem. B*, **108**, 16435–16440 (2004).

46. H. Park, J. Zhao, J. P. Lu, Effects of sidewall functionalization on conducting properties of single wall carbon nanotubes, *Nano Lett.*, **6**, 916–919 (2006).

47. J. Chen, H. Liu, W. A. Weimer, M. D. Halls, D. H. Waldeck, G. C. Walker, Noncovalent engineering of carbon nanotube surfaces by rigid, functional conjugated polymers, *J. Am. Chem. Soc.*, **124**, 9034–9035 (2002).

48. L. Yang, K. Setyowati, A. Li, S. Gong, J. Chen, Reversible infrared actuation of carbon nanotube-liquid crystalline elastomer nanocomposites, *Adv. Mater.*, **20**, 2271–2275 (2008).

49. N. B. McKeown, P. M. Budd, Polymers of intrinsic microporosity (PIMs): organic materials for membrane separations, heterogeneous catalysis and hydrogen storage, *Chem. Soc. Rev.*, **35**, 675–683 (2006).

50. Y. Yang, Z. Pei, X. Zhang, Y. Ji, Carbon nanotube-Vitrimer composite for facile and efficient photo-welding of epoxy, *Chem. Sci.*, **5**, 3486–3492 (2014).

51. Y. Yang, Z. Pei, Z. Li, Y. Wei, Y. Ji, Making and remaking dynamic 3D structures by shining light on flat liquid crystalline vitrimer films without a mold, *J. AM. Chem. Soc.* **138**, 2118–2121 (2016).

52. C. J. Camargo, H. Campanella, J. E. Marshall, N. Torras, K. Zinoviev, E. M. Terentjev, J. Esteve, Localised actuation in composites containing carbon nanotubes and liquid crystalline elastomers, *Macromol. Rapid Commun.*, **32**, 1953–1959 (2011).

53. W. Wang, X. Sun, W. Wu, H. Peng, Y. Yu, Photoinduced deformation of crosslinked liquid-crystalline polymer film oriented by a highly aligned carbon nanotube sheet, *Angew. Chem.*, **124**, 4722–4725 (2012).

54. T. Ozawa, M. Kondo, J.-I. Mamiya, T. Ikeda, Enhancement of mechanical stability in hydrogen-bonded photomobile materials with chemically modified single-walled carbon nanotubes, *J. Mater. Chem. C*, **2**, 2313–2315 (2014).

55. X. Sun, W. Wang, L. Qiu, W. Guo, Y. Yu, H. Peng, Unusual reversible photomechanical actuation in polymer/nanotube composites, *Angew. Chem. Int. Ed.*, **51**, 8520–8524 (2012).

56. J. E. Marshall, Y. Ji, N. Torras, K. Zinoviev, E. M. Terentjev, Carbon-nanotube sensitized nematic elastomer composites for IR-visible photo-actuation, *Soft Matter*, **8**, 1570–1574 (2012).

57. M. Hamon, M. Itkis, S. Niyogi, T. Alvaraez, C. Kuper, M. Menon, R. Haddon, Effect of rehybridization on the electronic structure of single-walled carbon nanotubes, *J. Am. Chem. Soc.*, **123**, 11292–11293 (2001).

58. S. Ahir, Y. Huang, E. Terentjev, Polymers with aligned carbon nanotubes: active composite materials, *Polymer*, **49**, 3841–3854 (2008).

59. N. Torras, K. Zinoviev, J. Marshall, E. Terentjev, J. Esteve, Bending kinetics of a photo-actuating nematic elastomer cantilever, *Appl. Phys. Lett.*, **99**, 254102 (2011).

60. R. R. Kohlmeyer, J. Chen, Wavelength-selective, IR light-driven hinges based on liquid crystalline elastomer composites, *Angew. Chem. Int. Ed.*, **52**, 9234–9237 (2013).

61. C. Camargo, H. Campanella, J. Marshall, N. Torras, K. Zinoviev, E. Terentjev, J. Esteve, Batch fabrication of optical actuators using nanotube-elastomer composites towards refreshable Braille displays, *J. Micromech. Microeng.*, **22**, 075009 (2012).

62. N. Torras, K. Zinoviev, C. Camargo, E. M. Campo, H. Campanella, J. Esteve, J. Marshall, E. Terentjev, M. Omastová, I. Krupa, Tactile device based on opto-mechanical actuation of liquid crystal elastomers, *Sensors and Actuators A: Physical*, **208**, 104–112 (2014).

63. C. Li, Y. Liu, X. Huang, H. Jiang, Direct sun-driven artificial heliotropism for solar energy harvesting based on a photo-thermomechanical liquid-crystal elastomer nanocomposite, *Adv. Funct. Mater.*, **22**, 5166–5174 (2012).

Chapter 19

Ferromagnetic and ferroelectric nanoparticles in liquid crystals

Yuriy Reznikov,[a,*] Anatoliy Glushchenko[b] and Yuriy Garbovskiy[b]

[a] Institute of Physics of National Academy of Sciences, Kyiv, Ukraine
[b] Univ. of Colorado Colorado Springs, Colorado Springs, Colorado, USA
**yurireznikov@hotmail.com*

This chapter introduces the basic principles of physics of magnetic and ferroelectric nanoparticles suspensions in thermotropic liquid crystals (LCs). It also covers the main features of such suspensions along with the look at the challenges that researchers in the field are facing today. Special attention is paid to understanding of major physical mechanisms responsible for the influence of nanoparticles on the properties of LCs. In the case of magnetic nanoparticles, their dipole moments are aligned by an external magnetic field that, in turn, results in a reorientation of the LC due to the surface anchoring between the nanoparticles and the LC. This mechanical coupling between the LC and the magnetic particles determines the unique sensitivity of the suspension to magnetic fields. In regard to the ferroelectric particles, their effect on LCs is due to a strong electric field by the permanent electric dipoles of the particles. This field is strong enough to change the orientational ordering of the LC surrounding the particle. In addition, the above-mentioned mechanism of the surface anchoring may also take place. The ongoing scientific and technological problems related to the suspensions are discussed. Among such problems are the stability of the suspensions, selection of the proper surfactants, formation of the particle chains, and the effect of the electric charges on the properties of the ferroelectric liquid crystal suspensions.

Contents

1. Introduction

The history of nanophysics of liquid crystals began in the summer of 1970 when F. Brochard and P. G. de Gennes published a theory of magnetic suspensions in liquid crystals (LCs),[1] and J. Rault *et al.* reported about magnetic properties of a firstly produced suspension of small magnetic particles in a nematic matrix.[2] The main idea of these pioneering studies was to use small elongated magnetic particles for controlling the director of a liquid crystal due to a mechanical coupling between the particles and the director; any turning of the particle in a magnetic field causes a reorientation of the nematic nearby due to the anchoring of the director with the particle surface (Fig. 1). The reorientation of the nematic by magnetic particles is a reverse analog of a well-known "guest - host" effect[3] in which the director of LCs, being switched by an external field, mediates the switching of dichroic dye molecules. This idea determined the direction of studies of suspensions of the magnetic nanoparticles for next few decades and promised the development of unique sensitive anisotropic magnetic materials. However, the first follow-up studies showed that the optimistic expectations were not fully met; although the magnetic sensitivity of the suspensions was indeed uniquely high (the suspensions could "feel" even the Earth's magnetic field) but the suspensions themselves were rather unstable and usually the par-

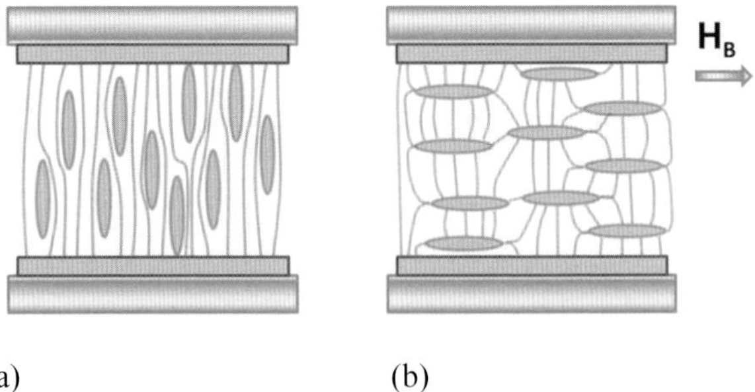

(a)   (b)

Fig. 1. The orientation of the elongated particles in a cell with homeotropic boundary conditions; (a) – planar boundary conditions on the particles' surfaces, (b) – homeotropic boundary conditions on the particles' surfaces. In the case (b) a bias field is applied to remove orientation degeneracy of the particles in the plane of the cell.

ticles coagulated within tens of minutes. This circumstance slowed down the interest to the experimental research of LC magnetic suspensions in 80s and 90s (we know only a few publications on this topic,[4-8] despite the fact that the theoretical studies remained to be very active at that time (see, e.g. Refs. 9–13)

The situation changed at the beginning of 2000s with a boom of the development of composite LC materials. It became apparent by this time that long-distance orientation at interactions in mesophase lead to a strong impact of particles on the mesogenic properties of the LC and vice versa; the LC matrix can rearrange the positional and translational ordering of the particles. Therefore, the combination of the orientational ordering and relative translational freedom in LCs with properties of the dispersed particles allows scientists to impose unique properties to the composite, which are not inherent to its components. The development of suspensions of the particles of different nature (ferroelectric, dielectric, metallic) initiated active studies of the stability of the suspensions and the search of new effective surfactants. It promised the solution of the stability of the magnetic LC suspensions and returned interest to their studies. Recent few years brought several principal results. Particularly, after 43 years since the tentative observations of Rault *et al.*,[2] Mertelj *et al.* univocally reported the existence of ferromagnetic ordering in the suspension of magnetic platelets in nematic LC,[14] and a big progress in the development of stable paramagnetic suspensions was achieved.[15]

One of the important consequences of the Brochard & De Gennes theory is a transfer of the magnetic ordering onto the underlying liquid crystal due to the coupling between the magnetic particles and the LC director, i.e. magnetic particles share their properties with LCs. This idea inspired Reznikov *et al.* to dope a nematic LC with ferroelectric nanoparticles to impart ferroelectric properties to the LC. The first try[16] showed that the particles partially share their ferroelectric properties with the LC; the nematic loses its centre-symmetry and becomes sensitive to the sign of the applied electric field, although the polarization disappears with the switching the electric field off. Such a behavior is similar to the paramagnetic behavior of the magnetic LC suspension and allows for expecting a possibility of ferroelectric ordering in the suspension analogically with the ferromagnetic ordering, observed in Mertelj *et al.*[14] The follow up studies showed that doping nematics with ferroelectric particles strongly changes the LC's basic properties, increasing their birefringence and dielectric anisotropy due to a change of the LC ordering near the particles. It is recognized that the main cause of these changes is a strong electric field around the ferroelectric particles. These results promised innovative simple and effective means to control precisely the physical properties of liquid crystalline materials and initiated a keen interest in ferroelectric LC suspensions last decade.

In this chapter we present primary properties of the suspensions of magnetic and ferroelectric nanoparticles in LCs. We consider basic mechanisms of the particles' coupling with liquid crystal molecules and provide our present view on the picture of physical phenomena occurring in these systems.

2. Magnetic liquid crystal suspensions

2.1. *Basic concept of ferronematics*

Conventional thermotropic LCs are usually diamagnetic materials with a small anisotropy of magnetic susceptibility ($\sim 10^{-7}$). Therefore, rather high magnetic fields ($H \geq 1$ kOe) are required to reorient the director and, in opposite to electro-optical effects, the magneto-optics effects have not found any significant application in the liquid crystal industry, so far. Consequently, a great interest in suspensions of magnetic particles in nematics (frequently called *ferronematics*) is caused mostly by the astonishing physics of these materials and not by their potential applications in extra-sensitive magneto-optical devices. If a stable, optically transparent, and homogeneous ferronematics are created, it would give a strong push for the development of many kinds of new magnetically controlled LC-devices.

As it was said in the introduction, the operation of ferronematics is based on the effect of a mechanical coupling between the elongated magnetic particles and the director. The magnetic particles of different nature (ferromagnetics, ferrimagnetics, paramagnetics and superparamagnetics) are used as dopants for a nematic matrix. At no magnetic field applied, the rod-like magnetic particles are oriented in LCs in such a way as to minimize the director distortion caused by the particles. The concentration of the particles in a nematic is usually small and, therefore, the magnetic dipole-dipole interaction between them is negligible.[1] In this case, planar boundary conditions for the director on particles surfaces encourage the orientation of the particles' long axes parallel to **n**; homeotropic boundary conditions impose the orientation of the particles perpendicular to **n** (Fig. 1).

The detailed theoretical description of the reorientation of ferronematics in a magnetic field was provided by Raikher and Burilov[10,11] and Zadorozhnii *et al.*[17–19] taking into account a finite anchoring of a nematic with the particles' surfaces. The free energy of the suspension in a one-elastic constant approximation reads:

$$F = \int_V \left[\frac{1}{2} K (\nabla \mathbf{n})^2 + \frac{f_v k_B T}{v_p} \ln f_v - M f_v (\mathbf{m} \cdot H) + \frac{f_v W_p}{d_p} (\mathbf{n} \cdot \mathbf{m})^2 \right] dV \tag{1}$$

Here K is the Frank elastic constant, f_v is the volume fraction of the particles, v_p is the volume of a particle, $\mathbf{m}$ is the unit vector in a direction of the sample magnetization, M is the saturation magnetization per unit volume within a particle, W_p is the anchoring energy of LC with the surface of a particle, and d_p is the diameter of a particle.

The first term in (1) describes Frank elastic energy of the nematic. The second term is the mixing entropy of the particles in the LC matrix. The entropic term favors homogeneous distribution of the particles. In the case of segregation this term increases and this is compensated by the decrease of the elastic energy. The third term describes the direct coupling of the magnetic field, $\mathbf{H}$, with the magnetic moments, $\mathbf{m}$, of the particles. The last term is responsible for the mechanical coupling between the magnetic moment of a particle and the director of LCs due to the anchoring of the director with the particle surface. Since $f_v \ll 1$, the particles dipole-dipole interaction in (1) is ignored. The direct magnetic-nematic diamagnetic interaction is also neglected with respect to much more strong mechanical coupling term. It is supposed that there is a preferable polar alignment of the magnetic moments of the particles in one direction (in the experiment it can be achieved by the application of a weak bias magnetic field or the magnetic field can impose the magnetic ordering when it switches on).

The minimization of the functional (1) at a given geometry and boundary conditions of the director at the cell substrates and the particles surfaces gives the director distribution in the sample and its behavior in a magnetic field. A crucial parameter that describes this behavior is the dimensionless coupling parameter:

$$w = \frac{\pi f_v d_p l_p L^2}{4 v_p K} W_p \tag{2}$$

where l_p is the length of the particle, L is the cell thickness, which substrates impose strong boundary conditions.

At $w \gg 1$ the coupling is strong and the director follows the particles in a magnetic field (Fig. 2b). Since the particles are oriented by a magnetic field

                    Y. Reznikov, A. Glushchenko and Y. Garbovskiy

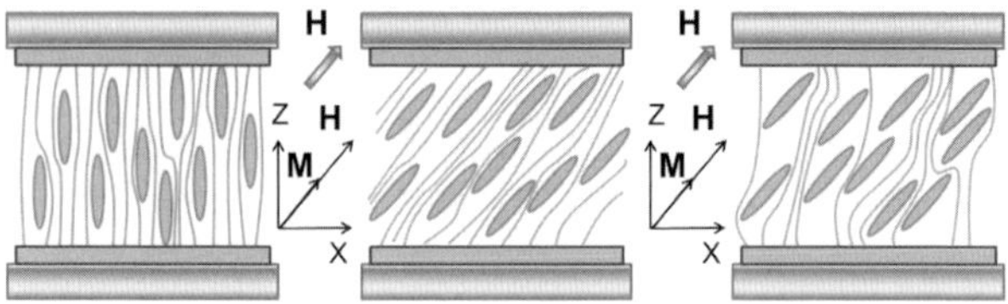

Fig. 2.   Reorientation of the initial suspension (a) in a magnetic field in a case of a strong (b) and weak (c) coupling between the particles and the director.

without a threshold, *the reorientation of the director in the suspension is also thresholdless even when* **H** *is perpendicular to* **n**. At a weak magnetic field the reorientation is proportional to **H** and the reorientation of the suspension is saturated at a high field.

In the case of a weak coupling (w<<1), a mismatch between the particles orientation and the director occurs (Fig. 2c). At w small enough the reorientation of the director becomes not-monotonic; after reaching a maximum the reorientation angle decreases and the director finally returns to the initial not-disturbed state. This effect is caused by a competition between the restoring elastic force that acts on the director and gains with the increase of the reorientation angle and the aligning force due to the mechanical coupling of a nematic with a particle. At some reorientation angle the aligning force from the particles cannot overcome the elasticity of the director that causes a return of the director back to the initial position (this effect is described by the authors of Refs. 17–19 in terms of an inverse Frederiks effect).

Magnetic particles also should change hydrodynamic properties of nematics. It is predicted that flow alignment, heat conduction, diffusion, thermodiffusion and viscosity are all modified by the presence of magnetic particles in a magnetic field.[20,21]

The basic experiments on the magnetically-induced reorientation of a magnetic suspension were carried out by Chen and Amer in 1983.[5] Since that time other numerous experimental papers were published, but the main features of the suspension behavior were established in that work, and the paper[5] provided a basis for a comparison of experiments with the theoretical model.[17–19]

Chen and Amer used ferromagnetic rods γ-Fe$_2$O$_3$ of $l_p \approx 500$ nm long with the aspect ratio $k_p = 7$ and magnetization $M = 340$ G. The volume fraction of the particle in a LC MBBA, $f_v = 10^{-6} - 10^{-7}$. The surfaces of the particles were coated with a surfactant DMOAP to prevent an aggregation. The cells both with homeotropic and planar boundary conditions were used. The thickness of the cells varied in the range of several hundred micrometers. For the homeotropic boundary conditions on the cell substrates the geometry of the experiment is depicted in Fig. 3. The cells were put between the crossed polarizers and a vertical magnetic field, $\mathbf{H}$, was applied parallel to the director. The long axes of the particles and their magnetic moments, $\mathbf{m}$, were perpendicular to the director, and a weak (< 1 G) bias horizontal magnetic field, $\mathbf{H}_b$, was applied in the plane of the cell to induce an initial polar ordering of the magnetic moments of the particles.

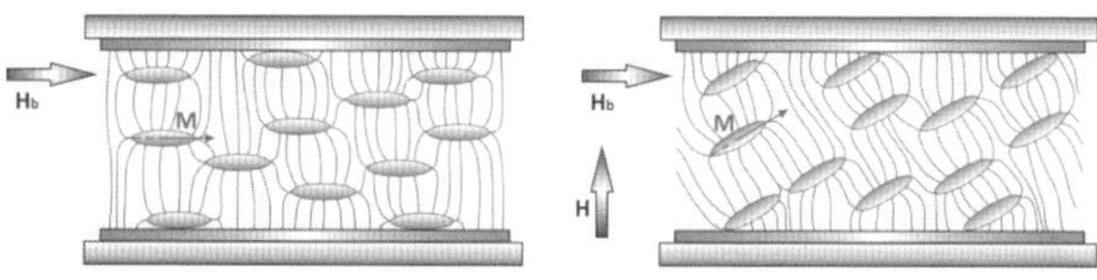

Fig. 3.   The geometry of the experiment of Chen and Amer.[5]

Upon application of the vertical field $\mathbf{H}$, a strong birefringence was observed in the cell. This birefringence could not be caused by the reorientation of the particles themselves as their own birefringence was negligibly small. Therefore, the reason for the induced birefringence was the reorientation of the nematic that followed the reorientation of the particles. The observed birefringence increased with the increase of $\mathbf{H}$ at the given cell thickness. The typical dependencies of the birefringence of the cell on the magnetic field are presented in Fig. 4. The lower curve in Fig. 4 corresponds to the low concentrated suspension ($f_v = 3.72 \cdot 10^{-7}$), at which the aggregation could be considered negligible within the experiment duration. The upper curve was measured for more concentrated suspension ($f_v = 7.44 \cdot 10^{-7}$), when the aggregation in the magnetic field is essential.

In Fig. 4 a fit of the experimental data by Chen and Amer to the theory of Zadorozhnii *et al.*[19] is presented with continuous curves. The best fit was obtained at the material parameters of the particles close to what was used[5] ($l_p = 470$ nm, $k_p = 7.7$, $f_v = 3.72 \cdot 10^{-7}$; $7.44 \cdot 10^{-7}$, $M = 340$ G) and the reasonable value of the anchoring energy $W_p = 4.9 \cdot 10^{-5}$ J/m^2. These parameters correspond to the weak coupling regime ($w \approx 0.2$) of the suspension reorientation. One can see a good match between the experimental data and the fitting for $f_v = 3.72 \cdot 10^{-7}$. A clear decrease of the

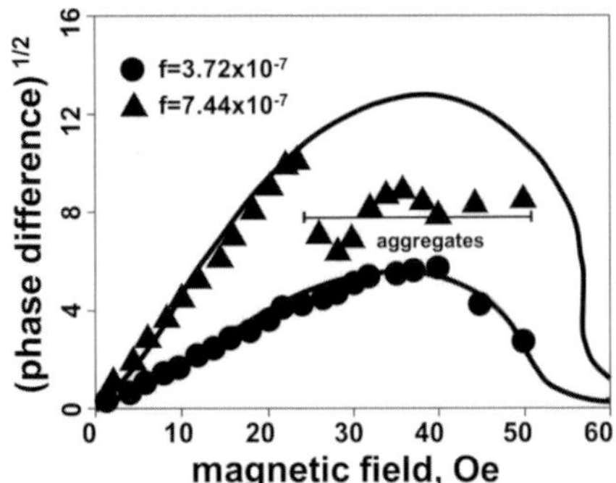

Fig. 4. The dependence of the magnetically-induced phase difference *vs* the magnetic field at different fractions, *f*, of the particles[5] and the theoretical curves.[19]

birefringence (e.g. of the reorientation angle) for $H > 40$ Oe is in agreement with the prediction of the behavior of the suspension at a weak coupling. There is an evident discrepancy between the experiment and the theory at the high field in the suspension with larger concentration, $f_v = 7.44 \cdot 10^{-7}$. Evidently, this is related to the formation of aggregates and clumping of the suspension, which is promoted by the field.

2.2. *Main directions of experimental studies of ferronematics*

2.2.1. *Basic materials*

In the most cases the ferromagnetic particles of iron(III) oxide (γ-Fe$_2$O$_3$, maghemite) and iron(III+II) oxide (Fe$_3$O$_4$, magnetite) are used as magnetic dopants for LCs. γ-Fe$_2$O$_3$ is a ferromagnetic material ($M_s = 350$ G), although it transforms to a supermagnetic phase when the size of the particles is less than 10-20 nm. Fe$_3$O$_4$ is a compound of Fe$_2$O$_3$ and FeO; this material is ferromagnetic ($M_s = 350$ G) and also transforms to a supermagnetic phase at $d_p \leq 10 - 20$ nm. Spherical nanoparticles of these materials are now available on a market in different sizes and their synthesis is described in literature in details (see, e.g. Refs. 22, 23). They are also available in elongated shape and in rods. Usually the aspect ratio of the rods $k = 5 - 7$ and the length of the rods varies from tens to hundreds nanometers and the easy magnetization axis is along the long axis of the nanoparticle.

Besides γ-Fe_2O_3 and Fe_3O_4 nanoparticles, more exotic magnetic materials are used. Martinez-Miranda *et al.* explored spherical particles $Fe_{52}Co_{48}$ (2 and 11 nm),[24] Lapointe *et al.* doped LCs with a long ($l = 5 - 35$ μm) Ni wires,[25] Podoliak *et al.* used weakly magnetic rods (250-600 nm) of γ-Fe_2O_3,[22] Buluy *et al.* applied multi-wall carbon nanotubes ($l = 3 - 10$ μm) filled with γ-Fe_2O_3.[26] Kopčanský *et al.* studied LCs doped with single-wall carbon nanotubes functionalized with magnetite particles.[27] This team also used chain-like magnetic particles obtained from magnetotactic bacteria; the chains of the mean length of 446 nm consisted of several spherical magnetic particles with a mean diameter of 34 nm. Recently, Mertelj *et al.*, suggested using 2-D magnetic nanoparticles, namely scandium-doped barium hexaferrite single-crystal nanoplatelets.[14] The thickness of the platelets is around 70 nm and the preferred direction of the magnetization is oriented perpendicular to the plane of the platelets.

The necessity of a high magnetic sensitivity of the suspensions requires a strong mechanical coupling ($w \gg 1$), which is in a conflict with a need of optically homogeneous samples. Indeed, the values W_p are in the range of $10^{-4} - 10^{-6}$ Jm^{-2}, $K \approx 10^{-11}$ N and $L = 10 - 50$ μm. The typical concentration of the particles at which an aggregation is still not severe, $c_p \leq 10^{10} - 10^{11}$ cm^{-3}, and usually the aspect ratio of the particle $k_p \leq 10$. For these characteristic values the condition $w \gg 1$ corresponds to the length of the particles, $l_p \gg 100$ nm. This value is much larger than a wavelength of light and it causes an unnecessary light scattering. Besides, the aspect ratio of the elongated magnetic particles, $k_p = l_p/d_p$ rarely exceeds $k_p = 5$, i.e. the anchoring parameter corresponding to the short axis of the particles $\xi_d = W_p d_p/K < 1$ at $d_p < 50$ nm. It means that the director of a liquid crystal is distorted at the ends of long particles causing additional light scattering.

Thus, to realize the potential of the application of the ferronematics, one shall find a subtle balance between the coupling efficiency, which requires long particles, and the optical quality, which requires particles short enough in order not to disturb the director of a nematic and do not scatter light much. We also should remember that in sufficiently large colloidal particles, the ferromagnetics and ferrimagnetics form a polydomain structure that usually transforms into a single domain structure when the particles become smaller than 100 - 300 nm; the application of this size is preferable. The further decrease of the size of the particles may result in a transition to a single domain superparamagnetic phase. This usually occurs when the size gets smaller than 20 nm. It means that it is difficult to expect ferromagnetic behavior of such particles, although paramagnetic and super-paramagnetic nanoparticles retain their magnetic properties even when their sizes approach scales of several nanometers. So, the optimal length of the ferromagnetic and ferrimagnetic particles is from several tens of nanometers untill several hundred nanometers. Regarding paramagnetic and super-paramagnetic particles, small particles can be used (< 20 nm) because of their tendency to form chain-like aggregates, which can play a role of a long magnetic particle (Fig. 5).

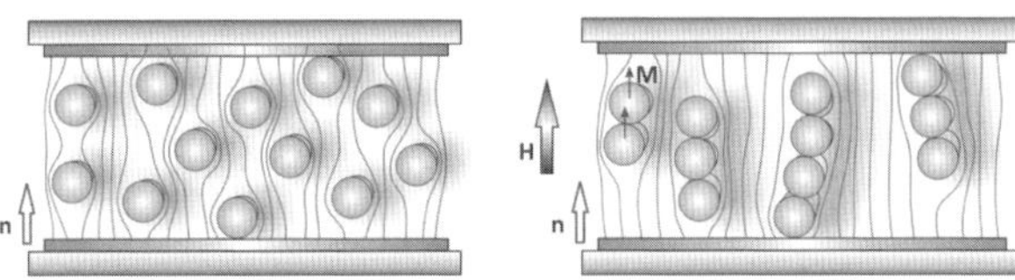

Fig. 5.   Formation of the chains of superparamagnetic nanoparticles in a magnetic field.

The technique of producing ferronematics is described elsewhere (see, e.g. Refs. 22, 23) Despite that the recipes of the magnetic nematic suspensions preparation differ in details, basically the surfactant-covered nanoparticles are dispersed in a solvent (e.g. choloroform or heptane), sonicated and then the dispersion is added to a pure liquid crystal and is left at elevated temperature so that the solvent evaporates. In some cases, the nanoparticles are dispersed in LCs directly, without preliminary dispersion in a solvent.

2.2.2. *Stability problem*

As it was noted above, the problem of the stability of the magnetic suspension is very severe. For diluted magnetic LC colloids of the particles less than 10 nm the direct magnetic interaction is not crucial and the strong aggregation of the small nanoparticles is directly related to the orientational ordering in a mesophase.[28] The interaction of a nanoparticle with an LC matrix changes the arrangement of LC molecules around the particle disturbing the order parameter. It increases the free energy of the system, and aggregation of the particles is a mechanism of the compensation of these energy expenses. For large nanoparticles (usually for the particles with $R_{\mathrm{part}} \geq 100$ nm) the distortion of the director around them becomes essential[29] and a nematic elasticity mediated attractive interaction plays a dominant role in the aggregates formation.

In order to suppress aggregation, nanoparticles are usually coated with various surfactants. The main role of a surfactant is to increase the excluded volume of the particle. In other words, the surfactant increases the steric repulsion radius of the particles, and prevents the particles from approaching each other to the distance of direct attractive interactions. At the same time, the presence of surfactants that usually have elongated molecular architectures, which penetrate into LC matrix, can seriously alter the mesogenic characteristics of the matrix, thereby affecting the ordering, elastic properties, and the phase transitions. Therefore, a good surfactant should not only suppress aggregation however, it should minimally affect the properties of LC matrices. From this point of view, standard, mostly used surfactants do not solve these problems well. Up to now the most popular surfactant is oleic acid, whose molecules are chemosorbed to magnetic nanoparticles.[30] Despite of its popularity, it does not prevent fully the aggregation of magnetic particles, even at a very small concentration of the colloid. In our experience, covering of small (5-7 nm) and weakly concentrated ($f_v = 10^{-5}$) particles of Fe_3O_4 or Fe_2O_3 with oleic acid do not prevent their aggregation and the suspensions notably sediment within tens of hours and larger particles sediment even faster. In addition, oleic acid is not only chemisorbed to nanoparticles but physically adsorbed to their surfaces and a notable fraction of the surfactant remains in the LC bulk. It decreases the order parameter and the phase transition temperature T_c of LCs and can modify other LC properties (elastic constants, pretilt, anchoring energy, etc).

Therefore, the development of effective surfactants for the LC magnetic suspension is a crucial task of the physics of nematic magnetic nano-colloids. Unfortunately, except as in the paper,[15] there are no detailed studies of the stability of the magnetic suspensions, in spite of the fact that the aggregation of the particles was observed in most of the papers devoted to magnetic LC suspensions. In our experience, if the low concentrated ($f_v \leq 10^{-5}$) suspensions of ultra small magnetic nanoparticles (2-5 nm) can be prepared without visible aggregation, the larger particles always aggregates and the aggregation and sedimentation become severe at the size of the particles larger than 20-30 nm. Evidently, instability of the suspensions affects the magneto-optical response of the suspensions and makes the comparison of the experimental results with the theory difficult and sometimes problematic.

The promising surfactant material for stabilization of magnetic nematic suspension is 4-n-octyloxybiphenyl-4-carboxylic acid (OBPh).[31] As compared to the conventional oleic acid coating, this coating well stabilizes LC-magnetic nanorods in nematic liquid crystal E7.

Recently, Vashchenko *et al.* suggested a concept that may pave a way for the development of true stable LC colloids.[32] This concept is based on an idea of the minimization of the distortion of the LC ordering around the particles using specially designed surfactants. Minimization of the LC distortion is achieved by a special architecture of the surfactant coating of the nanoparticles that provides: (a) effective penetration of the LC molecules into the surfactant layer and (b) effective interaction between LC molecules and the surfactant molecules, which results in the adjustment of ligand ordering with the LC molecules. In order to build such a structure, the authors[32] suggested a two-component surfactant. The first, main component consists of relatively long molecules, structurally compatible with LC host. It provides a big excluded volume around the particles. The second, accessory component consists of much shorter molecules, distributed within the main surfactant component. Such "tree-meadow" arrangement allows the LC molecules to penetrate between the main surfactant molecules and form an interface region, which softens the ordering distortion around the particle. An example of such a surfactant coating is presented in Fig. 6. The concentration ratio between the main and accessory surfactant molecules is 4:1 in this coating. The two-component surfactant was applied to make a suspension of the ferromagnetic 10 nm spherical particles $CoFe_2O_4$ in a nematic LC E7 (Merck).[33] The resulted suspension reported to be stable; there was no notable sedimentation of the 5 wt.-% suspension in a vessel during 2 years, although single aggregates of a few micrometers were observed in thin (20 μm) LC cells at $f_v \geq 5 \cdot 10^{-6}$.

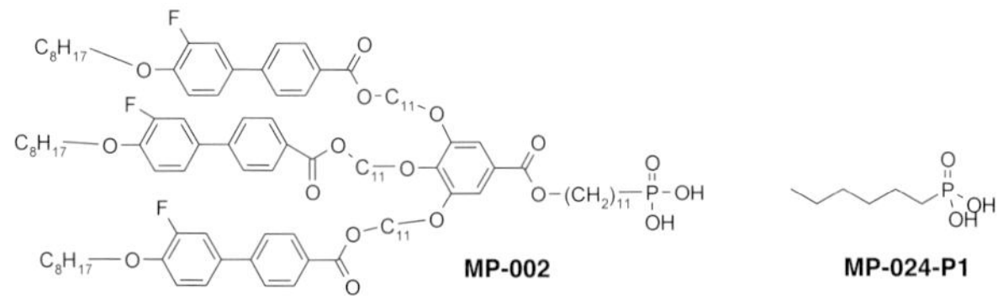

Fig. 6.   The two component surfactant for the stabilization of magnetic nanoparticles according to Ref. 32.

Ending the section, one can say that at the present time the problem of the development of true suspensions of magnetic nanoparticles has not been solved fully, although the last achievements in this field allows to look into the future with a cautious optimism.

2.2.3. *Magneto-optical effects in ferronematics*

Despite the fact that the main features of the director response of magnetic LC suspensions were established more than 30 years ago,[5] the diversity of physical processes in magnetic suspensions, complexity of the system and potential applications encourage scientists to continue studies of these materials. Below we consider the recent experimental works that we think reflect the modern trend of the research of ferronematics.

One of unexpected results, reported by Kopcansky *et al.*[27] and Podolyak *et al.*[22] is an evident effect of spherical magnetic particles on the magneto-optical response of a nematic. Rotation of a spherically symmetric particle in a nematic does not change the free energy of the suspension. Consequently, this rotation should not disturb the director. At the same time, the change of the Frederiks transition field was observed.[6,17,22,27] Surprisingly, a cause of this effect has not been studied and discussed in literature. V. Reshetnyak suggested that angular-depended adsorption of LC molecules may result in a formation of an anisotropic aligning layer on the particles surface.[34] It breaks a spherical symmetry of the interaction of the nematic with the particles and results in the angular mechanical coupling between the particles and the director. Another explanation can be a formation of the chains-like aggregates of the particles, which plays a role of quasi-rods in a nematic (Fig. 5). In the case of ferromagnetic particles these chains are formed due to a head-to-tail arrangement of the permanent magnetic dipoles and in the case of paramagnetic and superparamagnetic particles the chains are formed in a magnetic field (see, e.g. Ref. 35). Particularly, our studies showed that a mean length of the chains of 10 nm superparamagnetic particles Fe_3O_4 in water is 60 nm, and these particles can be considered as magnetic rods being doped into the LC suspension of V_2O_5 ribbons in water.[36]

As it was mentioned above, the achievement of Chen and Amer[5] was a unique magnetic sensitivity of the dispersion. It was achieved owing to the use of rather long (500 nm) particles, which provided although not a strong but rather effective mechanical coupling ($w \approx 0.22$). The cost of the strong magneto-optical response of the suspension was its clumping and the formation of large ($\sim$50 μm) aggregates. To reduce the aggregation, much shorter particles were used in the later publications. Podoliak *et al.*[22] found that suspension of 15–20 nm magnetic spherical Fe_yO_x particles with $f_v = 2 \cdot 10^{-4}; 10^{-4}$ and $2 \cdot 10^{-5}$ are stable, although some aggregation were noted after 6 months in the suspensions with $f_v = 2 \cdot 10^{-4}$ and 10^{-4}. These suspensions showed an evident increase of the magneto-optics response. The fitting of the experimental data by the theory,[22] taking into account diamagnetic response of LCs, showed that the suspensions can be described by the coupling parameters of the same order as it was obtained by Chen and Amer; $w \approx 0.07$; 0.3 and 0.4. It means that the suspension of spherical nanoparticles behaves as a suspension of elongated particles. We believe that the chain formation is a cause of this effect.

The strong influence of the spherical nanoparticles on the magneto-optical response was also observed,[24,37] where the magnetically-induced reorientation in the presence of an electric field was studied. The authors of these publications found that depending on the geometry of the experiments, the particles can both decrease and increase the governing magnetic field. The latter case the authors of these publications explained by the initial perpendicular orientation of the magnetic moment of the particle relatively to the LC director.

Despite that a lot of efforts were spent to fight the aggregation of the magnetic nanoparticles and to produce stable suspensions, Buluy *et al.*[26] showed that even aggregated suspension can be interesting from application and fundamental points of view. The authors of this publication studied the suspension of multi-wall carbon nanotubes filled with Fe_2O_3 in a nematic LC. They found that magnetic dipole interactions and van der Waals interactions between ferromagnetic nanotubes lead to their strong aggregation. Being in a nematic, the aggregates are elongated in shape, have several micrometers in length and preferably oriented along the director. The LC dispersion of these aggregates shows an effective response to extremely weak (<5 mT) magnetic field due to an individual reorientation of the aggregates in a magnetic field that leads to the reorientation of the director in the surrounding regions. So, in opposite to the collective character of the suspension's response, the local response is realized in the aggregated system.

The direct dipole interaction between magnetic nanoparticles in a nematic is much smaller than the thermal energy $k_B T$ and the directions **n** and -**n** are equivalent. Therefore, magnetic dipoles of particles have no polar ordering in a nematic matrix. As a result, magnetic LC suspensions should have no macroscopic permanent magnetization and they show a paramagnetic behavior. Such a behavior was proved in many experimental works, in which no hysteresis was obtained. At the same time, a ferromagnetic phase was predicted[1,38] and in the first experimental work on nematic magnetic suspensions, an evident hysteresis, diminishing in the isotropic phase, was observed.[2] It led to the fact that these suspensions started to be called *ferronematic*. The origin of the observed hysteresis was not discussed in details. One of the possible causes of the observed hysteresis may be a presence of incontrollable bias field in the experiment.

A true ferronematic with an evident ferromagnetic behavior was prepared just recently by Mertelj *et al.* in the suspension of magnetic nanoplateletes in a nematic LC.[14] When the system was quenched from the isotropic phase to the nematic state in the absence of the external field, magnetically polydomain sample was obtained, while quenching in the magnetic field produced monodomain sample. In both cases the system had polar ferromagnetic ordering induced by the combination of magnetic and nematic mediated interactions.

The magnetization of the sample is switched by the domain wall movement during the change of the magnetic field direction. The key point of these studies is a mechanism of the retaining of the magnetic ordering in a nematic phase. According to the authors,[14] the orientation of quadrupolar defects around the platelets produce some kind of network in the LC matrix that prevents aggregation of the particles, seriously impede the disordering by thermal fluctuations and encourage a ferromagnetic ordering.

Producing of the true ferromagnetic nematic suspension allowed Mertelj *et al.* observed new effects, which are not present in a pure nematic and are a consequence of the coupling between the nematic director and the magnetization of the sample.[39] The electro-optic effect, which is in the ferromagnetic phase the same as in the pure nematic, is accompanied by a converse magnetoelectric effect. Contrary to the pure nematic, no critical field needs to be exceeded for the system to respond to a perpendicular field, but a critical field needs to be exceeded to observe a response to the field parallel to the director and antiparallel to the magnetization.

2.3. *Conclusions*

At the present stage of the research one can state that we understand the basic physics of the ferronematics and the comprehensive theory of the re-orientation of the ferronematics in magnetic field has been developed. An anchoring of the nematic at the nanoparticle's surface results in a mechanical coupling between the director of the LC and the nanoparticle. This coupling is regarded as the basic effect that governs the behavior of the suspensions of magnetic nanoparticles in nematics. Regarding experimental studies, despite that the main features of the ferronematics are clear and the basic effects are found and well described (magnetically-induced reorientation in different geometries; paramagnetic and ferromagnetic behavior), there is a broad field where many discoveries are to be made. It is mainly related to the development of really stable suspensions, detailed characterization of the magnetic and anchoring properties of the nanoparticles and a role of the chain formation in the reorientation process. New extra-sensitive magneto-optic LC devices will create a strong competition to the existing optical isolators, non-reciprocal optical waveguides,[40] magnetophotonic crystals,[41] etc. when the described above problems are solved.

3. Ferroelectric liquid crystal suspensions

3.1. *Basic concept*

The idea of the use of magnetic nanoparticles in LCs is to reorient them with a magnetic field and, due to their anchoring with the director, reorient a surrounding liquid crystal. A magnetic field generated by the magnetic dipoles of the particles, is much less than the intermolecular interaction field in a mesophase and therefore it does not affect the properties of the LC matrix notably. However, in the case when ferroelectric nanoparticles are used, the field generated by the electric dipoles of ferroelectric particles can be comparable or even stronger than the field due to the intermolecular interaction. For a rough estimation, consider a ferroelectric particle as a dielectric sphere with a permanent polarisation, P_{part}. In this case the field around the particle reads:[42]

$$\mathbf{E}_{\mathrm{part}} = \frac{R_{\mathrm{part}}^3}{3\epsilon_0}\left(3\frac{(\mathbf{P}_{\mathrm{part}}\cdot\mathbf{r})\mathbf{r}}{r^5} - \frac{\mathbf{P}_{\mathrm{part}}}{r^3}\right) \tag{3}$$

The value of this field is very strong; for the particles of $BaTiO_3$ with $d_{\mathrm{part}} = 10$ nm the field is 10^9 Vm^{-1} in the vicinity of the particles. The estimation of the ratio of the electrostatic interaction associated with this field to the thermal energy, $U_{\mathrm{part}}/k_B T$, gives the number[43] of the order of 10^4 and the orientational intermolecular interaction in the mesophase is close to $k_B T$.[44] Therefore, even if the anisotropic part of the electrostatic interaction is small, the particle directly effects the orientation of LC molecules near the particle surface providing the field coupling between the director and the dipole moments of the particles, and the change of the local order parameter.

The direct effect of the field from the particle on the orientation of the LC molecules ("particle – LC molecule interaction, U_{E-LC}") allows expecting an effective coupling between the dipole moments of the particles, $\mathbf{G}_{\mathrm{part}}$, and the local director. In other words, most of the dipole moments of the particles are aligned parallel or antiparallel to the local director, $\mathbf{n}$, of a matrix and effective anchoring energy $\bar{W}_{eff}$ that describes the coupling between $\mathbf{G}_{\mathrm{part}}$ and $\mathbf{n}$, is strong even for the spherical particles. If the particles are elongated and $\mathbf{G}_{\mathrm{part}}$ is parallel to their long axis, the orientational coupling between the particles and the LC is further strengthened for the planar boundary conditions. As a result, by analogy with magnetic particles, the reorientation of ferroelectric nanoparticles by external electric field leads to the reorientation of the LC, and a strong impact of the ferroelectric particles on electrically-controlled orientational effects is expected. It should be noted that in opposite to the case of magnetic nanoparticles, the origin of the orientational coupling is not a steric interaction but an electrostatic interaction between the particle and LC molecules.

The particles impact on the reorientation Frederiks transition in a nematic LC was considered.[43] Shelestyuk *et al.* studied how permanent polarisation of the particles, $\mathbf{P}_{\mathrm{part}}$, affects the effective permittivity of the LC, ϵ_{eff}, and the free energy of the LC, F. Assuming strong particle-LC coupling, small particles (~ 10 nm), and E of the order or less than the field of Frederiks transition, the expression for Frederiks transition voltage is similar to the expression for a pure nematic and is given by:

$$V_{\mathrm{Fr}} = \pi \sqrt{\frac{K_1}{\epsilon_0 \Delta \epsilon_{\mathrm{eff}}}} \qquad (4)$$

where K_1 is the Frank constant, $\Delta \epsilon_{\mathrm{eff}}$ is the anisotropy of the effective dielectric constant of the suspension. The bulky expressions for $\Delta \epsilon_{\mathrm{eff}}$[43] depend on the polarization, P_{part} and permittivities of the LC and the particles. Due to the permanent polarization, P_{part} effective permittivity of the suspension along the director, $\epsilon_{\|,\mathrm{eff}}$, is larger than the permittivity of the pure matrix, $\epsilon_{\|,\mathrm{LC}}$. Numerical estimation shows that for the weight volume fraction of the particles of a few percents, the value $\epsilon_{\|,\mathrm{eff}}$ can be almost twice as large as $\epsilon_{\|,\mathrm{LC}}$. It results in a corresponding decrease of the Frederiks transition voltage (Fig. 7).

In Shelestiuk *et al.*[43] the increase of the dielectric constant of the suspension is related to the alignment of the dipoles of the particles; any possible changes of the dielectric constant and elastic constant of the nematic matrix are not considered in the model. At the same time, besides the coupling with the director, the strong field (3) can change the intermolecular interaction in the vicinity of the particle. According to Buchnev *et al.*,[45] the field from the particle polarises the LC molecules and induces

               Y. Reznikov, A. Glushchenko and Y. Garbovskiy

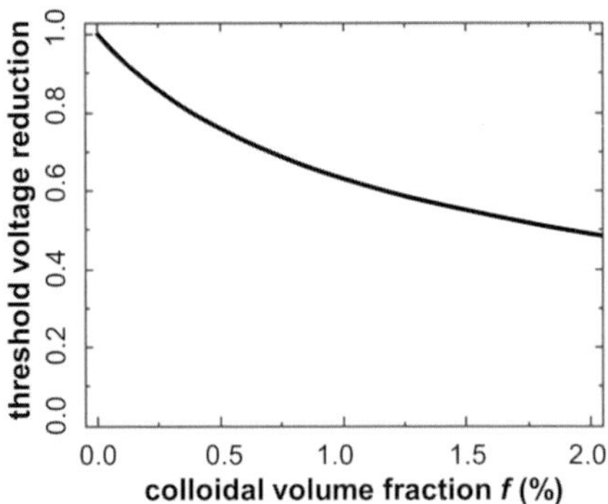

Fig. 7.   Dependence of the Frederiks threshold voltage reduction of the ferroelectric LC suspension on the colloidal volume fraction (based on the dependence presented[43]).

an additional dipole moments in LC molecules, $\mathbf{G}(\mathbf{E}_{\text{part}})$. This leads to the increase of the angular part of intermolecular van der Waals interaction $U_{a,i,j} \sim \mathbf{G}_i(\mathbf{E}_{\text{part}})\mathbf{G}_j(\mathbf{E}_{\text{part}})$. In the frame of the Maier-Saupe theory the increased interaction in the nematic LC means the higher order parameter of the surrounding molecules, S, and of the average order parameter of the suspension, $\bar{S}$.

The increased ordering of LC molecules results in changes of basic properties of the nematic LC which are determined by the order parameter S. First of all, it is related to the birefringence, $\Delta n(\bar{S})$, dielectric anisotropy, $\Delta\epsilon(\bar{S})$, and elastic constants, $K(\bar{S}^2)$. A change of $\Delta\epsilon(\bar{S})$ and elastic constants, $K(\bar{S}^2)$, should seriously affect the Frederiks transition voltage of the suspension (see (4) and Fig. 7).

Another bright consequence of the increased ordering in the ferroelectric nematic suspension is the increase of the clearing temperature, T_c. In the frame of the Maier-Saupe molecular field theory[45] the shift of T_c does not depend on the size of the particles at the fixed volume fraction f_v and is proportional to $\mathbf{P}^2_{\text{part}}$:

$$\Delta T_c = \frac{Z f_v N_{LC} (\Delta\beta)^2}{36\pi\epsilon_0 l^3_{m-m} 4.54 k_B} \mathbf{P}^2_{\text{part}} \tag{5}$$

where Z is nearest number of neighbouring molecules separated by the distance l_{m-m}, N_{LC} is the LC molecular concentration, $\Delta\beta$ is the anisotropy of the molecular polarisability. For the weight fractions $c = 0.1$-1% of typical ferroelectric particles we obtain the characteristic value of $\Delta T_c \approx (1-10)°C$, i.e. the effect of the particles can be strong.

In Buchnev *et al.*,[45] the perfect alignment of all the particles in one direction was assumed. Lopatina and Selinger[46,47] considered how the orientational distribution of the nanoparticles affects the orientational order of the liquid crystal. It is shown that the distributions of the particles and liquid crystal molecules are characterized by two orientational order parameters, which interact with each other. Lopatina and Selinger[47] postulated that the interaction energy of two ensembles of nanoparticles and LC molecules is described as:

$$F_{\text{part-LC}} = kc_{\text{part}}SS_{\text{part}} \tag{6}$$

where S_{part} is the order parameter of nanoparticles, k is the coupling coefficient, which is proportional to $\Delta\epsilon$. This expression shows that the orientational order of the nanoparticles favors the orientational order of the LC, and vice versa.

One should note that an approach largely similar to Lopatina and Selinger[47] had been proposed by Lisetski *et al.* much earlier,[48] with possible contributions of large molecular dipoles to the orientational order parameter described by accounting for terms with odd Legendre polynomials (P1) in the distribution function.

Expansion in Taylor series of the expression of the total free energy in power series S_{part} and S gives a term proportional to S^2 that determines the increase of the clearing temperature:

$$\Delta T_c = \frac{1.03 f_v \Delta\epsilon}{135\rho_{LC}k_B\epsilon_0\epsilon^2}\mathbf{P}^2_{\text{part}} \tag{7}$$

This formula gives the shift of T_c on the order of less than predicted by the formula (5). It should be noted that in (7) $\Delta T_c \sim \Delta\epsilon$ while according to Buchnev *et al.*[45] $\Delta T_c \sim (\Delta\beta)^2$. This difference arises because the polarisation of LC molecule is proportional to $\Delta\beta$ and therefore the additional interaction between the LC molecules in Buchnev *et al.*[45] scales as $\Delta\beta^2$. In the theory of Lopatina and Selinger the direct influence of the nanoparticles' electric field which scales linearly with $\Delta\epsilon$ is considered. At the present stage it is unclear which model describes the reality better, but in any case both approaches predict a notable increase of the order parameter and the clearing temperature of the nematic LC.

Suspensions of ferroelectric particles in a ferroelectric LC promises additional interesting effects and applications, since in chiral smectic LCs the permanent dipole moment of the ferroelectric particles, P_{part}, interact not only with the director but with the spontaneous polarisation of the LC, P_{LC}. Usually ferroelectric particles carry the dipole moment, which is comparable or larger than the spontaneous polarisation of ferroelectric LC, $P_{LC} \sim 1$ Debye. For instance, the metal oxide nanoparticles possessing wurtzite structure, carry dipole moments typically of the order of 50 Debye. Therefore, one can expect a notable impact of nanoparticles on the ferroelectric properties of smectics. The theory of ferroelectric smectic LCs doped with ferroelectric nanoparticles was developed by Lahiri, Majumder and Ghosh.[49] It predicts that the particles induce greater dipolar ordering in the smectic matrix and increase its overall polarization.

3.2. *Main directions of experimental studies of ferroelectric liquid crystal suspensions*

As was noted above, the enhancement of the intermolecular interaction should lead to serious changes of mesogenic properties of the LC matrix by ferroelectric nanoparticles. The first experiments[16,45] confirmed this predictions; suspension of ferroelectric nanoparticles in nematic LCs revealed an enhanced order parameter, a dielectric anisotropy and a birefringence, and an increased temperature of the transition to isotropic phase. These results promised new, simple, and effective means to control precisely the physical properties of liquid crystalline materials and development of unique LC compositions. However, as it is often the case in science, the follow up experimental works identified many problems. The main of them was instability of the suspensions and poor reproducibility of the results. The ferroelectric LC suspensions turned up even more "capricious" than the suspensions of magnetic particles.

As was described above, there are two primary effects related to the presence of ferroelectric nanoparticles in LCs. *First*, in analogy with magnetic nanoparticles, there is a coupling between the permanent dipole moments of the particles and the director of LC. This coupling gives a possibility of the mutual control of the orientation of the LC and the nanoparticles by electric field and changes electro-optics response of the LCs. *Second*, ferroelectric nanoparticles increase the order parameter in the vicinity of the particles, and, as a consequence, increase the average order parameter, $\bar{S}$, and the clearing temperature T_c. The raise of this values should be accompanied by the corresponding increase of all the parameters of a mesophase that are determined by the LC ordering, such as dielectric anisotropy, $\Delta\epsilon(\bar{S})$, birefringence, $\Delta n(\bar{S})$, Frank constants, $K(\bar{S}^2)$ etc.

The coupling and ordering effects promise significant changes of LC properties. At the same time, the theories[45–47] considered rather simplified system, composed of single, identical, single-domain and noninteracting neutral particles in a one-component nematic matrix. In fact, the suspensions are much more complicated systems.

First, in contrast to magnetic nanoparticles, the direct electrostatic interaction between the ferroelectric particles is strong. For two ferroelectric particles with antiparallel dipoles the electrostatic interaction is:

$$E_{\mathrm{el}} \sim \frac{p_{\mathrm{part}}^2}{4\pi\epsilon_0 r^3} \tag{8}$$

where $p_{\mathrm{part}} = P_{\mathrm{part}} V_{\mathrm{part}}$ is a permanent dipole moment of the particle, V_{part} is the particle volume, r is the distance between the particles.

The interaction (8) is much stronger than thermal disordering at the interparticle distance of the order of 100 nm. For instance, for typical ferroelectric material $BaTiO_3$ ($P_{\mathrm{part}} = 0.26$ C/m^2) and $d_{\mathrm{part}} = 10$ nm the ratio $E_{\mathrm{el}}/k_B T \approx 40$. This determines a strong aggregation of ferroelectric nanoparticles in a mesophase and producing a true suspension of single ferroelectric particles is a difficult task, which is still not completely solved.[28]

Second, the suspensions always contain free electric charges, concentration of which is difficult to control. These charges screen the electric field generated by the permanent electric dipoles and decrease/destroy the effect of the particles' ferroelectricity. Moreover, as was found recently,[50] in addition to permanent polarization, ferroelectric particles can bear own electric charge. This charge, which can strongly affect the surrounding LC ordering and behavior of the suspension in external field is also difficult to control.

Besides these two main problems, there are a lot of other difficulties, arising in the experiments. For example, the single domain approximation is valid for the limited range of the particles size; too small particles ($d_{\mathrm{part}} \leq 10$ nm) lose ferroelectricity and too large particles ($d_{\mathrm{part}} \geq 100$ nm) are polydomain.[51] The surfactants (e.g. oleic acid) can be partially dissolved in the LC and mask the effect of the particles.[52,53] In multi-component LC mixtures additional problems can arise due to the micro/nano separation of different components with different molecular masses and dipole moments. Indeed, the local electrical field is inhomogeneous in LCs, even if it is partially compensated by free charges which always exist in LCs. Motion of the polar molecules with various dipole moments and various molecular weights in the gradient of the local electric field, as well as various different adsorption affinities of various mixtures' molecular components on the particle's surface can lead to a spatial redistribution of the individual components of the LC matrix. This may provide additional contribution to the changes of the dielectric and reorientation properties of the ferroelectric colloids based on multi-component LCs and mask the effect of the orientation amplification.

All of this makes the development and study of the suspension of ferroelectric nanoparticles in LCs a difficult task. Nevertheless, the experimental data, described below, clearly demonstrate a validity of the main predictions of the basic properties of ferroelectric suspensions.

3.2.1. *Preparation of the colloids*

For now the primary technique of ferroelectric particles preparation is a mechanical grinding of ferroelectric materials.[54] Usually the ferroelectric material (e.g. $Sn_2P_2S_6$, $BaTiO_3$) is milled together with a surfactant in a non-ionic liquid carrier. The most popular surfactant is oleic acid and heptane or ethyl alcohol is taken as the carrier. It should be noted that oleic acid does not look as an optimized surfactant since its molecules are weakly bonded to the particle surface and sufficient part of them are dissolved in the LC matrix.

Large ferroelectric particles form a polydomain structure and very small particles can lose their ferroelectricity. Besides, to get the stable colloid with no director disturbance, it is preferable to have the smallest particles possible. Therefore, only the narrow region of the particles' size around 10-20 nm can provide efficient influence of the ferroelectric particles and stable suspensions. The final size of the nanoparticles (usually 8 - 20 nm) is determined by the milling time. This, in turn, strongly depends on the relative concentration of the components (surfactant, solvent, ferroelectric material), type of the mill (power of the mill, material and weight of the jar and the ball(s) are important) and the temperature of the milling. Depending on the type of the mill and the ferroelectric material, the time to get single domain ferroelectric particles varies from tens of minutes to hundreds of hours.

All listed factors show how delicate the mechanical grinding technique is. Each combination of the milling machine and the material being ground requires a specific recipe to produce the single domain ferroelectric particles. The details of the grinding technique are described in Refs. 54, 55.

The alternative method of preparation of ferroelectric nanoparticles is based on a sol-gel technique.[50,56] This chemical method provides particles with narrow size distribution. It was applied recently to obtain rather big particles of $BaTiO_3$, $d_{part} = 54\pm4$nm.

Due to the size dispersion, electric charges in the solvent, presence of the particles with the cubic symmetry and other factors only a part of the produced nanoparticles have an essential polarization. Moreover, some particles may carry an electric charge. Therefore the important stage of the producing of the suspension is a selection of the particles with a permanent polarization and no charge. A selection of the dipole particles is produced by the so called "harvesting technique" proposed by Cook *et al.*[55] The idea of the technique was to use gradient electric field, in which the particles with a permanent dipole moment move, whereas non-polarized particles do not "feel" the gradient of the field. The harvesting is usually performed in a small sealed glass container with the dispersion of ferroelectric particles and surfactant in non-ionic and non-conducting solvent (usually heptane) (see Fig. 8).

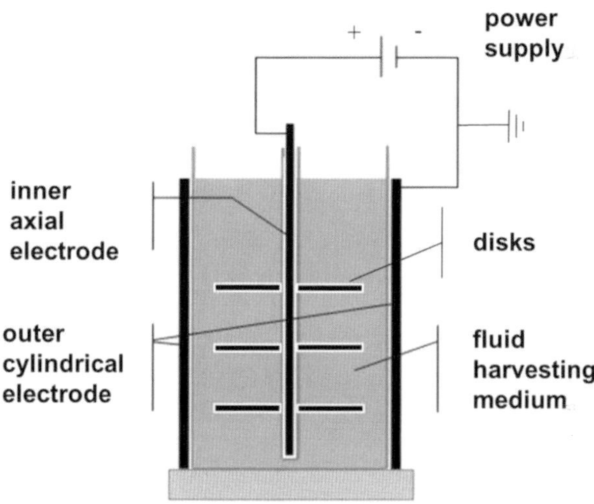

Fig. 8.   Harvesting set-up.

There is a thin inner wire electrode at the center of the container and an external radial foil electrode that wrapped around the container. The inner wire electrode is put within a thin-walled sealed glass capillary tube. A high dc potential (typically 10 - 20 kV) is applied to the inner wire electrode while the outer foil electrode is grounded. When the dc-field is applied, the harvested nanoparticles with permanent dipoles were accumulated on the inner wire electrode and nonpolar particles without dipole moments remained within the fluid or went down to the bottom of the container.

If the particles are charged, their behavior in a gradient of the field becomes more complicated and the results of the harvesting can be confusing. To check if the particles are charged, one can apply a dc-field to a flat cuvette with outer electrodes and filled with the particles in a solvent. If the geometry of the cuvette provides homogeneous electric field, the accumulation of the particles on the electrodes points to the charge of the particles.[50]

Our experience has shown that chemically the same ferroelectric materials obtained from different sources or treated differently have different harvesting efficiency and the particles are often charged. Therefore, a charge checking and a harvesting are necessary procedures for the preparation of the reliable ferroelectric LC colloids.

3.2.2. *Impact of the ferroelectric particles*

The important point of the studies of the suspensions of ferroelectric particles in LCs is a proof of the ferroelectric origin of the modification of the LC properties by its doping with the particles. In fact, even an isotropic spherical dielectric particle changes the mesogenic properties of LCs, effectively "diluting" it and decreasing the ordering and the clearing temperature.[57] Therefore, besides the impressive tuning of the liquid crystal properties by ferroelectric nanoparticles (see below), the complexity of the system and insufficient reproducibility of the results cause debates weather the effect of the particles is imposed by ferroelectricity and not by other phenomena. A simple yet fundamentally important experiment unambiguously shows that intrinsic ferroelectricity of the nanoparticles is responsible for the alteration of physical properties of liquid crystals. An immediate impact of the ferroelectricity of nanoparticles on optical properties of liquid crystals is clearly seen by utilizing a twin-cell (Fig. 9). The twin cell is the cell separated with a polymer stripe into two identical regions of the same thickness, boundary conditions, anchoring strength of nematic liquid crystals and aligning surfaces. One of these regions is filled with a pure nematic and the other region is filled with the liquid crystal doped with nanoparticles. When the temperature of the cell is below the Curie point of the particles, $T_{Curie} \approx 67^\circ C$, there is a difference in colors, well perceived by the naked eye, between plain liquid crystals and liquid crystal nano-colloids (Fig. 9a). It points to the different birefringence of the pure liquid crystal and the dispersion. Above the Curie point ferroelectricity disappears, and this phase transitions results immediately in the change

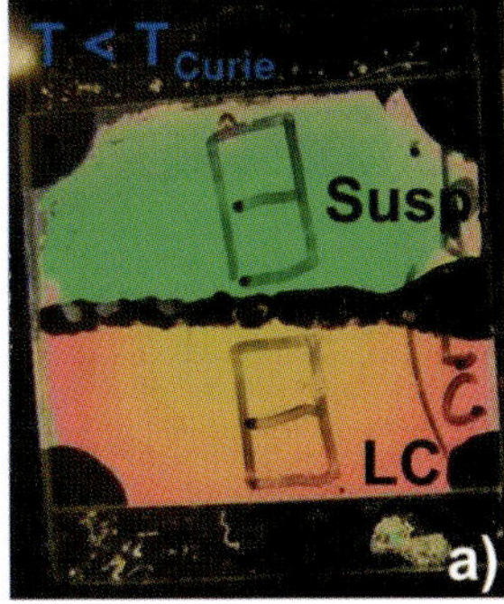

Fig. 9. The photograph of the twin cells placed in between two crossed polarizers at two different temperatures: a) the temperature of the twin cell is lower than T_{Curie}; b) the temperature of the twin cell is higher than T_{Curie}.

of the observed colors – both plain liquid crystals and colloids exhibit the same colors (Fig. 9b). This experimental result unambiguously proves an impact of the ferroelectricity: non-ferroelectric phase of the same nanoparticle does not alter optical properties of liquid crystals (Fig. 9b) while the ferroelectric phase does (Fig. 9a).

Despite the proof of the ferroelectric origin of the effect of ferroelectric particles on the nematic LC properties, the results of the experimental studies of the ferroelectric suspensions are still contradictive. For example, several authors[45,58–61] confirmed the theoretical predictions of the increase of the clearing point and the order parameter in suspensions of ferroelectric particles in nematics. A strong increase of the anisotropy of the conductivity in the ferroelectric LC suspension also was observed.[62] In the work[59] the increase of T_c in the LC 5CB with $Sn_2P_2S_6$ particles achieved 10°C and the order parameter increase was accompanied by the consistent increase of the dielectric anisotropy and birefringence. At the same time, it was pointed out in the same work that despite identical fabrication procedure, in some cells a decrease of the average order parameter and clearing temperature was observed. The decrease of the clearing temperature was also observed.[52,61–68]

The experimental data about influence of ferroelectric nanoparticles on the reorientation of the nematic LCs and electro-optics effects are also inconsistent. Kurochkin *et al.* reported a slight increase of the Frederiks transition ac-voltage, V_{Fr}, in the suspension of $Sn_2P_2S_6$ in the one-component LC 5CB[59] but Sing *et al.* found the evident decrease of ac-voltage, V_{Fr}, in the suspension of $BaTiO_3$ in a single component LC 6CHBT.[62] The decrease of ac-voltage V_{Fr} was also reported by Blach *et al.*[60] for $BaTiO_3$ particles in 5CB. Klein *et al.* observed no change of the Frederiks transition ac-voltage in the suspension of $BaTiO_3$ particles in the one component LC 5CB and the LC mixture ZLI 2293.[69]

Usually the ferroelectric nematic suspensions are paraelectrics; they do not reveal notable hysteresis of electro-optics response and have no macroscopic polarisation. Despite the sensitivity of the director of the ferroelectric LC suspension to the sign of the external electric field, the electrically-induced polarisation of the particles' ensemble disappeared after removing the field, e.g. the cell behaved as a superparalectric material.[16]

The only experiment, in which macroscopic polarisation was presumably observed, was reported by Cook *et al.*[70] In this paper the Frederiks transition in dc-field in the cell with the LC suspension of ferroelectric particles was studied. It was found that the electrical pre-history of the cells imparts polarity sensitivity to the Frederiks characteristics. Depending on the polarity of the previously applied dc-field, the Frederiks transition threshold increases or decreases with respect to the value of V_{Fr} of the cell before application of any electric field (a so called "virgin" cell). The asymmetry of the Frederiks transition can be large. Depending on the polarity of the applied voltage, the value V_{Fr} increases or decreases by 0.8 V, giving a net 1.6 V Frederiks threshold asymmetry for 8 μm thick cells filled with TL205 liquid crystal. The observed asymmetry is explained by the electrically-induced alignment of the dipoles of the nanoparticles. Their preferable orientation results in a macroscopic polarization of the cell which behaves as a ferroelectric material. The lined-up dipoles create an internal bias field which either adds or subtracts from the externally applied field, leading to an asymmetry in the external Frederiks transition threshold. The authors suggested that once aligned, dipole-dipole interaction between neighbouring nanoparticles is enough to allow the nanoparticles to keep the alignment after removing the external field. The stability of the polarised state of the nanoparticles can be also due to a strong coupling of the dipoles with the director of the matrix.

A possibility of a polar arrangement of the ferroelectric particles in nematic matrix is confirmed by the studies of the director fluctuations in suspension of $Sn_2P_2S_6$ nanoparticles in LC E7, which showed that at least locally macroscopic polarisation is present.[71]

There is only one publication related to the influence of ferroelectric particles on the properties of cholesteric LCs.[72] This work reports a strong change in the mesogenic, optical and electro-optics properties of the cholesteric based on nematic matrix with a chiral dopant. The most impressive impact of the ferroelectric nanoparticles is the 45% decrease of the driving voltage in a cell filled with cholesteric suspension.

There are several publications of the experimental studies of the ferroelectric smectic LC doped with ferroelectric nanoparticles. As in the case of nematic LC, the results of these studies are somewhat contradictory. In Refs. 73–76 the suspensions of the ferroelectric metal oxide nanoparticles possessing wurtzite structure in ferroelectric chiral smectic LC were studied. The authors of these publications reported the increase of the spontaneous polarization in these suspensions as compared to a pure nematic. Similar results were observed also for $BaTiO_3$.[77] Liang *et al.* found that the spontaneous polarization of ferroelectric LCs with $BaTiO_3$ nanoparticles is about twice of that for a pure LC.[78] At the same time, the authors of Refs. 67, 79 found an evident decrease of the spontaneous polarization of the ferroelectric LC doped with $BaTiO_3$. The decrease of the spontaneous polarization was also observed when antiferroelectric LC are doped with multiferroic $BiFeO_3$ nanoparticles.[80]

In our opinion, the depressing inconsistency in the experimental data is caused by uncertain differences in the suspensions producing procedures and numerous factors that can mask, change or prevent the effects considered in the theoretical models.[43,45–47] The main of them are the following.

- *Aggregation of the ferroelectric particles.* At the present stage of studies the aggregation of the particles is practically unavoidable. The presence of aggregation is noted in almost all the experimental papers. Moreover, even if the suspension looks stable with no visible aggregates, small aggregates, which size is less than the light wavelength, probably exist. The aggregates diminish the permanent polarisation, change effective concentration of the particles in the suspension and make comparison with the theory problematic.
- *Effect of the surfactant.* Dissolution of the surfactant in LCs results in the disordering of the matrix, which can mask the enhancement of the LC ordering due to the particles. Usually the presence of the surfactant in the bulk is not controlled in the experiments.
- *Charging of the particles.* In our experience, the ferroelectric particles are charged even after the harvesting. The presence of electrical charge on the particles complicates the description of the suspensions significantly, it distorts the field of the particle and may result in their

redistribution in an electric field. Usually, charging of the particles is not controlled in the experiments.

- *Size of the particles and their dispersion.* The characteristics of the suspensions and their response to an electric field strongly depend on the size of the particles. Besides, the spontaneous polarization of the nanoparticles depends on the particle size.
- *Properties of the LC matrix.* Free electric charges are always present in LCs. These charges can efficiently screen the permanent polarization of the particles. Even more, a micro/nano separation of the components of multi-component LC mixtures can affect the properties of the suspensions.

Despite the ambiguity of the experimental results one can state that ferroelectric particles do modify the properties of LCs, increasing their ordering and improving electro-optics characteristics. There are also strong unambiguous evidences about the essential increase of $T_c, \bar{S}_{\mathrm{col}}, \Delta\epsilon, \Delta n$, as well as improvement of electro-optics characteristics of the suspensions in cholesteric and smectic matrixes.

3.2.3. *Application aspects*

Ferroelectric nanoparticles added to the liquid crystalline host lead to the improvements of the electro-optical response (a lower threshold voltage, a higher birefringence, a shorter switching time, better contrast) of the thermotropic liquid crystals,[28] polymer dispersed liquid crystals,[81] and blue phase liquid crystals.[61] In addition, colloids of ferroelectric nanoparticles in liquid crystals exhibit enhanced nonlinear-optical properties (highly efficient gain of the beam coupling that is promising for the development of nonlinear-optical light valves in optical processing systems).[82,83]

An ideal performance of liquid crystal devices assumes that liquid crystals are dielectric materials. In fact, the majority of liquid crystals exhibit finite ionic electrical conductivity of the order of $10^{-11} - 10^{-9}$ S/m.[84] Ions that cause an electric conductivity of liquid crystals compromise an overall performance of liquid crystal devices leading to such undesirable phenomena as an image sticking, an image flickering and slow time response.[85] These ions are generated by several factors such as (i) by-products and/or impurities originated during chemical synthesis; (ii) injection from the alignment layers and glue during the cell assembling. While the former factor can be mediated by improving chemical procedures (by using materials of ultra-high purity and post-chemical synthesis purification), the latter one is practically inevitable since the alignment layers and glue commonly used in industry are prone to generate ions. Recent research conducted by independent groups on various types of nanoparticles embedded in liquid crystals suggested an elegant solution to this very important issue. It has been shown that nanoparticle can act as an ion trap thus leading to the reduction of the electrical conductivity of liquid crystals (for more references see reviews[85,86]). Among the other nanoparticles such as diamond, tin-doped indium oxide, alumina, zinc oxide, zirconium dioxide and montmorillonite, ferroelectric nanoparticles have the greatest potential to trap ions due to their permanent electric dipole. This electric dipole leads to strong electrostatic interactions between ions and ferroelectric nanoparticles. As a result, the concentration of mobile ions in liquid crystal host decreases. Our earlier research unambiguously proved the decrease in the mobile ions concentrations in liquid crystals caused by ferroelectric nanoparticles.

This effect is clearly demonstrated by the example of relaxation nematic LC after the application of a DC electric field. Consider a planar liquid crystal cell with ionic impurities. When a DC- field is applied, the director of the nematic reorients from a planar state toward to a homeotropic state. At the same time ionic impurities begin to drift in this field, form a charge layer on the substrates and create a 'screening' electric field E_{scr}. Such a screening field is formed during a 'drift' time $t_\mu = \frac{d^2}{\mu V}$ (μ charge carrier mobility, d thickness of the cell, V applied voltage; for typical values $\mu = 10^{-10} - 10^{-9}$ m^2/Vs, $d = 10^{-5}$ m, $V = 10^6$ V an estimated value of t_μ is $10^{-7} - 10^{-6}$ s). Direction of the 'screening' field is opposite to the external field so the effective field applied to the bulk liquid crystal decreases. When the external electric field is switched off, the electric field of screening charges does not vanish immediately but decreases slowly during the 'diffusion' time $t_d = \frac{d^2}{4D}$ (D is the diffusion coefficient of ions; for typical values $D = 10^{-12} - 10^{-11}$m^2/s, $d = 10^{-5}$ m, t_D equals 0.25 – 2.5 s). As a result, mobile ions in liquid crystal host alter the reorientation of liquid crystals and increase the total relaxation time of the director.

The geometry of the experiment corresponded to the birefringence mode (the cell with a planarly aligned LC is between crossed polarizers, the initial direction of the director made the angle 45° with the polarizers' axes). In this geometry the intensity of the light behind the analyzer is related to the birefringence of the cell, which in turn, is determined by the direction of the director.

The dependence of the intensity of the probe light beam after the switching the DC-field off is presented in Fig. 10. One can see that ferroelectric

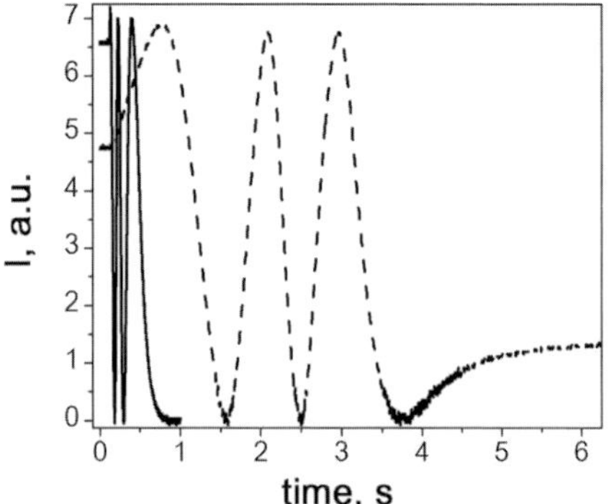

Fig. 10. Dependence of the light intensity behind the LC cells in the birefringence mode geometry (see the text). Dashed curve: LC TL-205 doped with ionic impurities; solid curve: LC TL-205 doped with ferroelectric particles $Sn_2P_2S_6$.

nanoparticles reduce the total relaxation time of the director relaxation by the factor of ten thus proving the concept of the liquid crystal purification by using ferroelectric nanoparticles as ion traps.

Another promising application of colloids of ferroelectric nanoparticles in liquid crystals is in the domain of microwave technologies. During last decade liquid crystal find an ever increasing application in microwave and millimeter-wave devices such as resonators, filters, phase shifters, delay lines and antennas.[87] This type of applications requires high birefringence liquid crystals to provide high performance of the device. As a rule, the newly synthesized liquid crystalline compounds with high birefringence ($\Delta n \sim$0.4-0.8) are usually very viscous, and this physical property sets a limit on the speed of microwave devices based on such materials. While the slow "time on" can be compensated by applying higher electric field, the "turn-off time" for non-dual-frequency liquid crystals is not governed by the electric field. Colloids of magnetic and ferroelectric nanoparticles in liquid crystals offer at least two independent ways to address this serious challenge. As it was mentioned early, the use of ferroelectric nanoparticles can lead to the enhancement of the birefringence of liquid crystal host. In this case the desired level of the performance is reached by mixing low-viscous liquid crystal host with ferroelectric nanoparticles. Another option is based on a concept of crossed electric and magnetic fields when an electric field is used to switch on liquid crystal devices, and a magnetic field pulls liquid crystalline molecules back thus speeding up the device's "turn-off time".

Garbovskiy *et al.* showed that applying a magnetic field along the direction perpendicular to the applied electric field leads to a decrease of the "turn-off time" by a factor of 6 for pure liquid crystals, and by a factor of 9 for ferronematics.[88] In this example homogeneously distributed magnetic nanorods create a spatially distributed aligning network within the liquid crystal host. When the magnetic field is applied, each particle of this aligning network follows the field and accelerates the relaxation of liquid crystalline molecules to their initial alignment.

3.3. *Conclusions*

The experimental results and theoretical studies show that a huge electric field generated by the permanent dipoles of ferroelectric nanoparticles determines the unique properties of their suspensions in liquid crystals. This field is incomparably larger that any reasonable external electric field which can be applied to the LC and serves both to couple the particles with the LC and to control the LC properties. Taking into account that nanoparticles do not deform a local director, they can be considered as a molecular dopant with a colossal dipole moment that drastically affect the LC order and related physical properties. The considered experimental results unambiguously show that improvements in the electro-optical performance of the colloids of ferroelectric nanoparticles in liquid crystals set a solid foundation for the design of the next generation devices which are cheaper, faster, and better than currently existing products. Of course, there is a set of the both scientific and technological challenges highlighted in the previous sections that should be overcome.

Acknowledgments

The authors are grateful to V. Zadorozhnii, V. Reshetnyak and V. Vashchenko for reviewing the manuscript and the valued advice, to Yu. Raikher and N. Tomašovičová for the introducing their activity in a field of ferronematics and to D. Lysenko for the help. The authors (YG and AG) gratefully acknowledge the support from the NSF grant #1102332 "Liquid Crystal Signal Processing Devices for Microwave and Millimeter Wave Operation", the NSF grant # 1446958 "EAGER: Single-step processing of self-assembled magneto-dielectric hybrid composites for microwave phased array sensors", and the support provided by the UCCS BioFrontiers Center at the University of Colorado.

References

1. F. Brochard and P. G. de Gennes, Theory of magnetic suspensions in liquid crystals, *Journal de Physique.* **31**, 691 (1970).
2. J. Rault, P. Cladis, and J. Burger, Feronematics, *Physics Letters.* **32**, 199–200 (1970).
3. G. H. Heilmeier and L. A. Zanoni, Guest-Host Interactions in Nematic Liquid Crystals. A New Electro-Optic Effect, *Appl. Phys. Lett.* **13**, 91–92 (1968).
4. S. H. Chen and B. J. Liang, Electro-optical effect of a magnetically biased ferronematic liquid crystal., *Opt. Lett.* **13**, 716–718 (1988).
5. S. Chen and N. Amer, Observation of macroscopic collective behavior and new texture in magnetically doped liquid crystals, *Phys. Rev. Lett.* **51**, 2298 (1983).
6. M. Koneracká and V. Závišová, Study of the magnetic Fredericksz transition in ferronematics, *Journal of Magnetism and Magnetic Materials and magnetic materials.* **157/158**, 589–590 (1996).
7. B. Liang and S. Chen, Electric-field-induced molecular reorientation of a magnetically biased ferronematic liquid-crystal film, *Phys. Rev. A.* **39**, 1441 (1989).
8. I. Potocŏvá, M. Koneracká, P. Kopčanský, M. Timko, L. Tomčo, J. Jadz̄yn, and G. Czechowski, The influence of magnetic field on electric Fredericksz transition in 8CB-based ferronematic, *J. Magn. Magn. Mater.* **196-197**, 578–580 (1999).
9. S. V. Burylov and Y. L. Raikher, Orientation of a solid particle embedded in a monodomain nematic liquid crystal, *Phys. Rev. E.* **50**, 358–367 (1994).
10. S. V. Burylov and Y. L. Raikher, Macroscopic properties of ferronematics caused by orientational interactions on the particle surfaces. I: Extended continuum model, *Molecular Crystals and Liquid Crystals Science and Technology. Section A. Molecular Crystals and Liquid Crystals.* **258**, 107–122 (1995).
11. S. V. Burylov and Y. L. Raikher, Macroscopic properties of ferronematics caused by orientational interactions on the particle surfaces. II. Behavior of real ferronematics in external fields, *Molecular Crystals and Liquid Crystals Science and Technology. Section A. Molecular Crystals and Liquid Crystals.* **258**, 123–141 (1995).
12. Y. L. Raikher. Orientational Frederiks-like transitions in ferronematics. In eds. A. F. N. Toledano and P., *Phase Transitions in Complex Fluids*, pp. 295–315. World Scientific (1998).
13. Y. L. Raikher and V. I. Stepanov, Transient field-induced birefringence in a ferronematic. **201**, 182–185 (1999).
14. A. Mertelj, D. Lisjak, M. Drofenik, and M. Copic, Ferromagnetism in suspensions of magnetic platelets in liquid crystal, *Nature.* **504**, 237–241 (2013).
15. O. Buluy, D. Burseva, M. R. Hakobyan, and J. W. Goodby, Influence of surface treatment of ferromagnetic nanoparticles on properties of thermotropic nematic liquid crystals, *Mol. Cryst. Liq. Cryst.* pp. 37–41 (2012).
16. Y. Reznikov, O. Buchnev, O. Tereshchenko, V. Reshetnyak, A. Glushchenko,

and J. West, Ferroelectric nematic suspension, *Appl. Phys. Lett.* **82**, 1917 (2003).

17. V. I. Zadorozhnii, V. Y. Reshetnyak, A. V. Kleshchonok, T. J. Sluckin, and K. S. Thomas, Inverse Frederiks effect and bistability in ferronematic cells, *Mol. Cryst. Liq. Cryst.* **475**, 221–231 (2007).

18. V. I. Zadorozhnii, A. Vasilev, V. Y. Reshetnyak, T. K, and T. J. Sluckin, Nematic director response in ferronematic cells, *EPL (Europhysics Letters).* **73**, 408–414 (2005).

19. V. Zadorozhnii and T. Sluckin, The Frederiks effect and related phenomena in ferronematic materials, *SIAM J.App. Math.* **68**, 1688–1716 (2008).

20. E. Jarkova and H. Pleiner, Hydrodynamics of nematic ferrofluids. *Eur. Phys. J. E.* **588**, 583–588 (2001).

21. E. Jarkova, H. Pleiner, H.-W. Müller, and H. R. Brand, Macroscopic dynamics of ferronematics, *J. Chem. Phys.* **118** (2003).

22. N. Podoliak, O. Buchnev, O. Buluy, G. DAlessandro, M. Kaczmarek, Y. Reznikov, and T. J. Sluckin, Macroscopic optical effects in low concentration ferronematics, *Soft Matter.* **7**, 4742 –44749 (2011).

23. N. Tomašovičová, P. Kopčanský, and N. Éber, *Magnetically Active Anisotropic Fluids Based on Liquid Crystals, in Anisotropy Research: New Developments.* Nova Science Pub Incorporated (2012).

24. L. Martinez-Miranda, Effect of the surface coating on the magnetic nanoparticle smectic-a liquid crystal interaction, *Appl. Phys. Lett.* **89**, 151917 (2006).

25. C. P. Lapointe, D. H. Reich, and R. L. Leheny, Manipulation and organization of ferromagnetic nanowires by patterned nematic liquid crystals, *Langmuir* **24**(19), 11175–11181 (2008).

26. O. Buluy, S. Nepijko, V. Reshetnyak, E. Ouskova, V. Zadorozhnii, A. Leonhardt, M. Ritschel, G. Schönhense, and Y. Reznikov, Magnetic sensitivity of a dispersion of aggregated ferromagnetic carbon nanotubes in liquid crystals, *Soft Matter.* **7**, 644 – 649 (2011).

27. P. Kopcansky, N. Tomasovicova, M. Koneracka, V. Zavisova, M. Timko, A. Dzarova, A. Sprincova, N. Iber, K. Fodor-Csorba, T. Toth-Katona, A. Vajda, and J. Jadzyn, Structural changes in the 6CHBT liquid crystal doped with spherical, rodlike, and chainlike magnetic particles, *Physical Review E* **78**, 4–8 (2008).

28. Y. Reznikov. Ferroelectric colloids in liquid crystals. In ed. Q. Li., *Liquid Crystals Beyond Displays: Chemistry, Physics, and Applications*, pp. 403–426. John Wiley & Sons, Inc. (2012).

29. A. Ryzhkova and I. Muševič, Particle size effects on nanocolloidal interactions in nematic liquid crystals, *Phys. Rev. E.* **87**, 032501 (2013).

30. L. Zhang, R. He, and H. C. Gu, Oleic acid coating on the monodisperse magnetite nanoparticles, *Appl. Surf. Sci.* **253**, 2611–2617 (2006).

31. N. Podoliak, O. Buchnev, D. V. Bavykin, A. N. Kulak, M. Kaczmarek, and T. J. Sluckin, Magnetite nanorod thermotropic liquid crystal colloids: Synthesis, optics and theory, *J. Colloid Interface Sci.* **386**, 158–166 (2012).

32. M. F. Prodanov, N. V. Pogorelova, A. P. Kryshtal, A. S. Klymchenko, Y. Mely, V. P. Semynozhenko, A. I. Krivoshey, Y. A. Reznikov,

S. N. Yarmolenko, J. W. Goodby, and V. V. Vashchenko, Thermodynamically stable dispersions of quantum dots in a nematic liquid crystal., *Langmuir* **29**, 9301–9309 (2013).

33. M. Prodanov, O. Buluy, E. Popova, O. Kurochkin, S. Gamzaeva, Y. Reznikov, and V. Vashchenko, Preparation of stable colloids of nanoparticles in liquid crystals and their dielectric and magneto-optical properties, *in ILCC2014* (2014).

34. V. Reshetnyak, Private communication. .

35. K. Nakata, Y. Hu, O. Uzun, O. Bakr, and F. Stellacci, Chains of superparamagnetic nanoplarticles, *Adv. Mater.* **20**, 4294–4299 (2008).

36. S. Kredentser, O. Buluy, P. Davidson, I. Dozov, S. Malynych, V. Reshetnyak, K. Slyusarenko, and Y. Reznikov, Strong orientational coupling in two-component suspensions of rod-like nanoparticles, *Soft Matter.* **9**, 5061 (2013).

37. P. Kopčanský, N. Tomašovičová, M. Koneracká, V. Závišová, M. Timko, L. Tomčo, N. Éber, K. Fodor-Csorba, T. Tóth-Katona, A. Vajda, J. Jadzyn, E. Beaugnon, and X. Chaud, Néel and brownian rotations in ferronematics, *Physics Procedia.* **9**, 82–86 (2010).

38. H. Pleiner, E. Jarkova, H.-W. Müller, and H. R. Brand, Nematic order in ferrofluids, *J. Magn. Magn. Mater.* **252**, 147–149 (2002).

39. A. Mertelj, N. Osterman, D. Lisjak, and M. Čopič, Magneto-optic and converse magnetoelectric effects in a ferromagnetic liquid crystal, *Soft Matter.* **10**, 9065–9072 (2014).

40. Y. Shoji and T. Mizumoto, Magneto-optical non-reciprocal devices in silicon photonics, *Sci. Technol. Adv. Mat.* **15**, 14602 (2014).

41. S. Keramati, M. Zamani, and M. Ghanaatshoar, Tunable multifunctional magneto-optical devices based on magnetophotonic crystals comprising liquid crystal defect layers, *J. Appl. Phys.* **114**, – (2013).

42. L. Landau, L. Pitaevskii, and E. Lifshitz, *Electrodynamics of Continuous Media, 2nd Ed.* vol. 29 (1984).

43. S. M. Shelestiuk, V. Y. Reshetnyak, and T. J. Sluckin, Frederiks transition in ferroelectric liquid-crystal nanosuspensions, *Physical Review E* **83**, 1–13 (2011).

44. P. G. de Gennes, *The Physics of Liquid Crystals*. Clarendon Press, Oxford (1974).

45. F. Li, O. Buchnev, C. I. Cheon, A. Glushchenko, V. Reshetnyak, Y. Reznikov, T. J. Sluckin, and J. L. West, Orientational coupling amplification in ferroelectric nematic colloids., *Phys. Rev. Lett.* **97**, 147801 (2006).

46. L. M. Lopatina and J. V. Selinger, Theory of ferroelectric nanoparticles in nematic liquid crystals, *Phys. Rev. Lett.* **102**, 197802 (2009).

47. L. M. Lopatina and J. V. Selinger, Maier-Saupe-type theory of ferroelectric nanoparticles in nematic liquid crystals, *Phys. Rev. E.* **84**, 1–7 (2011).

48. V. V. Belyaev, A. A. Gerasimov, M. F. Grebenkin, and L. N. Lisetskii, Effect of noncentrosymmetry of mesogenic molecules on the macroscopic properties of nematic liquid crystals, *Sov. Phys. JETP.* **59**, 557–561 (1984).

49. T. Lahiri, T. Pal Majumder, and N. K. Ghosh, Theory of nanoparticles doped

in ferroelectric liquid crystals, *J. Appl. Phys.* **113**, 064308 (2013).

50. O. Kurochkin, E. Mavrona, V. Apostolopoulos, J.-F. Blach, J.-F. Henninot, M. Kaczmarek, S. Saitzek, M. Sokolova, and Y. Reznikov, Electrically charged dispersions of ferroelectric nanoparticles, *Appl. Phys. Lett.* **106**, 043111 (2015).

51. E. Erdem, H.-C. Semmelhack, R. Böttcher, H. Rumpf, J. Banys, A. Matthes, H.-J. Gläsel, D. Hirsch, and E. Hartmann, Study of the tetragonal-to-cubic phase transition in $PbTiO_3$ nanopowders, *J. Phys.: Condens. Matter.* **18**, 3861 (2006).

52. H. Atkuri, K. Zhang, and J. West, Fabrication of paraelectric nanocolloidal liquid crystals, *Mol. Cryst. Liq. Cryst.* **508**, 183–190 (2009).

53. A. Mertelj, L. Cmok, M. Čopič, G. Cook, and D. Evans, Critical behavior of director fluctuations in suspensions of ferroelectric nanoparticles in liquid crystals at the nematic to smectic-A phase transition, *Phys. Rev. E.* **85**, 1–7 (2012).

54. H. Atkuri, G. Cook, D. R. Evans, C.-I. Cheon, A. Glushchenko, V. Reshetnyak, Y. Reznikov, J. West, and K. Zhang, Preparation of ferroelectric nanoparticles for their use in liquid crystalline colloids, *Journal of Optics A: Pure and Applied Optics.* **11**, 024006 (2009).

55. G. Cook, J. L. Barnes, S. A. Basun, D. R. Evans, R. F. Ziolo, A. Ponce, V. Y. Reshetnyak, A. Glushchenko, and P. P. Banerjee, Harvesting single ferroelectric domain stressed nanoparticles for optical and ferroic applications, *J. Appl. Phys.* **108**, 64309 (2010).

56. W. Li, Z. Xu, R. Chu, P. Fu, and J. Hao, Structure and electrical properties of $BaTiO_3$ prepared by sol–gel process, *J. Alloys Compd.* **482**, 137–140 (2009).

57. M. V. Gorkunov and M. A. Osipov, Mean-field theory of a nematic liquid crystal doped with anisotropic nanoparticles, *Soft Matter.* **7**, 4348 (2011).

58. M. Hakobyan, R. Alaverdyan, R. Hakobyan, and Y. Chilingaryan, Enhanced physical properties of nematics doped with ferroelectric nanoparticles, *Arm. Journ. Phys.,.* **7**, 11–18 (2014).

59. O. Kurochkin, H. Atkuri, O. Buchnev, A. Glushchenko, O. Grabar, K. R, V. Reshetnyak, J. West, and Y. Reznikov, Nano-colloids of $Sn_2P_2S_6$ in nematic liquid crystal, *Condensed Matter Physics.* **13**, 1–9 (2010).

60. J. F. Blach, S. Saitzek, C. Legrand, L. Dupont, J. F. Henninot, and M. Warenghem, $BaTiO_3$ ferroelectric nanoparticles dispersed in 5CB nematic liquid crystal: Synthesis and electro-optical characterization, *J. Appl. Phys.* **107**, 1–7 (2010).

61. L. Wang, W. He, X. Xiao, M. Wang, M. Wang, P. Yang, Z. Zhou, H. Yang, H. Yu, and Y. Lu, Low voltage and hysteresis-free blue phase liquid crystal dispersed by ferroelectric nanoparticles, *J. Mater. Chem.* **22**, 19629 (2012).

62. U. B. Singh, R. Dhar, R. Dabrowski, and M. B. Pandey, Enhanced electro-optical properties of a nematic liquid crystals in presence of $BaTiO_3$ nanoparticles, *Liq. Cryst.* **41**, 953–959 (2014).

63. M. Hasegawa, Characterization of $BaTiO_3$ nanoparticles suspension in liquid crystal, *Journal of Photopolymer Science and Technology.* **25**, 295–299 (2012).

64. A. Lorenz, D. M. Agra-Kooijman, N. Zimmermann, H. S. Kitzerow, D. R. Evans, and S. Kumar, Bilayers in nanoparticle-doped polar mesogens, *Phys. Rev. E.* **88**, 62505 (2013).

65. A. Lorenz, N. Zimmermann, S. Kumar, D. R. Evans, G. Cook, M. Fernández Martínez, and H.-S. Kitzerow, Doping a mixture of two smectogenic liquid crystals with barium titanate nanoparticles., *J. Phys. Chem. B.* **117**, 937–941 (2013).

66. S. N. Paul, R. Dhar, R. Verma, S. Sharma, and R. Dabrowski, Change in dielectric and electro-optical properties of a nematic material (6CHBT) due to the dispersion of $BaTiO_3$ nanoparticles, *Mol. Cryst. Liq. Cryst.* **545**, 105/[1329]–111/[1335] (2011).

67. A. Rudzki, D. R. Evans, G. Cook, and W. Haase, Size dependence of harvested $BaTiO_3$ nanoparticles on the electro-optic and dielectric properties of ferroelectric liquid crystal nanocolloids., *Appl. Opt.* **52**, E6–14 (2013).

68. K. P. Sigdel and G. S. Iannacchione, Calorimetric study of phase transitions in ocylcyanobiphenyl-barium titanate nanoparticle dispersions., *J. Chem. Phys.* **139**, 204906 (2013).

69. S. Klein, R. M. Richardson, R. Greasty, R. Jenkins, J. Stone, M. R. Thomas, and A. Sarua, The influence of suspended nanoparticles on the Frederiks threshold of the nematic host., *Philosophical transactions. Series A, Mathematical, physical, and engineering sciences.* **371**, 20120253 (2013).

70. G. Cook, V. Y. Reshetnyak, R. F. Ziolo, S. A. Basun, P. P. Banerjee, and D. R. Evans, Asymmetric Freedericksz transitions from symmetric liquid crystal cells doped with harvested ferroelectric nanoparticles., *Opt. Express.* **18**, 17339–17345 (2010).

71. M. Čopič, A. Mertelj, O. Buchnev, and Y. Reznikov, Coupled director and polarization fluctuations in suspensions of ferroelectric nanoparticles in nematic liquid crystals, *Phys. Rev. E.* **76**, 1–5 (2007).

72. O. Kurochkin, O. Buchnev, A. Iljin, S. K. Park, S. B. Kwon, O. Grabar, and Y. Reznikov, A colloid of ferroelectric nanoparticles in a cholesteric liquid crystal, *Journal of Optics A: Pure and Applied Optics.* **11**, 024003 (2009).

73. J. Huang, L. Li, and M. Chen, Probing molecular binding effect from zinc oxide nanocrystal doping in surface-stabilized ferroelectric liquid crystal with two-dimensional infrared correlation technique, *J. Phys. Chem. C.* **112**, 5410–5415 (2008).

74. T. Joshi, A. Kumar, J. Prakash, and A. M. Biradar, Low power operation of ferroelectric liquid crystal system dispersed with zinc oxide nanoparticles low power operation of ferroelectric liquid crystal system dispersed with zinc oxide nanoparticles, *Appl. Phys. Lett.* **253109**, 1–4 (2010).

75. L.-S. Li and J. Y. Huang, Tailoring switching properties of dipolar species in ferroelectric liquid crystal with zno nanoparticles, *J. Phys. D: Appl. Phys.* **42**, 125413 (2009).

76. A. Malik, A. Choudhary, P. Silotia, and A. M. Biradar, Effect of zno nanoparticles on the SmC *-SmA * phase transition temperature in electroclinic liquid crystals, *J. Appl. Phys.* **064111** (2011).

77. I. Coondoo, P. Goel, A. Malik, and A. M. Biradar, Dielectric and polariza-

tion properties of $BaTiO_3$ nanoparticle/ferroelectric liquid crystal colloidal suspension, *Integrated Ferroelectrics.* **125**, 81–88 (2011).

78. H.-H. Liang, Y.-Z. Xiao, F.-J. Hsh, C.-C. Wu, and J.-Y. Lee, Enhancing the electro-optical properties of ferroelectric liquid crystals by doping ferroelectric nanoparticles, *Liq. Cryst.* **37**, 255–261 (2010).

79. A. Mikulko, P. Arora, A. Glushchenko, A. Lapanik, and W. Haase, Complementary studies of $BaTiO_3$ nanoparticles suspended in a ferroelectric liquid-crystalline mixture, *EPL (Europhysics Letters).* **87**, 27009 (2009).

80. S. Ghosh, S. K. Roy, S. Acharya, P. K. Chakrabarti, M. Zurowska, and R. Dabrowski, Effect of multiferroic $BiFeO_3$ nanoparticles on electro-optical and dielectric properties of a partially fluorinated orthoconic antiferroelectric liquid crystal mixture, *EPL (Europhysics Letters).* **96**, 47003 (2011).

81. M. R. Darla, S. Hegde, and S. Varghese, Effect of $BaTiO_3$ nanoparticle on electro-optical properties of polymer dispersed liquid crystal displays. **2013**, 60–63 (2014).

82. O. Buchnev, A. Dyadyusha, M. Kaczmarek, V. Reshetnyak, and Y. Reznikov, Enhanced two-beam coupling in colloids of ferroelectric nanoparticles in liquid crystals, *Journal of the Optical Society of America B.* **24**, 1512 (2007).

83. G. Cook, A. Glushchenko, V. Reshetnyak, A. Griffith, M. A. Saleh, and D. R. Evans, Nanoparticle doped organic-inorganic hybrid photorefractives., *Opt. Express.* **16**, 4015–4022 (2008).

84. L. Blinov and V. G. Chigrinov, *Electrooptic Effects in Liquid Crystal Materials* (1994).

85. Y. A. Garbovskiy and A. V. Glushchenko, Liquid Crystalline Colloids of Nanoparticles: Preparation, Properties, and Applications. *Solid State Phys:* vol. 62, 1–74 (2010).

86. Y. Garbovskiy and I. Glushchenko, Nano-objects and ions in liquid crystals: Ion trapping effect and related phenomena, *Crystals.* **5**, 501–533 (2015).

87. Y. Garbovskiy, V. Zagorodnii, P. Krivosik, J. Lovejoy, R. E. Camley, Z. Celinski, A. Glushchenko, J. Dziaduszek, and R. Dąbrowski, Liquid crystal phase shifters at millimeter wave frequencies, *J. Appl. Phys.* **111**, 2010–2014 (2012).

88. Y. Garbovskiy, J. R. Baptist, J. Thompson, T. Hunter, J. H. Lim, S. G. Min, J. B. Wiley, L. M. Malkinski, A. Glushchenko, and Z. Celinski, Increasing the switching speed of liquid crystal devices with magnetic nanorods., *Appl. Phys. Lett.* **101**, 181109/1–181109/5 (2012).

Chapter 20

Nanoparticle guests in lyotropic liquid crystals

Sarah Dölle,[a] Ji Hyun Park,[b] Stefan Schymura,[c] HyeRan Jo,[d]
Giusy Scalia[b,*] and Jan P. F. Lagerwall[b,†]

[a] *Otto-von-Guericke-University of Magdeburg,*
Institute of Experimental Physics, D-39106 Magdeburg, Germany
[b] *University of Luxembourg, Physics & Materials Science Research Unit,*
1511 Luxembourg, Luxembourg
[c] *Helmholtz-Zentrum Dresden - Rossendorf e.V., Forschungsstelle Leipzig,*
Institut für Ressourcenökologie, 04318 Leipzig, Germany
[d] *Department of Nanoscience & Technology,*
Graduate School of Convergence Science & Technology,
Seoul National University, 443-270 Suwon, Korea
[*] *Giusy.Scalia@solcanta.com,* [†] *Jan.Lagerwall@lcsoftmatter.com*

In this chapter we discuss the benefits, peculiarities and main challenges related to nanoparticle templating in lyotropic liquid crystals. We first give a brief bird's-eye view of the field, discussing different nanoparticles as well as different lyotropic hosts that have been explored, but then quickly focus on the dispersion of carbon nanotubes in surfactant-based lyotropic nematic phases. We discuss in some detail how the transfer of orientational order from liquid crystal host to nanoparticle guest can be verified and which degree of ordering can be expected, as well as the importance of choosing the right surfactant and its concentration for the stability of the nanoparticle suspension. We introduce a method for dispersing nanoparticles with an absolute minimum of stabilizing surfactant, based on dispersion below the Krafft temperature, and we discuss the peculiar phenomenon of filament formation in lyotropic nematic phases with a sufficient concentration of well-dispersed carbon nanotubes. Finally, we describe how the total surfactant concentration in micellar nematics can be greatly reduced by combining cat- and anionic surfactants, and we discuss how nanotubes can help in inducing the liquid crystal phase close to the isotropic–nematic boundary.

Contents

1. Introduction

Most work on liquid crystal templating of nanoparticles has been done with thermotropic hosts, mainly because of the excellent means of controlling alignment, the (apparent) simplicity in handling, as well as the ease in reorienting the director dynamically with an electric field. However, lyotropic hosts provide some interesting unique advantages, which in certain cases may be of decisive impact. Many types of nanoparticle have been dispersed in a variety of lyotropic hosts, with useful, surprising as well as mysterious consequences.

Several demonstrations of templating of metal nanoparticles have been reported, for instance for ZnS quantum dots (synthesized *in-situ* from a dissolved precursor) in virus-based lyotropic cholesterics and smectics[1] or for clusters of spherical metal nanoparticles in surfactant-based hexagonal or sponge phases.[2,3] Gold nanorods have been dispersed in and aligned by chromonic nematics,[4] lyotropic cholesterics formed by cellulose nanocrystals[5-7] (CNC; see Chap. 27 for more on this class of lyotropics) and in surfactant-based nematic and hexagonal phases.[8] Some works focus on the effects of nanoparticles on the lyotropic mesomorphism, for instance with spherical silica nanoparticles in lamellar and hexagonal phases of nonionic surfactants[9] or magnetic nanorods dispersed in a lamellar phase of nonionic surfactant.[10,11] In one case[11] the system was a hybrid liquid crystal, as the nanorods formed a nematic phase within the lamellar host. Finally, much work has been devoted to carbon nanotubes dispersed in and aligned by lyotropic hosts, including chromonic nematics,[12] virus-based cholesterics,[13] as well as (most commonly) surfactant-based nematics, cholesterics or hexagonal phases.[14-22]

Conversely, the symbiosis between nanoparticles and lyotropic hosts can be used in the opposite direction, the nanoparticles aligning the liquid crystal macroscopically. Such an effect was demonstrated by Mezzenga and co-workers for the case of magnetite nanoparticles dispersed in lipid-based lyotropic hexagonal or lamellar phases.[23] Anisotropic nanoparticles have also been used to induce new phases, not present in the phase diagram of the pristine lyotropic host,[24] and they can promote macroscopic liquid crystalline ordering in surfactant solutions with such low concentration that the phase is isotropic without the nanorods.[25]

In this chapter we focus strongly on the case of carbon nanotubes (CNTs) dispersed in surfactant-based lyotropic liquid crystals, due to the peculiarities of carbon nanotubes as discussed in other chapters. Our aim is to make the reader aware of the potential of lyotropic-based templating of carbon nanotubes or similar nanorods, the issues that one needs to be aware of in order to succeed when working with surfactant-based systems, as well as the main challenges for future development. We make no claim of completeness, hence this should not be considered a review, but rather an introduction to the field.

2. Evidence of transfer of order from lyotropic hosts to dispersed anisometric nanoparticles

It can be quite challenging to confirm that the liquid crystal host has in fact aligned the dispersed nanoparticles, for two main reasons. First, the concentration of nanoparticles can be so low that they are difficult to detect, an assessment of their alignment being even more challenging. This was in particular a serious problem in the early studies. Second, lyotropic liquid crystals can be difficult to align uniformly over macroscopic areas, and then a quantitative assessment of how well aligned dispersed nanoparticles are, becomes very difficult.

The earliest report of CNT alignment with lyotropic liquid crystals was published by Regev and co-workers,[14] dealing with single-wall nanotubes (SWCNTs) introduced into a hexagonal phase formed by aqueous solutions of the non-ionic surfactant Triton X-100 (see Chap. 2 for structure). The high viscosity of a hexagonal phase makes the introduction of CNTs highly challenging, hence the authors dispersed the CNTs in a 1 wt% solution of either Triton X-100 or SDS (full name and structure in Chap. 2) and this dispersion was then mixed into a preformed hexagonal phase of Triton X-100, adjusted such that the final surfactant concentration was 50 wt%.

The final nanotube concentration was 0.25 wt%. The reported evidence of alignment is based on textural features that are common in lyotropic liquid crystals, also without guest particles, hence additional experimental evidence would be desirable. Small-angle x-ray scattering experiments (see Chap. 6) revealed a small but significant increase in the lattice parameter as more CNTs were added.

Independently, Lagerwall and co-workers at the same time explored SWCNT dispersion in lyotropic nematic[15] and cholesteric[16] phases formed by aqueous solutions of SDS and decanol. The decanol functions as co-surfactant, promoting an anisotropic micelle shape thanks to its much smaller hydrophilic headgroup than SDS (see Chap. 2), and its addition thus induces relatively broad and stable nematic phases formed by disc- or rod-micelles depending on the exact mixture composition.[26] The CNT concentration in these studies was very low, only about 0.01 wt%, hence optical microscopy studies could not probe CNT alignment, it could only confirm that the CNTs were well dispersed at macroscopic scale. Instead the authors investigated capillaries filled with the composites using polarized Raman spectroscopy (see Chap. 7), which—thanks to the resonant Raman response of SWCNTs—allows assessment of CNT alignment even at minute concentrations. This study provided unequivocal evidence that the CNTs align along the lyotropic liquid crystal director, for cylindrical as well as disc-shaped micelles.

A major advance was achieved about a year later by changing the surfactants used for CNT dispersion as well as for lyotropic liquid crystal formation.[17] The CNTs were now dispersed with the anionic surfactant SDBS (full name and structure in Chap. 2), particularly well suited for nanotube dispersion due to its phenyl ring close to the head group, allowing aromatic interactions between surfactant and nanotube surface. This dispersion was then mixed with the cationic surfactant CTAB (full name and structure in Chap. 2) with all component amounts calculated such that the final mixture would develop a lyotropic nematic phase. This new approach allowed a dramatic increase of CNT concentration while still having a good nanotube dispersion, to 0.2 wt%, which was sufficient to observe the uniform CNT alignment by the naked eye, assisted by a linear polarizer. CNTs have higher absorption of light polarized along the tube axis, and no or lower absorption for polarization perpendicular to the tube axis. This means that a sample with uniformly aligned CNTs, at sufficient concentration, acts like a linear polarizer, which could easily be verified with these systems as shown in Fig. 1. By filling the composite by vacuum suc-

Polarizer | | capillary   Polarizer ⊥ capillary

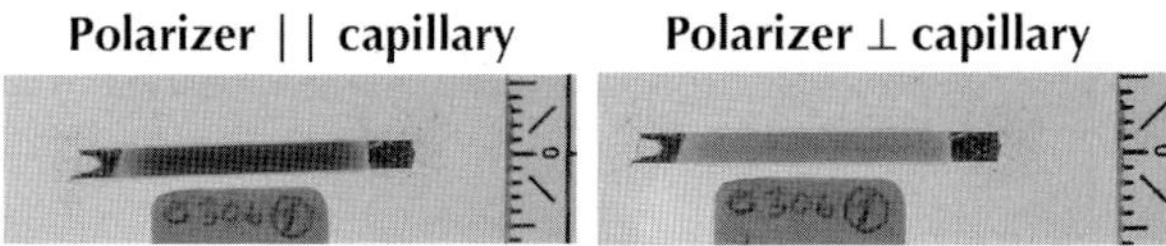

Fig. 1. A capillary filled with a catanionic lyotropic nematic doped with 0.2 wt% SWC-NTs, the director uniformly aligned by shear flow during filling, acts macroscopically as a linear polarizer, as demonstrated by rotating a polarizer foil above the sample. Reproduced from Ref. 17 with permission from The Royal Society of Chemistry.

tion into a flat capillary, the liquid crystal director was aligned along the capillary axis, hence also the SWCNTs were aligned along this direction, as verified by holding a linear polarizer over the sample and rotating it, cf. Fig. 1. The successful transfer of orientational order was also verified by polarized Raman spectroscopy, allowing an estimation of the large-scale orientational order parameter to $S \approx 0.3$ in the capillary. This low degree of order is surprising, considering that the liquid crystal phase, in this case being close to hexagonal order, should have distinctly higher orientational order. It was explained by the imperfect control of the macroscopic director achieved by shear flow during capillary filling, as proved by the higher order parameter (about 0.6) when probing a smaller area, thus approaching the local order of unidirectionally oriented monodomains. Also, when promoting the uniformity of the order by pulling a fiber (see below) the measured order parameter increased to 0.7, indicating the importance of large scale alignment on the measured values.

The test for this 'polarizing effect' from the liquid crystal-dispersed nanotubes can be a very convenient verification of sufficient dispersion quality and alignment, and it was subsequently confirmed also for DNA-stabilized SWCNTs and for MWCNTs stabilized by SDBS.[18] The protocol for preparing the composite of anionic-stabilized CNTs in a cationic phase is, however, not entirely trivial, and some temporary CNT aggregation always takes place at intermediate stages. An excellent dispersion quality in the CNT dispersion is imperative, but even so, there will be additional sonication necessary after mixing with the liquid crystal-forming surfactant. Stefan Schymura has formalized a useful protocol in his Ph.D. thesis.[27,a]

Polarized Raman spectroscopy was the technique used to confirm CNT alignment in the study by Puech *et al.*, where the lyotropic host was a cholesteric formed by fd virus.[13] The authors were able to quantify the orientational order S of the CNT guests and the virus liquid crystal host

---

[a]Available free of charge from http://www.lcsoftmatter.com.

separately, by using Raman spectroscopy to address the CNT order and establishing S of the liquid crystal host based on birefringence measurements. In this way they found clearcut evidence that the CNT orientational order is always lower ($0.1 < S_{CNT} < 0.35$) than that of the liquid crystal host ($0.55 < S_{LC} < 0.75$). The experimental observations were also corroborated with a theoretical treatment of the guest-host system. In addition, in their theoretical analysis they compared the effects of CNT length and polydispersity on the efficiency of orientational order transfer, finding that polydispersity is surprisingly unimportant, whereas the length of the CNT guest influences the achieved order considerably.

In their study of alignment of gold nanorods by a CNC-based chiral nematic phase,[5,6] Smalyukh and co-workers used the orientation-dependent surface plasmon resonance to verify the transfer of orientational order. Polarizing microscopy revealed polarization-dependent colors and polarization-sensitive spectroscopy confirmed a strong change in signal for incoming light polarized parallel and perpendicular to the liquid crystal director, respectively. By shear-aligning a gold nanorod-loaded CNC phase at the relatively high concentration of 20 wt%, yielding a kinetically arrested state (see Chap. 27), they obtained a sample with macroscopically uniform orientation of $\mathbf{n}$. They could then establish, from the polarization sensitive surface plasmon resonance signal, an orientational order parameter for the gold nanorods of $S \approx 0.47$.

3. Carbon nanotubes dispersed in surfactant solutions of varying type and concentration

One of the main motivations to explore carbon nanotubes in surfactant-based lyotropic liquid crystals is that the same standard surfactants, such as SDS and CTAB, that are commonly used for dispersing CNTs in aqueous suspension, also form a variety of liquid crystal phases at higher concentration, tunable with the addition of co-surfactants. However, for CNTs dispersed with SDS, a modest increase of concentration beyond the $\sim 1\%$ range that is typical for nanoparticle dispersion, to around 5%, was found to induce rapid aggregation.[28] The effect was attributed to depletion attraction because of excess micelles acting as depletants. In addition, the reduced stabilization efficiency due to increasing ionic strength of the solution as the concentration of an ionic surfactant is increased must certainly also have an influence, as discussed further below.

Interestingly, and counter-intuitively considering this observation, it is still possible to achieve very good CNT dispersion, at least for the right surfactant and a limited amount of time, in the higher surfactant concentration range where lyotropic liquid crystal phases form, if one follows an appropriate preparation protocol. It is far from obvious why this works and it turns out that the behavior of CNT suspensions provide some interesting surprises as the concentration of surfactant is increased. One of us investigated the behavior of aqueous suspensions of ionic surfactant-stabilized SWCNTs in the rarely studied regime between $\sim$ 1 wt% and $\sim$ 25 wt% surfactant concentration in the frame of her thesis.[29] The main results and conclusions are summarized in this section.

Dispersions with surfactant concentrations up to $\sim$ 2.5 wt% are widely used in the CNT research field and appreciated for their stability. The dry CNT powder (typically on the order of a mg) is first weighed out in a vial, in which the surfactant solution (on the order of a mL) is then dispensed. Typically a sonotrode ('probe' or 'tip' sonicator) is then immersed into the liquid and the sample is sonicated at high power for some tens of minutes. It is wise to keep the vial in an ice bath during the process, to dissipate the heat produced during the high-power sonication in the small amount of liquid. The aqueous surfactant solution has essentially no CNT dissolving power,[30] but it is the cavitation generated by the strong ultrasound treatment that breaks up bundles of CNTs and individualizes them.

The exposed hydrophobic surface is then quickly covered by surfactant molecules thanks to the hydrophobic effect (see Chap. 2), and at that stage the surfactant can serve its function, which is to prevent reaggregation. The repulsion induced by the surfactant is electrostatic (for ionic surfactants) or steric (for nonionic surfactants, less commonly employed for CNT dispersion). This procedure generally works very well when the surfactant concentration is in this low regime, yet there is always a certain fraction of CNTs that remains poorly dispersed after the sonication. In order to remove the residual CNT bundles it is common to centrifuge the sample and decant the supernatant. If the dispersion procedure has been appropriate, the extracted supernatant can be considered to be a practically stable[b] suspension of individualized CNTs or small bundles.

A quite different behavior can be found for intermediate surfactant concentrations, from around 5 wt%. In this regime, a phase separation into a CNT-rich and a CNT-depleted phase occurs over time. Naturally, this

---

[b]It is not thermodynamically stable, but it can remain unchanged over a time scale of many years.

unstable regime is avoided when homogeneous dispersions are the target. Remarkably, several surfactants start to form promising dispersions again from surfactant amounts of 16 wt% and higher. These suspensions are very viscous and close to the formation of lyotropic liquid crystalline phases.

We investigated the cationic surfactants MTAB (Myristyl Trimethyl Ammonium Bromide) and CTAB as well as the anionic surfactants SDS and SDBS. All four satisfy the precondition of being able to stabilize CNT suspensions reasonably at ~ 1 wt% surfactant. The chemical structures and full names of CTAB, SDS and SDBS were introduced in Chap. 2. MTAB is similar to CTAB but its hydrophobic chain is two methylene groups shorter, being built from 14 rather than 16 carbon atoms along the backbone. Our sample preparation included a brief sonication using a sonotrode and a subsequent treatment in a VialTweeter^c for 12 hours. The dispersions were stored at room temperature in an upright position. Only CTAB samples were kept at $40°$C to enable micelle formation equally to the other surfactants (as discussed in Sec. 4, the Krafft temperature of CTAB is about room temperature). The concentration of SWCNTs (of HiPCO type) was kept constant at 0.01 wt% in all samples.

When looking closely at the different surfactants in their function as CNT stabilizers explicit differences become evident at higher concentrations. We begin by discussing the results obtained with cationic surfactants. The stabilizing effect of MTAB seems to be limited to low concentrations since only the 1 wt.-% MTAB sample renders a stable dispersion, cf. the upper part of Fig. 2. The samples with MTAB concentration in the range $\sim 2- \sim 5$ wt% display a phase separation into a dense CNT-rich and a less dense CNT-depleted phase. At higher concentrations, up to ~ 25 wt%, large-scale flocculation of CNTs occurs within a single dark phase, whereas the top (eventually also the bottom) phase is clear, signifying almost complete absence of nanotubes.

Surprisingly, the addition of just two carbon atoms in the hydrophobic chain when switching to CTAB leads to considerably enhanced stabilizing ability, as can be seen in the lower half of Fig. 2. The CTAB dispersions generally appear deeply black throughout, indicating a high concentration of well dispersed CNTs. Additionally, the phase separation is slowed down considerably and its concentration range is smaller compared to MTAB. Only after four weeks can phase separation be clearly seen in the range from $\sim 9- \sim 15$ wt% CTAB. No phase separation can be detected in

---

^{c}A sonicator allowing contamination-free sonication at power levels intermediate between sonotrodes and sonication baths; cf. www.hielscher.com.

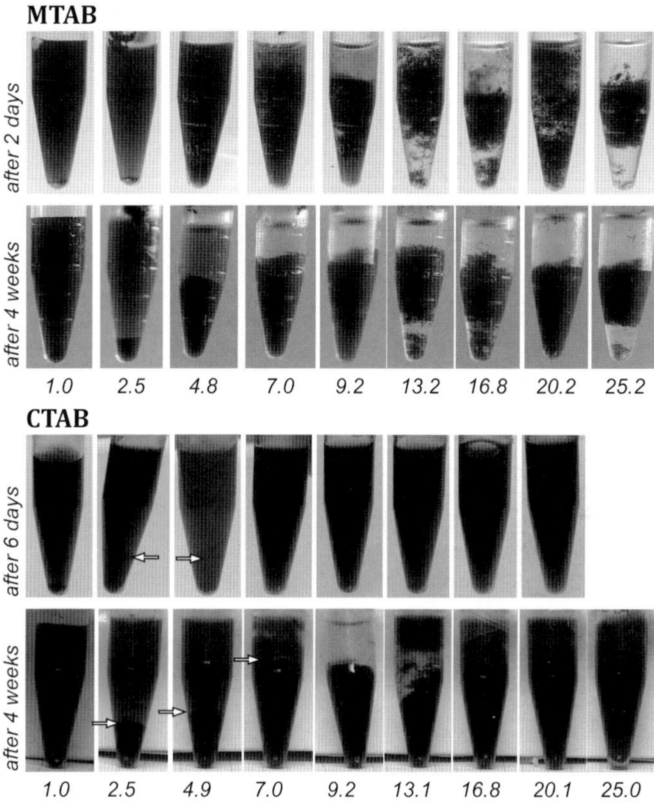

Fig. 2. Suspensions of SWCNTs stabilized by cationic surfactants MTAB and CTAB. The CNT concentration is fixed at 0.01 wt% and the surfactant concentration (in wt%) is given below each column. The time elapsed since sample preparation is indicated to the left of each series of concentrations. In the CTAB series, small arrows point out onsets of sediments that are hardly visible due to the intensely black supernatant.

the samples with 20 wt% CTAB and higher. Even after four weeks these homogeneous dispersions remain stable.

Moving to the performance of the anionic surfactants, the samples with CNTs stabilized by SDS showed, after four days, only a small range of phase separation at intermediate surfactant concentration, cf. Fig. 3. However, the dispersions age substantially and after four weeks, phase separation is detected all the way up to 20 wt% surfactant and the CNT-rich phase is considerably compacted. Comparing with the MTAB series, there is a striking difference. While the suspensions in MTAB grew continuously

                    S. Dölle et al.

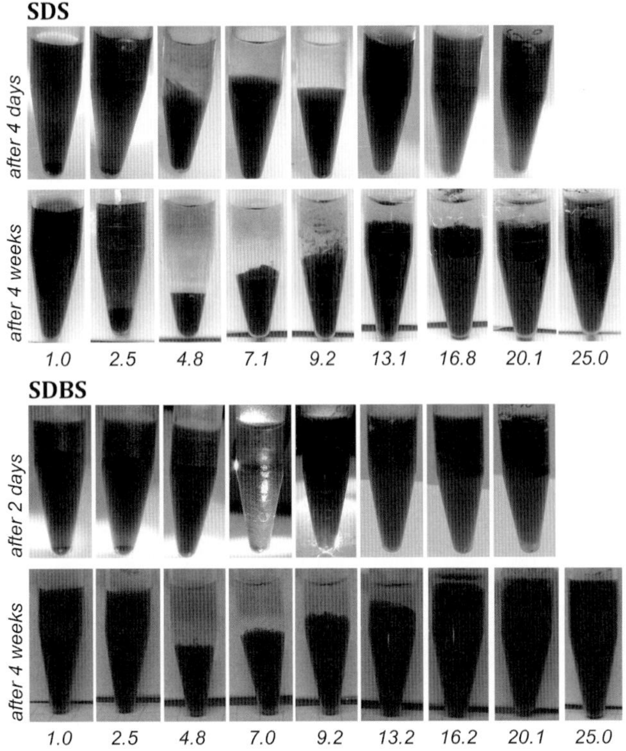

Fig. 3.   Suspensions of SWCNTs stabilized by anionic surfactants SDS and SDBS. The CNT concentration is fixed at 0.01 wt% and the surfactant concentration (in wt%) is given below each column. The time elapsed since sample preparation is indicated to the left of each series of concentrations.

worse with increasing surfactant concentration, the CNT-rich phase in SDS solutions grows in prominence with increasing surfactant concentration, to eventually extend throughout the whole sample volume at 25 wt%.

The surfactant SDBS appears as a good anionic alternative to CTAB, providing more uniformly black samples than SDS, even over an extended period of time. For at least two days, SDBS provides fully homogeneous dispersions over the whole concentration range studied, as seen in the lower part of Fig. 3. Similarly to SDS, the suspensions age, and phase separation arises from $\sim$ 5 wt% surfactant. However, the recurrence of stable, fully homogeneous CNT dispersions at higher concentrations sets in already at $\sim$ 20 wt% SDBS.

When comparing the performance of SDBS with the other surfactants, one should remember an important practical difference: while SDS, MTAB and CTAB can all be purchased with very high chemical purity, SDBS is commercially available only as 'technical grade', which means 80 % purity. The remaining 20% are mainly isomers of the 'ideal' SDBS molecule, where the phenyl ring is attached at various intermediate carbons in the dodecyl chain.[31,32] The mixture of isomers present in the SDBS used in this study (and all other studies of SDBS-dispersed CNTs that we are aware of) should be kept in mind when interpreting the observations, an issue we will come back to below.

If dispersions with a high surfactant concentrations are desirable, as is generally the case if the aim is to develop a micellar liquid crystalline phase, SDBS or CTAB could be the amphiphile of choice. Not only do they yield short-term stable dispersions covering a concentration range from 0-25 wt%. At surfactant concentrations from 20 wt%, their dispersions stay homogeneous for at least a month. The stability–instability phenomena of these phase diagrams are not fully understood. Nevertheless, a short excursion addressing possible explanations are made in the following.

The phase separation into a CNT-rich and a CNT-depleted phase arises with a relatively small concentration of surfactant, yet considerably higher than the ~ 1 wt% range usually employed for CNT stabilization. Possibly, this indicates aggregation driven by depletion attraction, as suggested by Zakri and Poulin.[28] Depletion attraction (see Chap. 3 for an in-depth discussion) occurs if 20-30 vol% of the sample is occupied by small particles (depletants; in the Zakri–Poulin scenario these would be excess spherical surfactant micelles) that are repelled from the main suspended particles.[33] Then, the larger particles, like CNTs, are forced towards coaggulation.[34,35]

The micelle polydispersity is known to rise with increasing surfactant concentration and a transition from spherical to worm-like micelles will typically take place at surfactant concentrations around 10 wt%.[36] If the worm-like micelles grow up to a size comparable to CNTs, the necessary size difference required for depletion attraction is lost. This process might explain the swelling volume of the CNT-rich phases with increasing surfactant concentration. As more and more worm-like micelles incorporate into the coagulated phase, the miscibility gap vanishes eventually.

Due to the higher packing parameter of a surfactant with long hydrophobic chain, the transition from spherical to wormlike micelles will happen at lower concentrations for a long-chain surfactant, like CTAB, than for short-chain surfactants, like MTAB or SDS. For SDBS the phenyl ring makes an estimate of the packing parameter less straight-forward, but in a first approximation this surfactant can be compared with CTAB in its hydrophiliic-hydrophobic balance. One should not be misled by the fact that SDS and SDBS both have dodecyl (12 carbon atoms) chains, thinking therefore that the lengths of their hydrophobic chains are similar. The phenyl ring of SDBS between the sulfate head group and the alkyl chain must in this context be considered part of the hydrophobic chain, as it interacts very well with the aromatic CNT surface, hence an ideal SDBS molecule effectively has a hydrophobic tail that is very similar in length to that of CTAB. Obviously, the mixture of isomers in a commercial SDBS sample also means that we have a mixture of packing parameters, but as discussed in a moment, the presence of CNTs may also lead to a certain fractionation of the SDBS sample, reducing this effect.

The higher packing parameter, and thus stronger tendency to form wormlike micelles, for CTAB and linear SDBS could thus be a major reason why it is easier to prepare stable CNT suspensions with high surfactant concentration when using these surfactants, compared to the cases of SDS and MTAB. Depletion attraction may be more or less absent already at some 10 wt% surfactant in case of CTAB and SDBS. On the other hand, one must also consider that the better performance of the latter two surfactants may be related to their stronger affinity for the hydrophobic CNT surface, due to their more extended hydrophobic tail. It could thus be that these surfactants provide the CNTs with a stronger protection against aggregation, thanks to their more intense binding to the nanotube surface. Although we have a mixture of isomers in the SDBS sample, the hydrophobic interaction area with the CNT surface is always larger than that of SDS or MTAB, even though one should take the chain branching into account. It could, however, also be that the stronger interaction with the curved aromatic CNT surface of certain SDBS isomers leads to a fractionation of the sample, such that the relative purity of the SDBS that actually covers CNTs is higher than 80%. On the other hand, we do not know if it is the 'ideal' linear SDBS that has the highest affinity for CNTs, or perhaps one of the branched isomers. This would need to be investigated in detail in future studies.

Considering that we are dealing with ionic surfactants, we must also take the alternative into account, that the differences seen as the surfactant concentration is increased is primarily due to the rising content of ions in the system. As discussed in Chap. 3 the effective range of electrostatic repulsion can be estimated by the Debye screening length λ_D. This length decreases dramatically as the salt content of the continuous phase (the ionic strength) increases, to such an extent that electrostatic repulsion becomes ineffective at a certain salt concentration. Indeed, destabilization of colloids by salt addition is a well known phenomenon.[37] In this view, the CNT aggregation seen around ~ 5 wt% surfactant would largely be due to ionic screening in addition to depletion attraction. At first sight the restabilization at higher surfactant concentrations seen for all surfactants but MTAB then becomes even more mysterious.

It has been suggested[d] that the surfactants may adsorb with multiple layers on the CNT surface at higher surfactant concentrations. Such a scenario might be an explanation, as the multilayer adsorption would require co- as well as counter ions to be incorporated in the increasingly thick disperse phase components, comprised by a CNT at the core of a growing localized lamellar phase that surrounds it. This would effectively reduce the ionic strength of the solvent and might thus explain the increasing stability with increasing surfactant concentration. Unfortunately, experimental verification of such a scenario is extremely difficult, thus this remains a speculative alternative scenario at present. Similar experiments with appropriate nonionic surfactants would certainly provide valuable complementary data.

A kinetic reason for the restabilization may also be found by looking at the viscosities of the samples. Only the MTAB samples not showing restabilization at high surfactant concentrations have a comparably low viscosity. All homogeneous samples with high amount of surfactant are highly viscous. This may indicate that the phase separation is inhibited kinetically and that all samples would phase separate, with possible CNT aggregation, if left to stand sufficiently long. On the other hand, this should not necessarily be attributed to the surfactant alone: it is well known that suspensions with well-dispersed CNTs can form physical gels if the concentration is above the threshold for rigidity percolation, on the order of 0.3 wt%.[38] Even though the CNT concentration is below this threshold in our case, it could thus be the combination of well-dispersed SWCNTs and worm-like micelles at high concentration that gives rise to strongly increasing viscosity, much higher than that of the corresponding surfactant phase without the CNTs.

When discussing the differences in performance between the different surfactants, we should also consider the effect of the different ionic head groups, although the currently available data only allow us to speculate

---

[d]Susanne Klein, personal communication.

about possible effects. The influence of the head group design appears to be the only possible explanation for the much better performance of SDS compared to MTAB, which after all has two carbon atoms more in its hydrophobic chain. (The cationic analog to SDS, 12TAB, with a dodecyl hydropobic chain and a trimethyl ammonium head group, fails utterly for dispersing CNTs, regardless of concentration.) There may be a different interaction between the π electron rich CNT surface and cat- and anionic ions, respectively. The positive ammonium ion of MTAB and CTAB might be expected to adsorb stronger to the CNT than the anionic sulfate group of SDS and SDBS, which might yield a different arrangement of the surfactants on the CNT surface. On the other hand, the aromatic attraction to the CNT surface of the phenyl ring of SDBS, positioned right next to the ionic head group, may compensate for this difference, driving the SDBS molecules just as close to the nanotube surface as the surfactant molecules with cationic head groups.

An equally (or possibly more) important difference are the three methyl groups surrounding the positive charge at the core of the ammonium ion, which will surely affect the hydration sheath compared to the case of the sulfate ions, where water molecules have direct access to the excess charge as well as to two oxygen atoms, which are excellent hydrogen bonding partners. There may also be an effect of the different counter ions, considering that Br after all has almost four times the atomic mass of Na, and only about half of the radius (the radii of the ions should, however, be more similar than for the neutral atoms). All these phenomena will surely have an impact on the efficiency of CNT stabilization. Much research remains to be done to better understand these subtle effects, which to the best of our knowledge have not yet been thoroughly investigated.

4. Advantages of dispersing carbon nanotubes below the Krafft temperature

Many nanoparticles of interest in today's scientific research are hydrophobic, apart from carbon nanotubes also for instance fullerenes, graphene flakes and nano diamond. All these particles are typically handled in the form of a suspension, prepared by sonicating a surfactant solution to which the particles have been added. However, while the surfactant is very useful in keeping the nanoparticles suspended, it also gives some critical disadvantages. It is very difficult to get rid of the surfactant after the particles have been deposited in a targeted area in a device configuration. If the surfactant molecules remain at this stage, they become obstacles that can negatively affect the performance of the system. Another problem is the already mentioned risk of excess surfactant forming micelles that can trigger particle aggregation by depletion attraction. Typically, the surfactant concentrations used for dispersing nanoparticles are on the order of 1 wt%, which is tens or hundreds times the critical micelle concentration (CMC) of the surfactant (see Chap. 2), thus micelles are present in these systems together with the particles, rendering depletion attraction-induced aggregation a risk that must be taken into account.

Dölle *et al.* introduced a very simple method for reducing the amount of surfactant used for nanoparticle dispersion to the absolute minimum,[39] thereby avoiding any risk of depletion attraction and minimizing residue surfactant at the final stage of device fabrication. It may appear surprising that we discuss a method for minimizing surfactant concentration in a chapter on dispersion of nanoparticles in lyotropic liquid crystals, but there are good reasons to consider it in this context. First, as mentioned above, nanoparticles can be successfully dispersed also in lyotropic liquid crystals that are not formed by surfactant micelles but rather by nanoparticles, e.g. rod-like viruses or CNC. In such cases, we do not want any excess surfactant from the nanoparticle suspension, beyond what is needed for stabilizing the suspension, as that will certainly influence the lyotropic liquid crystal phase formation. Second, we may want to use other surfactants for building the liquid crystal phase than those used for keeping the nanoparticles in suspension, an example given in Sec. 6, and also then we have a strong interest in minimizing the amount of particle-stabilizing surfactant in the continuous phase.

The approach takes advantage of the behavior of surfactants below their *Krafft temperature*. The solubility of ionic surfactants is highly temperature dependent, decreasing on cooling, cf. Fig. 4. At low enough temperature the solubility is equal to the CMC, hence no micelles can form at lower temperatures. The threshold temperature is called the Krafft temperature (after its discoverer Friedrich Krafft), which we abbreviate T_K. If we introduce an amount of surfactant into the system greater than the solubility limit, the excess will phase separate out as needle-like crystallites, the solution below T_K containing only individually dissolved surfactant molecules, without any micelles being formed.

If we disperse nanoparticles at $T < T_K$ this gives some attractive advantages. First, we can work with excess surfactant in the system, relying on the fact that whatever surfactant is not used for the nanoparticle dispersion

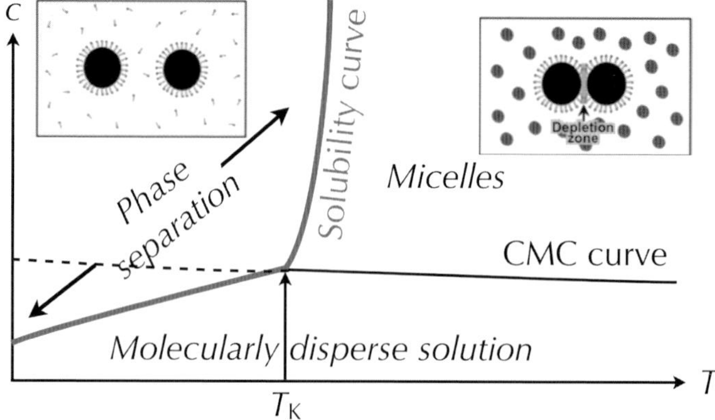

Fig. 4. Schematic diagram of the temperature (T) dependence of surfactant solubility, defining the Krafft temperature T_K as the point where the critical micelle concentration (CMC) curve crosses the solubility curve. The c axis represents surfactant concentration. The insets schematically illustrate how the presence or absence of micelles above and below T_K, respectively, influences particle aggregation by depletion attraction.

in the end can easily be removed after dispersion, as it will sediment on its own if the system is left standing for some time, or one can centrifuge the sample to speed up the process. With excess surfactant in the system, we can work with any concentration of nanoparticles we want, knowing that whatever surface is exposed to the aqueous continuous phase will be covered by surfactant molecules, since the hydrophobic effect promotes adsorption onto hydrophobic surfaces compared to molecular dissolution of the surfactant.

As we start sonicating the sample, taking care to keep the sample at $T < T_K$, particle aggregates are broken up and fresh hydrophobic surface not covered by surfactant is exposed to the solution. The dissolved surfactant molecules will rapidly adsorb to cover the new surface. This reduces the concentration of molecularly dissolved surfactant in the solution below the solubility limit, and some surfactant will thus be dissolved from the crystallites, which act as a surfactant reservoir throughout the sonication process. As more and more nanoparticle surface is exposed when the sonication-induced cavitation breaks up aggregates, this cycle of surfactant adsorption from solution, and dissolution of new surfactant from the reservoir crystallites, will repeat, until no further individualization of nanoparticles takes place. At that stage sonication should be stopped and the sample either left standing for a few days or centrifuged. All remaining excess surfactant needles as well as any poorly dispersed nanoparticles are collected in the sediment, whereas the supernatant, which we extract for later usage, contains well-dispersed nanoparticles with just the amount of surfactant needed to stabilize the suspension, but no micelles.

The concept was demonstrated in the study by Dölle *et al.* on the example of SWCNTs of HiPCO type ($d \approx 1$ nm, $l \approx 500$ nm). Figure 5a shows five samples with different concentrations of CNTs, in each case in a 1 wt% CTAB solution, that have been standing at 20°C for one week after high-power ultra-sonication. The CMC of CTAB is 0.036 wt% and the Krafft temperature is 25°C. The interesting part in these photos is the size of the sediment, which clearly decreases as the CNT content is raised from left to right. The variation in sediment size confirms that CTAB from the phase-separated crystallites contributed to the nanotube dispersion during the sonication process, leaving less crystalline sediment when the amount of nanotubes in the sample is increased.

Well dispersed CNTs with greatly minimized amount of excess surfactant can be extracted from the cleanly separated supernatant. Figures 5b and c show atomic force microscope (AFM) phase images of CNTs de-

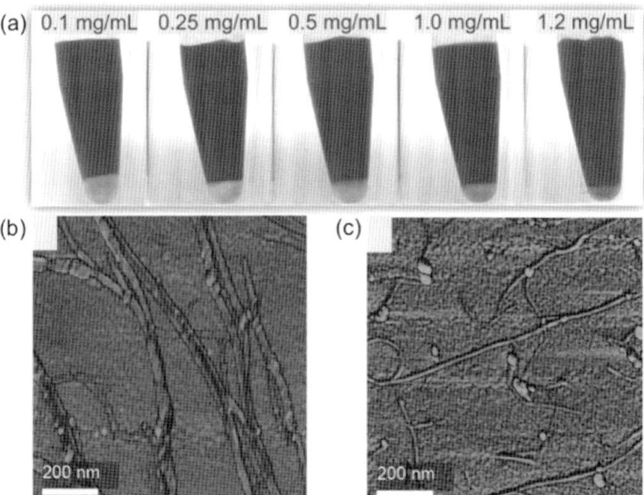

Fig. 5. (a) Macroscopic photos of five samples with different SWCNT concentrations (indicated above each photo) in 1 wt% CTAB solutions, that have been standing at 20°C for one week after sonication at $T < T_K$. (b,c) AFM phase image of deposited SWCNTs that have been dispersed at (b) $T > T_K$ and (c) $T < T_K$, clearly revealing the much reduced excess surfactant after dispersion below the Krafft temperature. Copyright (2012) Wiley. Adapted with permission from Ref. 39.

posited on a silicon wafer, in the former case for CNTs dispersed at $T > T_K$, in the latter case at $T < T_K$. The $T < T_K$ image contains clearly distinguishable features that match in shape and size what is expected for individually suspended SWCNTs, together with a few bright spots which may be islands of solid CTAB. In the $T > T_K$ sample, in contrast, the features are irregular in shape and much wider, indicating that the tubes are embedded in large amounts of remaining excess solid surfactant. The improved dispersion quality of CNTs prepared at $T < T_K$ was also confirmed by comparing absorbance spectra from suspensions prepared below and above the Krafft temperature.[39] Individually dispersed CNTs shows clear oscillations in absorbance spectra, whereas the spectra flatten if the nanotubes are aggregated.[40,41] For suspensions prepared at $T < T_K$ the oscillations were much more prominent than for the control samples, prepared above 25°C, confirming that the CNTs were better suspended also in the liquid sample state.

5. Filament formation in lyotropic liquid crystalline carbon nanotube suspensions

As described in Sec. 2, the order parameter for CNTs dispersed in lyotropic nematic phases filled into capillaries was surprisingly low, on the order of $S \approx 0.3$. Although the theoretical component of the study by Puech *et al.* suggests that this should be expected even for perfect alignment of the liquid crystal host,[13] there will certainly be a reduction in the achieved order from the difficulty in achieving uniform director orientation throughout macroscopic samples. An interesting, and useful, peculiarity of the nematic composites where anionically suspended CNTs could be dispersed in a liquid crystal phase formed by cationic surfactant, is that these phases show drastically altered viscoelastic properties above a certain CNT threshold concentration. A distinct rise in extensional viscosity of these compounds enables the extraction of long filaments (Fig. 6), and it turns out that the CNTs in these filaments are highly aligned along the filament direction, with an order parameter of $S \approx 0.7$.[17,22]

This behavior can be seen as analogous to filament-forming behavior of polymers in solution, connected to a transition from a coiled to a stretched conformation upon shear or extensional flow. This transition increases the extensional viscosity (and decreases the shear viscosity), causing the solution to show increasingly elastic properties, thus reminding more of a solid, in contrast to the classic viscous properties of a fluid. Under these condi-

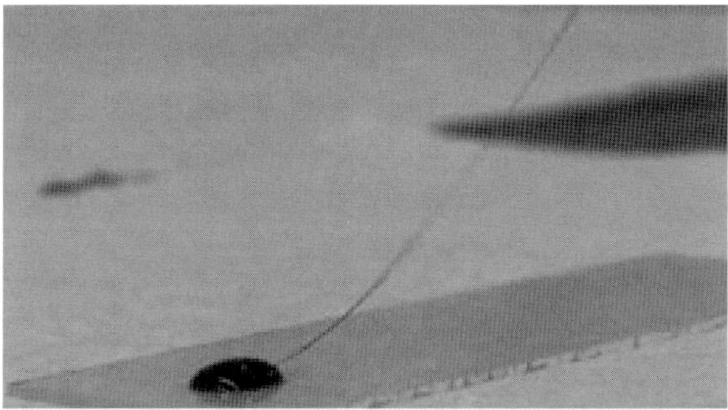

Fig. 6. Filament drawn from a drop of lyotropic liquid crystal-CNT composite. Reproduced from Ref. 42 with permission from The Royal Society of Chemistry.

tions the extraction of filaments becomes possible. In case of the lyotropic nematic-CNT composites we propose[22] that the role of the stretched-out polymer is played by a chain of CNT-containing micelles and stiffened adjacent micelles formed by a supramolecular polymerization[43,44] caused by the peculiar condition of a lyotropic liquid crystal phase with high enough CNT content under extensional flow.

While lyotropic phases of aqueous CTAB show no tendencies of filament forming whatsoever, a CNT content beyond a threshold between 0.5 and 1 mg/mL SWCNTs (HiPCO) causes filaments to be formed upon application of an extensional flow. We induce this flow by dipping a spatula into the composite and pulling it out. In the vicinity of the threshold concentration, short (centimeters) and rather unstable filaments can be drawn from the bulk composites, while above 1 mg/mL CNT content long stable filaments can be extracted. The same holds true for other CNT types, including MWCNTs, although the exact threshold concentration was not established in these cases. A necessary condition apart from the minimum concentration is that the CNTs are well dispersed, since partially aggregated CNTs will disrupt the filament formation. Another prerequisite is the liquid crystallinity of the sample. CNT dispersions in isotropic aqueous CTAB will not form filaments.

Shear viscosity measurements revealed a distinctly different behavior of the composites below and above the threshold in CNT content for filament formation (Fig. 7). The pure lyotropic liquid crystal shows a shear thinning behavior with a distinct transition from a high-viscosity regime to a low-viscosity regime with increasing shear rate as the alignment of $\mathbf{n}$ along the shear flow decreases micelle entanglements.[45] Small additions of CNTs of

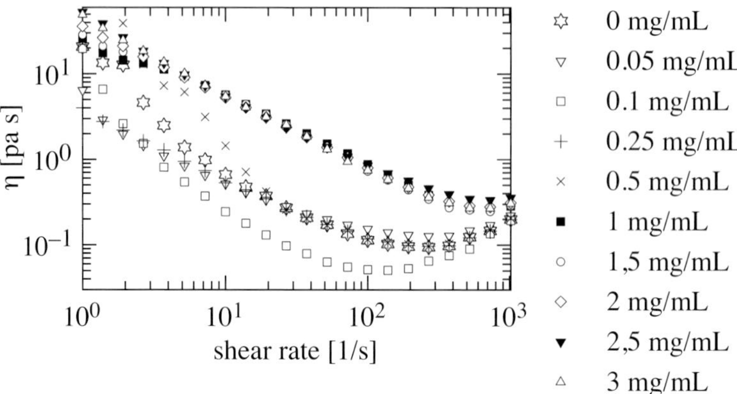

Fig. 7. Shear viscosity data of lyotropic nematic-CNT composites in dependence of shear rate and CNT concentration. Reproduced from Ref. 22 with permission from The Royal Society of Chemistry.

only 0.1 mg/mL decrease the shear viscosity of the compound and suppress any transition behavior as the viscosity data now fall exclusively in the low-viscosity regime. At the filament formation threshold, again a transition regime can be observed while at even higher concentrations the data fall exclusively in the high-viscosity regime. There is no transition behavior observable and no discernible change in viscosity upon further increase in CNT concentration.

The observed variation of the rheological properties in dependence of CNT content which goes in hand with the formation of filaments can be understood as a consequence of supramolecular polymerization.[43,44] When subjected to a quadrupolar ordering field (here the shear/extensional stress and the liquid crystalline phase) sufficiently long and stiff micelles align along the field, enhancing the orientational order and promoting subsequent further growth of the micelles. In the case at hand the CNTs cause the stiffening of the adjacent micelles[46–48] that is needed to set in motion a feedback loop of increasing micelle orientation and growth.

At low CNT concentrations this leads to an inhibition of micelle entanglements and consequent reduction in shear viscosity. Upon growing CNT content it becomes more likely that fusing micelles will contain a CNT or be adjacent to a CNT-containing micelle. This would lead to a sufficient stiffening, such that the feedback loop does not break down and a quasi-infinite chain supporting an ever growing filament can be formed (Fig. 8). These

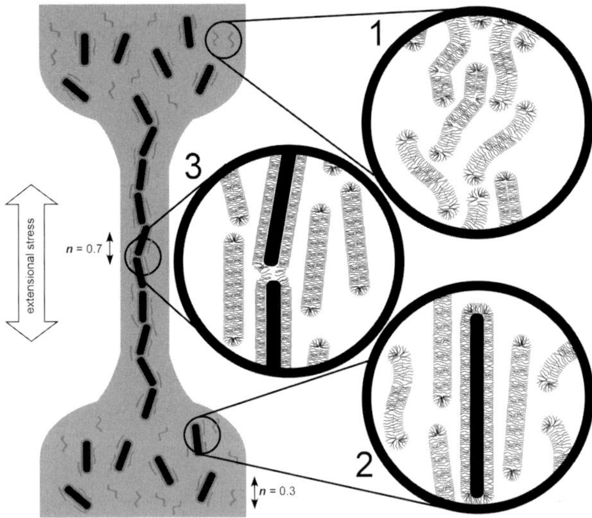

Fig. 8. Schematic depiction of the proposed filament formation process: (1) wormlike, flexible micelles of bulk liquid crystal phase, (2) stiffening of micelles in the vicinity of CNTs and (3) formation of percolating chain of CNTs under extensional stress via supramolecular polymerization. See main text for further explanation.

filaments can be deposited in any continuous shape and be used to deposit aligned carbon nanotube networks. However, it is still highly challenging to rinse away the surfactant after deposition. Unfortunately, the process tends to also remove most of the nanotubes, providing a considerable limitation of the practical usefulness of this method under present conditions.

6. Lyotropic nematic hosts with exceptionally low surfactant concentration by combining cat- and anionic surfactants

As described above, different strategies for realizing lyotropic liquid crystal-CNT composites have been presented in the literature, like the use of the same surfactant for forming the liquid crystal phase as was used for dispersing the nanotubes, or using different types, with opposite charges, for a better packing of the micelles and CNTs.[17] The combination of cat- and anionic surfactants is a powerful but delicate tool in the field of lyotropic liquid crystals. Lack of optimization of the composition can lead to severe aggregation without liquid crystal formation, but it can also greatly facilitate nematic phase formation at surfactant concentrations far below those where these surfactants normally develop anisotropic order,[25] an effect we can explain with the dramatic change in effective packing parameter when cat- and anionic molecules effectively form a 'twin' surfactant dimer.

In Ref. 25 a CNT-liquid crystal composite was realized with the aim of minimizing the overall surfactant content by combining a suspension of CNTs dispersed below the Krafft temperature of the stabilizing surfactant, with a very low-surfactant content lyotropic nematic host formed by cat- and anionic surfactants. The two surfactants used for forming the host liquid crystal were anionic SDS and cationic 12TAB. These surfactants were chosen because they form very long worm-like micelles at a total concentration equal to 1 wt%.[49] This behavior suggests that the combination is suitable for obtaining LC phases at a very low threshold concentration due to the tendency of forming highly anisotropic micelles. The easy formation of cylindrical micelles is likely related to the fact that the surfactants have similar chain length, on top of the important reduction of effective head group area as positive and negative ionic head groups form a pair. The ratio between the two surfactants turns out to be very relevant for the characteristics of the lyotropic host. Small variations in relative composition, still keeping a total concentration of surfactants constantly equal to only 8 wt%, results in very different macroscopic properties, like the appearance or not of a nematic phase.

HiPCO SWCNTs were dispersed with a different surfactant than the host to try to avoid that the surfactant molecules used for stabilizing the CNT suspension would leave the nanotube surface to enter in the host micelles. Interestingly, the addition of CNTs had also a strong impact on the behavior of the host. As shown in Fig. 9 for the reported ratio of cat- and anionic surfactants (molar ratio of SDS to 12TAB equal to 2.3 to 1) the undoped lyotropic exhibited no birefringence in the capillary, even if it did after strong shearing in vials. However, after the addition of CNTs birefringence was clearly observed even in a still-standing sample, indicating the formation of an equilibrium nematic phase (Fig. 9, images C and D).

The CNTs also affected a host with slightly different composition (molar ratio of surfactants 2.7 to 1), showing a flow-induced nematic phase after filling capillaries. The CNT influence is apparent in the phase transition behavior, as shown in Fig. 10. A drastic increase of the clearing temperature can be recognized in the doped sample with more than $10°C$ increase of T_{NI}. The reason for the nanotube-induced stabilization of the nematic phase is not fully clear, but a possibility is that the isotropic phase, just below the onset of liquid crystal formation, is formed by microscopically disordered anisotropic micelles. The high aspect ratio of the CNTs, their

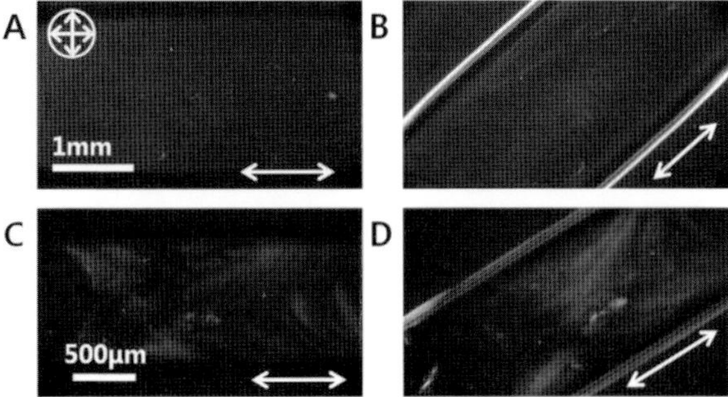

Fig. 9. Lyotropic systems prepared with a surfactant molar ratio of SDS and 12TAB equal to 2.3 to 1 without (images A and B) and with CNTs (C and D) in capillaries investigated by polarizing optical microscopy. The double arrow at the bottom right of each panel indicates the capillary axis, and thus the shear flow direction during filling. Reproduced with permission from Ref. 25.

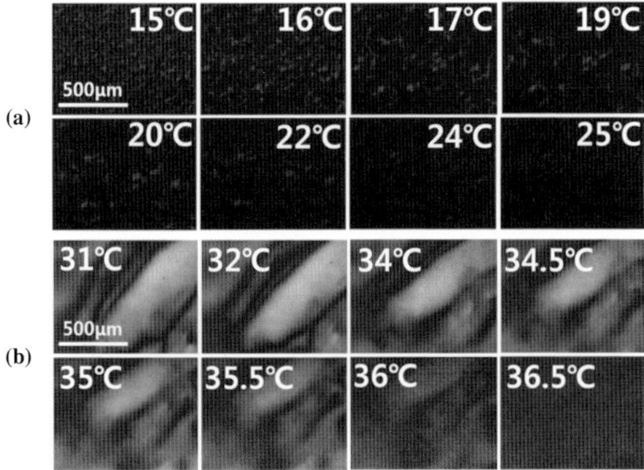

Fig. 10. The phase transition between the nematic and isotropic phase in the undoped (a) and CNT-doped lyotropic nematic systems (in both cases SDS and 12TAB in 2.7:1 molar ratio, total surfactant concentration 8 wt.-%). Reproduced with permission from Ref. 25.

higher rigidity compared to the surfactant micelles and the presence of surrounding surfactant micelles can induce a biasing effect on the alignment of the micelles as sketched in Fig. 11. On a local scale such influence was confirmed by cryogenic electron microscopy by Regev and co-workers.[46]

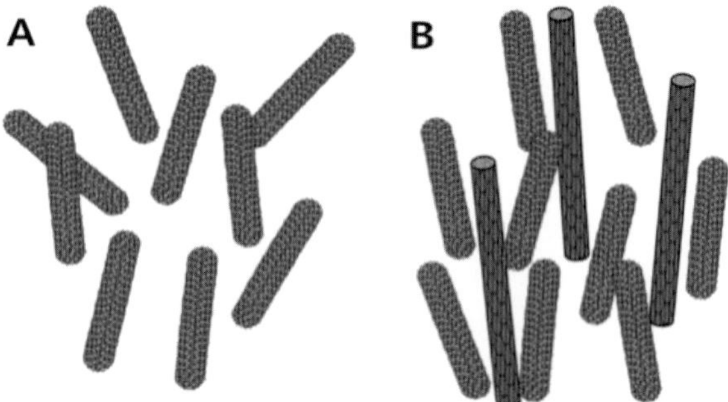

Fig. 11. Scheme of pristine lyotropic nematic prepared by charge combination of SDS and 12TAB surfactants (A) with anisotropically shaped micelles locally aligned with a lower degree of order and macroscopically misaligned. The CNT-doped sample is drawn in (B) with the nanotubes bringing the alignment of the local domains into a common direction. For simplicity the surfactant molecules on the CNT surface have been omitted in the drawing. Reproduced with permission from Ref. 25.

7. Conclusions and outlook

Comparatively little efforts have been done to explore the control of alignment (and possibly of position) of nanoparticles in lyotropic liquid crystal phases, but the existing reports clearly hint at some attractive advantages. To the best of our knowledge, the surfactant-based lyotropic nematic is so far the only liquid crystal phase that has been shown to be capable of dispersing a sufficient amount of carbon nanotubes, at sufficient degree of orientational order, to achieve a macroscopic light polarizing effect. The filament formation is another unique aspect of these systems, which could be interesting in developing deposition methods with control of nanotube order, or perhaps to spin very strong, thin and conductive wires, based on the presence of a high concentration of aligned carbon nanotubes.

A major problem with surfactant-based liquid crystal formation in this context is, however, that it is not trivial to remove the surfactant without also removing the nanoparticles, once the composite system has been deposited on a target substrate or incorporated in a target material. Generally, the surfactant is highly detrimental to the further use of nanoparticles such as carbon nanotubes or graphene, hence their presence at the stage of application must be minimized. In this sense, the method to disperse hydrophobic nanoparticles below the Krafft temperature, in order to remove all surfactant that is not actively participating in keeping the nanoparticles suspended, is of great interest. This can then be combined with novel approaches for forming the liquid crystal host phase, for instance by appropriately combining cat- and anionic surfactants to achieve nematic phases at total surfactant concentrations much lower than usual, or with lyotropic phases that are not formed by surfactants at all, for instance virus- or CNC-based lyotropics. These phases also have the attractive ability to get kinetically arrested at an early stage of solvent evaporation, with retained liquid crystalline order, hence it is easy to transfer the composite into a solid without loss of the macroscopic order. However, if the virus or CNC particles are not desirable in the end product, which would normally be the case if the electronic properties of, for instance, carbon nanotubes are to be utilized, then their removal can be very challenging indeed.

Much remains to be done in terms of analyzing how the details of surfactant chemical design influence the performance in nanoparticle dispersion. Empirical data clearly demonstrate that the differences between surfactants can be considerable, and the behavior as the surfactant concentration is increased is far from trivial to understand. Issues like depletion attraction, electrostatic screening, and possible multi-layer adsorption are scenarios that need to be taken into account when modeling the behavior. Computer simulations may be helpful to advance the understanding, and also experiments with non-ionic surfactants should be performed to provide valuable complementary data.

References

1. S. Lee, C. Mao, C. Flynn, and A. Belcher, Ordering of quantum dots using genetically engineered viruses, *Science.* **296**(5569), 892–895 (2002).
2. E. Eiser, F. Bouchama, M. Thathagar, and G. Rothenberg, Trapping metal nanoclusters in "soap and water" soft crystals, *ChemPhysChem.* **4**(5), 526–528 (2003).
3. V. Gaikwad, Anil, P. Verschuren, T. van, der Loop, G. Rothenberg, and E. Eiser, Stable soap and water sponges doped with metal nanoparticles, *Soft Matter.* **5**(10), 1994–1999 (2009).
4. H. Park, A. Agarwal, N. Kotov, and O. Lavrentovich, Controllable side-by-side and end-to-end assembly of au nanorods by lyotropic chromonic materials, *Langmuir.* **24**(24), 13833–13837 (2008).
5. Q. Liu, M. Campbell, J. Evans, and I. Smalyukh, Orientationally ordered colloidal co-dispersions of gold nanorods and cellulose nanocrystals., *Adv. Mater.* **26**(42), 7178–7184 (2014).
6. M. Campbell, Q. Liu, A. Sanders, J. Evans, and I. Smalyukh, Preparation of nanocomposite plasmonic films made from cellulose nanocrystals or mesoporous silica decorated with unidirectionally aligned gold nanorods, *Materials.* **7**(4), 3021–3033 (2014).

720   *S. Dölle et al.*

7. A. Querejeta-Fernández, B. Kopera, K. Prado, A. Klinkova, M. Methot, G. Chauve, J. Bouchard, A. Helmy, and E. Kumacheva, Circular dichroism of chiral nematic films of cellulose nanocrystals loaded with plasmonic nanoparticles., *ACS Nano.* **9**(10), 10377–10385 (2015).

8. Q. Liu, Y. Cui, D. Gardner, X. Li, S. He, and I. Smalyukh, Ivan, Self-alignment of plasmonic gold nanorods in reconfigurable anisotropic fluids for tunable bulk metamaterial applications, *Nano. Lett.* **10**(4), 1347–1353 (2010).

9. E. Venugopal, K. Bhat, Suresh, J. Vallooran, Jijo, and R. Mezzenga, Phase behavior of lipid-based lyotropic liquid crystals in presence of colloidal nanoparticles, *Langmuir.* **27**(16), 9792–9800 (2011).

10. K. Beneut, D. Constantin, P. Davidson, A. Dessombz, and C. Chaneac, Magnetic nanorods confined in a lamellar lyotropic phase, *Langmuir.* **24**(15), 8205–8209 (2008).

11. D. Constantin, P. Davidson, and C. Chaneac, Lyotropic lamellar phase doped with a nematic phase of magnetic nanorods, *Langmuir.* **26**(7), 4586–4589 (2010).

12. N. Ould-Moussa, C. Blanc, C. Zamora-Ledezma, O. D. Lavrentovich, I. I. Smalyukh, M. F. Islam, A. G. Yodh, M. Maugey, P. Poulin, E. Anglaret, and M. Nobili, Dispersion and orientation of single-walled carbon nanotubes in a chromonic liquid crystal, *Liq. Cryst.* pp. 1–8 (2013).

13. N. Puech, M. Dennison, C. Blanc, P. van, der Schoot, M. Dijkstra, R. van, Roij, P. Poulin, and E. Grelet, Orientational order of carbon nanotube guests in a nematic host suspension of colloidal viral rods, *Phys. Rev. Lett.* **108**(24), 247801 (2012).

14. V. Weiss, R. Thiruvengadathan, and O. Regev, Preparation and characterization of a carbon nanotube-lyotropic liquid crystal composite, *Langmuir.* **22**(3), 854–856 (2006).

15. J. P. F. Lagerwall, G. Scalia, M. Haluska, U. Dettlaff-Weglikowska, S. Roth, and F. Giesselmann, Simultaneous alignment and dispersion of carbon nanotubes with lyotropic liquid crystals, *Phys. Stat. Sol. (b).* **243**(13), 3046–3049 (2006).

16. J. P. F. Lagerwall, G. Scalia, M. Haluska, U. Dettlaff-Weglikowska, S. Roth, and F. Giesselmann, Nanotube alignment using lyotropic liquid crystals, *Adv. Mater.* **19**(3), 359–364 (2007).

17. G. Scalia, C. von Bühler, C. Hägele, S. Roth, F. Giesselmann, and J. P. F. Lagerwall, Spontaneous macroscopic carbon nanotube alignment via colloidal suspension in hexagonal columnar lyotropic liquid crystals, *Soft Matter.* **4**(3), 570–576 (2008).

18. S. Schymura, E. Enz, S. Roth, G. Scalia, and J. P. F. Lagerwall, Macroscopic-scale carbon nanotube alignment via self-assembly in lyotropic liquid crystals, *Synth. Met.* **159**(21-22), 2177–2179 (2009).

19. K. Okano, I. Noguchi, and T. Yamashita, Anisotropic carbon nanotube films fabricated from a lyotropic liquid-crystalline polymer, *Macromolecules.* **43**(13), 5496–5499 (2010).

20. S. Mauter, Meagan, M. Elimelech, and O. Osuji, Chinedum, Nanocomposites

of vertically aligned single-walled carbon nanotubes by magnetic alignment and polymerization of a lyotropic precursor, *ACS Nano.* **4**(11), 6651–6658 (2010).

21. F. Tardani and C. La Mesa, Elasticity of dispersions based on carbon nanotubes dissolved in a lyotropic nematic solvent, *J. Phys. Chem. C.* **115**(19), 9424–9431 (2011).

22. S. Schymura, S. Dölle, J. Yamamoto, and J. Lagerwall, Filament formation in carbon nanotube-doped lyotropic liquid crystals, *Soft Matter.* **7**(6), 2663 – 2667 (2011).

23. J. Vallooran, Jijo, S. Bolisetty, and R. Mezzenga, Macroscopic alignment of lyotropic liquid crystals using magnetic nanoparticles, *Adv. Mater.* **23**(34), 3932–3937 (2011).

24. H.-S. Jang, T.-H. Kim, C. Do, M.-J. Lee, and S.-M. Choi, Single-walled carbon nanotube induced re-entrant hexagonal phases in a pluronic block copolymer system, *Soft Matter.* **9**(11), 3050–3056 (2013).

25. H. R. Jo, J. Yamamoto, J. Lagerwall and G. Scalia, *Effects of carbon nanotubes on a very low surfactant concentration lyotropic liquid crystal host.* SPIE proceedings 9004, doi. 10.117/12.204918 (2014).

26. L. Q. Amaral and M. E. Marcondes Helene, Nematic domain in the sodium lauryl sulfate water decanol system, *J. Phys. Chem.* **92**(21), 6094–6098 (1988).

27. S. Schymura. *Liquid Crystalline Carbon Nanotube Suspensions: From Unique Challenges to Unique Properties.* PhD thesis, Martin-Luther-Universität Halle-Wittenberg, Halle, Germany (2013).

28. C. Zakri and P. Poulin, Phase behavior of nanotube suspensions: From attraction induced percolation to liquid crystalline phases, *J. Mater. Chem.* **16** (42), 4095–4098 (2006).

29. S. Dölle. *Dispersion und Organisation von Kohlenstoffnanoröhrchen in lyotropen Flüssigkristallen - Vergleichende Untersuchungen zum Einfluss der Amphiphiltypen.* Diploma thesis, Martin-Luther-Universität Halle-Wittenberg, Halle (2009).

30. S. Schymura, M. Kühnast, V. Lutz, S. Jagiella, U. Dettlaff-Weglikowska, S. Roth, F. Giesselmann, C. Tschierske, G. Scalia, and J. Lagerwall, Towards efficient dispersion of carbon nanotubes in thermotropic liquid crystals, *Adv. Funct. Mater.* **20**(19), 3350–3357 (2010).

31. J. Stewart, A. Saiani, A. Bayly, and G. Tiddy, The phase behaviour of lyotropic liquid crystals in linear alkylbenzene sulphonate (LAS) systems, *Colloid Surf. A-Physicochem. Eng. Asp.* **338**(1-3), 155–161 (2009).

32. S. Ramaraju, B. Carroll, J. Chambers, and G. Tiddy, The liquid crystalline phases formed by linear-dodecylbenzene sulphonic acid during neutralisation with sodium carbonate, *Colloid Surf. A-Physicochem. Eng. Asp.* **288**(1-3), 77–85 (2006).

33. D. Marenduzzo, K. Finan, and P. R. Cook, The depletion attraction: An underappreciated force driving cellular organization., *J. Cell Biol.* **175**(5), 681–686 (2006).

34. S. Asakura and F. Oosawa, Interaction between particles suspended in so-

lutions of macromolecules, *Journal of Polymer Science.* **33**(126), 183–192 (1958).

35. A. Yodh, K. Lin, J. Crocker, A. Dinsmore, R. Verma, and P. Kaplan, Entropically driven self-assembly and interaction in suspension, *Philos. Transact. A Math. Phys. Eng. Sci.* **359**(1782), 921–937 (2001).

36. D. F. Evans and H. Wennerström, *The Colloidal Domain: Where Physics, Chemistry, Biology, and Technology Meet (Advances in Interfacial Engineering).* Wiley-VCH, New York, NY, USA (1999).

37. R. J. Hunter, *Foundations of Colloid Science.* Oxford University Press, USA (2001).

38. L. Hough, M. Islam, P. Janmey, and A. Yodh, Viscoelasticity of single wall carbon nanotube suspensions, *Phys. Rev. Lett.* **93**(16), 168102 (2004).

39. S. Dölle, B.-D. Lechner, J. H. Park, S. Schymura, J. P. F. Lagerwall, and G. Scalia, Utilizing the krafft phenomenon to generate ideal micelle-free surfactant-stabilized nanoparticle suspensions, *Angew. Chem. (Int. Ed.).* **51**(13), 3254–3257 (2012).

40. A. Blanch, C. Lenehan, and J. Quinton, Optimizing surfactant concentrations for dispersion of single-walled carbon nanotubes in aqueous solution., *J. Phys. Chem. B.* **114**(30), 9805–9811 (2010).

41. M. OConnell, S. Bachilo, C. Huffman, V. Moore, M. Strano, E. Haroz, K. Rialon, P. Boul, W. Noon, C. Kittrell, J. Ma, R. Hauge, R. Weisman, and R. Smalley, Band gap fluorescence from individual single-walled carbon nanotubes, *Science.* **297**(5581), 593–596 (2002).

42. J. P. F. Lagerwall and G. Scalia, Carbon nanotubes in liquid crystals, *J. Mater. Chem.* **18**(25), 2890–2898 (2008).

43. M. Turner and M. Cates, Flow-induced phase-transitions in rod-like micelles, *J. Phys.-Condens. Mat.* **4**(14), 3719–3741 (1992).

44. P. P. A. M. van der Schoot. Theory of supramolecular polymerization. In ed. A. Ciferri, *Supramolecular Polymers*, pp. 77–106. Taylor & Francis, Boca Raton, USA (2005).

45. L. Coppola, R. Gianferri, I. Nicotera, C. Oliviero, and G. Ranieri, Structural changes in $CTAB/H_2O$ mixtures using a rheological approach, *Phys. Chem. Chem. Phys.* **6**(9), 2364–2372 (2004).

46. E. Nativ-Roth, R. Yerushalmi-Rozen, and O. Regev, Phase behavior and shear alignment in SWNT-surfactant dispersions, *Small.* **4**(9), 1459–1467 (2008).

47. E. Nativ-Roth, O. Regev, and R. Yerushalmi-Rozen, Shear-induced ordering of micellar arrays in the presence of single-walled carbon nanotubes, *Chem. Commun.* (17), 2037–2039 (2008).

48. O. Ben-David, E. Nativ-Roth, R. Yerushalmi-Rozen, and M. Gottlieb, Rheological investigation of single-walled carbon nanotubes - induced structural ordering in CTAB solutions, *Soft Matter.* **5**(9), 1925–1930 (2009).

49. A. Renoncourt. *Study of supra-aggregates in catanionic surfactant systems.* PhD thesis, University of Regensburg (2005).

Chapter 21

Control of nanoparticle self-assemblies using distorted liquid crystals

Emmanuelle Lacaze* and Delphine Coursault

*Institut des Nano-Sciences de Paris (INSP), UMR-CNRS 7588,
Université Pierre et Marie Curie-Paris 6, 75005 Paris, France*
emmanuelle.lacaze@insp.jussieu.fr

This chapter concerns the structure and the optical properties of nanoparticle (NP)/liquid crystal (LC) composites in the presence of LC distortion. After a first description of the general behaviour of NPs at the proximity of distorted LC areas, the first section of the chapter discusses the stabilization of the LC phases, characterized by the presence of topological defects in presence of NPs. The assemblies of NPs induced by distorted LC films is addressed in the second section. The last section then extensively develops the structure and optical properties of NP assemblies created within topological defects. Specific localisation and orientations of the NPs will be discussed, but also possible control of the size and shape of the NP assemblies, together with control of the distances between NPs in the assemblies, leading to original optical properties of the composites as far as fluorescent or gold NPs are concerned.

Contents

1. General behavior of nanoparticles embedded in distorted liquid crystals

1.1. *Direct proof of attraction by the defects*

The localisation of a nanoparticle in a LC distorted area allows the decrease of the free energy due to the release of the elastic energy in the volume occupied by the particle. In the presence of a distortion gradient, the NPs will be automatically attracted to the most deformed area.[1] Moreover, in presence of topological defects, associated with highly elastically distorted areas around a defect core, a localisation of the NPs within the core usually occurs. The energy density is indeed higher within the core, associated with disordered matter and this is now the disorder energy that is released. The first example of such a phenomenon corresponds to the trapping of NPs in the nematic Saturn ring disclination (see Chap. 10) around a micron-sized colloid.[2–4] In LC cells containing silica beads, one can play on the thickness of the cell to induce either a point defect (hedgehog) or a line defect (saturn-ring) around the micron-sized particle. Trapping in hedgehog defects of micron-sized colloids (see Chap. 10) has also been intensively studied.[4–6] If we consider a nematic defect, the elastic energy density, at a distance D from the defect, can be roughly estimated of the order of K/D^2, with K the elastic constant (see Chap. 2, Sec. 4). The replacement of the corresponding volume of distorted liquid crystal by a spherical NP of radius R, leads to an elastic energy benefit of $4K\pi R^3/3D^2$. For a particle of diameter 10 nm, the attraction by the defect becomes efficient (larger than k_BT, where k_B is the Boltzmann constant and T the temperature) at a distance D from the defect equal or smaller than 85 nm for a typical $K = 7.10^{-12}$ J.m^{-1}.[7] Experimentally, for nanorods of volume around two times larger, an attraction has been shown to be already measurable at a distance of 2μm from a micron-sized colloid associated with a saturn-ring defect (Fig. 1b).[4] It is clear however that the specificity of the involved distortion around the defect and the influence of the LC anchoring at the NP surface may play a role. In case of anisometric NPs, the surface anchoring will tend to align them either parallel (planar anchoring) or perpendicular (homeotropic anchoring) to the nematic director.[8,9] With gold nano-objects, the NP presence in the LC matrix can be evidenced using two photon luminescence. For two nanorods with anchoring varying between planar and homeotropic and NP volumes varying by a factor 8, different trajectories are then observed toward the saturn-ring defect (Fig. 1b).

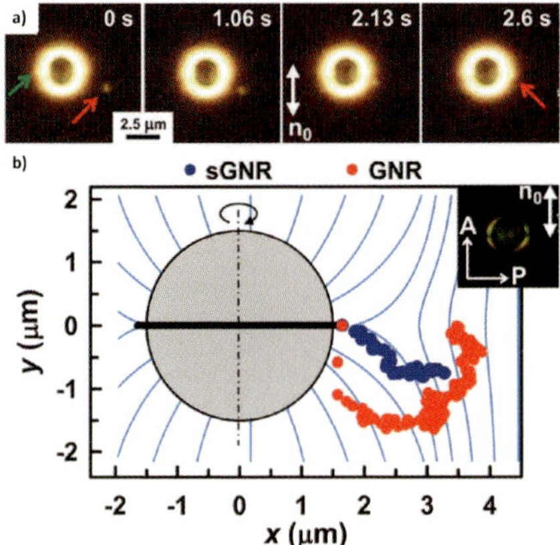

Fig. 1. (a) Dark-field images showing attraction of a gold nanorod (marked by a red arrow) to a saturn-ring defect (marked by a green arrow). (b) Trajectories of gold nanorods (red filled circles - homeotropic anchoring and blue filled circle - planar anchoring) attracted to the saturn-ring (black line). Ordinary index, n_0 is shown by white double-headed arrows and the nematic director N(r) is shown by blue lines in (b). Inset in (b) shows the polarizing microscope texture of the microsphere with the saturn-ring defect. Reprinted with permission from Ref. 4. Copyright 2012 by the American Chemical Society.

However the final localisation is within the saturn-ring defect for the two nanorods (Fig. 1a-b).[4] An experiment such as this shows that topological defects of micron-sized colloids can be used to trap NPs with highly precise spatial localisation since, independently of the trajectory towards the defect, the two nanorods both become localised on the saturn-ring.[2,4] A problem can arise due to NPs which become "stuck" in a metastable state close to the defects. The use of a laser beam to overcome the corresponding repulsive barrier energy may thus become necessary.[4] This shows that it is important to build distorted LC matrices that are efficient from the point of view of NP attraction towards the desired location for the NPs.

1.2. *Stabilisation of liquid crystal phases with topological defects induced by the nanoparticles*

The interactions between NPs and defects have also been probed indirectly. In the presence of NPs, existing LC phases with topological defects can be stabilized, with a larger temperature range. A number of experiments on composite systems, NPs/blue phases, have been performed with NPs of size between 3.5 and 9 nm.[10–12] Blue phases (BPs) are formed by highly chiral liquid crystals. They are stable in a very narrow temperature range and are characterized by three-dimensional lattices of disclinations of periods of several hundred nanometers (for further details the reader can refer, among others, to the review by Seideman[13] or the book chapter by Crooker in "Chirality in Liquid Crystals" edited by Kitzerow and Bahr[14]). For NPs of diameter 3.5 nm, covered by organic ligands made of grafted alkyl chains, a combination of experiment and theory was used to demonstrate that almost all NPs can be trapped within topological defects of the blue phases.[11] In contrast, this trapping is less efficient for a second kind of NPs of diameter 9 nm with OH groups at their surface,[12] possibly in relation with the well-known induced degenerate planar anchoring by these OH groups. The planar anchoring around the NPs may induce less distortion/disorder in the surrounding LC than the homeotropic anchoring due to the organic ligands.[15] As a consequence, it may be of greater energetic advantage to position NPs in defect cores for homeotropic anchoring, possibly due to a double energetic gain: disordered core energy is eliminated for a volume corresponding to that of the NP, but also the additional distortion/disorder induced around the NPs located in initially non distorted LCs is avoided. The first energy term is independent of the LC anchoring, but not the second one. This last term is of higher energy for homeotropic anchoring with respect to planar anchoring, explaining the better trapping efficiency for the homeotropic anchoring.

Generally speaking, a stabilisation of the LC phases with topological defects in the presence of NPs only holds for NPs of small enough diameter. If the NP size is larger than the defect core, some additional disorder may be induced.[16] This disorder may depend on the anchoring around the NPs. For NPs larger than the defect core, a stabilisation of the LC phases with topological defects in the presence of NPs may thus hold for appropriate anchoring only. A larger disorder outside the defect cores than the one that the NPs would have induced elsewhere in the distorted liquid crystal should be avoided. Indeed Ravnik *et al.* demonstrated that a NP of diameter beyond 10 nm must present anchoring energy small enough (smaller than 10^{-5} Jm^{-2}) to stabilize the composite system NPs/blue phases.[17] On the other hand, Stratford *et al.* demonstrated that by playing with anchoring strength at the NP/ LC interface as well as with NP density, various blue phases may be obtained for NPs of sizes up to 50 nm.[18] Thereforth, if the size of NPs matters for the stability of the trapping within the topological defect core,[19] appropriate anchoring may finally enable the balancing of these effects.

This stabilizing property of the NPs is of interest for further applications, in particular for blue phases which exhibit a reflexion band whose wavelength is related to the defect lattice. While the structure of NPs/blue phases composites might be switched by applying an external electric field, it opens the route for "future multistable device application".[18] Moreover new phases can also appear in the presence of NPs. This has been shown to occur for Twist Grain Boundary (TGB) phases, characterized by arrays of screw dislocations, which can be evidenced in the presence of NPs only.[20] For the chiral liquid crystal phases, like blue phases and TGB phases, the presence of chiral ligands around the NPs has been suggested to be a key parameter that enhances the stabilisation of the LC phases in presence of defects.[11,20]

2. Nanoparticle assemblies induced in distorted liquid crystals

2.1. *Introduction*

We just described how NPs are attracted by the elastically deformed liquid crystal areas, thanks to the elastic energy advantage associated with the replacement of a deformed LC area by a NP. This suggests that these areas can be used as templates for NP self-assemblies, in a top-down approach, similar to the one tested for micron-sized colloids.[4] However, how does self-assembly occur in distorted areas, in absence of topological defects with singular cores? We expect an accumulation of NPs within the distorted areas, but to allow for fine control over their behavior, it appears crucial to be able to manipulate the structures of the NP assemblies induced in distorted LCs at the single NP level. The behavior of the NP is very sensitive to its surroundings and usually modified by the interactions which take place within the NP assemblies. This is particularly true for metallic NPs which display localized surface plasmon resonance (LSPR). The response to incident light is dependent on the electromagnetic coupling which can occur between NPs.[21,22] This coupling is first determined by the shape of the assemblies. For an anisotropic shape, we expect a larger coupling for an incident polarization along the long axis of the assembly. In consequence, the LSPR can become activated by the appropriate light polarization. However the electromagnetic coupling is obviously also related to the distance between the NPs and we also have to understand how to control the spacing ("side to side" distance) between NPs.

2.2. *Liquid crystals without topological defects*

2.2.1. *The example of distorted cholesterics*

To answer these questions, oriented distorted LCs can be used. Cholesteric LCs (CLCs-see Chap. 2), frustrated by competing anchorings at the substrate/CLC (planar unidirectional anchoring on rubbed polymer substrate) and CLC/air (homeotropic anchoring) interfaces, are associated with a 90° rotation of the cholesteric helix (scheme on Fig. 2b).[23,24] For well-defined thicknesses, distorted cholesteric films are characterized by a helix perpendicular to the substrates, rotating close to the CLC/air interface to become aligned parallel to the substrate, along a well-defined direction (Fig. 2). This leads to the fingerprint texture evidenced by the optical microscopy picture of Fig. 2a (helix close to the CLC/air interface perpendicular to the stripes) and schematically shown on Fig. 2b. The presence of oriented distorted areas may be induced around the 90° tilt of the helix, together with the well known presence of an array of disclinations with no singular cores at the proximity of the CLC/air interface.[25,26] Thin distorted cholesteric films have been prepared on rubbed PVA substrate and solvent droplets with gold nanoparticles (radius $R = 2.1$ nm) have been deposited on top of these films to favor localization of the nanoparticles close to the CLC/air interface.[27,28]

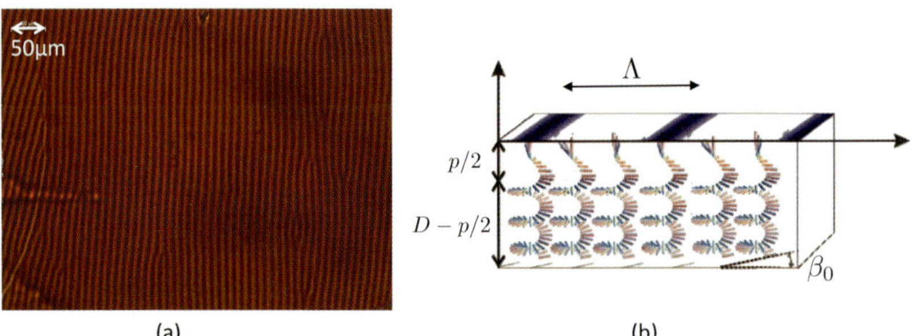

(a)   (b)

Fig. 2.   (a) Optical microscopy image (crossed polarizers) of a typical area of a CLC sample with competing anchorings, which exhibits the expected striped texture, associated with a planar helix close to the CLC/air interface. (b) The director field of the aligned CLC sample. The helical axis is perpendicular to the planar aligning surface over a thickness $D - p/2$, p being the cholesteric pitch and D being in that case the sample thickness. It gives way to a rotation of the cholesteric helix within a thickness around $p/2$ from the CLC/air interface to allow the director to meet the homeotropic boundary condition at the interface. The rods show the orientation of the director in the film. Λ is the period of the stripes (see (a)), β_0 is the angle between the normal to these stripes and the orientation of the director on the substrate.

By combining atomic force microscopy (AFM, see Chap. 9) that probed the topography of NP assemblies, ultraviolet-visible spectroscopy (UV-vis) that probed LSPR light absorption of gold NPs[a] and Generalized Mie Theory (GMT) for the simulations of LSPR of gold NPs,[b] the formation of needle-like structures of the spherical gold NPs within the distorted cholesterics has been demonstrated.[28] They are referred as "ribbons" in the following. In the CLC, the gold NP LSPR varies with the incident light polarization, depending mainly, for a given CLC thickness, on the polarization orientation with respect to the LC anchoring on the substrate (Fig. 3b). In the simpler case of nematics with a well-defined orientation of the director, Park and Stroud[30] have shown that the LSPR is weakly dependent on the orientation of the electric field along the ordinary or the extraordinary direction. The large LSPR shift between the two polarizations, parallel and perpendicular to the anchoring on the substrate, ($\Delta\lambda = 18$ nm) is expected to be linked to the ribbons presence (evidenced by AFM as shown in Fig. 3a) and to the anisotropic coupling between NPs induced in the ribbons, the ribbons being partly oriented by the CLC matrix. The LSPR measurements, together with simulations, allow modeling of the ribbon structure. They are long (larger than 200 nm - 41 NPs) and, on average, of one or two NPs in width. Moreover the ribbons are oriented in average only, since a LSPR anisotropy around $\Delta\lambda = 50$ nm would be expected for strictly oriented ribbons, instead of the measured $\Delta\lambda = 18$ nm. The large number of ribbons, together with the observation of ribbon orientation not related to the disclination orientation at the proximity of the CLC/air interface suggest that the ribbons are more likely formed around the 90° tilt of the helix. This shows that NP trapping can be different from trapping of micro-sized colloids. Micro-sized colloids are indeed usually trapped by the disclinations at the proximity of the CLC/air interface.[25] This underlines the different process of trapping for nano and microparticles, NPs being more sensitive to local distortions.

---

[a]UV-vis spectroscopy allows to probe the extinction properties of a sample. Light, from near UV to near infra-red, can be absorbed or scattered by the probed sample, it correspond to electronic transition from the ground state to an excited state. For noble metal like gold, silver and copper, collective oscillations of the conductive electrons corresponding to intraband transition, show a strong resonance known as localized surface plasmon resonance (LSPR) in the visible range.

[b]The Mie Theory allows to solve the Maxwell equation for a sphere (with a diameter that can be of several wavelength and a complex refractive index) illuminated by a plane wave. The GMT is the extension of the Mie Theory to multiple scatterers of different geometry illuminated by beam of different shape.[29]

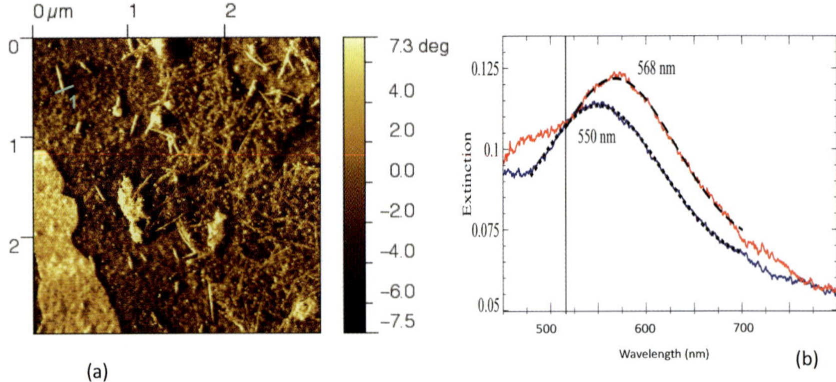

Fig. 3. (a) AFM image of gold NPs self-assembled in ribbons after the evaporation of most of the cholesteric film. The AFM phase data are shown to better evidence the presence of the disordered ribbons (needle-like structures), concentrated at the right side of the image. At the left side isolated, ribbons are visible, one being underlined by "1". (b) Optical extinction of the gold NP ribbons prior to evaporation of the cholesteric film; red: polarization perpendicular to LC anchoring on the substrate; blue: polarization parallel to LC anchoring on the substrate.

The observed large anisotropic LSPR wavelength in Fig. 3b is not only related to the anisotropic shape of NP assemblies oriented by the CLC matrix, but is also enhanced by the small distance between NPs, induced by the surrounding CLC matrix (red-shift with respect to isolated NPs of 52 nm for light polarized perpendicular to anchoring and 34 nm parallel to anchoring - Fig. 3(b)). Calculations using Generalized Mie theory[31] lead to spacings between the NPs of the order of 0.6 nm, associated with a strong interdigitation/compression of the dodecanethiol ligands, localised between the NPs. This is smaller than 0.98 nm, the spacing found in 2D NP monolayers formed on the bare rubbed polymer substrates (the pure colloidal solution is drop-casted in absence of CLC in the solution). On the other hand, this latter value of 0.98 nm is close to the one simulated with the same NPs for 2D monolayers in air,[16,32,33] suggesting that the spacing in 2D monolayers without CLC is mainly controlled by the van der Waals interactions between the dodecanethiol ligands balanced by the steric repulsions.[32] In CLC, an additional attraction between NPs (LC-induced compression) occurs and decreases the spacing value to 0.6 nm. This compression may arise from the disorder induced by the NPs in the cholesteric sample. If the trapping area is not a singular defect core, the presence of NPs locally induces disorder in the liquid crystal, entailing an additional energy term. Consequently in CLC, the distance between two nanoparticles must be as small as possible to reduce the disordered volume around the NPs.

2.2.2. *Conclusion*

In distorted LCs, *a priori* in the absence of singular defect cores,[23,24] the localization of NPs appears different from that of micron-sized colloids and in relation to the presence of oriented distorted areas. Anisotropic assemblies of NPs can be formed, but without perfect orientation. As a result, the localized surface plasmon resonances (LSPR) of the gold NPs become activated by light polarization which yields an added value to these composite films of gold NPs/distorted LCs when the distortion can become oriented by the substrate. A strong modification of the LSPR with respect to that of isolated NPs is observed. It arises due to the LC-induced attraction between NPs associated with the disorder created by the NPs in the surrounding LCs. As a consequence, the electromagnetic coupling between NPs in LCs may be controlled by the nature of the ligands coating the NPs, which may vary the distortion/disorder around the NPs.

3. In the presence of topological defects

When the trapping sites are topological defects associated with a disordered defect core, the energy gain of the NP presence will be particularly high. It minimizes the free energy by decreasing the disordered volume of the defect core. This is the case of the defects associated with micron-sized colloids (hedgehog or "saturn ring" defects - see Chap. 10), disclinations in blue phases,[2–6] screw dislocations in twist-grain-boundary phases[20] and dislocations in smectics.[16,34,35] These topological defects can be used in the directed assembly of nanoparticles, a way to build original nanostructured materials on a large scale.[36] In the following, the first subsection concerns the situation where properties of isolated NPs must be retained without electromagnetic coupling between NPs. The modification of the coupling properties of the NPs in a controlled way is discussed in the last subsection.

3.1. *Single nanoparticles*

3.1.1. *Localisation of NPs*

As mentioned earlier, hyperbolic hedgehog defects (point defects: 0D) associated with a micron sized colloid (embedded in the LC matrix) can attract
and entrap a single NP (of various size and shape).[4–6] In a second step,
the assembled micro/nanoparticle object can be used as a building block
for 1D or 2D assembly designed with optical tweezers. This process enables
the periodic arrangement of NPs of large period, preserving their individual
properties since no electromagnetic coupling between the NPs occurs,[4] but
without any easy production on a large scale (Fig. 4.1).

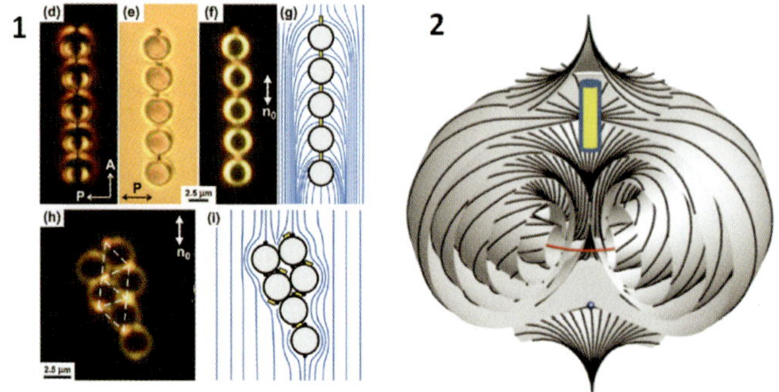

Fig. 4. 1. Colloidal superstructure of gold nanoparticles and dielectric microspheres
in nematic liquid crystal. Reprinted with permission from Ref. 4. Copyright 2012 by
the American Chemical Society. 2. Schematic structure of a toron with a gold nanorod
trapped in the upper hedgehog defect perpendicular to the toron axis. Reprinted with
permission from Ref. 37. Copyright 2013 by the American Physical Society.

Similar attraction/entrapment for single particles may be achieved using
cholesteric torons created by laser irradiation of a cholesteric film.[37] A toron
consists of two hyperbolic hedgehog defects connected by a looped double
twist cylinder (see scheme in Fig. 4.2). Scanning a cholesteric film with a
Gaussian beam enables the creation of extended 1D or 2D arrays of defects
as shown on Fig. 5. The stabilisation of the film through partial polymerization then allows for successive liquid crystal layer deposition/laser irradiation cycles, leading to 3D structures (Fig. 5b). The polymerized bottom
layer acts as a template and generates the upper layer with similar defect
structures. The nature of the defects may also be varied in each layer. In
the case of torons, Evans and coworkers evidenced that gold nanorods (with

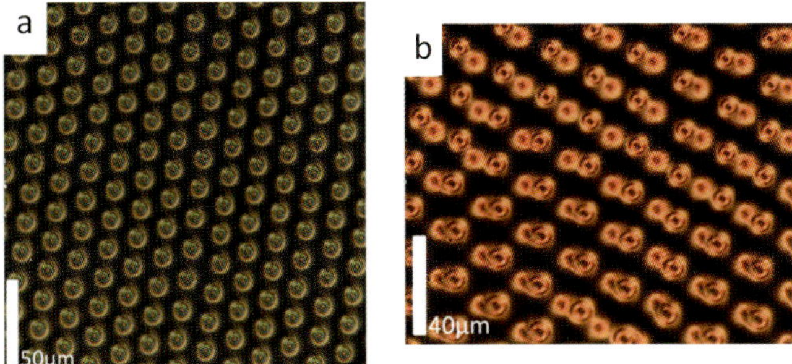

Fig. 5.   a) Polarized optical microscopy (POM) image of 2D arrangement of optically generated torons; b) POM image of polymerized torons in a two-layer cholesteric film. Reprinted with permission from Ref. 37.   Copyright 2013 by the American Physical Society.

a long axis as small as 65 nm and a diameter of 25 nm) can be trapped in the hyperbolic hedgehog point defect on top of the toron, with an average orientation perpendicular to the toron axis as revealed by dark field microscopy (Fig. 4.2). This demonstrates that not only the localisation of the NPs can be imposed by the defect but its orientation as well. It has been shown that partial polymerization of the film can be achieved. First it may suppress the residual Brownian motion of the trapped nanorods. Second it may allow for an exchange of the unpolymerized liquid crystal with oil, in order to alter the gold nanorod properties by varying its surrounding.[38,39] Extended 2D or 3D arrays of nanorod/toron composites remain to be realized, with the difficulty related to the two step process for layer formation: aggregation or inhomogeneity of the nanorod density in the matrix must be avoided prior to laser irradiation. Microgrooves can be used to create extended arrays of defects.[40,41] However, until now, only microspheres have been efficiently trapped in this kind of array.[41]

A promising alternative consists in using self-organized arrays of topological defects in a one step process where NPs are trapped during the LC film formation. A solution containing the LC molecules together with the NPs can be deposited on the substrate, such that, during the solvent evaporation, in the same time the topological defects form and the NPs become trapped in the defects. This kind of defect array can be formed in smectic films due to antagonistic anchorings at the two interfaces, with a homeotropic anchoring at the LC/air interface and a planar unidirectional anchoring on the substrate. The advantage lies in the formation of the array on the whole sample, with the array homogeneity only related to the thickness homogeneity. There are two typical structures corresponding to arrays of smectic topological defects:

(1) for planar degenerate anchoring[42,43] or for planar unidirectional anchoring with large liquid crystal film thickness,[44] hexagonally or quasi-hexagonally packed focal conic domains are created. Focal conics are elliptical topological defects around which the smectic layers rotate (see Fig. 6a). For planar degenerate anchoring, they form for all thicknesses, as they are only associated with a linear defect perpendicular to the substrate. For planar unidirectional anchoring, focal conics are associated with grain boundaries and local anchoring breaking at both interfaces.[44] They consequently become less favorable than oily streaks for small thicknesses,[44,45] oily streaks presenting extended 2D grain boundaries but not any anchoring breaking.

(2) Smectic oily streaks thus correspond to the second kind of array, associated with planar unidirectional anchoring and small liquid crystal film thickness (100 nm-300 nm). They have been described in various papers.[45–49] In the oily streaks, the smectic layers are stacked in flattened hemicylinders, perpendicular to the anchoring direction on the substrate (see Fig. 6b).[45,46] It has been shown that between and below the hemicylinders, grain boundaries may be present, with a number of straight edge dislocations dispersed along the grain boundaries and parallel to the hemicylinder axis (Fig. 6).[46–49] Oily streaks are thus associated with a dense array of straight dislocations perpendicular to the anchoring. Dislocation orientation can be identified by optical microscopy which detects the hemicylinders orientation (Figs. 6(b) and 8(b)). The drawback is that topological defects in these arrays are not 0D defects, but 1D defects with defect cores of width of the order of the NP size. As a consequence, a well defined localization in the dislocation is expected, but without any specific localization along this 1D defect. For small NP concentrations only, we expect a dispersion of the NPs along the 1D defects. In oily streaks, the first experiments were performed with spherical quantum dots with low density (10^{-5} %vol), in order to visualize *in situ* the NP assembly. Fluorescence microscopy reveals chains of non interacting particles (Fig. 7a).[34]

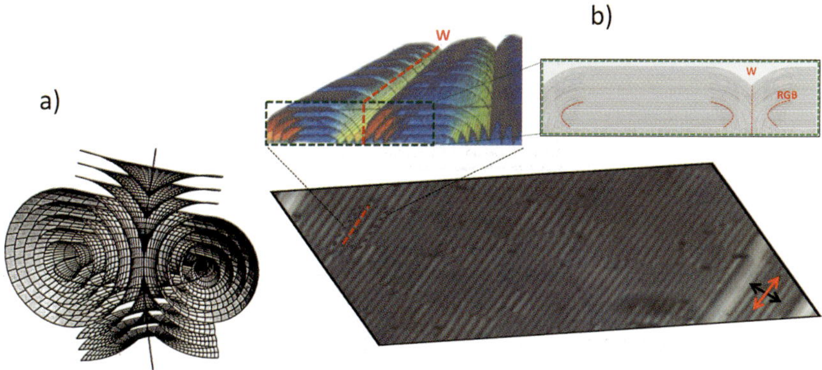

Fig. 6.   (a) Schematic illustration of the internal structure of focal conic domains (courtesy of C. Blanc) (b) Oily streaks leading to straight lines viewed in top view by optical microscopy between crossed polarizers, the lines being associated with smectic layers organized in flattened hemicylinders parallel to the substrate. The flattened hemicylinder internal structure is shown in side view (on the right). It is associated with grain boundaries represented in red, along which straight dislocations, oriented parallel to the hemicylinder axis, are dispersed.

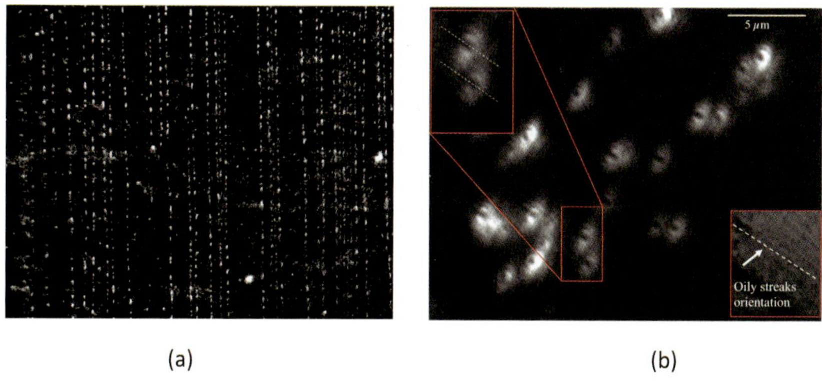

Fig. 7.   (a) Chains of quantum dots formed in smectic oily streaks (density $10^{-5}\%$vol), parallel to the 8CB hemicylinders (80 μm $\times$ 60 μm) (b) Photoluminescence of DRs illuminated with the 436 nm band of a Hg lamp in defocused configuration: the objective is defocused by setting the focal plane 500 nm away from the DR. (Left-inset) Zoom on two defocusing spots. (Right-inset; 5×6 μm^2) In absence of high-pass filter and in focused configuration, the oily streaks are observed with the same source.

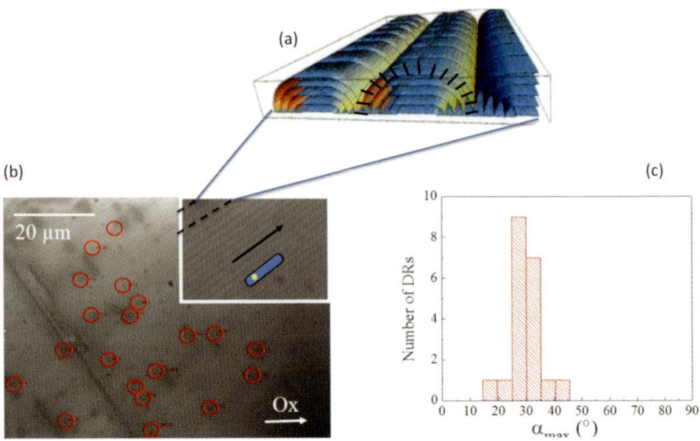

Fig. 8. (a) Scheme of the flattened hemicylinders of smectic layers, represented in relation to the optical microscopy. (b) 8CB smectic oily streak film of 130 nm thickness observed through optical microscopy between crossed polarizers. The position of the nanorods is found in the smectic oily streaks, via fluorescence microscopy and is highlighted by red circles on the picture. The inset shows a zoom of size 13.5 μm x 9 μm. The arrow indicates the axis of the oily streaks, the in-plane orientation of the dipoles (as deduced from panel (c)) is shown with the blue icon. (c) Histogram of the angle value corresponding to the fluorescence maximum for the 20 DRs measured on panel b.

3.1.2. *Orientation of nanorods*

Using fluorescent nanorods, the orientation of nanorods within topological defects has been confirmed and extended to a large scale by using these arrays of smectic dislocations, created in smectic oily streaks.[50] If the nanorod width matches that of the smectic dislocation cores (of the order of the smectic layer thickness[51]), the size matching, in addition to the nanorod's elongated shape, promotes the nanorod trapping inside the line defects. The localisation of nanorods within and parallel to the dislocation core maximizes the volume of disordered liquid crystal expelled by the nanorods. It thus decreases the disorder energy of the smectic liquid crystal film in the presence of dislocations. If we consider elementary smectic dislocations, their energy per unit of length has been measured in free standing smectic films to be 0.5 k_BT/Å.[52] As a consequence a single nanorod of length $l = 23$ nm (diameter around 7 nm), trapped in the dislocation core and parallel to its axis, allows a decrease in the liquid crystal disorder energy of 115 k_BT, leading to a significant advantage for the liquid crystal film. The nanorods, once trapped in smectic dislocations, may be particularly well-stabilised.

The efficiency, in terms of induced-nanorod orientation, has been investigated using fluorescent CdSe/CdS Dot-in-Rods (DRs).[50] Although those DRs can be viewed as a model system, the technology can be easily extended to a wide class of anisotropic nano-objects. The choice of these particles was dictated by:

- their geometrical properties, a one-dimensional shape used in combination with the linear liquid crystal structures of oily streaks in order to obtain orientation of the rods.
- their quantum properties, they behave as single photon emitters with reduced blinking.[53]
- their polarized emission,[54] in order to control the polarization of the emission of single emitters.

The direct observation of the emitting DRs is obtained with a defocused microscopy experiment (Fig. 7b). This consists of varying the focalization with respect to the quasi-punctual nanorods by 500 nm to reveal the shape of the emitted spot. Almost all DRs appear oriented parallel to the oily streak's hemicylinder axis, and thus parallel to the smectic dislocations (hemicylinder orientation visible by optical microscopy on the same area - Fig. 7b).

On rubbed polymer substrates, the emission polarization of each nanorod, underlined by red circles in Fig. 8b, has been measured. It appears oriented, as shown on the histogram of Fig. 8b, at an average angle value of $\phi = 29.9°$ (standard deviation of 5.6°), equal to the oily streak stripe orientation angle (Fig. 8b). These results are finally interpreted by DRs parallel to the dislocations and thus embedded within the dislocations cores, at the same time forced to orient parallel to the linear dislocation core.[50] They also show that orienting the DRs, we accordingly finely tune the polarization of single photon emitters.

This work shows the feasibility of a large-scale orientation of anisotropic emitters. Smectic dislocations not only trap but also align elongated nano-objects. It paves the way for macroscopic assemblies into linear arrays, nonetheless of nano-emitters that are sources of well polarized single-photon emission, but also more generally of elongated nanoparticles. In the case of metallic nanorods, we expect to induce an anisotropic (plasmonic) extinction. For composite films of very low NP density, similar to the cholesteric case with torons,[37] one could polymerize the smectic oily streaks in order to annihilate Brownian motion of the NPs along the defect core. In contrast, to achieve dense assemblies of NPs, motion of NPs within the defects may be favoured (increase of temperature).

3.2. *Control of nanoparticle assemblies*

One major advantage of directed assembly is that ultra-small distances between NPs can be achieved, in contrast with other micro-fabrication techniques such as e-beam lithography. When composite materials include metallic or fluorescent NPs, promising modifications of the NP's optical response are expected due to the induced electromagnetic coupling between the NPs. The first question is: can liquid crystal topological defects be used for an accurate control of size and shape of NP assemblies? We address this question in the first part of the section (Sec. 3.2.1). The second question is then addressed in the second part (Sec. 3.2.2). It is: can liquid crystal topological defects be used for the design of interactions between NPs? There is a complex interplay between NP size, NP ligands and topological defect nature for the control of these interactions. If we want to allude to the possibility of manipulating NP properties, either individual or collective, by the smart use of topological defects to finely direct their assemblies, the understanding of this interplay is essential. To reach this goal, while the nano-objects become too small to be observed by conventional and direct imaging techniques, the combination of various experiments, from linear and non linear spectroscopies to X-Ray diffraction (as described in Chap. 6), may be used to characterize assembly, position and orientation of the NPs in the composites.

3.2.1. *From ribbons to chains*

Smectic Liquid crystal wedge cells with gold nanoparticles
Smectic edge dislocations appear to be good candidates to control NP assemblies, in particular to direct highly anisotropic assemblies due to their linear geometry. Without NP, it is known that linear arrays of smectic edge dislocations are created in the center of wedge cells with a periodicity of the order of some microns, defined by the angle of the cells (top of Figure 9).[55] The dislocations appear at the nematic/smectic A transition. Using wedge cells with homeotropic anchoring on both sides (top of Figure 9), Milette and coworkers created 8CB edge dislocation arrays decorated with gold NPs.[35]

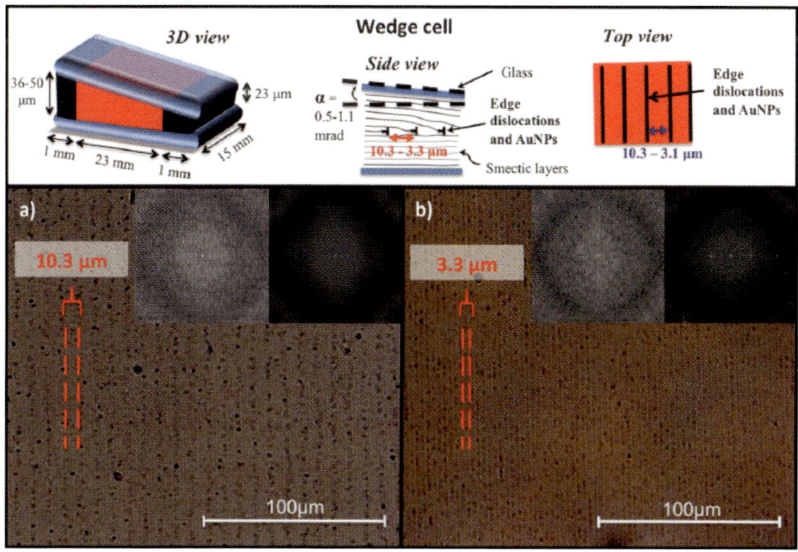

Fig. 9. Polarized optical microscopy images, between parallel polarisers of gold NPs (0.1%) self-assembled in large ribbons in 8CB confined in a homeotropic wedge cell with an angle a) 0.5 mRad; b)1.1 mRad. Inset rights are the fast fourier transform of the polarized optical microscopy images. The NP ribbons are localized around the dislocations contained in the film and thus reveal the presence of the dislocations. On top are schematics of the wedge cell. Reproduced from Ref. 35 with permission of The Royal Society of Chemistry.

Observation of gold NPs (of a diameter around 5 nm) around the dislocations is obtained for concentrations below 0.5%vol and a film thin enough to avoid aggregation of gold NPs in the nematic phase. Initially homogeneously dispersed in the nematic phase thanks to their partial mesogenic coating, the gold NPs aggregate along the dislocations at the smectic phase transition. They form large ribbons (micron size) visible by optical microscopy (Fig. 9). While varying the angle of the wedge cell, the period of the gold NP ribbons changes, following the trend of the period of the defects (Figs. 9(a)–(b)). Furthermore the increase in dislocation density (associated with a decrease of the angle leading to small Burger vectors for the dislocations) diminished the size of gold NP aggregates as shown in Fig. 9. This is in agreement with almost all gold NPs being trapped in the vicinity of the dislocations, which is confirmed by the observation that in the cavity cell (open cell), where dislocations are expected to be rejected to the glass plate interface,[56] the aggregates appear, by optical microscopy, closer to the substrate interface than to the air interface. To understand the trapping by the dislocations, the mobility of the dislocations is compared with and without nanoparticles.[57] The localisation of the gold NPs is modeled similarly to the so called Cottrell clouds in metals. These are impurities (foreign atoms) in the metal crystal that accumulate in the vicinity of dislocation:[57,58] On the one hand, the impurities tend to be segregated around the dislocations lowering their elastic energy. On the other hand, the dislocations are attached to the impurities diminishing the plasticity of the material.[59] The gold NP distribution within the dislocations was statistically modeled using a Boltzmann distribution: $C = C_0 e^{-\frac{E_I}{k_B T}}$, with C_0 the gold NP concentration far from the defect, E_I the interaction energy between the NP and the defect, being proportional to the deformation volume representing a gold NP.

As a result, the Cotrell Cloud corresponds to the area where $C > C_0$ and it appears that the gold NP cloud is localized in a single plane around the dislocation core, where the dilation of smectic layers is not negligible. The investigation of the variation of the dislocation mobility, evidences a hardening of the LC in the plane perpendicular to the layers. Although the theoretical model did not include NP interactions (aggregations) and considered no disorder induced by the gold NP ligands, the good fit to the experimental data warranted the model.[57] This work highlights again that smectic edge dislocations are highly attractive, but the trapping by the dislocation core is not demonstrated, the NPs concentration being so large that the majority of gold NPs may be localized in elastically distorted areas.

This work also shows that an increase in dislocation density, for a given gold NP concentration, leads to a decrease of the ribbon width. This suggests that obtaining straight single chains or ribbons of controlled width at the single NP level could be possible, leading to highly anisotropic optical properties for the composite films (see Sec. 3.2.2). This could occur if the majority of gold NPs becomes trapped in the dislocation cores which can be almost strictly linear. For such a purpose, a critical gold NP density in combination with a high defect density is required. The wedge cell geometry offers to easily vary the dislocation density. However the associated critical NP density is limited to a maximum of 0.05%vol. This is too small to induce a significant optical adsorption at the macroscopic level.

Smectic liquid crystal oily streaks with gold nanoparticles

In the case of the wedge cells presented above, the period of the dislocations varies between 2 and 10 μm. In comparison, the dislocation density in oily streaks is expected to be 100 times higher.[48,49] If the density of gold NPs is not too high, the NPs should mostly become located in the dislocation core. The small core width of the dislocations should lead to a linear confinement for the gold NPs, already evidenced for quantum dots (Sec. 3.1.1)[34] and for fluorescent nanorods (Sec. 3.1.2).[50] Can we now densify the composites, still preserving a linear assembly of the NPs, but with a small distance between NPs in the chains? For such a purpose, an increase of 10^4 in NP density has become necessary with respect to quantum dot experiment (Fig. 7(a)): the distance between the gold NPs needs to be smaller than twice their diameter in order to induce a non negligible electromagnetic coupling between them. Direct observation of the gold NPs being impossible, extinction measurements related to LSPR properties of gold NPs have been performed using UV-vis spectroscopy under a microscope probing an area of 50×50 μm^2. The LSPR has been compared for a polarization along and perpendicular to the defects. An example is shown in Fig. 10a. An anisotropy of the plasmon resonance is observed. The LSPR parallel to the dislocations is red-shifted compared to the perpendicular one. Furthermore the superposition of the extinction spectrum of the colloidal suspension (gold NP dispersed in toluene) fit the extinction for a polarization perpendicular to the dislocations, highlighting that an in-phase electromagnetic coupling occurs only along the dislocations. Chains of interacting NPs have grown along the dislocations. The fact that no electromagnetic coupling is observed perpendicular to the dislocations demonstrates that the induced NP chains are not only individual but also straight. They are strictly oriented along a single direction of the substrate, the dislocation orientation which is perpendicular to the anchoring direction.[34] This suggests a better accuracy of liquid crystal topological defect cores to impose a well-defined shape and orientation to the NP assemblies, with respect to elastically distorted liquid crystal areas (compare with Sec. 2.2.1). Accordingly the anisotropy of the LSPR, $\Delta\lambda \times 2$ is larger for similar gold NPs (in oily streaks $\Delta\lambda = 35$ nm[16] with respect to $\Delta\lambda = 18$ nm in cholesterics (Sec. 22.1)[28]). This is due to the small size of the liquid crystal defect cores, together with the ability to strictly orient them in oily streaks, thanks to the presence of orienting interfaces. Trapped within nematic disclinations, chains of micron-sized colloids were also created between the two interfaces of closed cells, where the substrate polymer had been appropriately rubbed.[60,61] They did not appear as straight as the chains of NPs created in smectic oily streaks. This is due to the fact that the colloids were considerably larger than the disclination cores, whereas the NP size is of the same order of magnitude. Therefore, this last parameter appears crucial for a good control of the NP organization.

3.2.2. *Control of the electromagnetic coupling between NPs*

Directed assembly of NPs using topological defects as templates may enable manipulation of NP assemblies through the control of their size and shape. The study of the NP chains created in oily streaks also allows the study of the parameters defining the spacing value ("side-to-side" distance between NPs). The spacing value strongly influences the electromagnetic coupling between NPs and, consequently, the induced optical response of the composites. On the same composites with smectic oily streaks as in Sec. 3.2.1, UV-vis measurements (Fig. 10a) have been analyzed using dipolar approximation to extract the corresponding spacing between NPs. These measurements can be combined with X-ray diffraction measurements (Fig. 10b), performed with synchrotron radiation.[16] Figure 10b confirms the creation of single chains with a unique orientation along the smectic dislocations: the grazing incidence small angle scattering (GISAXS) bands are only observed along the defects. Moreover the value of the spacing between the NPs in the chain can be also obtained, through a fitting of the GISAXS data.[16] The spacing values obtained for NP chains trapped within smectic dislocations have been compared to the spacing between NPs without liquid crystal. The gold NPs and the smectic 8CB being mixed in the same solvent (toluene in this case), the drop-casting on top of the rubbed polymer substrate can be compared with and without smectic 8CB. Without 8CB, 2D monolayers of gold NPs are created on the substrate and analysis of UV-vis data with dipolar approximation still allows the extraction of the corresponding spacing between NPs. With smectic 8CB, in a one-step process, NP chains are created by the trapping of NPs in the dislocations during the solvent evaporation.[34] After the complete solvent evaporation, different spacing values have been found, depending on the solvent evaporation rate,[16] demonstrating the dual influence of ligands and presence of topological defects on the induced electromagnetic coupling between NPs.

For an abrupt evaporation, the spacing is small, of the order of 0.7 nm, in other words, much smaller than twice the ligand length (1.4 nm for a single extended dodecanethiol[62]). Between NPs, not only the ligands are

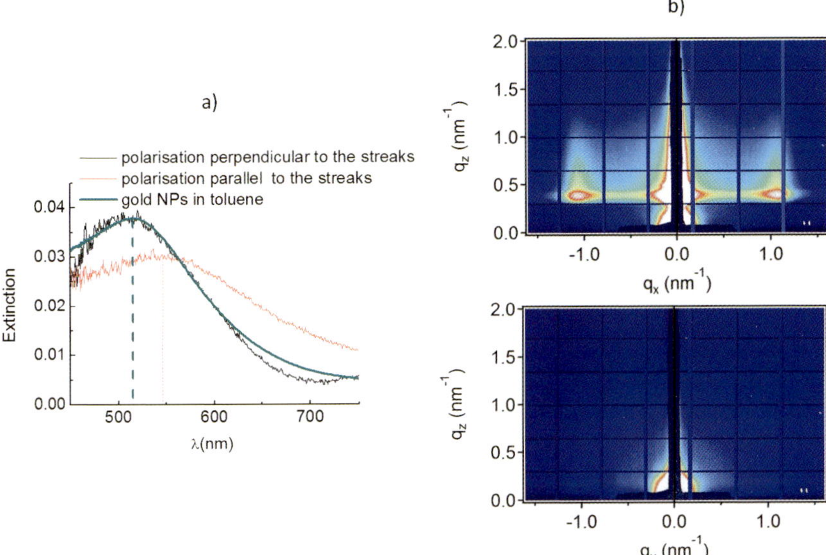

Fig. 10.   a) Extinction spectra for NP/LC composites with average volume fraction $\phi = 0.13\%$. Measurements with incident light polarized parallel and perpendicular to the LC stripes (visible by optical microscopy - Fig. 6b) are plotted in red and black, respectively. The blue dotted line is indicative of the position of the LSPR maximum of NPs in toluene and corresponds to the spectrum of the colloidal solution (bold black). The fact that there is red-shift only for polarization parallel to the dislocations indicates that there is electromagnetic coupling between NPs only in this direction. In other words, there is formation of single chains parallel to the dislocations. b) GISAXS pattern for controlled solvent evaporation (volume fraction of NPs in LC film $\phi = 0.026$ %) in oily streaks oriented at $90°$ (top) and $0°$ (bottom) from the incident X-ray beam. The intensity scale is the same for both patterns. There is no signal parallel to the beam demonstrating that we only have single chains parallel to the dislocations.

interdigitated, but they are even confined in a ring of width smaller than one ligand length (at least 30% smaller). The ring is much smaller than the 8CB molecule length (2 nm), meaning that there are almost no LC molecules between NPs within the chains. It is observed that the spacings are similar in NP chains formed in dislocation cores and in 2D NP assemblies without liquid crystal. These obtained similar spacing values indicate that there is no liquid crystal-induced compression (LC-induced attraction between NPs) like that found in elastically distorted liquid crystals (Sec. 2.2.1).[32] This is because NPs are already trapped in disordered areas (the defect cores) and do not induce additional disorder in the liquid crystal. As a consequence of the strong ligand interdigitation, the dominating interactions between neighboring NPs are Van der Waals interactions between the ligands of neighboring NPs together with steric repulsion. As a result, there is no significant impact of the dislocations cores on the spacing between NPs, which is imposed by the ligand's interdigitation. The spacing is similar in smectic oily streaks and in 2D monolayers without LC.

For slower solvent evaporation, the ligands around the NPs become swollen by the solvent,[63,64] leading to an increase of steric interactions between NPs during the self-assembly. As a consequence, the induced spacings are larger than for abrupt evaporation. The Van der Waals attraction between the ligands of neighboring NPs decreases and the influence of the dislocation cores is revealed. As we already discussed, in the presence of NPs within the dislocation core, the disorder is decreased thanks to the expulsion of disordered molecules from the cores. In contrast with elastically distorted liquid crystals (Sec. 2.2.1: observation of LC-induced attraction between NPs), an additional repulsion between NPs along the chains is expected: the energy advantage due to the dislocation line tension replacement by NPs is expected to be larger in the presence of NPs far from each other. It is maximum when the distance between NPs is equal to twice the length of the ligands. Accordingly, with slow solvent evaporation an increase in the spacing between NPs has been measured from 0.94 nm for 2D monolayers without liquid crystal to 1.9 nm for smectic oily streaks.

These results demonstrate that, within topological defects in smectic films, the distance between NPs can be increased with respect to the case without liquid crystal, if the solvent evaporation is controlled. On the other hand for all solvent evaporation, the spacing between NPs remains small, mostly smaller than the NP diameter and is controlled by the ligand length. This should induce the presence of a large number of hot spots between neighboring gold NPs. The so-called hot spots are areas characterized by strong field exaltation and occur mainly when gold NPs are strongly electromagnetically coupled. They are interesting for a number of applications, in particular to induce surface enhanced Raman scattering, allowing for accurate measurements of organic molecules at the proximity of the hot spots. In oily streaks, we expect that these hot spots become activated by light polarization. This could constitute a unique system for efficient surface enhanced Raman scattering phenomenon of particularly large enhancement if the liquid crystal can be eliminated in a second step.

4. Conclusion

In conclusion, the combination NPs/distortion-defects in LCs appears fruitful and of high potential for future applications. The LC phases formed by networks of topological defects are stabilised with NPs. On the other hand, depending on the topological defects, a number of specific NP organizations become possible, converting these distorted LCs into matrices of high potential for a directed NP self-assembly. Localization of the NPs in specific areas can be achieved, as can orientation along a single direction. For higher NP concentrations, in elastically distorted areas or in topological defects, accumulation of NPs occurs. Topological defects allow for well-defined NP assemblies, single NP chains in particular, due to the small width of the defect cores. In contrast if LC-induced compression occurs in elastically-distorted LCs, a LC-induced extension can take place within topological defects. This finally bridges the gap between two extreme cases, mainly observed in LCs without distortion: (1) aggregation of NPs, where LC-induced attraction between NPs (LC-induced compression) and small distances between NPs take place; (2) correct dispersion of NPs, which induces distances between NPs, that can be considered as quasi-infinite, with no electromagnetic coupling.

References

1. D. Voloschenko, O. P. Pishnyak, S. V. Shiyanovskii and O. D. Lavrentovich, Effect of director distortions on morphologies of phase separation in liquid crystals, *Phys. Rev. E.* **65**, 060701 (2002).
2. M. Skarabot, M. Ravnik, S. Zumer, U. Tkalec, I. Poberaj, D. Babic and M. I., Hierarchical self-assembly of nematic colloidal superstructures, *Phys. Rev. E.* **77**, 061706 (2008).
3. G. Koenig, J. de Pablo and N. L. Abbott, Characterization of the reversible interaction of pairs of nanoparticles dispersed in nematic liquid crystals, *Langmuir.* **25**, 13318 (2009).
4. B. Senyuk, J. S. Evans, P. J. Ackerman, T. Lee, P. Manna, L. Vigderman, E. R. Zubarev, J. van de Lagemaat and I. I. Smalyukh, Shape-dependent oriented trapping and scaffolding of plasmonic nanoparticles by topological defects for self-assembly of colloidal dimers in liquid crystals, *Nano Letters.* **12**, 955–963 (2012).
5. B. Senyuk and I. I. Smalyukh, Elastic interactions between colloidal microspheres and elongated convex and concave nanoprisms in nematic liquid crystals, *Soft Matter.* **8**, 8729–8734 (2012).
6. A. V. Ryzhkova and I. Musevic, Particle size effects on nanocolloidal interactions in nematic liquid crystals, *Phys. Rev. E.* **87**, 032501 (2013).

7. M. J. Bradshaw, E. P. Raynes, J. D. Bunning and T. E. Faber, *J. Phys. (Paris).* **46**, 1513 (1985).

8. S. V. Burylov and Y. L. Raikher, On the orientation of an aniso-metric particle suspended in a bulk uniform nematic, *Phys. Lett. A.* **149**, 279 (1990).

9. S. V. Burylov and Y. L. Raikher, Orientation of a solid particle embedded in a monodomain nematic liquid-crystal, *Phys Rev. E.* **50**, 358 (1994).

10. H. Yoshida, Y. Tanaka, K. Kawamoto, H. Kubo, Tsuda, A. Fujii, S. Kuwabata, H. Kikuchi and M. Ozaki, Nanoparticle-stabilized cholesteric blue phases, *Applied physics express.* **2**, 121501 (2009).

11. E. Karatairi, B. Rozic, Z. Kutnjak, V. Tzitzios, G. Nounesis, G. Cordoyiannis, J. Thoen, C. Glorieux and S. Kralj, Nanoparticle-induced widening of the temperature range of liquid-crystalline blue phases, *Phys. Rev. E.* **81**, 041703 (2010).

12. B. Rozic, V. Tzitzios, E. Karatairi, U. Tkalec, G. Nounesis, Z. Kutnjak, G. Cordoyiannis, R. Rosso, E. Virga, I. Musevic and S. Kralj, Theoretical and experimental study of the nanoparticle-driven blue phase stabilisation, *Eur. Phys. J. E.* **34**, 1 (2011).

13. T. Seideman, The liquid-crystalline blue phases, *Reports on Progress in Physics.* **53** (6), 659 (1990).

14. P. Crooker, Blue phases. In eds. H.-S. Kitzerow and C. Bahr, *Chirality in Liquid Crystals*, Partially Ordered Systems, pp. 186–222. Springer New York (2001).

15. Q. Liu, Y. Yuan and I. I. Smalyukh, Electrically and Optically Tunable Plasmonic Guest-Host Liquid Crystals with Long-Range Ordered Nanoparticles, *Nanoletters.* **14**, 4071 (2014).

16. D. Coursault, J.-F. Blach, J. Grand, A. Coati, A. Vlad, B. Zappone, D. Babonneau, G. Lévi, N. Félidj, B. Donnio, J.-L. Gallani, M. Alba, Y. Garreau, Y. Borensztein, M. Goldmann and E. Lacaze, Towards a control of anisotropic interactions between soft nanospheres using dense arrays of smectic liquid crystal edge dislocations, *ACS Nano.* **9**(12), 11678 (2015).

17. M. Ravnik, G. Alexander, J. Yeomans and S. Žumer, Three-dimensional colloidal crystals in liquid crystalline blue phases, *Proc. Natl. Acad. Sci. USA.* **108**, 5188 (2011).

18. K. Stratford, O. Henrich, J. Lintuvuori, M. Cates and D. Marenduzzo, Self-assembly of colloid-cholesteric composites provides a possible route to switchable optical materials, *Nature communications.* **5**, 3954 (2014).

19. R. Jose, G. Skačej, V. S. S. Sastry and S. Žumer, Colloidal nanoparticles trapped by liquid-crystal defect lines: A lattice monte carlo simulation, *Phys. Rev. E.* **90**, 032503 (2014).

20. G. Cordoyiannis, V. S. Rao Jampani, S. Kralj, S. Dhara, V. Tzitzios, G. Basina, G. Nounesis, Z. Kutnjak, C. S. Pati Tripathi, P. Losada-Perez, D. Jesenek, C. Glorieux, I. Musevic, A. Zidansek, H. Ameinitsch and J. Thoen, Different modulated structures of topological defects stabilized by adaptive targeting nanoparticles, *Soft Matter.* **9**, 3956 (2013).

21. S. K. Ghosh and T. Pal, Interparticle coupling effect on the surface plasmon resonance of gold nanoparticles: From theory to applications, *Chemical*

reviews. **107**(11), 4797 (2007).

22. N. J. Halas, S. Lal, W.-S. Chang, S. Link and P. Nordlander, Plasmons in Strongly Coupled Metallic Nanostructures, *Chemical reviews.* **111**, 3913 (2011).
23. J. Baudry, M. Brazovskaia, L. Lejcek, P. Oswald and S. Pirkl, Arch-texture in cholesteric liquid crystals, *Liquid Crystals.* **21**(6), 893 (1996).
24. A. Bosco, M. G. M. Jongejan, R. Eelkema, N. Katsonis, E. Lacaze, A. Ferrarini and B. L. Feringa, Photoinduced reorganization of motor-doped chiral liquid crystals: Bridging molecular isomerization and texture rotation, *Journal of the American Chemical Society.* **130**(44), 14615 (2008).
25. J. S. Lintuvuori, P. A. C. K. Stratford, M. E. C. P. S. Clegg and D. Marenduzzo, *Phys. Rev. Lett.* **110**, 1187801–187805 (2013).
26. P. Rofouie, P. D. and R. A. D., Nano-scale surface wrinkling in chiral liquid crystals and plant-based plywoods, *Soft Matter.* **11**, 1127 (2015).
27. H. Ayeb, J. Grand, H. Sellame, S. Truong, J. Aubard, N. Félidj, A. Mlayah and E. Lacaze, Gold nanoparticles in a cholesteric liquid crystal matrix: self-organization and localized surface plasmon properties, *Journal of Materials Chemistry.* **22**, 7856 (2012).
28. J. S. Pendery, O. Merchiers, D. Coursault, J. Grand, H. Ayeb, R. Greget, B. Donnio, J.-L. Gallani, C. Rosenblatt, N. Felidj, Y. Borensztein and E. Lacaze, Gold nanoparticle self-assembly moderated by a cholesteric liquid crystal, *Soft Matter.* **9**, 9366 (2013).
29. G. Gouesbet and G. Gréhan, *Generalized Lorenz-Mie Theories.* Springer Science & Business Media (2011).
30. S. Park and D. Stroud, Splitting of surface plasmon frequencies of metal particles in a nematic liquid crystal, *Applied physics letters.* **85**, 2920 (2004).
31. D. W. Mackowski, Calculation of total cross sections of multiple-sphere clusters, *J. Opt. Soc. Am. A.* **11**(11), 2851 (1994).
32. P. Schapotschnikow, R. Pool and T. J. Vlugt, Molecular simulations of interacting nanocrystals, *Nano letters.* **8**, 2930 (2008).
33. P. Schapotschnikow and T. J. H. Vlugt, Understanding interactions between capped nanocrystals: Three-body and chain packing effects, *The Journal of Chemical Physics.* **131**, 124705 (2009).
34. D. Coursault, J. Grand, B. Zappone, H. Ayeb, G. Lévi, N. Félidj and E. Lacaze, Linear self-assembly of nanoparticles within liquid crystal defect arrays, *Adv. Mater.* **24**, 1461 (2012).
35. J. Milette, S. Relaix, C. Lavigne, V. Toader, S. J. Cowling, I. M. Saez, R. B. Lennox, J. Goodby and L. Reven, Reversible long-range patterning of gold nanoparticles by smectic liquid crystals, *Soft Matter.* **8**, 6593 (2012).
36. M. Grzelczak, J. Vermant, E. M. Furst and L. M. Liz-Marzan, Directed self-assembly of nanoparticles, *ACS Nano.* **4**(7), 3591 (2010).
37. J. S. Evans, P. J. Ackerman, D. J. Broer, J. van de Lagemaat and I. I. Smalyukh, Optical generation, templating, and polymerization of three-dimensional arrays of liquid-crystal defects decorated by plasmonic nanoparticles, *Phys. Rev. E.* **87**, 032503 (2013).
38. P. Mulvaney, Surface plasmon spectroscopy of nanosized metal particles,

Langmuir. **12**(3), 788 (1996).

39. J. Muller, C. Sonnichsen, H. von Poschinger, G. von Plessen, T. A. Klar and J. Feldmann, Electrically controlled light scattering with single metal nanoparticles, *Applied Physics Letters.* **81**, 171 (2002).

40. Y. H. Kim, D. K. Yoon, H. S. Jeong, O. D. Lavrentovich and H.-T. Jung, Smectic liquid crystal defects for self-assembling of building blocks and their lithographic applications, *Advanced Functional Materials.* **21**, 610 (2011).

41. T. Ohzono and J. Fukuda, Zigzag line defects and manipulation of colloids in a nematic liquid crystal in microwrinkle grooves, *Nature Communications.* **3**, 701 (2012).

42. J. B. Fournier and G. Durand, Focal conic faceting in smectic-A liquid crystals, *J. Phys. II (Paris).* **1**, 845 (1991).

43. C. Blanc and M. Kleman, The confinement of smectics with a strong anchoring, *Eur. Phys. J. E.* **4**, 241 (2001).

44. B. Zappone, C. Meyer, L. Bruno and E. Lacaze, Periodic lattices of frustrated focal conic defect domains in smectic liquid crystal films, *Soft Matter.* **8**, 4318 (2012).

45. B. Zappone and E. Lacaze, Surface-frustrated periodic textures of smectic-A liquid crystals on crystalline surfaces, *Physical Review E Stat Nonlin Soft Matter Phys.* **78**, 061704 (2008).

46. J. Michel, E. Lacaze, M. Alba, M. de Boissieu, M. Gailhanou and M. Goldmann, Optical gratings formed in thin smectic films frustrated on a single crystalline substrate, *Physical Review E.* **70**, 011709 (2004).

47. J. Michel, E. Lacaze, M. Goldmann, M. Gailhanou, M. de Boissieu and M. Alba, Structure of smectic defect cores: x-ray study of 8cb liquid crystal ultrathin films, *Physical Review Letter.* **96**, 027803 (2006).

48. D. Coursault, B. H. Ibrahim, L. Pelliser, B. Zappone, A. de Martino, E. Lacaze and B. Gallas, Modeling the optical properties of self-organized arrays of liquid crystal defects, *Opt. Express.* **22**(19), 23182 (2014).

49. D. Coursault, B. Zappone, A. Coati, A. Boulaoued, L. Pelliser, D. Limagne, N. Boudet, B. H. Ibrahim, A. de Martino, M. Alba, M. Goldmann, Y. Garreau, B. Gallas and E. Lacaze, Self-organized arrays of dislocations in thin smectic liquid crystal films, *Soft Matter.* **12**, 678 (2016).

50. L. Pelliser, M. Manceau, C. Lethiec, D. Coursault, S. Vezzoli, G. Lemenager, L. Coolen, M. DeVittorio, F. Pisanello, L. Carbone, A. Maitre, A. Bramati and E. Lacaze, Alignment of rod-shaped single photon emitters driven by line defects in liquid crystals, *Advanced Functionnal Materials.* **25**(under press), 1719 (2015).

51. M. Kléman, *Points, lignes, parois dans les fluides anisotropes et les solides cristallins.* Number vol. 1 in Points, lignes, parois dans les fluides anisotropes et les solides cristallins, Éditions de physique (1977).

52. J.-C. Géminard, C. Laroche and P. Oswald, Edge dislocation in a vertical A film: Line tension versus film thickness and burgers vector, *Phys. Rev. E.* **58**, 5923 (1998).

53. F. Pisanello, G. Lemenager, L. Martiradonna, L. Carbone, S. Vezzoli, P. Desfonds, P. D. Cozzoli, J. P. Hermier, E. Giacobino, R. Cingolani, V. M. De

and A. A. Bramati, Non-Blinking Single-Photon Generation with Anisotropic Colloidal Nanocrystals: Towards Room-Temperature, Efficient, Colloidal Quantum Sources, *Adv. Mat.* **25**, 1974 (2013).

54. F. Pisanello, L. Martiradonna, G. Lemenager, P. Spinicelli, A. Fiore, L. Manna, J.-P. Hermier, R. Cingolani, E. Giacobino, M. De Vittorio and A. Bramati, Room Temperature Dipole-like Single Photon Source with a colloidal dot-in-rod, *Appl. Phys. Lett.* **96**, 033101 (2010).

55. I. Lelidis, C. Blanc and M. Kléman, Optical and confocal microscopy observations of screw dislocations in smectic-*a* liquid crystals, *Phys. Rev. E.* **74**, 051710 (2006).

56. L. Lejcek and P. Oswald, Influence of surface tension on the stability of edge dislocations in smectic a liquid crystals, *Journal de Physique II.* **1**(8), 931 (1991).

57. P. Oswald, J. Milette, S. Relaix, L. Reven, A. Dequidt and L. Lejcek, Alloy hardening of a smectic a liquid crystal doped with gold nanoparticles, *EPL Europhysics Letters.* **103**, 46004 (2013).

58. A. H. Cottrell and B. A. Bilby, Dislocation theory of yielding and strain ageing of iron, *Proceedings of the Physical Society. Section A.* **62**, 49 (1949).

59. J. Friedel, R. Smoluchowski and N. Kurti, *Dislocations: International Series of Monographs on Solid State Physics.* International series of monographs on solid state physics, Elsevier Science (2013).

60. D. Pires, J.-B. Fleury and Y. Galerne, Colloid particles in the interaction field of a disclination line in a nematic phase, *Phys. Rev. Lett.* **98**, 247801 (2007).

61. J. B. Fleury, D. Pires and G. Y., Self-connected 3D architecture of microwires, *Phys. Rev. Lett.* **103**, 267801 (2009).

62. P. Laibnis, R. Nuzzo and G. Whitesides, Structure of monolayers formed by coadsorption of 2 normal-alkanethiols of different chain lenghts on gold and its relation to wetting, *Journal of physical chemistry.* **96**, 5097 (1992).

63. N. Goubet, J. Richardi, P.-A. Albouy and M.-P. Pileni, Which forces control supracrystal nucleation in organic media?, *Advanced Functional Materials.* **21**, 2693 (2011).

64. M. Gauvin, Y. Wan, I. Arfaoui and M.-P. Pileni, Mechanical properties of au supracrystals tuned by flexible ligand interactions, *The Journal of Physical Chemistry C.* **118**(9), 5005 (2014).

Chapter 22

Nanoparticles and networks created within liquid crystals

Shin-Wong Kang* and Sudarshan Kundu

*Department of BIN Convergence Technology, Chonbuk National
University, Jeonju, Republic of Korea 54896*
*swkang@jbnu.ac.kr

We report the *in situ* creation of growing polymer nanoparticles and resulting polymer networks formed in liquid crystals. Depending on the concentration of monomer, polymerization-induced phase separation proceeds in two distinct regimes. For a high monomer concentration with a good miscibility, phase separation is initiated through the nucleation and growth mechanism in the binodal decomposition regime and rapidly crosses over to the spinodal decomposition process, consequently resulting in interpenetrating polymer networks. For a dilute system, however, the phase separation mainly proceeds and completes in the binodal decomposition regime. The system resembles the aggregation process of colloidal particles. For a dilute system, the reaction kinetics is limited by the reaction between *in situ* created polymer aggregates and hence the network morphologies are greatly influenced by the diffusion of reactive growing polymer particles. The thin polymer layers localized at the surface of substrate are frequently observed and can be comprehended by the interfacial adsorption and further cross-linking reaction of *in situ* created polymer aggregates at the interface. This process provides a direct perception on understanding polymer stabilized liquid crystals accomplished by the interfacial polymer layer formed by polymerization of dilute reactive monomers in liquid crystal (LC) host.

Contents

1. Introduction

Nanoparticles and networks in liquid crystals, either introduced by ready-made particles or formed by the *in situ* polymerization followed by phase separation, play crucial roles for optical, electro-optical, and mechanical properties of the LC-composite systems. The LC-nanoparticle inclusion systems, described in the previous chapters, present unique physical properties such as anchoring transition of LCs, optical and electro-optical responses,[1,2] and anisotropic colloidal interactions between particles.[3,4] In addition, liquid crystals can serve as a medium for chemical reactions. *In situ* polymerization in LCs, as anisotropic solvents, results dramatically distinct network morphologies from those obtained from conventional isotropic solvents.[5,6]

Polymer-LC inclusion systems for the polymer dispersed liquid crystals (PDLC) with high polymer content have been vastly investigated over the last decades. The optical and electro-optical properties mainly rely on the combination of polymers and liquid crystals.[7] On the other hand, relatively small amount of polymer networks have been used for the polymer stabilized liquid crystals (PSLC), where the networks stabilize a certain state of LC configuration or facilitate a preferred switching route of LC devices.[8] The optical and electro-optical effects are mainly attributed to the state of LC component. For both cases, morphologies of the networks, formed by *in situ* polymerization, are critically affected by the orientational and spatial order of LCs as a reaction medium. Phase separation, morphology and its property relationships have been widely investigated.[7,8]

In this chapter, we discuss the *in situ* creation of growing polymer nanoparticles and resulting networks formed within liquid crystals. Eventuating network morphologies have been discussed based on the phase separation processes. After general considerations on the polymerization-induced phase separation, the main focus is placed on the PSLC systems with relatively low monomer concentration. For a dilute system, *in situ* created reactive polymer aggregates behave like colloidal particles. The consequent local morphologies and spatial distributions of polymer networks are deliberated based on the concentration sensitive process of polymerization-induced phase separation and interfacial cross-linking of reactive polymer nanoparticles.

2. Materials and experimental

2.1. *Materials*

Nematic liquid crystals with either positive (E7, $\Delta\varepsilon = 13.8$ at 1 kHz) or negative (MLC-6608, $\Delta\varepsilon = -4.2$ at 1 kHz) dielectric anisotropy have been supplied by Merck Advanced Technology in Korea and used as a host LC for the study. Relatively small amount (0.1–5.0 wt.-%) of photo-reactive mesogenic (RM-257, Merck) and nonmesogenic (HDDA, Sigma-Aldrich) monomers have been homogeneously dissolved in a host LC. Irgacure-651 (Ciba Specialty Chemicals Inc.) has been used as photo-initiator. The O,O'-fluorescein diacrylate, Sigma-Aldrich) was additionally doped in LCs for the fluorescent confocal microscopy. The chemical structures of photo-polymerizable monomers, used in the study, have been shown in Fig. 1.

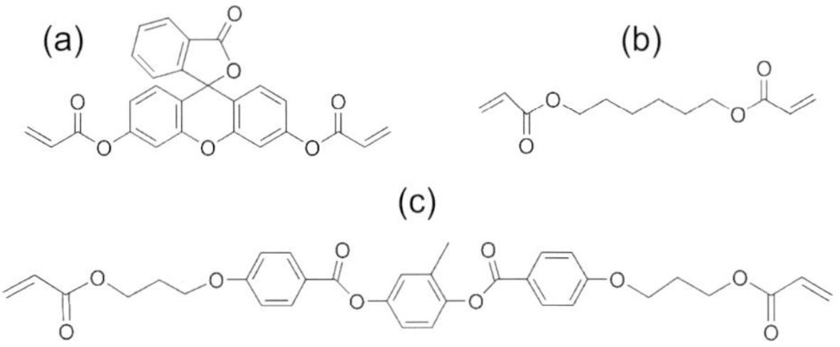

Fig. 1. Chemical structures of photo-polymerizable acrylate monomers: (a) Fluorescent monomer O,O'-fluorescein diacrylate, (b) nonmesogenic HDDA (1,6-hexanediol diacrylate), and (c) mesogenic RM-257.

2.2. *Sample preparation*

Bare glass and ITO-coated glass plates have been used to fabricate LC cells. Polyimide (PI) alignment layers with either planar or homeotropic anchoring have been spin-coated at the inner surface of cells with and without mechanical rubbing. The cell gaps are maintained at 4, 10, or 60 μm by using a spacer tape (JWT-84000, Zenith in Korea). Mesogenic monomer (RM-257, Merck) and nonmesogenic monomer 1,6-hexanediol diacrylate (HDDA,

Sigma-Aldrich) have been independently used as received without further purification. Monomers have been dissolved in the host LCs by a gentle heating without using solvent. The solubility at room temperature has been carefully examined by an optical microscope. For the fluorescent confocal microscopy (FCM), a fluorescent dye (O,O'-fluorescein diacrylate, Sigma-Aldrich) has been additionally dissolved in LCs. The mixtures have been loaded by capillary action in the isotropic phase. For the polymerization, 350–400 nm UV-light with normal incidence has been irradiated with various intensity, ranging between 100 μW/cm^2 to 50 mW/cm^2. The polymerization reaction has been initiated with or without adding photo-initiator. The free standing LC films have been formed by using unsupported TEM grids and kept in the chamber with UV- and visible-light transparent window. For polymerization, the chamber has been refreshed by the flow of an inert nitrogen gas during UV-light irradiation. The LC-liquid interfaces have been prepared by immersing the free standing film, formed on TEM grids, into immiscible liquids such as water and glycerol.

For the FE-SEM and AFM studies, the polymerized LC cells have been soaked in hexane/chloroform (80/20 wt.-%) co-solvent for three days. After complete drying, cells have been dismantled. Bare-network surface has been used for AFM imaging and a thin platinum layer has been deposited on the surface of the substrate for the FE-SEM imaging. For the particle size measurements, 20 wt.-% poly(dimethylsiloxane-co-methylphenylsiloxane, (Silicon oil, Sigma-Aldrich), has been added to the 0.2 wt.-% RM-257 solution in toluene. Homogeneous mixtures have been exposed with 200 mW/cm^2 UV-light for 5 minutes. The particle size has been measured before and after UV-irradiation as a function of time to monitor the creation and growth of particles.

2.3. *Characterizations*

For polarized optical textures of the sandwiched electrooptic (E.O.) cells, Nikon Eclipse LV100POL polarizing microscope has been used. The director orientation of a homeotropic LC has been identified by the conoscopic images before and after polymerization. Brookehaven 90 Plus particle size analyzer has been used to study the *in situ* creation and growth of polymer nanoparticles in different solvents before and after UV-irradiation. For fluorescence confocal microscopy, LSM 510 Meta from Carl Zeiss has been used to study the spatial distribution of fluorescent chromophore before and after polymerization of monomers. Cells have been prepared with one ITO-coated glass substrate and the other 100 μm, thick cover slip as substrates. The gap between substrates has been maintained by the tape spacer with 60 μm thickness. The Ar$^+$ ion laser at 488 nm for excitation and 505–530 nm bandpass filter for emission have been employed. The studies on nanoscopic morphologies of thin polymer layers or isolated beads, formed by photopolymerization of acrylate monomers, have been performed by using the atomic force microscope in tapping mode (Bruker, Nanoscope V) and a high resolution scanning electron microscope (Hitachi, SU-70).

3. *In situ* creation of nanoparticles

Photopolymerizable monomers used in our study exhibit a good miscibility to the host LCs. The initial mixture with a low concentration consists of a homogeneous distribution of monomers in LC solvent. Our results from the fluorescent confocal microscopy (FCM) clearly show that monomers are homogeneously dissolved and uniformly distributed throughout the entire LC cell. By assuming the same distribution of fluorescent and nonfluorescent monomers, both dissolved in LC, no specific localization of monomers is observed *prior to* polymerization.

Upon UV-irradiation, polymerization reaction is instantaneously initiated and polymers rapidly grow in their size by consuming monomers. It is interesting to note that a photoinitiator is not always necessary for the polymerization of acrylate monomer in LC solvent. Due to the improved electrical resistivity of LC mixtures, in general, polymerization is carried out without using photoinitiator for high performance display applications. As polymer grows, its solubility in LC solvent decreases and thus polymers are phase separated from the LC host. Initial polymer aggregates separated from solvent are likely to be spherical in their shape due to interfacial tension between LC and polymer surfaces. As they grow, however, particles evolve to different shapes depending on types of monomer and solvent. For nonmesogenic monomers and solvents, polymer particles retain their spherical shape as they grow, typically resulting in micrometer-sized beads. Polymerized mesogenic monomer in LC exhibits strong tendency to be evolved to an elongated grain-shape along the local director of LC.[9] The local morphology is influenced by various polymerization conditions such as concentration, irradiation intensity, UV-wavelength, temperature, chemical structure, and solubility.[9–12]

Direct measurements of creation and evolution of the reactive growing particles in LCs are limited by a light-scattering of LC solvent and rapid diffusion rate of monomer and particle. The mesogenic monomer solutions of 0.1–1.0 wt.-% in either LC or toluene solvent have been used to probe the creation of polymer particles. Immediately after 5 minutes of UV-irradiation, no measurable particles have been counted by the dynamic light scattering method. Instead, significant amount of polymers have been observed on the wall of cuvette cell. This may happen if created growing polymer particles have been rapidly diffused to the cell wall and cross-linked to form a polymer layer at the surface. To restrain diffusion of polymer particles, we have adjusted viscosity of the reaction medium by employing the mixture of toluene and viscous silicon oil. The initial transparent solution of mesogenic monomer in the mixed isotropic solvent immediately turns to a milky blend upon UV-irradiation, indicating the formation of phase separated polymer particles.

Figure 2 shows the results of particle size measurements after 5 minute UV-exposure for 0.2 wt.-% RM-257 in the mixed solvent. No particles have been counted *prior* to UV-treatment. The particle size has been measured as a function of time after halting 5 minute UV-irradiation. The graph in Fig. 2 reveals the creation of polymer particles with approximately 50 nm in diameter. Within 30 minutes, diameter reaches to 70 nm and particles gradually grow to about 80 nm (see filled circles in Fig. 2). As expected, count rate abruptly increases upon UV-irradiation and then gradually decreases as the particles grow in their size as represented by open circles

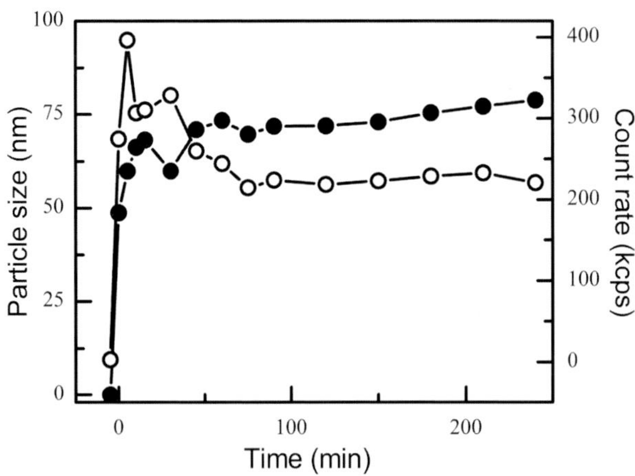

Fig. 2.   Measured sizes (filled circles) and count rates (open circles) of growing reactive particle as a function of time after halting 5 minute UV-irradiation at 200 mW/cm^2: Pristine mixture consists of 0.2 wt.-% RM-257 in toluene-silicon oil (80:20) mixed solvent.

in Fig. 2. The size of particle depends on polymerization conditions such as initiator concentration, monomer concentration, UV-light intensity and irradiation time. Since the viscosity of medium significantly increased to retard diffusion of both monomers and polymer aggregates, the reaction dynamics dramatically slows down. However, it clearly shows a formation and growth of polymer particles in tens of nanometer size at the early stage of polymerization and subsequent phase separation.

This is a typical process of phase separation occurring through the *binodal decomposition* which is characterized by *nucleation* and *growth* mechanism and isolated domain morphology of the appearing phase in a continuous phase.[7] Homogeneous mixture of low concentration monomer in LCs, generally adopted for PSLCs, follows this type of phase separation at early stage upon initiation of polymerization reaction. At the later stage, competition between reaction and diffusion rates of particles greatly affects the final local morphology and spatial distribution of polymer networks. The later stage is greatly influenced by the population and size of growing particles.[9] Therefore, it is important to control the initial polymerization conditions for achieving better regulation on LC-polymer inclusion systems.

4. Morphologies of polymer networks

4.1. *Phase separation and network morphology*

Two distinct mechanisms of *binodal* and *spinodal* decompositions are known for phase separation processes. Under the binodal curve in the phase diagram, the system requires activation energy for the induction of a new phase and thus phase separation proceeds by *nucleation* and *growth* mechanism. Alternatively, under spinodal curve, the second phase spontaneously appears without activation energy barrier leading to a spinodal decomposition mechanism.[7,8] Polymer morphologies formed through phase separation are critically influenced by the phase separation routes. In the binodal process, phase separation begins in random locations and leads to isolated domains of one phase within the other continuous phase. In the spinodal decomposition, however, new phase forms interconnected network structure resulting in interpenetrating (i.e., bicontinuous) networks of the two phases.[7,8]

On the other hand, the evolution of network morphology in these systems is similar to the aggregation process of colloidal particles.[10] The colloidal aggregation shows two types of kinetic processes (i.e., *reaction-limited* and *diffusion-limited* kinetics) which may be distinguished by compactness of the aggregate and characterized by their space filling.[13–15] If the polymerization process is *diffusion-limited*, dominant interparticle reaction forms porous clusters of particles uniformly through the sample. This process is preferable if spatial density of reactive particles is high. When the process is *reaction-limited*, dominant diffusion of particles toward reaction sites produces compactly packed and cross-linked polymers.[10,13–15]

For PDLCs with a high polymer content, both interpenetrating network morphologies and isolated domain morphologies have been well documented.[7,8] On the other hand, PSLCs with a relatively lower polymer content mainly exhibit interpenetrating fibril-like morphologies and clustered bead-like morphologies rather than surrounded domain morphologies of the LC phase within the other continuous polymer phase.[8,9] This could be attributed to either insufficient amount of polymers or different decomposition routes of phase separation, both originated mainly from the initial concentration. Decomposition route depends on various parameters such as concentration, solubility, temperature, radiation intensity, and chemical structure.[7–12]

For a high concentration, polymerization-induced phase separation produces a large number of polymer aggregates (i.e., gels or particles). These aggregates rapidly grow by depleting monomers at the early stage of polymerization. The highly populated reactive polymer particles coalesce through interparticle reaction and rapidly become unstable, causing a large density fluctuation. This leads to a rapid crossover of the phase separation to the spinodal decomposition regime. In the spinodal decomposition, density gradient spontaneously appears in an interconnected network structure. These density gradients grow sharper and larger as phase separation proceeds, resulting in interpenetrating networks of the two phases.[7]

For a low concentration, however, relatively slow or no crossover from binodal to spinodal decomposition occurs due to the wider gap between phase boundaries and lower spatial density of reactive polymer aggregates. No rapid crossover occurs to the spinodal decomposition regime. Therefore, the system behaves like the aggregation process of colloidal particles once the reactive polymer particles are formed at the early stage of polymerization. As the monomers are depleted by reaction due to their relatively faster diffusion over polymer aggregates, the reaction slows down due to a lower population and slower diffusion of the growing particles. Therefore, the diffusion of aggregates plays an increasingly important role in limiting morphologies. Since now the diffusion of particles determines a global network structure, the final morphology becomes a densely packed cluster of beads.[10,13–15] In this case, phase separation stays in the binodal decomposition regime mainly due to insufficient number of growing particles and their spatial density gradient to form interpenetrating networks. Unless a spatial localization occurs by the preferred diffusion of reactive particles to a specific region, the phase separation completes in the binodal regime, resulting in a discontinuous clustered bead-like morphology.[9–11,16] The localized thin-layered morphology obtained by the preferred diffusion of reactive particles is discussed in Sec. 5.

Since similar types of distinct morphologies have been observed in the PSLCs, we briefly discuss the progression of network morphology based on our experimental results.

4.2. *Phase separation in PSLCs*

Phase separation in PSLCs represents polymerization-induced phase separation of dilute monomers in LC solvent. The experimental results on nano-sized particle formation and the discussion above support that the phase separation in PSLCs begins under binodal curve through the nucleation and growth mechanism at the initial stage of polymerization. This is further complemented by the spherical bead-like morphology of the polymer network demonstrated in Sec. 5.2. The crossover of reaction kinetics may or may not occur depending on reaction conditions such as monomer concentrations and UV-light intensity. The system with relatively high monomer concentration (typically above ~ 5 wt.-%) and strong UV-irradiation rapidly crosses over the phase boundary line from binodal to spinodal decomposition regime. The reaction of highly populated polymer aggregates, nucleated at the early stage of polymerization, governs the morphology of phase separation and hence density gradient spontaneously appear in an interconnected network structure. Therefore, in this case, network formation proceeds mainly in the spinodal decomposition regime. Consequently, both major and minor phases possess a high degree of connectivity and interpenetration.

Figure 3 displays network morphology formed by this type of process. The E7 LC with 5.0 wt.-% mesogenic monomer RM-257 has been loaded into 10 μm cells with a homeotropic boundary condition. The polymerization has been performed by using 350–400 nm UV-light at the intensity of 20 mW/cm^2. As seen in Fig. 3, both images represent interpenetrating networks consisted of fine fibrils aligned normal to the substrate (*i.e.*, parallel to the LC director). The networks are distributed through the en-

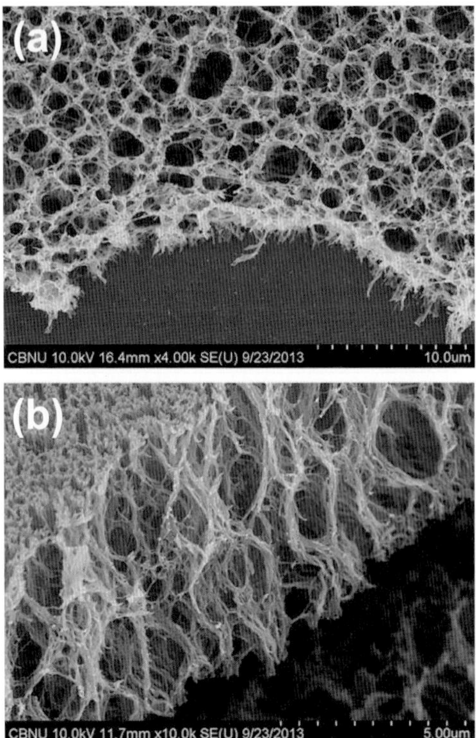

Fig. 3. Interpenetrating fibril-like morphology of the polymer networks obtained on the 5.0 wt.-% RM-257 in E7 host. Inner surfaces of the cells have been treated by homeotropic polyimide. Polymerization has been carried out by 350–400 nm UV-light at 20 mW/cm^2. The SEM images (a) and (b) represent near normal and cross-sectional views from the substrate plane, respectively.

tire cell. The height of fibrous network precisely matches to the thickness of LC layer. The networks in Fig. 3a, viewed from near normal to the substrate, exhibit a porous structure. These results strongly indicate that the phase separation has mainly proceeded and completed in the spinodal decomposition regime.

For the more dilute samples typically below 2.0 wt.-%, however, the networks are surface-localized and interpenetrating appearance has completely disappeared. Figure 4 shows the SEM images for 0.5 wt.-% and 0.1 wt.-% of RM-257 in E7 and MLC-6608 hosts, respectively. The samples have been polymerized independently both at 100 μmW/cm^2 and 20 mW/cm^2. Similar morphologies are observed on both top and bot-

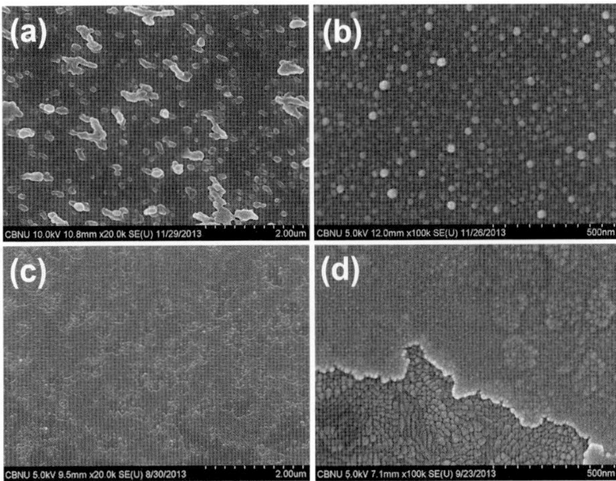

Fig. 4.   SEM micrographs of the polymer networks obtained on the dilute 0.5 wt.-% RM-257 in E7 host (a, c) and 0.1 wt.-% RM-257 in MLC-6608 host (b, d). Polymerizations have been carried out by 350–400 nm UV-light at 100 μmW/cm^2 for (a, b) and 20 mW/cm^2 for (c, d). For both concentrations, the stronger irradiation yields smoother and fused molten surface with much smaller particles, while the weaker irradiation results in larger isolated grains.

tom surfaces of each sample. No evidence for the bulk network is observed. In these cases, the networks are completely localized on the surfaces, forming either isolated grains (a) or thin-layered structure (b,c,d) as seen in Fig. 4. The formation of polymer particles has been strongly evidenced by the elongated grains and spherical beads in Figures 4a and 4b, respectively. It strongly indicates that the phase separation occurs mainly under the binodal decomposition process for a dilute system. Therefore, the final morphology is determined by the reaction kinetics as in the colloidal aggregation process.

The phase separation begins in the binodal regime, creating reactive growing polymer aggregates. Due to the dilute monomer concentration, the spatial density of aggregates and interparticle reaction are not sufficient enough to form interpenetrating networks through entire cell (*i.e.*, no high enough fluctuation of spatial density for spinodal decomposition). Therefore, phase separation proceeds in the binodal regime with no fast crossover to the spinodal regime. As mentioned earlier, in this case, the morphology is determined by the competition between interparticle reaction and diffusion of particles as in the colloidal aggregation.[13–15] Once monomers are mostly consumed, the reaction is significantly decelerated due to a low spatial density of reactive particles. The particles grow by depleting monomers, diffuse to the surface, and complete phase separation through coalescence at the surface, instead of forming porous networks at the bulk. The origin of particle diffusion and localization to the surface is discussed in Sec. 5.

Irradiation intensity can also affect phase separation procedure and thus resulting morphology of polymer networks. The contrasting SEM images in Fig. 4 show the effect of irradiation intensity on a local morphology. For both 0.5 wt.-% and 0.1 wt.-% concentrations, the stronger irradiation results rather continuous and smoother surface (see Figures 4c and 4d), while the weaker irradiation yields larger isolated grains on the surface (see Figures 4a and 4b). Under stronger UV-irradiation at the 20 mW/cm^2, more particles are simultaneously nucleated and deplete monomers. Since monomer concentration is fixed, in this case, the size of growing particles is limited due to their higher population. As a result, more populated and smaller particles are created and subsequent interparticle reaction produces a smoother molten surface of polymer networks. Similarly, a concentration of initiator may results in the same effect as UV-intensity. The higher concentration of initiator may induce the more populated and smaller polymer aggregates. For weaker irradiation, however, reactive particles grow larger since less number of nucleated particles consumes monomers at the same concentration. This eventuates in the formation of larger isolated grains on the surface or a thin continuous layer with rougher surface as in Figures 4a and 4b, respectively.

Although a local morphology of the network may depend on the mesogenicity of monomers,[9–12,16] the decomposition route of phase separation doesn't critically rely on the mesomorphic behavior of monomers. As observed in the mesogenic RM-257, the nonmesogenic HDDA also reveals a similar global morphology (see Fig. 5). The polymer beads with 30–50 nm in diameter are closely packed, eventuating in a thin localized layer with a protuberant surface. It is strongly evidenced that polymer particles in tens of nanometer size have been created by *in situ* polymerization and subsequently constitute a thin localized layer.

As shown above, the mixtures with lower monomer concentration, typically below 2.0 wt.-%, result in prominently localized polymer at the substrate surfaces. No network is observed in the bulk. This observation is not completely understood by the binodal and spinodal decomposition processes discussed above. An additional factor should be involved for the predominantly localized polymers at the surfaces. More details on the localization will be discussed in the next section.

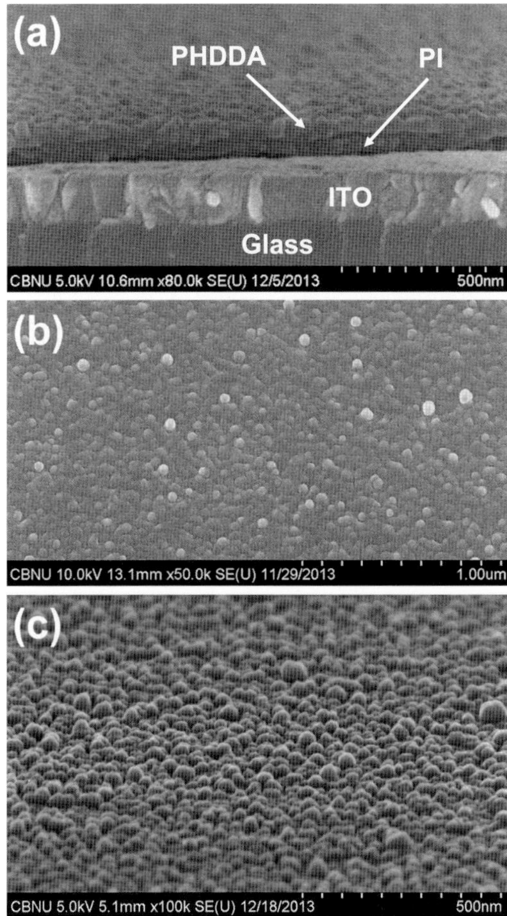

Fig. 5.   Entirely localized layers of polymer networks obtained on the 0.3 wt.-% HDDA in MLC-6608. Inner surfaces of the cells have been treated by homeotropic polyimide. Polymerization has been carried out by 350–400 nm UV-light at 100 μmW/cm^2. Images represent cross-sectional (a), low tilt (b), and high tilt (c) from the layer normal. PHDDA and PI denote polymerized HDDA and polyimide alignment layer, respectively.

5. Spatial distribution of polymer networks

The control of a spatial distribution of polymerized networks has been achieved, in general, by manipulating the spatial intensity of UV-light used for polymerization. Lithographic and holographic techniques have been employed to induce a patterned phase separation of polymer networks from LC host.[17,18] The initiation of polymerization reaction preferentially occurs and depletes monomers at regions with UV-irradiation. Subsequent monomer diffusion driven by the gradient in chemical potential and continued polymerization-induced phase separation yield patterned polymer networks, determined by the lithographic or holographic pattern.

The network distribution along UV-light propagation direction can also be controlled either by doping light-absorbing dye[19,20] or by properly selecting wavelength of light used for polymerization.[21] In either case, the light-intensity exponentially decays due to the absorption by LC medium and hence induces intensity gradient of UV-light along propagation direction. In this case, selective initiation of polymerization and depletion of monomers at near UV-side, followed by monomer diffusion to reaction sites, create denser networks at near UV-side substrate.[19-21] Patterned phase-separation, driven by the gradient in elastic deformation of LC host, has also been reported without using external patterning agencies. The pattern-forming state of a cholesteric LC has been used to template both spatial and orientational order of the LC into polymer networks without using holographic and lithographic techniques.[22-24]

Without utilizing the methods discussed above, the global spatial distribution of polymer networks is expected to be uniform throughout the sample. In fact, for the system with a high polymer content, no specific localization is observed and network distribution is spatially uniform throughout the cell. Type of decomposition for phase separation explains observed morphologies quite well.[7] However, a specific localization of polymer networks has been consistently observed for the photoinduced phase separation in LCs with a low monomer content. The dense networks are completely localized as a thin layer at the surfaces of both substrates. Mostly no networks are observed in the bulk of LCs. The cause of such an extreme localization is not clearly understood.

5.1. *Bulk and surface-localized networks*

As mentioned earlier, it has been confirmed by our confocal fluorescent microscopic study that no specific localization of reactive monomers is observed before polymerization. Monomers are homogeneously dissolved and uniformly distributed throughout the cell. After the completion of polymerization, however, polymer networks are distributed through entire cell or completely localized at the top and bottom surfaces depending on the monomer concentration. The spatial distribution of networks after polymerization has been confirmed by both FCM and FE-SEM. For a 5.0 wt.-%

mesogenic monomer in the homeotropically aligned LC, the interpenetrating fibril-like bulk networks are uniformly formed throughout the cell as shown in Fig. 3. For a low concentration monomer below 2.0 wt.-%, however, most of polymer networks are observed at near substrates. Figures 4 and 5 represent examples of the surface-localized polymers. Both mesogenic RM-257 and nonmesogenic HDDA have been completely localized as a thin layer at ITO- and PI-surfaces, respectively. Drastic difference in their spatial distribution is evident in Fig. 3 and Fig. 4. It should be noted that the UV-light used for polymerization is not absorbed by the host LCs. Therefore, the intensity distribution of UV-light is uniform throughout the cell.

It seems that such a contrast takes its origin from the decomposition process of phase separation. The system, depending on concentration, does or does not cross over the phase boundary from the binodal to spinodal decomposition regimes during the polymerization. If the system rapidly crosses over the phase boundary and phase separation proceeds and completes in spinodal decomposition regime, the polymer networks shows uniform spatial distribution and interpenetrating network morphology as seen in Fig. 3. However, when the phase separation completes in the binodal decomposition regime, the system composed of reactive polymer aggregates behaves like aggregation process of colloidal particles. It may result in a spatially localized network structure, as in Figures 4 and 5, since now diffusion of polymer aggregates is more influential for the final morphology.

5.2. *Interfacial localization of networks*

For the LC-Polymer binary systems formed by photo-polymerization with low monomer content, the spatial distribution of phase separated networks is critically affected by the competition between reaction rate and diffusion rate of growing polymer particles as in the aggregation process of colloidal particles. As discussed above, the diffusion of monomers towards the reaction sites and polymerization-induced phase separation of polymer particles are predominant at the early stage of polymerization reaction. The polymer aggregates, created by *in situ* photo-polymerization, remain reactive for continued polymerization and cross-linking reactions during UV-light irradiation. This makes the particles grow in their size by further consuming monomers and also particles react to others to form fused larger particles. The reaction rate between polymer aggregates critically depends on their population density. On the other hand, diffusion of the particles becomes much more sluggish compared to that of individual monomer due to the difference in their sizes. If the particles are highly populated and thus the inter-particle reaction is dominant over the diffusion of particles to a specific region, distribution of resulting polymer networks is uniform through the entire cell. This could be responsible for spatially uniform networks with a high degree of porosity in Fig. 3.

On the contrary, spatially nonuniform networks localized at specific region can be formed if the diffusion toward specific region is dominating the inter-particle reaction. For a dilute monomer, typically below 2.0 wt.-%, the spatial density of reactive particle is not high enough for the inter-particle reaction to predominate the diffusion of particles (i.e., *reaction-limited* regime). In addition, it seems that a certain type of driving force exists for tecific chemical attractions such as dipole-dipole interaction and hydrogen bonding. Our FCM study performed before and after polymerization shows no evidence for the pre-phase separation of monomer before UV-irradiation. There is no obvious reason for the prephase separation of monomer. Since the monomer has a similar chemical nature and good miscibility to the host LC, the entropy can prevail over enthalpy for a homogeneous mixing, especially for a dilute system.

Since now we have reactive growing particles in our systems, created by *in situ* photo-polymerization, we conjecture that the polymer nanoparticles are physically adsorbed by the interface to reduce interfacial tension between LC and solid surface. It is well known that small solid particles can be used as a surface active agent and emulsifier since they stabilize interfaces (so called, 'Pickering stabilization').[25] Solid particles can significantly reduce surface tensions by locating themselves at interfaces, as amphiphilic surfactant molecules do, and therefore stabilize interfaces. To confirm our inference, we have prepared monomer-mixed LC layer with three different types of interfaces. The LC layers have been sandwiched by solid (glass or ITO), liquid (glycerol), and gas (nitrogen) surfaces. Refer to the experimental section for more details. The FCM and FE-SEM studies, executed before and after polymerization, have clearly disclosed essentially the same results of localization of polymer networks at each interface. For all three samples, evenly distributed monomers in a LC layer *prior to* polymerization have turned into completely localized networks at interfaces after the completion of polymerization. Therefore, we believe that the main driving force for the spatial localization is an interfacial energy between liquid crystals and varied phases of gas, liquid, and solid. *In situ* created polymer particles diffuse to the interfaces and adsorbed by the interfacial energy primarily due to the *Pickering stabilization*. Thus polymer networks are preferably located at the interface.

Such a dramatic localization can also be rationalized by an elastic energy driven localization.[22–24] Since *in situ* created polymer particles disrupt the nematic order of the host, a LC medium has tendency to expel particles to the surface to maintain maximum degree of nematic order. This can reduce an elastic free energy of the system by minimizing elastic distortion of the host LC. However, it doesn't seem to be the primary factor for the localization, at least for the present study, since interfacial polymer layers are consistently observed even in isotropic liquid-solid interfaces. Polymerization of dilute monomers in isotropic solvents, proceeded in the binodal decomposition process, readily result in a thin localized interfacial layer with no elastic energy driven localizing force.

Another corroborative example for the interpretation is a nanoparticle induced homeotropic alignment of LCs. Although NP-induced homeotropic alignment of LCs has been reported previously, no clear explanation has been proposed for a driving force for the localization of NPs on the solid surface.[1,2] We believe that it is essentially the same interfacial adsorption on the analogy of 'Pickering effect' at the LC- solid interface as discussed above.[25,26] In fact, our FCM experiments performed by using fluorescent NPs unambiguously support the particle adsorption by interfacial energy.[26]

Figure 6 schematically illustrates polymerization-induced phase separation and interfacial localization of polymer for a dilute system. Figure 6a represents homogeneously mixed monomers in a LC solvent. The mixing entropy prevails over pre-phase separation *prior to* polymerization. Upon initiation of polymerization, insoluble polymer nanoparticles, denoted by circles in Fig. 6b, are nucleated and grow to spherical particles with tens of nanometer in diameter by depleting monomers. For a dilute system, phase separation proceeds under the nucleation and growth mechanism in the binodal decomposition regime. Reaction between growing particles is similar to the aggregation process of colloidal particles. Due to limited reaction between particles and interfacial energy at the surfaces, the reactive particles are driven to diffuse toward the interface (designated by the curved arrows in Fig. 6b) and closely packed at the surface as in Fig. 6c. The reactive particles adsorbed at the interface are further developed to a thin uniform layer of polymer networks through a continued polymerization and cross-linking reactions between particles as evidenced in Figures 4 and 5.

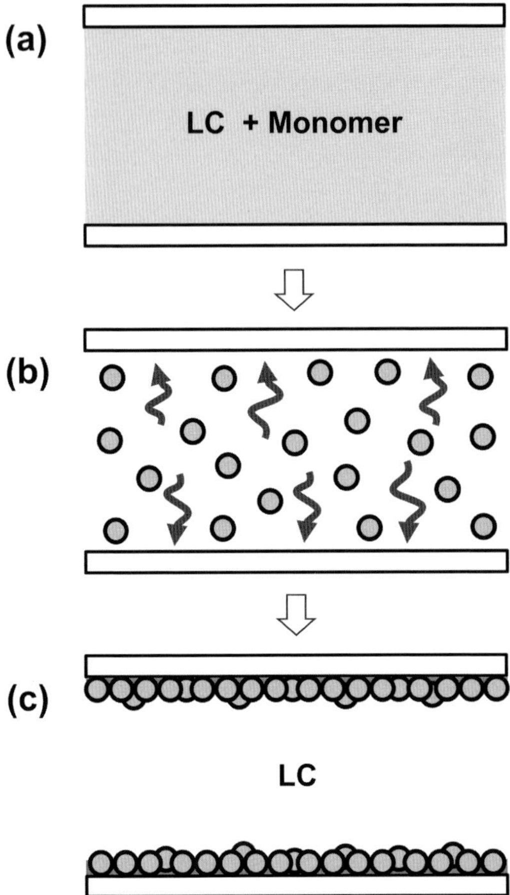

Fig. 6. Schematic illustration of *in situ* creation of reactive polymer nanoparticles, interfacial adsorption, and subsequent formation of protuberant layers at the interface: (a) Homogeneous mixture of LC host and photopolymerizable monomer before UV-irradiation, (b) nucleation and growth of phase separated polymer nanoparticles upon UV-irradiation, and (c) thin interfacial polymer layers consisted of fused polymer beads. The arrows in (b) represent diffusion toward the interface between LC and solid substrate. Absorbed reactive polymer beads are fused into a thin interfacial layer in (c) with protuberant surface.

Figure 5a demonstrates an entirely localized polymer layer (PHDDA, polymerized HDDA) formed at the interface between LC and polyimide (PI) alignment layer. Essentially the same uniform layers are observed through the entire cell symmetrically at both top and bottom surfaces. The low and high tilted views from the layer normal in Figures 5b and 5c, respectively, unambiguously reveal a protuberant surface composed of spherical nanoparticles with approximately 30–50 nm in diameter. The layer thickness can be estimated to the diameter of polymer nanoparticles, indicating approximately monolayer adsorption of particles at the interface. The FE-SEM images in Fig. 5 strongly support the *in situ* creation of polymer nanoparticles and localization by the interfacial adsorption, occurring in the binodal decomposition process during the phase separation. Since the localized layer has been formed by the interfacial adsorption and further cross-linking reactions of the polymer particles, the thickness and roughness of a localized layer are closely correlated to the size of created polymer particles. All these are greatly influenced by the initial polymerization conditions such as concentration and irradiation intensity.

6. Conclusion

We have discussed polymer nanoparticles and networks formed within liquid crystals by *in situ* polymerization. In LC-Polymer inclusion systems, the local morphology and spatial distribution of polymer networks are determined by the decomposition process of phase separation, which is sensitively affected by concentration. For a high monomer concentration, the phase separation mainly proceeds in the spinodal decomposition regime, resulting in the interpenetrating and bicontinuous polymer networks in LCs. For a dilute system, however, the phase separation remains in the binodal decomposition regime and thus the system behaves like the aggregation process of colloidal particles. The global morphology of networks is determined by the reaction kinetics of *in situ* created nanoparticles. The diminished reaction rate, due to insufficient number of reactive particles and their spatial density, leads the system to the reaction-limited regime. Therefore, the morphology is mainly influenced by diffusion of particles. If there is no preferred diffusion to a specific region, densely packed clusters are formed randomly in LCs. For the thin layered mixture confined by external surfaces, however, the interfacial energy provides a driving force for adsorption of particles, diffused toward interfacial area. The physically adsorbed particles, on the analogy of the 'Pickering stabilization', form approximate mono-layers symmetrically at top and bottom interfaces. The particles are fused into uniform layer with a protuberant surface through a further cross-linking reaction.

Even for the same host LC and monomer, the process can be easily affected by various parameters such as monomer concentration, radiation intensity, initiator concentration, temperature and interfacial energy between LC host and substrate. The interfacial layer, formed by polymerization-induced phase separation and adsorption, can play crucial roles for the stabilization of liquid crystals. Therefore it is important to understand the process and control the polymerization conditions for better performing tailor-made PSLCs.

Acknowledgment

This research was supported by Samsung Display Company in Korea. Authors thank Dr. Byung Wook Ahn, Dr. Heung-Shik Park, Dr. Changhoon Lee, Dr. Keun Chan Oh, Dr. Jae Jin Lyu, and Dr. Yong-Kuk Yun for their kind supports and valuable comments.

References

1. S. C. Jeng, C. W. Kuo, H. L. Wang, and C. C. Liao, Nanoparticle-induced vertical alignment in liquid crystal cell, *Appl. Phys. Lett.* **91** (2007).
2. H. Qi, B. Kinkead, and T. Hegmann, Unprecedented dual alignment mode and freedericksz transition in planar nematic liquid crystal cells doped with gold nanoclusters, *Adv. Func. Mater.* **10**, 212–221 (2008).
3. J. C. Loudet, P. Barols, and P. Poulin, Colloidal odering from phase separation in a liquid crystalline continuous phase, *Nature.* **407**, 611–613 (2000).
4. I. Musevic, M. Skarabot, U. Tkalec, M. Ravnik, and S. Zumer, Two-dimensional colloidal crystals self-assembled by topological defects, *Science.* **313**, 954–958 (2006).
5. K. Akagi, G. Piao, S. Kaneko, K. Sakamaki, H. Shirakawa, and M. Kyotani, Helical polyacetylene synthesized with a chiral nematic field, *Science.* **282**, 1683–1686 (1998).
6. R. M. A. Hikmet, Anisotropic gels andplasticized networks formed by liquid crystal molecules, *Liq. Cryst.* **9**, 405–416 (1991).
7. P. S. Drzaic, *Liquid Crystal Dispersions.* World Scientific, Singapore (1995).
8. S. Zumer and G. P. Crawford, eds., *Liquid Crystals in Complex Geometries Formed by Polymer and Porous Networks.* Taylor and Francis (1996).
9. S. W. Kang. *Spatio-orientationally organized polymer microstructures obtained on self-assembled pattern-forming state of cholesteric liquid crystals.* PhD thesis, Kent State University, Ohio, USA (2003).
10. C. V. Rajaram, S. D. Hudson, and L. C. Chien, Morphology of polymer stabilized liquid crystals, *Chem. Mater.* **7**, 2300–2308 (1995).
11. C. V. Rajaram, S. D. Hudson, and L. C. Chien, Effect of polymerization tem-

perature on the morphology and electrooptic properties of polymer stabilized liquid crystals, *Chem. Mater.* **8**, 2451–2460 (1996).

12. I. Dierking, Polymer network-stabilized liquid crystals, *Adv. Mater.* **12**, 167–181 (2000).

13. D. A. Weitz, J. S. Huang, M. Y. Lin, and J. Sung, Limits of the fractal dimension for irreversible kinetic aggregation of gold colloids, *Phys. Rev. Lett.* **54**, 1416–1419 (1985).

14. R. C. Ball, D. A. Weitz, T. A. Witten, and F. Leyvraz, Universal kinetics in reaction-limited aggregation, *Phys. Rev. Lett.* **58**, 274–277 (1987).

15. D. Asnaghi, M. Carpineti, M. Giglio, and M. Sozzi, Coagulation kinetics and aggregate morphology in the intermediate regimes between diffusion-limited and reaction-limited cluster aggregation, *Phys. Rev. A.* **45**, 1018–1023 (1992).

16. S. W. Kang, S. H. Jin, L. C. Chien, and S. Sprunt, Spatial and orientational templating of semiconducting polymers in a cholesteric liquid crystal, *Adv. Func. Mater.* **14**, 329–334 (2004).

17. J. Zhang, C. R. Carlen, S. Palmer, and M. B. Sponsler, Dynamic holographic gratings recorded by photopolymerization of liquid crystalline monomers, *J. Am. Chem. Soc.* **116**, 7055–7063 (1994).

18. C. F. van Nostrum and R. J. M. Nolte, Photoinduced opposite diffusion of nematic and isotropic monomers during patterned photopolymerization, *Chem. Mater.* **10**, 135–145 (1998).

19. D. J. Broer, J. Lub, and G. N. Mol, Wide-band reflective polarizers from cholesteric polymer networks wi a pitch gradient, *Nature.* **378**, 467–469 (1995).

20. H. Kemperman and R. M. A. Hikmet, Electrically swichable mirrors and optical components made from liquid-crystal gels, *Nature.* **392**, 476–479 (1998).

21. S. W. Kang, S. Sprunt, and L. C. Chien, Photoinduced localization of orientationally ordered polymer networks at the surface of a liquid crystal host, *Macromolecules.* **35**, 9372–9376 (2002).

22. S. W. Kang, S. Sprunt, and L. C. Chien, Structure and morphology of polymer- stabilized cholesteric diffraction gratings, *Appl. Phys. Lett.* **76**, 3516–3518 (2000).

23. D. Voloschenko, O. P. Pishnyak, S. V. Shiyanovskii, and O. D. Lavrentovich, Effect of director distortion on morphologies of phase separation in liquid crystals, *Phys. Rev. E.* **65**, 060701 (2002).

24. S. W. Kang, S. Sprunt, and L. C. Chien, Ordered polymer microstructures obtained using pattern forming state of a cholesteric liquid crystal as templates, *Adv. Mater.* **13**, 1179–1182 (2002).

25. B. P. Binks and T. S. Horozov, eds., *Colloidal Particles at Liquid Interfaces.* Cambridge University Press (2006).

26. P. Kumar, S. Y. Oh, M. B. Oh, S. H. Lee, and S. W. Kang, Nano-particle induced homeotripic alignment of nematic liquid crystals, *19th National Conference on Liquid Crystals.* p. 15 (2012).

Part 5

Liquid crystals formed by nanoparticle suspensions

Chapter 23

Nematic phase formation in suspensions of carbon nanotubes

Cecile Zakri and Philippe Poulin*

*Centre de Recherche Paul Pascal - CNRS, University of Bordeaux
115 avenue Schweitzer, 33600 Pessac, France
poulin@crpp-bordeaux.cnrs.fr

This chapter describes the chemical composition, phase behavior and structure of recently investigated carbon nanotube (CNT) based liquid crystals. Because nanotubes are long and thin rigid cylinders, their phase behavior shares several similarities with many other systems such as rigid polymers and rod-like particle suspensions. CNT liquid crystals are achieved in highly concentrated suspensions comprised of raw or chemically functionalized particles. But extreme aspect ratio, rigidity, high sensitivity to interactions, optical properties and structural features of CNTs make their liquid crystalline phases unique in several ways. In particular, the chapter discusses the importance of the CNT waviness on the phase ordering and the role of excess surfactant or biomolecules used to stabilize the CNTs. The unique resonant Raman scattering of CNT allows original and accurate measurements of order parameters at a micron-scale. Highly oriented nematic tactoids could even be characterized by polarized Raman microscopy. From a more applied point of view, nematic ordering is shown to be a route towards the processing of new materials such as anisotropic conductive films and high strength fibers made of oriented carbon nanotubes. Examples of functional materials and nanocomposites achieved from CNT liquid crystals are given.

Contents

1. Introduction

Carbon nanotubes (CNTs) are thin cylinders made of sp^2 carbon atoms. They are named singlewalled nanotubes (SWNTs) when formed by a single sheet of rolled graphene or multiwalled nanotubes (MWNTs) when formed by several coaxial cylinders. CNTs exhibit remarkable physical properties which have been scrutinized in the last two decades. In particular they exhibit a high mechanical strength coupled to excellent thermal and electrical conductivities and giant specific area. The structural features and properties of CNTs are excellently covered in many books and review articles[1–3] and are out of the scope of the present chapter. It is today recognized that CNTs are promising materials for a number of diverse applications: from reinforcement of composites and organic electronics to energy storage devices through electrochemical sensors or actuators.[4] However, in most applications and CNT based materials, the ordering of the CNTs is expected to play a critical role. Classical mechanics for example predicts optimal improvements of the mechanical properties of composites reinforced by fibers when these last are well-aligned.[5–8] An assembly of well-aligned conducting fibers can exhibit anisotropic conductivity and allow a more efficient current transport along a given direction.

However, processing materials with well-controlled CNT alignment is often challenging. Suspending nanotubes in a liquid via their dissolution or surfactant assisted dispersion has been the topic of extensive research over the last years because fluid processing is often used to make CNT based materials. When dispersed or dissolved in liquids, CNTs are most of the time diluted and form isotropic fluids. In solid forms such as polymer composites, fibers, mats, CNTs are often disordered, or artificially ordered in the presence of an external field: magnetic, electric, shear, composite and fiber spinning or drawing.[8–14] Another appealing approach consists in suspending CNTs in molecular or polymer liquid crystals.[15–19] This coupling of liquid crystallinity and CNTs is presented in another chapter of the present book and therefore not discussed here. Instead, we focus on nematic phase formation in CNT suspensions.

Because nanotubes are long and thin rigid cylinders, their phase behavior in fluid suspensions actually shares several similarities with many other systems such as rigid polymers and rod-like particle suspensions. In particular they can form liquid crystalline phases when suspended at high concentration in an isotropic solvent, forming thereby a lyotropic liquid crystal.[20–23] This state is particularly interesting from a technological point of view. Indeed, fluid processing of liquid crystals is a direct route towards well aligned structures such as thin films, fibers and composites. For example, rigid polyaramide polymers are processed into extremely strong fibers (Kevlar®) from liquid crystalline phases which can be more effectively aligned. Beyond their technological interest, CNT liquid crystals exhibit unique features due to the extreme aspect ratio, rigidity, high sensitivity to interactions, optical properties and structural features of nanotubes. In particular, the chapter discusses the importance of the CNT waviness on the phase ordering and the role of excess surfactant or biomolecules used to stabilize the CNTs. The unique resonant Raman scattering of CNTs allows original and accurate measurements of order parameters at a micron-scale. Highly oriented nematic tactoids could even be characterized by polarized Raman microscopy.

The present chapter covers various aspects related to the science and potential applications of CNT based liquid crystals. The suspension of CNTs in liquids is naturally discussed in the first section of the chapter. CNTs are insoluble in aqueous and classic organic solvents and their processing in liquid state is not straightforward. We will see that the use of superacids or CNT surface functionalization allowed the achievements of thermodynamically stable solutions of CNTs concentrated up to nematic phases. Another approach is based on the stabilization of CNTs by surfactant or polymers. These metastable colloids can also be concentrated so that they form nematic phases. The phase behavior of CNT based nematic can be altered by the interactions between the CNTs. The latter can in particular be varied by the nature of the solvents or by the presence of additives. The third section of the chapter is dealing with particular structural features of CNT based nematics. We will in particular discuss the role of the waviness of the CNTs on the order parameter of the materials and on the presence of defects. Lastly, the fourth section will present recent efforts towards the processing of materials made from CNT based liquid crystals. Those include strong fibers made by a wet-fiber spinning process, electronic components, biomaterials and films which exhibit anisotropic conductivity.

2. Chemistry and phase behavior of liquid crystalline suspensions of CNTs

Following Onsager's model on the competition of packing and rotational entropies,[24] carbon nanotubes, in analogy with other rod-like particles, are expected to form nematic phases when suspended in a solvent above a certain concentration. Nevertheless, suspending CNTs at high concentration in a fluid is not straightforward. Various chemical approaches have been developed in the last years to overcome this challenge. Two main classes of suspensions, named "solutions" or "dispersions" can be defined. Solutions are thermodynamically stable systems in which the CNTs are solubilized up to a certain concentration without additives. The solubility of CNTs in common solvents is extremely small. As a result raw CNTs do not easily form liquid crystals. But CNTs can become highly water soluble if their surface is modified by covalent functionalization. The main approach consists in using acid treatments which lead to the formation of oxygenated polar groups at the outer surface of the CNTs. This approach actually led to the first achievement of CNT based liquid crystals.[25,26] MWNTs were employed in this pioneering work. Examples are shown in Fig. 1. Surface functionalization is suitable for MWNTs, but poorly appropriate for SWNTs. Indeed, surface functionalization downgrades irreversibly the

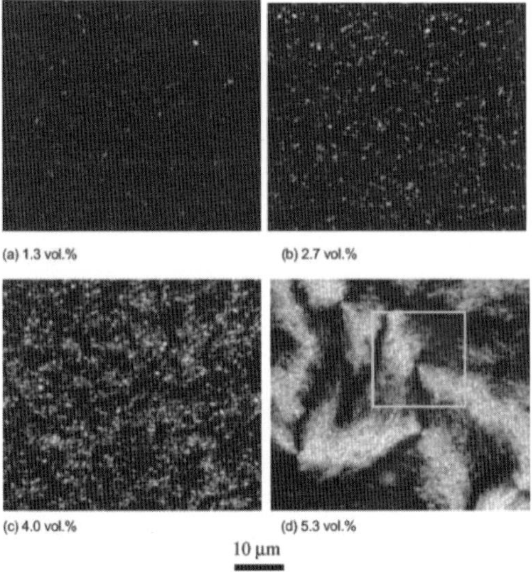

Fig. 1. Optical micrographs of MWNT dispersions at different aqueous concentrations respectively, imaged in reflected light with crossed polars: (a) 1.3 vol% dispersion, showing weak bireflection contrast from nematic nuclei; (b) 2.7 vol% dispersion, where the discrete entities appear larger and appear to represent growing nematic nuclei; (c) 4.0 vol% dispersion, where the nematic nuclei are beginning to "join up" in some regions; (d) 5.3 vol% dispersion, showing the Schlieren texture of nematic liquid crystals. Reprinted with permission from Ref. 26. Copyright (2005) American Chemical Society.

properties of SWNTs. However, Pasquali *et al.* observed that SWNTs could be efficiently solubilized without any chemical modification in superacids such as chlorosulfonic acid.[27,28] The mechanism of solubilization is based on the reversible protonation of the CNTs.[29] At high concentration such materials form liquid crystalline phases.

Soft and reversible reduction of CNTs via the intercalation of alkali metal ions[30] can also be used to achieve true solutions of CNTs in polar organic solvents such as dimethyl sulfoxide or N-methyl pyrrolidone. But the solubility of reduced CNTs has remained too low to achieve liquid crystals. A challenge for future research would consist in optimizing the soft dissolution method to achieve greater solubility and liquid crystalline materials.

By contrast to true solutions, CNT dispersions are metastable systems kinetically stabilized by additives. For example, CNTs can be homogeneously dispersed in water by using surfactants or polymers adsorbed at their interface.[31–39] The stabilization by appropriate surface active agents can be sufficiently strong so that the materials can be concentrated up to liquid crystalline states. For example, the stabilization of CNTs by single strand DNA (ssDNA) allowed the achievement of the first water based liquid crystals made of SWNTs.[40] The use of surfactant and polymers may be detrimental in certain situations but allows the nanotube structure and properties to be preserved. In addition, it is particularly suitable for making water based liquid crystals which can be easily processed and manipulated in environmentally friendly conditions.

Regardless of their mechanisms of stabilization, it has been shown that CNT based liquid crystals exhibit phase boundaries in rather good agreement with theoretical expectations. As motivated in Chap. 2, theory predicts that monodisperse and rigid rods of diameter D and length L form an isotropic phase for a volume fraction lower than $\phi_{I,the} = 3.3D/L$ and a nematic phase above a volume fraction $\phi_{N,the} = 4.5D/L$ ($\phi_{I,the}$ and $\phi_{N,the}$ are the volume fractions of the phase boundaries theoretically expected).[41] These values are expected in the limit of long rods. In between these boundaries, coexistence between a nematic and isotropic phase is expected. The ratio $\phi_{I,the}/\phi_{N,the}$ is 1.4. In the experiments reported in Ref. 40, the authors found a ratio of $\phi_{I,exp}/\phi_{N,exp} = 2$ ($\phi_{I,exp}$ and $\phi_{N,exp}$ are the volume fractions of the phase boundaries experimentally observed). This experimental value is greater than 1.4, the value theoretically expected for monodisperse rod-like and long particles. The discrepancy between experiments and theory was ascribed to the polydispersity of the samples in both diameter and length. Nevertheless, the phase boundaries were still consistent with the aspect ratio of CNT bundles estimated from light scattering experiments and electron microscopy observations. Similar conclusions were drawn in several studies of CNT based liquid crystals. Compared to other rod-like particle systems, CNT based liquid crystals can be achieved at relatively low concentration considering their very high aspect ratio. An extreme limit is attained in the case of SWNTs directly solubilized in superacids without any mechanical treatment that could induce the scission of the CNTs (see Fig. 2). In this limit, the aspect ratio L/D can be as high as 10^5 with a diameter of SWNTs of only 1 nm and a length of 10 μm. In more frequent cases, either MWNTs or SWNTs are shortened after their dispersion in a surfactant solution. This shortening is induced by the mechanical energy supplied to disperse the particles, often via sonication.[42–45] The CNT aspect ratio in typical dispersions lies in between 10^2 and 10^4, which is still very high compared to other rod-like particle materials.

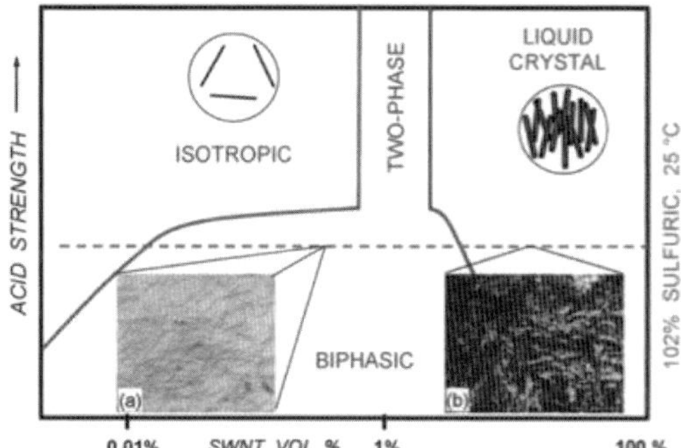

Fig. 2.   Postulated phase diagram of SWNTs in acids. In 102% sulfuric acid (depicted by the horizontal dashed line), the biphasic region extends from a concentration of 100 ppm to 8%. These critical concentrations are expected to vary with the strength of the acid used. Reprinted with permission from Ref. 28. Copyright (2006) American Chemical Society.

Attractive interactions are expected to alter the phase behavior of simple rod-like suspensions. In particular the isotropic-nematic biphasic domain is expected to become wider with increasing interactions. This was actually confirmed in both stable solutions[28] and metastable dispersions[46] of carbon nanotubes stabilized by biopolymers. In the first case the interactions between the CNTs were varied in superacids by tuning the acid strength. As schematized in Fig. 2, this allowed the observation of the so-called Flory chimney phase diagram type.[28,47,48] The biphasic domain becomes broader with increasing attractive interactions between the CNTs. The attraction is here increased with decreasing the acid strength.

For polymer stabilized suspensions, attractive interactions arose from depletion of non-adsorbing excess polymer in solution.[46,49] This type of interaction can be finely tuned by controlling the amount of additives. It was actually used to accurately control the percolation behavior of nanotube suspensions stabilized by surfactant.[50–52] Excess surfactant molecules in solution form micelles, which, such similar to the behavior of polymer coils, act as depleting agents.

The Flory chimney phase diagram type was used by Windle *et al.* to sort CNTs by their length.[53] As already mentioned, CNT materials are generally highly polydisperse in length. This leads to a broadening of the biphasic isotropic-nematic domain. As intuitively expected, the nematic phase was found to be enriched with the longest specimens. Separation of the nematic from the isotropic phase allowed therefore a fractionation of the CNTs by their length. This type of fractionation was named mesogenicity driven fractionation.[53]

Even though CNT liquid crystals exhibit features expected from classical theories of rod-like particles discussed in other chapters of the present book, it remains important to note that they quantitatively differ from many other systems because of their giant aspect ratio. As already mentioned their aspect ratio allows the achievement of nematic states at very low concentration. But in addition to this, the aspect ratio makes CNT based liquid crystals particularly sensitive to interactions. For sake of simplicity, let us consider CNTs as long rectangular parallelepipeds of length L and equal width and height D. They experience a surface interaction of amplitude u per unit surface area. The net energy between two perpendicular neighboring CNTs is expected to be on the order of uD^2 whereas it becomes on the order of uDL for two neighboring and aligned CNTs. A small variation of u can therefore be associated to a very large gain of energy when the CNTs change their orientation from a random state to an aligned structure. This explains the high sensivity of CNTs to interactions and also the general tendency of rod-like materials to form gels and kinetically arrested structures when their interactions largely exceed kT, the thermal energy.[54]

3. Structure of CNT liquid crystals

In spite of our current relatively good understanding of the phase behavior of CNT based liquid crystals seen in the previous section, the structure of such materials remains more puzzling. First of all, it is generally observed that it is difficult to align CNT liquid crystals on large scale. The materials are often under the form of small polydomains that don't coarsen with time. This means that the materials contain topological defects that don't annihilate with time as observed in more conventional and fluid liquid crystals.[55] As shown in Fig. 3, the first CNT liquid crystals reported by Windle *et al.* contained already a large density of defects[26] and even aligned domains displayed a significant waviness. Similar trends were observed in further

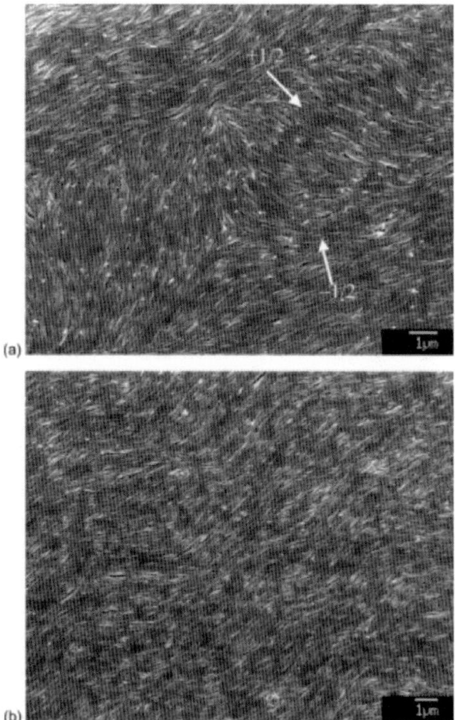

Fig. 3.   Scanning electron micrographs of a dried CNT film. (a) the director field around a pair of disclinations of topological strength +1/2 and -1/2 (b) monodomain free of disclinations. Reprinted with permission from Ref. 26. Copyright (2005) American Chemical Society.

discovered liquid crystals regardless their chemical composition.

This lack of homogeneity and of long range alignment has two main consequences. First, it makes the characterization of CNT liquid crystals, and in particular the measurement of their order parameter, often difficult. Second, it hinders applications in which CNT liquid crystals are used for the anisotropy of their properties. Efforts have thus been made to align nematic liquid crystals and characterize their order parameter. As shown in Fig. 4, Zamora-Ledezma *et al.* examined the ordering of surfactant or polymer stabilized lyotropic nematic suspension of single wall nanotubes and showed that a uniform macroscopic alignment can be obtained by mechanical shearing.[56] Drying of liquid crystals allowed the fabrication of anisotropic thin films with a thickness comprised in between 0.1 μm and 1 μm. The angular distribution of the nanotubes around the director can be described by the scalar nematic order parameter S, which, as defined in Chap. 2, writes:

$$S = \frac{1}{2}\langle 3\cos^2\beta - 1\rangle \tag{1}$$

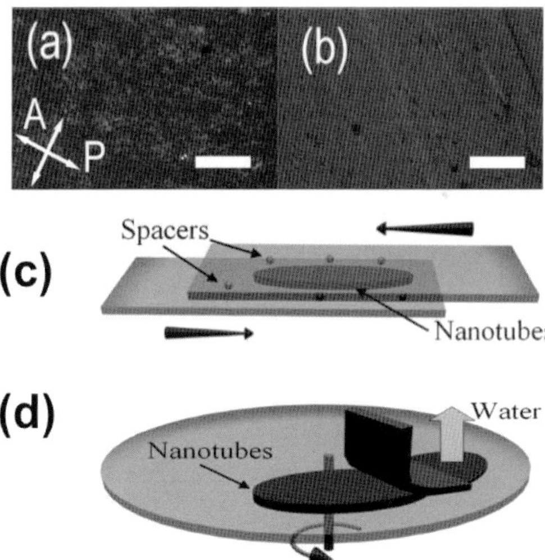

Fig. 4. Typical optical micrographs between crossed polarizers of a non-aligned thin layer of lyotropic aqueous suspension (a) and a thin layer aligned by shear between glass substrates (b) (thickness of the slab $= 10$ μm). The scale bar corresponds to 200 μm. Sketch of the methods used to shear align lyotropic nematic phases between glass substrates separated by spacer beads (c) or between glass substrates assisted by spin-coating (d). Reprinted with permission from Ref. 56. Copyright (2008) American Chemical Society.

for a three-dimensional (3D) system, and:

$$S_{2D} = \langle 2\cos^2 \beta - 1 \rangle \tag{2}$$

for a two-dimensional system (2D), where the brackets indicate an average over all the angles β between the local director and the main molecular axis (or the tube axis for a SWNT lyotropic phase).

Polarized resonant Raman spectroscopy (see Chap. 7) was used to measure S.[56–58] Raman scattering is a resonant process for nanotubes and absorption is strongly polarized parallel to the tube axis. Consequently, it is a good approximation to consider that the only non zero component of the Raman polarizability tensors is for incident and scattered light parallel to the tube axis. A typical order parameter of about 0.1 and 0.15 was found considering 2D or 3D analyses. This value is much lower than the theoretical order parameter of rigid rods at the isotropic nematic transition: $S \approx 0.8$, but also lower than the order parameter of flexible chains $S \approx 0.5$,[59] which exhibit Onsager-type excluded-volume interactions. Lu and Chen[60] have demonstrated that impurities could greatly hinder the ordering of nanotubes in concentrated suspensions and showed that purified nanotubes could be efficiently shear-aligned in composite membranes. Nevertheless, nanotubes of relatively high purity were also used in other studies and could not lead to materials aligned on macroscopic scale.

Song and Windle[61] have shown that the morphology of the nanotubes can affect the texture of nematic liquid crystals and the density of topological defects. In particular, the authors have demonstrated that long nanotubes could be bent around the core of topological defects. The stabilization of topological defects by deformed or imperfect nanotubes could explain the difficulty in aligning such materials over large monodomains. Even shear aligned and dried materials could indeed still contain defects at the microscopic scale which can neither be visualized by optical microscopy nor detected by polarized Raman spectroscopy. Such techniques, as other optical or scattering techniques, probe a surface area of a few microns square. Topological defects could be stabilized by long and deformed nanotubes and yield apparent low order parameters. Long and/or tortuous nanotubes can also increase the viscosity of the material and even yield some elastic behavior that hinders the spontaneous coarsening of topological defects as observed in conventional liquid crystals.

The importance of the nanotube waviness was in fact supported by studies of shortened nanotubes.[57] Indeed, sonication induced scission of nanotubes allows for the achievement of shorter and straighter particles.

Materials stabilized in water by bile salts acting as surfactants were used in this work. Liquid crystals have been made by dispersing these sorted nanotubes in water. It was found that short nanotubes could easily be shear aligned over large monodomains. More importantly, it was observed that the order parameter of dried nematic films increased with the sonication time used to prepare the materials. In other words, shorter but straighter nanotubes could be more efficiently aligned than long and wavy ones. The best systems tested by this approach displayed orientational order parameters up to $S = 0.55$.[57] As shown in Fig. 5, shortened nanotubes formed also uniform tactoids at the isotropic-nematic equilibrium.[62] The presence of tactoids reflected the remarkable alignment of the nanotubes into fluid droplets. The observation of such tactoids was an opportunity to probe a nematic monodomain and accurately measure the order parameter of a nanotube based liquid crystal of a non-dried material. The order parameter was found to be of about 0.65. This quantitative characterization was in relatively good agreement with the theoretically expected behavior of rigid rods in solution.

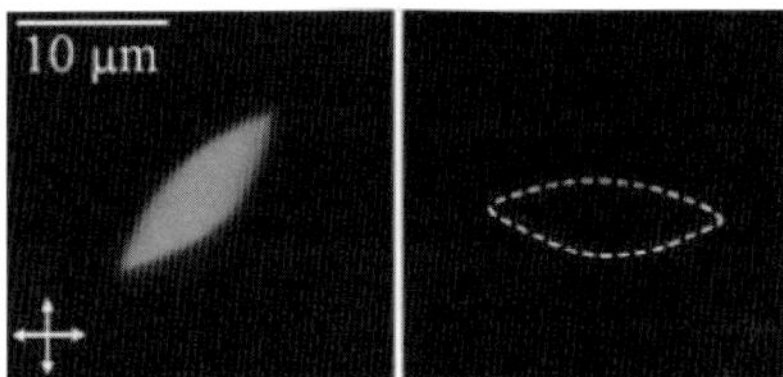

Fig. 5. Optical micrographs of a tactoid with the main body axis at 45° relative to the polarizers (left) and along one of the polarizers (right). Indicated by dashed line is the outline of the tactoid. Reprinted with permission from Ref. 62 Copyright (2010) by the American Physical Society.

4. Towards applications of CNT liquid crystals

CNTs exhibit remarkable physical properties, in particular a high electrical conductivity and a great mechanical strength. But manifestation of these properties on macroscopic scale for actual applications is often challenging. As indicated in the introduction of this chapter, long range alignment of the nanotubes is a necessary condition to achieve the best of their potential. Liquid crystal ordering of CNTs provides an appealing approach towards such an objective. Indeed, we have seen in the previous sections, that CNT liquid crystals can be achieved by several chemical approaches and that their ordering can be optimized by different treatments. As a matter of fact, first investigations of CNT liquid crystals properties and examples of exciting applications have emerged in the recent years. These advances are summarized in the present section.

Liquid crystals exhibit anisotropic physical properties such as optical birefringence and anisotropic dielectric constants.[63] They also exhibit conductivity anisotropy. In dielectric liquid crystals, the current carrying species are generally embedded ions. The conductivity anisotropy results from the differences of the ionic mobility parallel and perpendicular to the director field.[63] This phenomenon has been the topic of several studies in the past. By contrast, the current is carried by electrons travelling through the particles in a film made from a liquid crystal of intrinsically conductive particles. While conductivity anisotropy has been experimentally observed in a number of aligned CNT materials, a quantitative relationship between the conductivity anisotropy and the degree of ordering from liquid crystal materials was only recently determined.[64]

Different films made from more or less ordered liquid crystals were prepared. Their order parameters were measured by polarized Raman spectroscopy. The conductivity anisotropy defined by the ratio between the surface conductivity parallel to the nematic director and the perpendicular one $\sigma_{\mathrm{ani}} = \sigma_{\parallel}/\sigma_{\perp}$ was found to systematically increase with the order parameter. The anisotropy σ_{ani} is close to 1 for films that are weakly ordered (almost isotropic). It increases up to $\sigma_{\mathrm{ani}} \sim 8$ for the more ordered nematics tested in this work with an order parameter $S \sim 0.6$. Lu and Chen achieved a macroscopically aligned conductive film from a CNT liquid crystal and estimated from electron micrographs an order parameter of about 0.9.[60] The surface conductivity anisotropy was about 18. The experimental results were accounted for by a model that takes into account the number of intertube contacts and the density of conductive pathways in different directions, as introduced by J. Fischer *et al.* for magnetically aligned nanotubes.[65] A good agreement, without any fitting parameter, of the proposed model and experiments was obtained with considering a 2D Gaussian distribution of the nanotube orientation.

It can be concluded from the above studies that the conductivity along the main axis can typically be one order of magnitude greater than the conductivity along the perpendicular direction. This degree of anisotropy is much greater than the conductivity anisotropy of liquid crystals resultant from the mobility anisotropy of embedded ions. Indeed, anisotropy conductivity arising from differences in ionic mobility doesn't generally exceed a value of 2 in dielectric liquid crystals.[63] As shown in Fig. 6, Ko and Tsuruk[66] have elegantly taken advantage of the anisotropic electronic properties of CNT liquid crystals to make thin films transistors. The properties of aligned materials were shown to be significantly improved compared to misaligned materials.

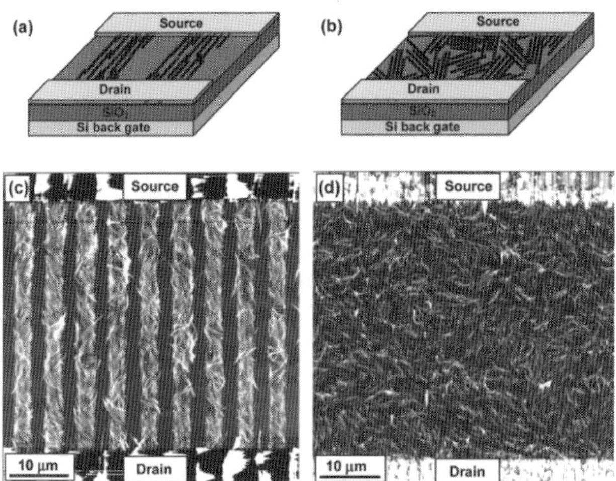

Fig. 6. Device configurations of back-gated oriented (a) and random thin film transistors (TFTs). AFM images of a CNT-TFTs with an ordered CNT array (c) and with a randomly oriented CNT film. Reprinted with permission from Ref. 66. Copyright (2006) American Chemical Society.

In analogy with the industrial liquid crystal fiber spinning of rigid polyaramid materials (high performance Kevlar® or Twaron® fibers), Pasquali *et al.* used CNT liquid crystals in super acids to make CNT fibers.[47,67] The main incentive is the achievement of fibers with densely packed and highly aligned carbon nanotubes, such as high performance polymer fibers, in order to efficiently take advantage of the CNT properties. However, this breakthrough was not yet accompanied by exceptional properties and a clear scalability in its early developments.[67] But less than ten years later, after deep fundamental investigations of the phase behavior of CNT liquid crystals, optimization of the processing conditions and progresses in the quality of the CNT materials, spectacular advances have been reported by Pasquali's group.[48,68]

CNT liquid crystals can be used to manufacture continuous and multifilament fibers. The fibers exhibit a uniform morphology, with very few defects and a high degree of CNT alignment. These lightweight fibers exhibit excellent mechanical properties.[68] Indeed, CNT fibers approach the high specific strength of polymeric and carbon fibers, while also achieving the high specific electrical conductivity of metals and the specific thermal conductivity of graphite fibers. Actually, if CNT fibers don't necessarily outperform a given material for a specific property, they clearly outperform any known material as combined properties are considered. This is why they open exciting opportunities in particular in the field of smart and strong materials that necessitate multifunctional and highly efficient constituents. Those include smart textiles, conductive composites, electric wires, etc.

Considering the intrinsic properties of their constituents, mechanical and electrical properties are the most natural targets in potential applications of CNT liquid crystals. Nevertheless, other uses can be envisioned. In particular the propensity of CNTs to form liquid crystals at low concentration because of their large aspect ratio can be exploited to alter the visco-elastic properties of soft materials. An example of potential biomedical interest was recently reported with the case of hyaluronic acid (HA) gels.[46] HA is a common component of synovial fluid extracellular matrix. This natural polysaccharide is of great interest for medical and cosmetic applications.[69] In most cases HA has to be used in a gel state. Unfortunately, raw HA in aqueous media does increase the viscosity of the solution but does not form elastic gels. Consequently extensive research work has been devoted over the last years to develop chemical modifications of HA and covalent cross-linkers.[69-72] These chemical modifications can lead to the formation of gels but involve heavy chemical processing.

As shown in Fig. 8, the addition of carbon nanotubes (CNTs) can also lead to the formation of HA gels.[46,73,74] These gels are achieved at relatively low concentrations without any covalent modifications of the polymer. The new HA-CNT biogels have already demonstrated promising properties and biofunctionalities. They are biocompatible, electrically conductive and can serve as scaffolds with electrically stimulated delivery of bioactive molecules such as neurotrophins.[46] Studies by optical microscopy and light scattering showed that the gelation results from an arrested liquid crystal phase separation of the CNTs. The formation of nematic gels is promoted by depletion attractive interactions due to the HA molecules in solution. The remarkable efficiency of CNTs at inducing the gelation of HA, without any chemical modification and with small amounts of materials, results from their propensity to easily phase separate as liquid crystals because of their giant aspect ratio.

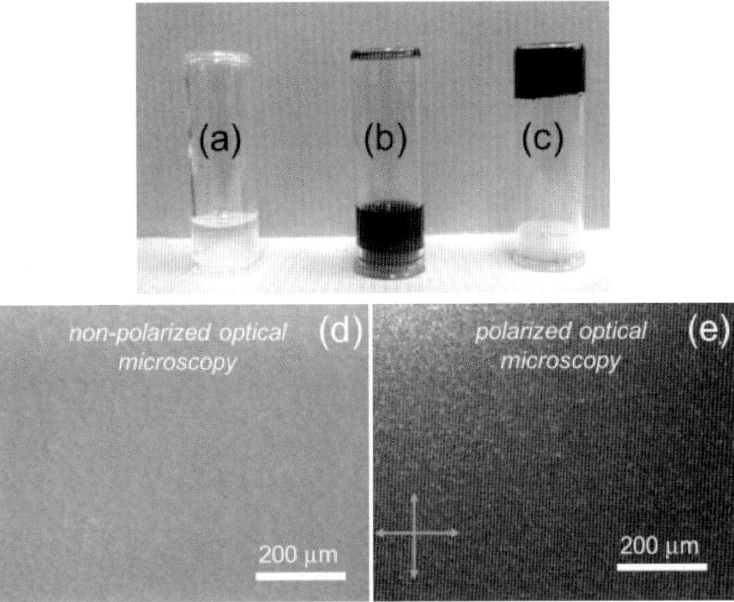

Fig. 7. Macroscopic photographs of (a) a 0.5 wt% HA aqueous solution; (b) an isotropic suspension with 0.3 wt% SWCNTs and 0.25 wt% HA and (c) a HA-CNT liquid crystal biogel with 0.6 wt% SWCNTs and 0.5 wt% HA. Vials have been turned upside down to show the effect of gelation. Optical micrographs of a sample of the biogel with 0.6 wt% SWCNT and 0.5 wt% of HA after one hour after preparation and confinement in a 10 μm thick quartz cell with (d) no polarization and (e) between crossed polarizers. Arrows indicate the orientations of the polarizers axes. Reprinted with permission from Ref. 74. Copyright (2006) American Chemical Society.

5. Conclusions and outlook

Carbon nanotubes, as other rod-like colloids, form lyotropic liquid crystals. The chemistry and phase behaviour of such materials are rather well understood after more than ten years of research in the field. Nevertheless, a number of challenges are still faced for their use in future applications. So far, only very few applications of CNT based liquid crystals have been explored. By contrast, conventional liquid crystals are found in a variety of devices and technologies. In particular molecular thermotropic liquid crystals are broadly used in optical, electro-optical, data storage and communication applications. It would be appealing to investigate whether specific features of carbon nanotubes, such as photoluminescence or high absorbance could not be useful for novel optical applications. Other applications such as actuators, sensors and electrostrictive nanocomposites will also deserve great attention in the years to come. Developments towards high performances materials, in particular fibers, are among the most exciting potential outcome of CNT liquid crystals. But, the properties of the best fibers achieved so far are yet a small fraction of the intrinsic properties of individual and defect free carbon nanotubes. It is therefore critical to further improve the quality and length of nanotubes used in such materials to progress in the field. Achieving high conductivity will also require the exclusive use of metallic nanotubes. But sorting nanotubes is still today a very difficult task. The synthesis methods have progressed tremendously over the last years. But the selective growth of metallic or semi-conducting has still to be achieved. From a general point of view, progresses in the uses of CNT liquid crystals are today more hindered by the intrinsic quality of raw materials rather than by the control of their liquid crystallinity.

Lastly, extension of chemical routes and formulation concepts used for CNT liquid crystals have recently been extended to graphene based liquid crystals. Graphene oxide liquid crystals are the topic of chapters of the present book, and interested readers can refer to them. Graphene oxide liquid crystals can easily be obtained in polar solvents, including water, without any stabilizing agents. Indeed, graphene oxide monolayers are stabilized by electrostatic interactions provided by charged groups at their surface. By contrast, liquid crystals of graphene are more difficult to process and can be either achieved in super acids[75] or in presence of stabilizing agents.[58,75] Like CNT liquid crystals, graphene based materials display great promises for future applications.[76] Nevertheless, graphene liquid crystals also raise new fundamental questions. In particular, the competition of liquid crystal phase transition and percolation is among the most exciting ones. The percolation threshold of long and rod like particles is expected to be lower than the typical concentration of the isotropic-nematic phase separation. Therefore liquid crystal transition and percolation do not interfere, at least from a thermodynamical point of view.

It could be possible that percolation slows down the dynamics of the system and reduces the freedom to reorganize, making the formation of liquid crystal phases at greater concentrations more difficult. Nevertheless, the formation of percolated networks at concentrations below the concentration of the isotropic-nematic phase separation is consistent with most simulations of penetrable as well as not penetrable particles, experimental and theoretical studies. The situation turns out to be different for platelets and in particular for graphene. Recent simulations of impenetrable particles[77] clearly show that liquid crystal phase separation affects the percolation behaviour. The percolation threshold is expected to be significantly greater than the threshold predicted from simple excluded volume arguments. This fundamental problem clearly needs further investigation in the years to come. Indeed, understanding the ordering and percolation behaviour in CNT or graphene based liquid crystals is the key towards the control and improvements of their so promising physical properties.

References

1. P. Ajayan, Nanotubes from carbon, *Chem. Rev.* **99**(7), 1787–1800 (1999).
2. H. Dai, Carbon nanotubes: synthesis, integration, and properties, *Accounts Chem. Res.* **35**(12), 1035–1044 (2002).
3. V. N. Popov, Carbon nanotubes: properties and application, *Materials Science and Engineering: R: Reports.* **43**(3), 61–102 (2004).
4. R. H. Baughman, A. A. Zakhidov, and W. A. de Heer, Carbon nanotubes - the route toward applications, *Science.* **297**(5582), 787–792 (2002).
5. W. Chen and X. Tao, Production and characterization of polymer nanocomposite with aligned single wall carbon nanotubes, *Appl. Surf. Sci.* **252**(10), 3547–3552 (2006).
6. M. Moniruzzaman and K. L. Winey, Polymer nanocomposites containing carbon nanotubes, *Macromolecules.* **39**(16), 5194–5205 (2006).
7. B. Vigolo, P. Poulin, M. Lucas, P. Launois, and P. Bernier, Improved structure and properties of single-wall carbon nanotube spun fibers, *Appl. Phys. Lett.* **81**(7), 1210–1212 (2002).
8. X.-L. Xie, Y.-W. Mai, and X.-P. Zhou, Dispersion and alignment of carbon nanotubes in polymer matrix: a review, *Materials Science and Engineering: R: Reports.* **49**(4), 89–112 (2005).
9. R. Haggenmueller, H. Gommans, A. Rinzler, J. E. Fischer, and K. L. Winey, Aligned single-wall carbon nanotubes in composites by melt processing methods, *Chem. Phys. Lett.* **330**, 219–225 (2000).
10. J. Hone, M. Llaguno, N. Nemes, A. Johnson, J. Fischer, D. Walters, M. Casavant, J. Schmidt, and R. Smalley, Electrical and thermal transport properties of magnetically aligned single wall carbon nanotube films, *Appl. Phys. Lett.* **77**(5), 666–668 (2000).
11. K. Iakoubovskii, Techniques of aligning carbon nanotubes, *Central European Journal of Physics.* **7**(4), 645–653 (2009).
12. P. Miaudet, S. Badaire, M. Maugey, A. Derre, V. Pichot, P. Launois,

P. Poulin, and C. Zakri, Hot-drawing of single and multiwall carbon nanotube fibers for high toughness and alignment, *Nano. Lett.* **5**(11), 2212–2215 (2005).

13. P. Pötschke, H. Brünig, A. Janke, D. Fischer, and D. Jehnichen, Orientation of multiwalled carbon nanotubes in composites with polycarbonate by melt spinning, *Polymer.* **46**(23), 10355–10363 (2005).

14. S. Ruan, P. Gao, and T. Yu, Ultra-strong gel-spun UHMWPE fibers reinforced using multiwalled carbon nanotubes, *Polymer.* **47**(5), 1604–1611 (2006).

15. J. P. F. Lagerwall, G. Scalia, M. Haluska, U. Dettlaff-Weglikowska, S. Roth, and F. Giesselmann, Nanotube alignment using lyotropic liquid crystals, *Adv. Mater.* **19**(3), 359–364 (2007).

16. J. P. F. Lagerwall and G. Scalia, Carbon nanotubes in liquid crystals, *J. Mater. Chem.* **18**(25), 2890–2898 (2008).

17. M. Lynch and D. Patrick, Organizing carbon nanotubes with liquid crystals, *Nano. Lett.* **2**(11), 1197–1201 (2002).

18. N. Puech, M. Dennison, C. Blanc, P. van, der Schoot, M. Dijkstra, R. van, Roij, P. Poulin, and E. Grelet, Orientational order of carbon nanotube guests in a nematic host suspension of colloidal viral rods, *Phys. Rev. Lett.* **108**(24), 247801 (2012).

19. P. van der Schoot, V. Popa-Nita, and S. Kralj, Alignment of carbon nanotubes in nematic liquid crystals, *J. Phys. Chem. B.* **112**(15), 4512–4518 (2008).

20. H. K. Bisoyi and S. Kumar, Carbon-based liquid crystals: art and science, *Liq. Cryst.* **38**(11-12), 1427–1449 (2011).

21. B. Dan, A. W. Ma, E. H. Ha roz, J. Kono, and M. Pasquali, Nematic-like alignment in SWNT thin films from aqueous colloidal suspensions, *Industrial & Engineering Chemistry Research.* **51**(30), 10232–10237 (2012).

22. V. A. Davis, Liquid crystalline assembly of nanocylinders, *J. Mater. Res.* **26**(2), 140–153 (2011).

23. S. Zhang and S. Kumar, Carbon nanotubes as liquid crystals, *Small.* **4**(9), 1270–1283 (2008).

24. L. Onsager, The effects of shape on the interaction of colloidal particles, *Ann. N. Y. Acad. Sci.* **51**(4), 627–659 (1949).

25. W. H. Song, I. A. Kinloch, and A. H. Windle, Nematic liquid crystallinity of multiwall carbon nanotubes, *Science.* **302**(5649), 1363–1363 (2003).

26. W. Song and A. Windle, Isotropic-nematic phase transition of dispersions of multiwall carbon nanotubes, *Macromolecules.* **38**(14), 6181–6188 (2005).

27. V. Davis, L. Ericson, A. Parra-vasquez, H. Fan, Y. Wang, V. Prieto, J. Longoria, S. Ramesh, R. Saini, C. Kittrell, W. Billups, W. Adams, R. Hauge, R. Smalley, and M. Pasquali, Phase behavior and rheology of SWNTs in superacids, *Macromolecules.* **37**(1), 154–160 (2004).

28. P. Rai, R. Pinnick, A. Parra-vasquez, V. Davis, H. Schmidt, R. Hauge, R. Smalley, and M. Pasquali, Isotropic-nematic phase transition of single-walled carbon nanotubes in strong acids, *J. Am. Chem. Soc.* **128**(2), 591–595 (2006).

29. S. Ramesh, L. M. Ericson, V. A. Davis, R. K. Saini, C. Kittrell, M. Pasquali, W. Billups, W. W. Adams, R. H. Hauge, and R. E. Smalley, Dissolution of pristine single walled carbon nanotubes in superacids by direct protonation, *J. Phys. Chem. B.* **108**(26), 8794–8798 (2004).

30. A. Penicaud, P. Poulin, A. Derre, E. Anglaret, and P. Petit, Spontaneous dissolution of a single-wall carbon nanotube salt, *J. Am. Chem. Soc.* **127**(1), 8–9 (2005).

31. D. Baskaran, J. W. Mays, and M. S. Bratcher, Noncovalent and nonspecific molecular interactions of polymers with multiwalled carbon nanotubes, *Chem. Mater.* **17**(13), 3389–3397 (2005).

32. R. Haggenmueller, S. S. Rahatekar, J. A. Fagan, J. Chun, M. L. Becker, R. R. Naik, T. Krauss, L. Carlson, J. F. Kadla, and P. C. Trulove, Comparison of the quality of aqueous dispersions of single wall carbon nanotubes using surfactants and biomolecules, *Langmuir.* **24**(9), 5070–5078 (2008).

33. M. F. Islam, E. Rojas, D. M. Bergey, A. T. Johnson, and A. G. Yodh, High weight fraction surfactant solubilization of single-wall carbon nanotubes in water, *Nano. Lett.* **3**(2), 269–273 (2003).

34. W. Jin, X. Sun, and Y. Wang, Solubilization and functionalization of carbon nanotubes, *New Carbon Materials.* **4**, 312–318 (2004).

35. O. Matarredona, H. Rhoads, Z. Li, H. Jeffrey, L. Balzano, and D. Resasco, Dispersion of single-walled carbon nanotubes in aqueous solutions of the anionic surfactant naDDBS, *J. Phys. Chem. B.* **107**(48), 13357–13367 (2003).

36. S. K. Samanta, M. Fritsch, U. Scherf, W. Gomulya, S. Z. Bisri, and M. A. Loi, Conjugated polymer-assisted dispersion of single-wall carbon nanotubes: the power of polymer wrapping, *Accounts Chem. Res.* **47**(8), 2446–2456 (2014).

37. V. A. Sinani, M. K. Gheith, A. A. Yaroslavov, A. A. Rakhnyanskaya, K. Sun, A. A. Mamedov, J. P. Wicksted, and N. A. Kotov, Aqueous dispersions of single-wall and multiwall carbon nanotubes with designed amphiphilic polycations, *J. Am. Chem. Soc.* **127**(10), 3463–3472 (2005).

38. B. Vigolo, A. Penicaud, C. Coulon, C. Sauder, R. Pailler, C. Journet, P. Bernier, and P. Poulin, Macroscopic fibers and ribbons of oriented carbon nanotubes, *Science.* **290**(5495), 1331–1334 (2000).

39. Y. Wu, J. Hudson, Q. Lu, J. Moore, A. Mount, A. Rao, E. Alexov, and P. Ke, Coating single-walled carbon nanotubes with phospholipids, *J. Phys. Chem. B.* **110**(6), 2475–2478 (2006).

40. S. Badaire, C. Zakri, M. Maugey, A. Derre, J. N. Barisci, G. Wallace, and P. Poulin, Liquid crystals of DNA-stabilized carbon nanotubes, *Adv. Mater.* **17**(13), 1673–1676 (2005).

41. A. Y. Grosberg and A. R. Khokhlov. Statistical theory of polymeric lyotropic liquid crystals. pp. 53–97. Springer Berlin Heidelberg, Berlin, Heidelberg (1981).

42. F. Hennrich, R. Krupke, K. Arnold, J. A. Rojas Stütz, S. Lebedkin, T. Koch, T. Schimmel, and M. M. Kappes, The mechanism of cavitation-induced scission of single-walled carbon nanotubes, *J. Phys. Chem. B.* **111**(8), 1932–1937 (2007).

43. A. Lucas, C. Zakri, M. Maugey, M. Pasquali, P. v. d. Schoot, and P. Poulin,

Kinetics of nanotube and microfiber scission under sonication, *J. Phys. Chem. C.* **113**(48), 20599–20605 (2009).

44. G. Pagani, M. J. Green, P. Poulin, and M. Pasquali, Competing mechanisms and scaling laws for carbon nanotube scission by ultrasonication, *Proceedings of the National Academy of Sciences.* **109**(29), 11599–11604 (2012).

45. Y. Y. Huang, T. P. J. Knowles, and E. M. Terentjev, Strength of nanotubes, filaments, and nanowires from sonication-induced scission, *Adv. Mater.* **21** (38-39), 3945–3948 (2009).

46. S. Moulton, M. Maugey, P. Poulin, and G. Wallace, Liquid crystal behavior of single-walled carbon nanotubes dispersed in biological hyaluronic acid solutions, *J. Am. Chem. Soc.* **129**(30), 9452–9457 (2007).

47. A. Davis, Virginia, A. N. G. Parra-Vasquez, J. Green, Micah, K. Rai, Pradeep, N. Behabtu, V. Prieto, D. Booker, Richard, J. Schmidt, E. Kesselman, W. Zhou, H. Fan, W. W. Adams, H. Hauge, Robert, E. Fischer, John, Y. Cohen, Y. Talmon, E. Smalley, Richard, and M. Pasquali, True solutions of single-walled carbon nanotubes for assembly into macroscopic materials, *Nat. Nanotechnol.* **4**(12), 830–834 (2009).

48. A. Windle, Processing: Superacids offer nanotube solution, *Nat. Nanotechnol.* **4**(12), 800–801 (2009).

49. R. J. Hunter, *Foundations of Colloid Science.* Oxford University Press, USA (2001).

50. A. Kyrylyuk and P. van, der Schoot, Continuum percolation of carbon nanotubes in polymeric and colloidal media, *Proc. Natl. Acad. Sci. USA.* **105** (24), 8221–8226 (2008).

51. T. Schilling, S. Jungblut, and M. Miller, Depletion-induced percolation in networks of nanorods, *Phys. Rev. Lett.* **98**(10), 108303 (2007).

52. B. Vigolo, C. Coulon, M. Maugey, C. Zakri, and P. Poulin, An experimental approach to the percolation of sticky nanotubes, *Science.* **309**(5736), 920–923 (2005).

53. S. J. Zhang, I. A. Kinloch, and A. H. Windle, Mesogenicity drives fractionation in lyotropic aqueous suspensions of multiwall carbon nanotubes, *Nano. Lett.* **6**(3), 568–572 (2006).

54. M. Solomon and P. Spicer, *Microstructural regimes of colloidal rod suspensions, gels, and glasses* .

55. I. Chuang, R. Durrer, N. Turok, and B. Yurke, Cosmology in the laboratory: Defect dynamics in liquid crystals, *Science.* **251**(4999), 1336–1342 (1991).

56. C. Zamora-Ledezma, C. Blanc, M. Maugey, C. Zakri, P. Poulin, and E. Anglaret, Anisotropic thin films of single-wall carbon nanotubes from aligned lyotropic nematic suspensions, *Nano. Lett.* **8**(12), 4103–4107 (2008).

57. N. Puech, C. Blanc, E. Grelet, C. Zamora-Ledezma, M. Maugey, C. Zakri, E. Anglaret, and P. Poulin, Highly ordered carbon nanotube nematic liquid crystals, *J. Phys. Chem. C.* **115**(8), 3272–3278 (2011).

58. C. Zakri, C. Blanc, E. Grelet, C. Zamora-Ledezma, N. Puech, E. Anglaret, and P. Poulin, Liquid crystals of carbon nanotubes and graphene, *Philos. Transact. A Math. Phys. Eng. Sci.* **371**, 20120499 (2013).

59. Z. Y. Chen, Nematic ordering in semiflexible polymer chains, *Macro-*

molecules. **26**(13), 3419–3423 (1993).

60. L. Lu and W. Chen, Large-scale aligned carbon nanotubes from their purified, highly concentrated suspension, *ACS Nano.* **4**(2), 1042–1048 (2010).

61. W. Song and A. Windle, Size-dependence and elasticity of liquid-crystalline multiwalled carbon nanotubes, *Adv. Mater.* **20**(16), 3149–3154 (2008).

62. N. Puech, E. Grelet, P. Poulin, C. Blanc, and P. van, der Schoot, Nematic droplets in aqueous dispersions of carbon nanotubes, *Phys. Rev. E.* **82**(2), 020702 (2010).

63. L. M. l. Blinov, Electro-optical and magneto-optical properties of liquid crystals., *John wiley & sons, inc., 605 Third ave., New york, ny 10158, USA, 1983, 350* (1983).

64. C. Zamora-Ledezma, C. Blanc, N. Puech, M. Maugey, C. Zakri, E. Anglaret, and P. Poulin, Conductivity anisotropy of assembled and oriented carbon nanotubes, *Phys. Rev. E.* **84**(6), 062701 (2011).

65. J. E. Fischer, W. Zhou, J. Vavro, C. Llaguno, C. Guthy, R. Haggenmueller, M. J. Casavant, D. E. Walters, and R. E. Smalley, Magnetically aligned single wall carbon nanotube films: Preferred orientation and anisotropic transport properties, *J. Appl. Phys.* **93**(4), 2157–2163 (2003).

66. H. Ko and V. Tsukruk, Liquid-crystalline processing of highly oriented carbon nanotube arrays for thin-film transistors, *Nano. Lett.* **6**(7), 1443–1448 (2006).

67. L. Ericson, H. Fan, H. Peng, V. Davis, W. Zhou, J. Sulpizio, Y. Wang, R. Booker, J. Vavro, C. Guthy, A. Parra-Vasquez, M. Kim, S. Ramesh, R. Saini, C. Kittrell, G. Lavin, H. Schmidt, W. Adams, W. Billups, M. Pasquali, W. Hwang, R. Hauge, J. Fischer, and R. Smalley, Macroscopic, neat, single-walled carbon nanotube fibers., *Science.* **305**(5689), 1447–1450 (2004).

68. N. Behabtu, C. C. Young, D. E. Tsentalovich, O. Kleinerman, X. Wang, A. W. Ma, E. A. Bengio, R. F. ter Waarbeek, J. J. de Jong, and R. E. Hoogerwerf, Strong, light, multifunctional fibers of carbon nanotubes with ultrahigh conductivity, *Science.* **339**(6116), 182–186 (2013).

69. G. Kogan, L. Soltes, R. Stern, and P. Gemeiner, Hyaluronic acid: a natural biopolymer with a broad range of biomedical and industrial applications, *Biotechnol. Lett.* **29**(1), 17–25 (2007).

70. M. N. Collins and C. Birkinshaw, Physical properties of crosslinked hyaluronic acid hydrogels, *Journal of Materials Science: Materials in Medicine.* **19**(11), 3335–3343 (2008).

71. A. Dhanasingh, J. Salber, M. Moeller, and J. Groll, Tailored hyaluronic acid hydrogels through hydrophilic prepolymer cross-linkers, *Soft Matter.* **6**(3), 618–629 (2010).

72. M. Mori, M. Yamaguchi, S. Sumitomo, and Y. Takai, Hyaluronan-based biomaterials in tissue engineering, *Acta Histochemica et Cytochemica.* **37**(1), 1–5 (2004).

73. B. Thompson, S. Moulton, K. Gilmore, M. J. Higgins, P. G. Whitten, and G. G. Wallace, Carbon nanotube biogels, *Carbon* (2009).

74. C. Zamora-Ledezma, L. Buisson, S. E. Moulton, G. Wallace, C. c. Zakri,

C. Blanc, E. Anglaret, and P. Poulin, Carbon nanotubes induced gelation of unmodified hyaluronic acid, *Langmuir.* **29**(32), 10247–10253 (2013).

75. N. Behabtu, J. Lomeda, M. Green, A. Higginbotham, A. Sinitskii, D. Kosynkin, D. Tsentalovich, A. Parra-Vasquez, J. Schmidt, E. Kesselman, Y. Cohen, Y. Talmon, J. Tour, and M. Pasquali, Spontaneous high-concentration dispersions and liquid crystals of graphene, *Nat. Nanotechnol.* **5**(6), 406–411 (2010).

76. S. Naficy, R. Jalili, S. H. Aboutalebi, R. A. Gorkin Iii, K. Konstantinov, P. C. Innis, G. M. Spinks, P. Poulin, and G. G. Wallace, Graphene oxide dispersions: tuning rheology to enable fabrication, *Materials Horizons.* **1**(3), 326–331 (2014).

77. M. Mathew, T. Schilling, and M. Oettel, Connectivity percolation in suspensions of hard platelets, *Phys. Rev. E.* **85**(6) (2012).

Chapter 24

Nematic phase formation in suspensions of graphene oxide

Nathalie Fresneau and Stéphane Campidelli*

*LICSEN, NIMBE, CEA, CNRS, Université Paris-Saday,
CEA Saday 91191 Gif-sur-Yvette Cedex, France*
**stephane.campidelli@cea.fr*

The last decade has seen the rise of graphene. Graphene is a single layer of graphite; it can be obtained by direct liquid phase exfoliation of the latter through harsh sonication. This technique presents the disadvantage to produce small graphene flakes (typically in the 0.05 to 0.4 μm^2 range for the monolayers) and multilayer graphene with uncontrolled thickness distributions. In order to improve the exfoliation process, one has to counter the strong van der Waals interactions between the carbon planes of graphite. This implies to increase the distance between two planes and it can be done, for example, by oxidizing graphite to introduce oxygen species in the graphenic planes. The fabrication of graphite oxide is known for almost 150 years, and it became popular again these last ten years. Generally, the oxidation of graphite is performed following a method described by Hummers in the 1950's and the material produced by this technique exfoliates quasi-spontaneously into monolayer species called graphene oxide (GO). The highly anisotropic shape of GO (several μm in length and width for a thickness of ca. 1 nm) combined with the presence of oxygenated functions on the sp^2 carbon structure of graphene lead to the formation of a lyotropic liquid crystalline phase in water. Above a certain concentration of graphene flakes the gain in translational entropy for a long-range ordered phase outweighs the loss in rotational entropy, and the liquid crystal phase then forms. The value of the threshold is affected by the aspect ratio of the graphene flakes but other factors such as the interactions also play a strong role.

Contents

1. Introduction

Graphene is a monolayer of sp^2-hybridized carbon atoms arranged into a two-dimensional (2D) honeycomb lattice. Each atom possess three sigma bonds (responsible of the mechanical properties) and an orbital p which is responsible of the $\pi\pi$-conjugation and therefore of the electronic properties of the materials. Although graphene has been known for more than sixty years as a 2D building block for graphitic material of all other dimensionalities (Fig. 1),[1] it was only in 2004 and 2005 that its experimental isolation was first achieved by Andre Geim and Konstantin Novoselov of Manchester University, UK.[2] From this date, graphene research has known a phenomenal growth and it was the subject of the Nobel Prize in Physics in 2010. Today, graphene is the most attractive nanomaterial because of its excellent electrical, thermal, mechanical and electronic properties. For example, it has ultrahigh surface area, intrinsic charge mobility, high optical

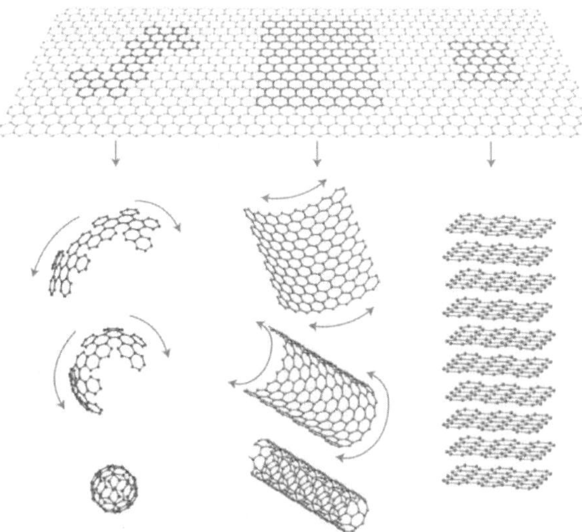

Fig. 1.   Graphene: the parent of all graphitic forms. (a) It can be wrapped up into 0D fullerenes, (b) rolled into 1D nanotubes or (c) stacked into 3D graphite. Reprinted from Ref. 7 with permission of Macmillan Publishers, Copyright (2007).

transmittance, high conductivity, high elasticity, impermeability to gas and liquid and tunable band gap.[2-8] These capacities have made graphene ideal for diverse applications in many technological fields such as nanocomposites, batteries, transistors, transparent conductive films, hydrogen storage, actuators and supercapacitors.[3,7,9,10]

2. Synthesis of graphene

There exist several routes to obtain graphene. The first isolation of graphene was carried out by micromechanical exfoliation, also called "Scotch tape" or "Peel-off" method. Typically, a cellophane tape is used to peel off graphene layers from a graphite flake. The tape is then pressed against a substrate and upon removing it, thinner graphite flakes are obtained. This process is repeated multiple times. Although this method permits to obtain monolayer graphene of high structural and electronic quality, yields are very poor. It is not possible to envisage a large scale production by this way.[2]

Exfoliation of graphite can be also achieved in solvents (direct liquid phase exfoliation). In organic solvents (DMF or NMP), exfoliation was carried out through harsh sonication and leads to small graphene flakes (typically in the 0.05 to 0.4 m^2 range for pure graphene monolayers) with limited yield.[11,12] The same problem was observed with exfoliation in aqueous medium (with surfactant). In these cases, the graphene flakes were obtained with uncontrolled thickness distributions (few layers in majority).[13-15]

On the other hand, obtaining graphene sheets is possible by epitaxial growth on silicon carbide (SiC) surfaces[17] and metal surfaces[16] or by chemical vapour deposition (CVD) of hydrocarbons on metal surfaces.[18,19] This technique permits the preparation of high-quality graphene in few quantities. Moreover, it has been demonstrated that graphene nanoribbons can be produced by unzipping of carbon nanotubes.[20,21]

Finally, the oxidative route is considered as one of the most promising ways to obtain purely monolayers Graphene Oxide (GO) flakes at a large scale. This alternative route implies to increase the distance between two planes by oxidizing graphite to introduce oxygen species in the graphenic planes and thus decrease the strong van der Waals interactions between the carbon planes of graphite. It consists on the oxidation of graphite followed by the exfoliation of graphite oxide in aqueous or polar organic solvents. GO is an insulating material and chemical and/or thermal treatments are necessary to recover, at least partially, the electronic properties of graphene. The material obtained is called reduced Graphene Oxide (rGO).

3. Graphene oxide

Despite the relative novelty of graphene as a material of broad interest and potential, graphite oxide is known for almost 150 years; it became popular again for the last eight years. Since 2008 the number of articles including the terms "graphene oxide" is superior to 15,000. The history of graphene oxide starts in 1859 when the British chemist, B. C. Brodie, was explored the structure of graphite by investigating the reactivity of graphite flakes. During his experiments, he added in one of the reactions potassium chlorate ($KClO_3$) to a slurry of graphite in fuming nitric acid (HNO_3).[22] The resulting material (graphite oxide) was composed of carbon, hydrogen, and oxygen and had a greater overall mass than the flake graphite. Nearly 40 years later, L. Staudenmaier revised Brodie's method by adding the potassium chlorate in small portions in concentrated sulfuric acid (H_2SO_4).[23] The resulting material is not much different from the previous one. Nearly 60 years after Staudenmaier, W. S. Hummers and R. E. Offeman presented a safer approach by utilizing potassium permanganate ($KMnO_4$) as oxidant in a mixture of concentrated sulfuric acid (H_2SO_4) and sodium nitrate.[24] The oxidative agent is the manganese heptoxide (Mn_2O_7) which is produced by the dehydratation of permanganic acid. This method achieved similar levels of oxidation but it was adopted by many researchers due to the absence of fuming nitric acid. Graphite oxide obtained after oxidative treatment can be readily exfoliated as individual graphene oxide sheets in water with or without ultrasonication.

The precise chemical structure of GO has been the subject to controversy over the years and even to this day, no unambiguous model exists. Certainly the most well-known model is the one established by A. Lerf and J. Klinowski.[25] By reacting Graphite Oxide under various conditions and characterizing the resulting materials by solid-state NMR, they revealed that this material have their basal decorated mostly with epoxide and hydroxyl groups (Fig. 2a).[26] A review of this model was proposed by incorporating some of the data obtained by infrared spectroscopy. Thus, another model has emerged taking into account the presence of carboxylic acids and ketones located presumably at the edges (Fig. 2b).[25]

By nature, GO is electrically insulating and can be converted into conducting graphene (rGO) by chemical/thermal reduction processes. The re-

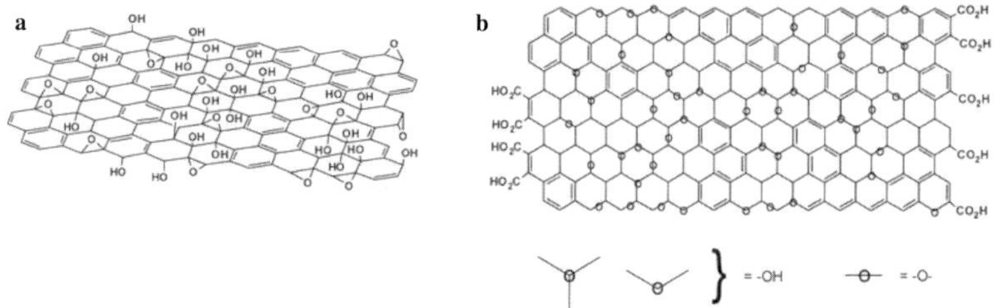

Fig. 2. Variations of the Lerf-Klinowski model. (a) In presence of carboxylic acids[25,27] or (b) in absence of carboxylic acids.[26,27] Adapted from Ref. 27 with permission of The Royal Society of Chemical, Copyright (2010).

covery of the π-conjugation system from a GO sheet takes place during the reduction and the following thermal annealing. It has been demonstrated that the chemical reduction of exfoliated graphene oxide sheets can be performed by several reducing agents[28,29] and one of the best to produce rGO is hydrazine hydrate (NH_2-NH_2, H_2O).[30] GO has been known to disperse well in water and therefore it has been thought for a long time that GO was hydrophilic. However, it has been demonstrated that GO sheets have both hydrophilic character attributed to the ionizable edge –COOH groups and hydrophobic character due to the graphitic domains in the basal plane. Thus, GO could be a 2D amphiphile with a largely hydrophobic basal plane and hydrophilic edges.[31–33]

The amphiphilicity of GO can be modified by variation of pH. Indeed, at high pH (pH = 10), COOH groups are fully charged and GO sheets became more hydrophilic but when the pH was decreased, GO becomes less charged and more amphiphilic.[31] Moreover, GO's amphiphilicity should be size-dependent; a study have shown that small GO sheets are hydrophilic while larger ones are amphiphilic.[31] Due to its amphiphilic character and electrostatic repulsions, GO can forms stable aqueous highly anisotropic colloidal suspensions. With its high aspect ratio, GO sheets can easily align to form a lyotropic liquid crystalline phase in water even at low concentration.[33] In contrast to the isotropic phase where the GO sheets show a random distribution, GO sheets with a high aspect ratio tend to align with their GO plane normal along an orientation vector **n** (the director, in the terminology of this book). Furthermore, due to the polydispersity of the particles, the only possible liquid crystal phase that can be formed is the nematic phase (Fig. 3).[34] As highly diluted phases contain a small amount of material, more concentrated solutions are more useful from a

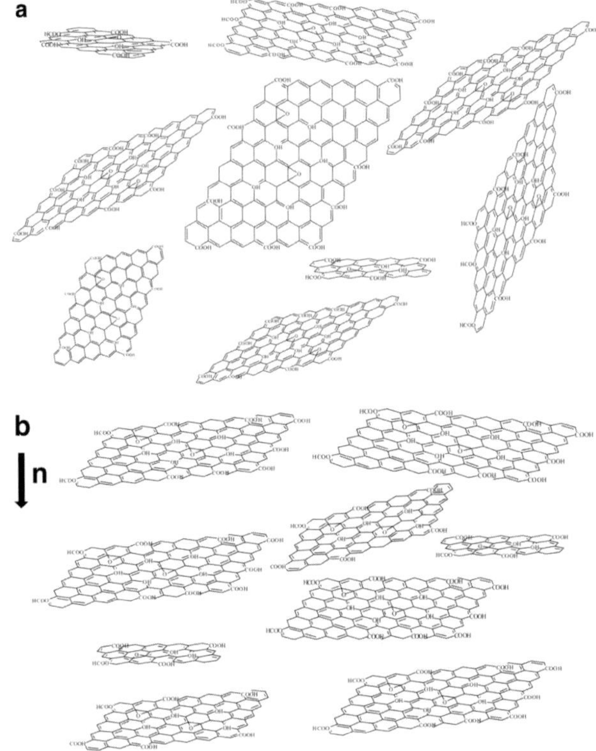

Fig. 3. Transition from an isotropic to nematic liquid crystal phase. a) Isotropic phase of a GO aqueous dispersion showing a random orientational distribution. b) Nematic phase of a GO aqueous dispersion showing alignment of the GO sheets. Reprinted from Ref. 34 with permission of John Wiley and Sons, Copyright (2011).

technological point of view and it appears that these more concentrated solutions are liquid crystalline. This should be taken into consideration for eventual processing.

Most of the works reported so far are focused on the liquid-crystalline properties of graphene oxide. However, it is worth mentioning that the first example of the formation of mesophase with graphene was reported by Behabtu *et al.* in 2010. The liquid-crystalline properties were obtained for graphene suspensions in chlorosulfonic acid at high graphene concentration (2 wt%, 20-30 mg mL^{-1}).[35] In the rest of this chapter we will discuss exclusively the properties of graphene oxide solutions.

4. GO-based liquid crystals

As introduced in Chap. 2, a simple model that predicts lyotropic phase transitions is the model proposed by Lars Onsager. According to Onsager's theory, suspensions of 2D materials with high aspect ratio (the ratio of the lateral size to the thickness) show a transition from a disordered isotropic phase to an ordered nematic phase above a critical concentration, through an entropy-driven process.[36] Thus, despite the loss of orientational entropy, the nematic phase is stabilized by a gain in translational entropy.[36]

4.1. *Studies of liquid crystal phase of GO formation*

In the case of GO, above the critical concentration for liquid crystal formation, or for ultra-high sheet aspect ratio, the GO sheets orientate parallel to each other, maximizing the positional entropy and favoring a nematic phase.[37] The liquid-crystalline structure is of technological interest because the self-aligned GO sheets produced by the liquid-crystalline process can give best optical, electrical and mechanical properties. Since Kim *et al.*[38] who first reported liquid crystallinity of GO in 2011, several groups have confirmed the observation and made some additional interesting discoveries.

Early studies have been carried out on the observation of liquid crystalline properties (LC) of GO at different concentrations. The characterization of LC-GO was performed between crossed polarized-light optical microscopy (POM). In 2011, Kim *et al.*[38] and Xu and Gao[39] reported discotic nematic fluid behavior in aqueous suspensions of GO (aspect ratio, $D/h \sim 1200$ and 2600, respectively). For example, Xu and Gao observed that GO dispersions evolve into three phases: isotropic (<0.025 wt%), biphasic coexistence (between 0.025 wt% and 0.5 wt%) and nematic (>0.5 wt%) (Fig. 4). They also found that the nematic phase of GO should evolve to a "pseudo" lamellar phase with higher concentration (1 wt%).[39] The nematic to lamellar transition is not clearly demonstrated and other characterization could be beneficial to prove formation of a new phase.

The same year, Dan *et al.* studied the lyotropic phase of giant graphene oxide flakes with high aspect ratio ($D/h \sim 10^4$) in aqueous suspension.[40] They demonstrated that higher aspect ratio leads to a qualitative change in the mesomorphic behavior. At 0.14 vol%, the sample appeared birefringent between crossed polarizers, indicating nematic phase formation. In the same time, Aboutalebi *et al.* reported the same observation with ultralarge

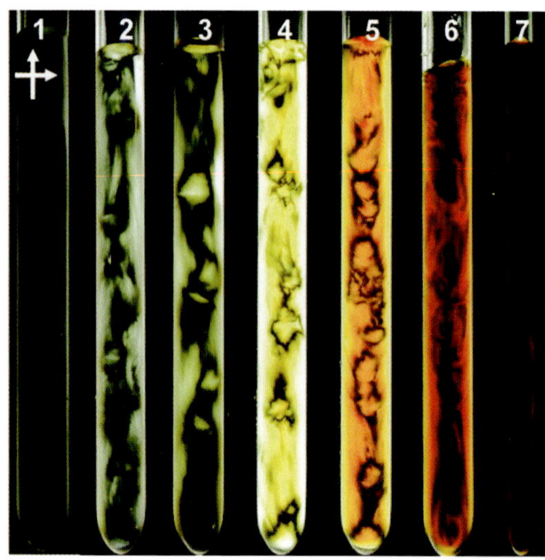

Fig. 4.   Macroscopic photographs between crossed polarizers of GO aqueous dispersions at various concentrations. 1) 0.01 wt%; 2) 0.025 wt%; 3) 0.05 wt%; 4) 0.1 wt%; 5) 0.5 wt%; 6) 1 wt%; and 7) 2 wt%. Reprinted from Ref. 39 with permission of American Chemical Society, Copyright (2011).

GO sheets in water ($D/h \sim 3 \cdot 10^4$) leading to spontaneous formation of lyotropic nematic liquid crystals at a GO concentration as low as 0.1 wt% (1.0 mg mL^{-1} (Fig. 5).[34] Two years later, Yang *et al.* observed only birefringence at low concentrations of GO (0.05 wt%) but no clear texture was observed. By contrast, with concentrations of 0.2 wt% (2 mg mL^{-1}) and higher, they noticed the formation of a typical Schlieren texture.[41] The optical birefringence shows the anisotropic property of the GO solution, whereas the changing of color indicates the wavelength variation (Fig. 6).

4.1.1. *GO in organic solvents*

Other studies focus on the formation of nematic liquid crystalline (LC) phase in dispersion of GO in a wide range of organic solvents to overcome the practical limitations imposed by water. In 2013, Jalili *et al.* discovered that the ability of GO to form self-organized structures is largely imposed by the polarity and capacity of the solvents to form hydrogen bonds with the GO flakes.[42] Indeed, the transition concentration from isotropic to the nematic phase was found to be ~ 0.025 wt% (0.25 mg mL^{-1}) for water, DMF and ethanol and ~ 0.05 wt% (0.50 mg mL^{-1}) for acetone and THF.

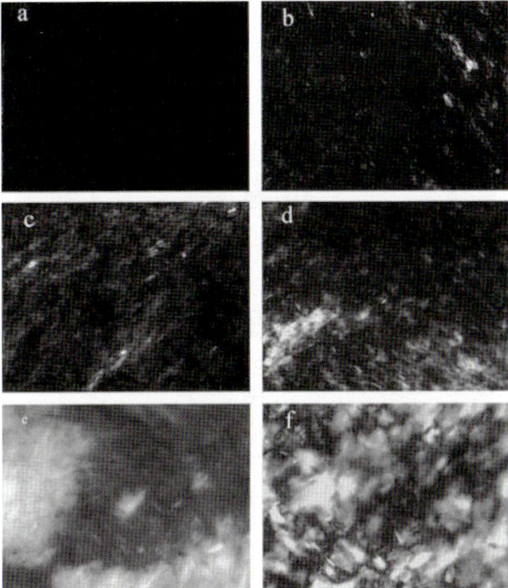

Fig. 5.   Aqueous dispersions of GO in deionized water in various concentrations. a) 0.05 wt% GO; b) 0.1 wt% GO; c) 0.15 wt% GO; d) 0.2 wt% GO; e) 0.5 wt% GO; f) 1.0 wt% GO. Reprinted from Ref. 34 with permission of John Wiley and Sons, Copyright (2011).

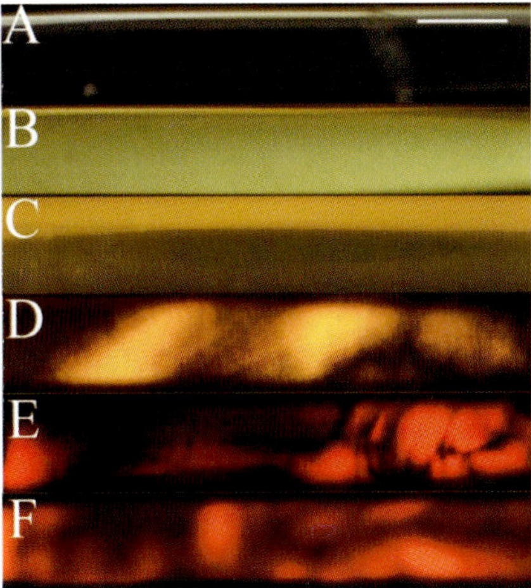

Fig. 6.   Macroscopic photographs of GO sheets aqueous solutions with various concentrations. A) 0 wt%, B) 0.05 wt%, C) 0.1 wt%, D) 0.2 wt%, E) 0.3 wt%, and F) 0.5 wt%. Reprinted from Ref. 41 with permission of American Chemical Society, Copyright (2013).

Shortly after Jalili, Gudarzi *et al.* have also reported nematic LC phase in GO dispersion in organic solvents at low concentration (2.0 mg mL^{-1}) (Fig. 7).[43]

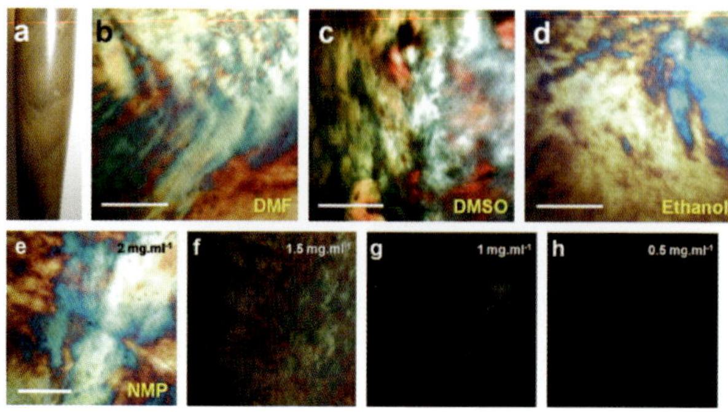

Fig. 7. GO dispersion in organic solvents. a) 0.2 wt% GO dispersion in DMF showing anisotropic texture. b-e) Optical micrographs of GO in organic solvents (0.2 wt%) observed between crossed polarizers demonstrating nematic texture. f-h) Polarized optical micrographs of GO dispersions at lower concentrations (0.05-0.15 wt%) showing isotropic and biphasic textures. Reprinted from Ref. 43 with permission of Elsevier, Copyright (2013).

4.1.2. *Effects of varying the GO sheet size*

As stated in the previous sections, several groups[34,37–39] demonstrated that the critical concentration in which isotropic-nematic transition occurs, depends on the lateral size of GO sheets which is consistent with Onsager's theory.[36] In this context, Jalili *et al.* studied the formation of LC GO with constant GO concentration (2.5 mg ml^{-1}) by varying the GO sheet size.[37] In order to do this, aqueous GO dispersion was exposed to a bath sonication to break down the lateral size of the GO sheets; during this process, small fractions were taken from the GO dispersion and analyzed by SEM. When the mean sheet size of the GO sheets was smaller than 0.7 μm (Fig. 8a), the nematic phase volume fraction was found to be negligible ($\phi_{\text{nem}} \approx 0$). With the mean sheet size between 0.7 and 1.5 μm (Fig. 8b), biphasic dispersions were obtained ($0 < \phi_{\text{nem}} < 1$). Finally, with the mean sheet size higher than 1.5 μm (Fig. 8c), a fully nematic phase ($\phi_{\text{nem}} = 1$) was formed and the dispersions were found to be fully processable and wet-spinnable (*i.e.* fibres were spun from suspensions in this region).

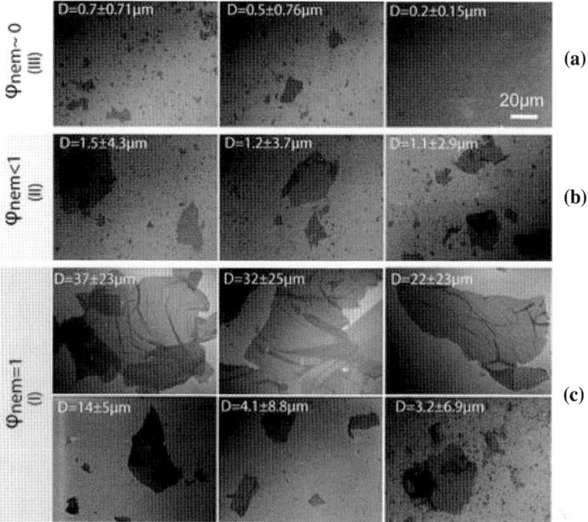

Fig. 8. Representative SEM images of GO sheets with different average lateral size as a function of nematic phase volume fraction (ϕ_{nem}) at a GO concentration of 2.5 mg ml^{-1}. Adapted from Ref. 37 with permission of The Royal Society of Chemistry.

4.1.3. *Effects of varying pH or salt concentration*

As previously reported, large GO sheets have an amphiphilic behavior because of the hydrophobicity of basal plane and the hydrophilicicity of the edges.[31–33] The ionisable groups render this amphiphilicity dependent on pH. As a result, isotropic-nematic transitions are dependent upon factors such as pH and salt concentration. In 2011, Xu *et al.* studied the effect of salt concentration on the interlayer spacing between GO flakes.[44] They reported that the electrostatic repulsion is the major interaction to stabilize the GO liquid crystalline phase; by increasing the salt concentration the interlayer distance decrease because of the charge screening and finally at high concentration, the GO suspensions start to flocculate. In 2014, Tkacz *et al.* varied the pH of GO solutions by adding concentrated NaOH or HCl and examined its influence on the LC properties of GO.[45] At pH 1 and 14, GO platelets aggregated and thus the suspension did not form liquid crystals. However, fully nematic phases are obtained at pH 6 and 9 for a concentration of 16 and 18 mg mg ml^{-1} and pH 2 for a concentration of 9.0 mg mg ml^{-1}.

4.2. *Properties and applications*

The orientation of GO in the LC phase can be controlled by a magnetic field or by mechanical deformation. In 2011, Kim *et al.* first reported the evolution of the birefringent texture of graphene oxide liquid crystals under a magnetic field (Fig. 9).[38] The magnetic field induced the macroscopic alignment of LC GO and a typical nematic schlieren texture evolved. The domains with different LC orientation gradually reoriented and merged into large domain. Shen *et al.* demonstrated a few years later that the direction of macroscopic alignment of LC GO can be readily controlled by applying low electric fields.[46] In particular, they found a Kerr coefficient of $1.8 \cdot 10^{-5}$ mV^{-2}, representing the dependence of the optical birefringence to the electric field. It's probably the highest value ever reported for a molecular LC. This extremely large Kerr coefficient allowed them to propose a prototype of GO liquid crystal displays (LCDs) with low power consumption (only 5 V mm^{-1} threshold field) for electrooptical switching. These findings are discussed in more detail in the following chapter of this book.

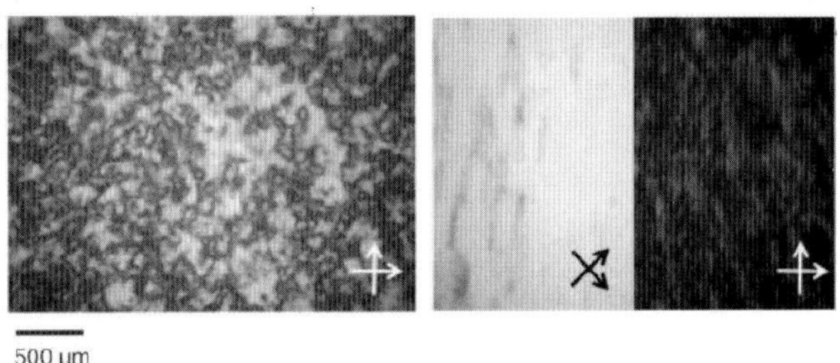

Fig. 9.   Magnetic-field-induced alignment of GO LC. a)Nematic schlieren morphology formed about 3 h after sample preparation without any external field. b)Top: magnetic-field-induced highly aligned liquid-crystal texture. Adapted from Ref. 38 with permission of John Wiley and Sons, Copyright (2011).

The liquid crystalline properties of GO have been studied for several years. Among these studies, in 2011 Guo *et al.* revealed a "shape memory" effect of GO LC gel.[47] To determine this, they studied the behahior of GO gel undergoing drying between two metal needles. Thus, they observed that evaporation caused gradual thinning of the drop until breakage and upon rehydration, the deposits swell and recover their initial size and shape (Fig. 10). This behavior could be a unique hydration-responsive folding and unfolding transition. This ability may find applications in controlled

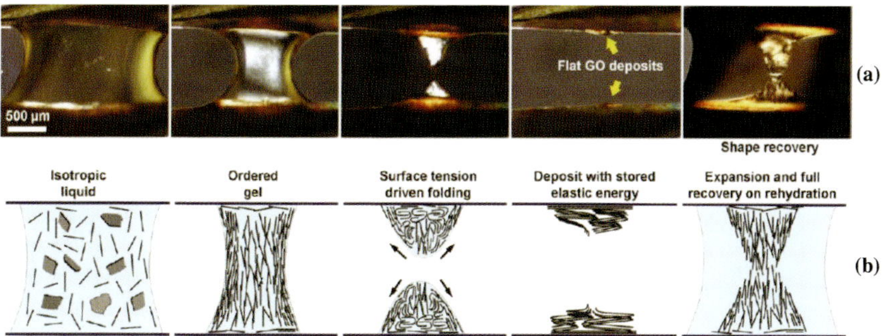

Fig. 10. Drying and rehydration process. (a) Optical micrographs of hourglass droplet (2 mg mg ml^{-1} aqueous GO) undergoing drying between two metal needles. (b) Proposed molecular assembly of GO plates during drying and rehydratation. Adapted from Ref. 47 with permission of the American Chemical Society, Copyright (2011).

release, in nano/microelectro-mechanical devices or in dynamic space filling or sealing. One years later, Senyuk and co-workers reported a visible range nonlinear photoluminescence (PL) from aqueous GO flakes, excited by near-infrared femtosecond laser light.[48] They showed that PL can be used for direct imaging of orientational order of nematic and lamellar LC phases formed by GO flakes. The photoluminescence of graphene is still not fully understood, it can be induced by the defects in the structure. Nevertheless, its photoluminescent properties can potentially lead to novel applications of GO such as biomedical applications[49] or new graphene-based composites.[50]

Recently, Li *et al.* prepared lyotropic photonic liquid crystals based on large-size GO through direct colloidal self-assembly approach. The color reflection of GO photonic crystal exhibited tunable structural color over the entire visible light spectrum by varying the GO concentration (Fig. 11).[51] Indeed, variations in the GO concentration (0.36 to 0.91 wt%) resulted in

Fig. 11. Visual images of GO dispersions of different structural colors. From left to right the weight fraction of GO is 0.91, 0.75, 0.67, 0.55, 0.51, 0.44, and 0.36 wt%. Adapted from Ref. 51 with permission of American Chemical Society, Copyright (2013).

a shift of the reflectance peak λ_{max} from 632 to 338 nm. The simple control of the GO photonic structure by changing GO concentration makes it attractive for many potential applications, such as tunable reflective filters, sensors or energy-efficient color display applications.

Among many possible applications of liquid crystalline GO, the fabrication of nanocomposites materials with polymer is the closest.[38,42,43] It was demonstrated that the liquid crystallinity of GO could be maintained in the polymers and the thermal and mechanical properties can be improved.[50,52,53] High hydrogen capacity (approximately 2.6 wt%) was also reported for highly aligned structures of GO-Multiwalled carbon nanotubes (MWCNTs) composite.[54] It can be a viable route for the fabrication of scalable hydrogen storage media.

The recent understanding of the rheological behavior of LC GO have expanded the range of possible industrial scalable fabrication methods such as spinning (wet and dry), printing (ink-jet and extrusion) and coatings (spray and electrospray).[37,55] This may allow the production of ultra-strong and electrically conducting graphene fibers and high performance supercapacitors.[56–58] It has been demonstrated that, LC GO goes through four distinct rheological regions as a function of their concentration: viscoelastic liquid, a transition state involving viscoelastic liquid and viscoelastic soft solide, viscoelastic soft solid and viscoelastic gel. Each of these regions is appropriated for unique industrial processing methods (spray coating / inkjet printing or extrusion printing / fiber spinning).[59]

GO is an insulating material and it is known that chemical and/or thermal treatments permit to recover partially the conductivity of graphene.[27–29] In 2012, the group of Poulin reported the formation of liquid crystals with rGO stabilized by bile salts (BSs).[60] This discovery can lead to new materials (electronic inks, sensors, electrodes, conductive coating...) that combine the advantages of liquid crystallinity for processing and ordering with the electronic properties of rGO.[61] In the case of high thermal stability of polymer, the conductivity of GO sheets could be recovered by thermal treatment of composite materials.[43]

5. Conclusion

After the strong interest of the scientific community for graphene, GO has also led to some interesting discoveries such as their use as colloidal surfactants, their 2D assembly and size-dependent amphiphilicity. More recently, due to its amphiphilic character and electrostatic repulsions, GO were shown to be able to form a nematic LC phase. Over the last five years, many authors studied this liquid-crystalline behavior and showed the self-aligned GO sheets produced by this process can give best optical, electrical and mechanical properties. Thus, these discoveries can provide access to high-performance nanocomposites, optical materials, energy storage materials and many others applications. These studies have also contributed to understand the solvophobic effect and the parameters affecting the self-assembly process. According to rheological properties of LC GO, the capacity of large GO sheets to be wet-spun led to the production of series of graphene-based fibers, developing many properties such as flexibility, high strength and high conductivity. Moreover, the aqueous surrounding of GO LC can also lead to biological applications, especially the fabrication of highly ordered, self-assembly biomolecules/graphene conjugates.

References

1. P. R. Wallace, The band theory of graphite, *Physical Review.* **71**(9), 622–634 (1947).
2. K. S. Novoselov, A. K. Geim, S. V. Morozov, D. Jiang, Y. Zhang, S. V. Dubonos, I. V. Grigorieva, and A. A. Firsov, Electric field effect in atomically thin carbon films, *Science.* **306**(5696), 666–669 (2004).
3. R. F. Service, Carbon sheets an atom thick give rise to graphene dreams, *Science.* **324**(5929), 875–877 (2009).
4. A. K. Geim, Graphene: Status and prospects, *Science.* **324**(5934), 1530–1534 (2009).
5. C. N. R. Rao, A. K. Sood, K. S. Subrahmanyam, and A. Govindaraj, Graphene: The new two-dimensional nanomaterial, *Angew. Chem. (Int. Ed.).* **48**(42), 7752–7777 (2009).
6. M. J. Allen, V. C. Tung, and R. B. Kaner, Honeycomb carbon: A review of graphene, *Chem. Rev.* **110**(1), 132–145 (2009).
7. A. K. Geim and K. S. Novoselov, The rise of graphene, *Nat. Mater.* **6**(3), 183–191 (2007).
8. K. S. Novoselov, D. Jiang, F. Schedin, T. J. Booth, V. V. Khotkevich, S. V. Morozov, and A. K. Geim, Two-dimensional atomic crystals, *Proc. Natl. Acad. Sci. U. S. A.* **102**(30), 10451–10453 (2005).
9. Y. Zhu, S. Murali, W. Cai, X. Li, J. W. Suk, J. R. Potts, and R. S. Ruoff, Graphene and graphene oxide: Synthesis, properties, and applications, *Adv. Mater.* **22**(35), 3906–3924 (2010).
10. U. K. Sur, Graphene: A rising star on the horizon of materials science, *International Journal of Electrochemistry.* **2012**, 12 (2012).
11. U. Khan, A. O'Neill, M. Lotya, S. De, and J. N. Coleman, High-concentration solvent exfoliation of graphene, *Small.* **6**(7), 864–871 (2010).
12. Y. Hernandez, V. Nicolosi, M. Lotya, F. M. Blighe, Z. Sun, S. De, I. T.

McGovern, B. Holland, M. Byrne, Y. K. GunKo, J. J. Boland, P. Niraj, G. Duesberg, S. Krishnamurthy, R. Goodhue, J. Hutchison, V. Scardaci, A. C. Ferrari, and J. N. Coleman, High-yield production of graphene by liquid-phase exfoliation of graphite, *Nat Nano.* **3**(9), 563–568 (2008).

13. S. De, P. J. King, M. Lotya, A. O'Neill, E. M. Doherty, Y. Hernandez, G. S. Duesberg, and J. N. Coleman, Flexible, transparent, conducting films of randomly stacked graphene from surfactant-stabilized, oxide-free graphene dispersions, *Small.* **6**(3), 458–464 (2010).

14. L. Guardia, M. J. Fernández-Merino, J. I. Paredes, P. Solís-Fernández, S. Villar-Rodil, A. Martínez-Alonso, and J. M. D. Tascón, High-throughput production of pristine graphene in an aqueous dispersion assisted by non-ionic surfactants, *Carbon.* **49**(5), 1653–1662 (2011).

15. M. Lotya, Y. Hernandez, P. J. King, R. J. Smith, V. Nicolosi, L. S. Karlsson, F. M. Blighe, S. De, Z. Wang, I. T. McGovern, G. S. Duesberg, and J. N. Coleman, Liquid phase production of graphene by exfoliation of graphite in surfactant/water solutions, *J. Am. Chem. Soc.* **131**(10), 3611–3620 (2009).

16. K. V. Emtsev, A. Bostwick, K. Horn, J. Jobst, G. L. Kellogg, L. Ley, J. L. McChesney, T. Ohta, S. A. Reshanov, J. Rohrl, E. Rotenberg, A. K. Schmid, D. Waldmann, H. B. Weber, and T. Seyller, Towards wafer-size graphene layers by atmospheric pressure graphitization of silicon carbide, *Nat. Mater.* **8**(3), 203–207 (2009).

17. P. W. Sutter, J.-I. Flege, and E. A. Sutter, Epitaxial graphene on ruthenium, *Nat. Mater.* **7**(5), 406–411 (2008).

18. A. Reina, X. Jia, J. Ho, D. Nezich, H. Son, V. Bulovic, M. S. Dresselhaus, and J. Kong, Large area, few-layer graphene films on arbitrary substrates by chemical vapor deposition, *Nano. Lett.* **9**(1), 30–35 (2009).

19. K. S. Kim, Y. Zhao, H. Jang, S. Y. Lee, J. M. Kim, K. S. Kim, J.-H. Ahn, P. Kim, J.-Y. Choi, and B. H. Hong, Large-scale pattern growth of graphene films for stretchable transparent electrodes, *Nature.* **457**(7230), 706–710 (2009).

20. D. B. Shinde, J. Debgupta, A. Kushwaha, M. Aslam, and V. K. Pillai, Electrochemical unzipping of multi-walled carbon nanotubes for facile synthesis of high-quality graphene nanoribbons, *J. Am. Chem. Soc.* **133**(12), 4168–4171 (2011).

21. M. Terrones, Sharpening the chemical scissors to unzip carbon nanotubes: Crystalline graphene nanoribbons, *ACS Nano.* **4**(4), 1775–1781 (2010).

22. B. C. Brodie, On the atomic weight of graphite, *Philosophical Transactions of the Royal Society of London.* **149**, 249–259 (1859).

23. L. Staudenmaier, Verfahren zur darstellung der graphitsäure, *Berichte der deutschen chemischen Gesellschaft.* **31**(2), 1481–1487 (1898).

24. W. S. Hummers and R. E. Offeman, Preparation of graphitic oxide, *J. Am. Chem. Soc.* **80**(6), 1339–1339 (1958).

25. A. Lerf, H. He, M. Forster, and J. Klinowski, Structure of graphite oxide revisitedñ, *J. Phys. Chem. B.* **102**(23), 4477–4482 (1998).

26. H. He, J. Klinowski, M. Forster, and A. Lerf, A new structural model for graphite oxide, *Chem. Phys. Lett.* **287**(1–2), 53–56 (1998).

27. D. R. Dreyer, S. Park, C. W. Bielawski, and R. S. Ruoff, The chemistry of graphene oxide, *Chem. Soc. Rev.* **39**(1), 228–240 (2010).

28. C. K. Chua and M. Pumera, Chemical reduction of graphene oxide: a synthetic chemistry viewpoint, *Chem. Soc. Rev.* **43**(1), 291–312 (2014).

29. S. Mao, H. Pu, and J. Chen, Graphene oxide and its reduction: modeling and experimental progress, *RSC Adv.* **2**(7), 2643–2662 (2012).

30. S. Stankovich, D. A. Dikin, R. D. Piner, K. A. Kohlhaas, A. Kleinhammes, Y. Jia, Y. Wu, S. T. Nguyen, and R. S. Ruoff, Synthesis of graphene-based nanosheets via chemical reduction of exfoliated graphite oxide, *Carbon.* **45**(7), 1558–1565 (2007).

31. J. Kim, L. J. Cote, F. Kim, W. Yuan, K. R. Shull, and J. Huang, Graphene oxide sheets at interfaces, *J. Am. Chem. Soc.* **132**(23), 8180–8186 (2010).

32. F. Kim, L. J. Cote, and J. Huang, Graphene oxide: Surface activity and two-dimensional assembly, *Adv. Mater.* **22**(17), 1954–1958 (2010).

33. J. Kim, L. J. Cote, and J. Huang, Two dimensional soft material: New faces of graphene oxide, *Accounts Chem. Res.* **45**(8), 1356–1364 (2012).

34. S. H. Aboutalebi, M. M. Gudarzi, Q. B. Zheng, and J.-K. Kim, Spontaneous formation of liquid crystals in ultralarge graphene oxide dispersions, *Adv. Funct. Mater.* **21**(15), 2978–2988 (2011).

35. N. Behabtu, J. R. Lomeda, M. J. Green, A. L. Higginbotham, A. Sinitskii, D. V. Kosynkin, D. Tsentalovich, A. N. G. Parra-Vasquez, J. Schmidt, E. Kesselman, Y. Cohen, Y. Talmon, J. M. Tour, and M. Pasquali, Spontaneous high-concentration dispersions and liquid crystals of graphene, *Nat Nano.* **5**(6), 406–411 (2010).

36. L. Onsager, The effects of the shape on the interaction of colloidal particles, *Ann. N. Y. Acad. Sci.* **51**(4), 627–659 (1949).

37. R. Jalili, S. H. Aboutalebi, D. Esrafilzadeh, K. Konstantinov, J. M. Razal, S. E. Moulton, and G. G. Wallace, Formation and processability of liquid crystalline dispersions of graphene oxide, *Materials Horizons.* **1**(1), 87–91 (2014).

38. J. E. Kim, T. H. Han, S. H. Lee, J. Y. Kim, C. W. Ahn, J. M. Yun, and S. O. Kim, Graphene oxide liquid crystals, *Angew. Chem. (Int. Ed.).* **50**(13), 3043–3047 (2011).

39. Z. Xu and C. Gao, Aqueous liquid crystals of graphene oxide, *ACS Nano.* **5**(4), 2908–2915 (2011).

40. B. Dan, N. Behabtu, A. Martinez, J. S. Evans, D. V. Kosynkin, J. M. Tour, M. Pasquali, and I. I. Smalyukh, Liquid crystals of aqueous, giant graphene oxide flakes, *Soft Matter.* **7**(23), 11154–11159 (2011).

41. X. Yang, C. Guo, L. Ji, Y. Li, and Y. Tu, Liquid crystalline and shear-induced properties of an aqueous solution of graphene oxide sheets, *Langmuir.* **29**(25), 8103–8107 (2013).

42. R. Jalili, S. H. Aboutalebi, D. Esrafilzadeh, K. Konstantinov, S. E. Moulton, J. M. Razal, and G. G. Wallace, Organic solvent-based graphene oxide liquid crystals: A facile route toward the next generation of self-assembled layer-by-layer multifunctional 3D architectures, *ACS Nano.* **7**(5), 3981–3990 (2013).

43. M. M. Gudarzi, M. H. M. Moghadam, and F. Sharif, Spontaneous exfoliation

of graphite oxide in polar aprotic solvents as the route to produce graphene oxide – organic solvents liquid crystals, *Carbon.* **64**(0), 403–415 (2013).

44. Z. Xu and C. Gao, Graphene chiral liquid crystals and macroscopic assembled fibres, *Nat. Commun.* **2**, 571 (2011).

45. R. Tkacz, R. Oldenbourg, S. B. Mehta, M. Miansari, A. Verma, and M. Majumder, ph dependent isotropic to nematic phase transitions in graphene oxide dispersions reveal droplet liquid crystalline phases, *Chem. Commun.* **50**(50), 6668–6671 (2014).

46. T.-Z. Shen, S.-H. Hong, and J.-K. Song, Electro-optical switching of graphene oxide liquid crystals with an extremely large kerr coefficient, *Nat. Mater.* **13** (4), 394–399 (2014).

47. F. Guo, F. Kim, T. H. Han, V. B. Shenoy, J. Huang, and R. H. Hurt, Hydration-responsive folding and unfolding in graphene oxide liquid crystal phases, *ACS Nano.* **5**(10), 8019–8025 (2011).

48. B. Senyuk, N. Behabtu, B. G. Pacheco, T. Lee, G. Ceriotti, J. M. Tour, M. Pasquali, and I. I. Smalyukh, Nonlinear photoluminescence imaging of isotropic and liquid crystalline dispersions of graphene oxide, *ACS Nano.* **6** (9), 8060–8066 (2012).

49. X. Sun, Z. Liu, K. Welsher, J. Robinson, A. Goodwin, S. Zaric, and H. Dai, Nano-graphene oxide for cellular imaging and drug delivery, *Nano Research.* **1**(3), 203–212 (2008).

50. S. Stankovich, D. A. Dikin, G. H. B. Dommett, K. M. Kohlhaas, E. J. Zimney, E. A. Stach, R. D. Piner, S. T. Nguyen, and R. S. Ruoff, Graphene-based composite materials, *Nature.* **442**(7100), 282–286 (2006).

51. P. Li, M. Wong, X. Zhang, H. Yao, R. Ishige, A. Takahara, M. Miyamoto, R. Nishimura, and H.-J. Sue, Tunable lyotropic photonic liquid crystal based on graphene oxide, *ACS Photonics.* **1**(1), 79–86 (2013).

52. S. Lu, S. Li, J. Yu, Z. Yuan, and B. Qi, Epoxy nanocomposites filled with thermotropic liquid crystalline epoxy grafted graphene oxide, *RSC Adv.* **3** (23), 8915–8923 (2013).

53. B. Qi, Z. Yuan, S. Lu, K. Liu, S. Li, L. Yang, and J. Yu, Mechanical and thermal properties of epoxy composites containing graphene oxide and liquid crystalline epoxy, *Fibers and Polymers.* **15**(2), 326–333 (2014).

54. S. H. Aboutalebi, S. Aminorroaya-Yamini, I. Nevirkovets, K. Konstantinov, and H. K. Liu, Enhanced hydrogen storage in graphene oxide-MWCNTs composite at room temperature, *Adv. Energy Mater.* **2**(12), 1439–1446 (2012).

55. S. Gambhir, R. Jalili, D. L. Officer, and G. G. Wallace, Chemically converted graphene: scalable chemistries to enable processing and fabrication, *NPG Asia Mater.* **7**, e186 (2015).

56. Z. Xu and C. Gao, Graphene in macroscopic order: Liquid crystals and wet-spun fibers, *Accounts Chem. Res.* **47**(4), 1267–1276 (2014).

57. S. H. Aboutalebi, R. Jalili, D. Esrafilzadeh, M. Salari, Z. Gholamvand, S. Aminorroaya Yamini, K. Konstantinov, R. L. Shepherd, J. Chen, S. E. Moulton, P. C. Innis, A. I. Minett, J. M. Razal, and G. G. Wallace, High-performance multifunctional graphene yarns: Toward wearable all-carbon energy storage textiles, *ACS Nano.* **8**(3), 2456–2466 (2014).

58. R. Jalili, S. H. Aboutalebi, D. Esrafilzadeh, R. L. Shepherd, J. Chen, S. Aminorroaya-Yamini, K. Konstantinov, A. I. Minett, J. M. Razal, and G. G. Wallace, Scalable one-step wet-spinning of graphene fibers and yarns from liquid crystalline dispersions of graphene oxide: Towards multifunctional textiles, *Adv. Funct. Mater.* **23**(43), 5345–5354 (2013).

59. S. Naficy, R. Jalili, S. H. Aboutalebi, R. A. Gorkin Iii, K. Konstantinov, P. C. Innis, G. M. Spinks, P. Poulin, and G. G. Wallace, Graphene oxide dispersions: tuning rheology to enable fabrication, *Materials Horizons.* **1**(3), 326–331 (2014).

60. C. Zamora-Ledezma, N. Puech, C. Zakri, E. Grelet, S. E. Moulton, G. G. Wallace, S. Gambhir, C. Blanc, E. Anglaret, and P. Poulin, Liquid crystallinity and dimensions of surfactant-stabilized sheets of reduced graphene oxide, *The Journal of Physical Chemistry Letters.* **3**(17), 2425–2430 (2012).

61. C. Zakri, C. Blanc, E. Grelet, C. Zamora-Ledezma, N. Puech, E. Anglaret, and P. Poulin, Liquid crystals of carbon nanotubes and graphene, *Philos. Transact. A Math. Phys. Eng. Sci.* **371**, 20120499 (2013).

Chapter 25

Electro-optical switching of liquid crystals of graphene oxide

Jang-Kun Song

*Sungkyunkwan University, School of Electronic & Electrical Engineering,
Jangan-gu, Suwon 440-746, Korea*
jk.song@skku.edu

Electric field effects on aqueous graphene-oxide (GO) dispersions are reviewed in this chapter. In isotropic and biphasic regimes of GO dispersions, in which the inter-particle friction is low, GO particles sensitively respond to the application of electric field, producing field-induced optical birefringence. The electro-optical sensitivity dramatically decreases as the phase transits to the nematic phase; the increasing inter-particle friction hinders the rotational switching of GO particles. The corresponding Kerr coefficient reaches the maximum near the isotropic to biphasic transition concentration, at which the Kerr coefficient is found be c.a. $1.8 \cdot 10^{-5}$ mV^{-2}, the highest value ever reported in all Kerr materials. The exceptionally large Kerr effect arises from the Maxwell–Wagner polarization of GO particles with an extremely large aspect ratio and a thick electrical double layer (EDL). The polarization sensitively depends on the ratio of surface and bulk conductivities in dispersions. As a result, low ion concentration in bulk solvent is highly required to achieve a quality electro-optical switching in GO dispersions. Spontaneous vinylogous carboxylic reaction in GO particles produces H$^+$ ions, resulting in spontaneous degradation of electro-optical response with time, hence the removal of residual ions by using a centrifuge cleaning process significantly improves the electro-optical sensitivity. GO particle size is another important parameter for the Kerr coefficient and the response time. The best performance is observed in a GO dispersion with c.a. 0.5 μm mean size. Dielectrophoretic migration of GO particles can be also used to manipulate GO particles in solution. Using these unique features of GO dispersions, one can fabricate GO liquid crystal devices similar to conventional liquid crystal displays; the large Kerr effect allows fabricating a low power device working at extremely low electric fields.

Contents

1. Introduction

Single-layered graphene-oxide (GO) particles with abundant functional groups such as carboxyl and hydroxyl groups disperse well in water and the aqueous GO dispersion exhibits liquid crystalline assembly at low concentrations,[1-6] which can be a significant benefit for solution processes in flexible electronics, energy storage etc.[1,7-10] After Onsager's theory was introduced for describing the phase transition in mono-disperse and rod-like colloids,[11] the theory has been further developed to be applicable to other types of materials, in particular, including disk-like and poly-disperse colloids, which aqueous GO dispersions belong to.[12-14] According to those models, the aspect ratio (diameter/thickness) is one of the most critical factors to determine the liquid crystalline behavior. Since GO particles have an extremely large aspect ratio,[2,15-17] it is naturally expected that aqueous GO dispersion is a good lyotropic liquid crystal (LC), which was recently confirmed in 2011 by three independent groups.[2,4,18] After then, the liquid crystalline properties of GO dispersions have been intensively studied including its aligning methods.[2,3,18]

It was reported that the capillary effect during the injection of GO LC into a cell can induce a large sized uniform GO-LC alignment and the application of magnetic fields can also control the GO alignment,[2,4] but these methods have clear limitations that prevent the fine and arbitrary control of GO alignment. An electric field is the easiest and most widely used method to dynamically control the alignment of LCs in conventional LCDs using molecular LCs. The commercial success in LCD business is significantly attributed to the facile alignment of LCs using a surface treatment and the precise manipulation of dynamic switching of LCs using electric fields, and these features are regarded as intrinsic advantages of LCs.[19,20] Dierking *et al.* and Tie *et al.* demonstrated the alignment and electrical switching of carbon nanotubes and graphene flakes by mixing with molecular nematic liquid-crystal host.[21–23] However, Kim *et al.* reported that GO flakes in aqueous dispersions cannot be simply aligned by applying an electric field because of several critical issues such as insensitivity to electric fields, electrolysis of water, and electrophoretic migration of GO flakes toward the anode.[2] The insensitivity of nematic GO LC to electric fields arises from viscous rheology similar to polymeric liquid crystals and is considered as an intrinsic limitation.[2,24] GO particles are negatively charged due to the protonation of functional groups on GO basal plane, which causes the electrophoretic migration. Recently, Shen *et al.* reported that these issues could be overcome by applying high-frequency alternating current (AC) fields and reducing the interparticle interactions between GO flakes.[17] Moreover, they discovered an interesting phenomenon that the optical Kerr coefficient of GO is the highest reported for all Kerr materials. The finding provides new possibility of electro-optical devices with low power consumption using GO dispersions.

In this chapter, the electro-optical switching behaviors of aqueous GO dispersions are precisely reviewed including the relevant theory, dynamic response time, ionic effect, particle size effect, and dielectrophoretic migration. This chapter is majorly based on the works reported by the author's group in the references.[17,25–27]

2. Theory

The electric polarizability of colloidal particles can be formulated using the Maxwell–Wagner–O'Konski model. Usually, a colloid is stabilized by electrostatic repulsion that arises from the electrical double layer on the surface. The movable ions in the electrical double layer (EDL) are the origin of the field-induced polarization of the particles in colloids, that is, Maxwell–Wagner polarization.

Let us assume that a dielectric GO particle in water is a spheroid for convenience of the calculation, although actual GO particles have irregular two-dimensional shapes that can be partially crumpled. In this approximation, the dielectric spheroid has three principal axes, where two ordinary axes have lengths of $2b$ and the extraordinary axis has a length of $2a$ (Fig. 1), and the diameter (D) is $2b$ and the thickness (T) is $2a$.

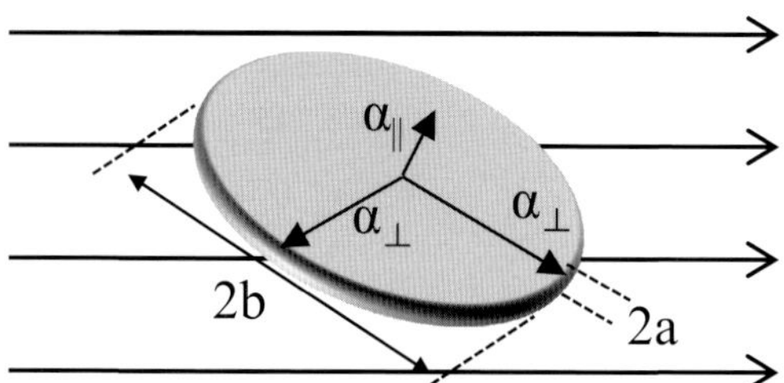

Fig. 1. Illustration of a 2-dimensional GO particle in an electric field. The parameters $2a$ and $2b$ denote the thickness and the diameter of the GO particle.

The Maxwell–Wagner polarizability of a spheroid particle can be expressed as:[17,28]

$$\alpha_{||,\perp} = \frac{4\pi ab^2}{3}\epsilon_0\epsilon_e^* \frac{\epsilon_p^* - \epsilon_e^*}{\epsilon_e^* + (\epsilon_p^* - \epsilon_e^*)L_{||,\perp}} \tag{1}$$

where ϵ_0, ϵ_p^*, ϵ_e^* and $L_{||,\perp}$ are the permittivity in a vacuum, the complex relative permittivities of the particle (ϵ_p^*) and of solvent or electrolyte (ϵ_e^*), and the ordinary geometrical depolarisation factor $(L_{||,\perp})$, respectively, and the parallel and perpendicular notations in the subscripts denote the directions parallel and perpendicular to the extraordinary axis, respectively.

When the conductivities of particle (κ_p) and solvent (κ_e) are given, the permittivity of the particle can be expressed by the following equations by neglecting the anisotropy of the real part of relative permittivity:

$$\epsilon_{p,||,\perp}^* = \epsilon_p + i\frac{\kappa_{p,||,\perp}}{\omega\epsilon_0} \text{ and } \epsilon_e^* = \epsilon_e + i\frac{\kappa_e}{\omega\epsilon_0} \tag{2}$$

The conductivity has an ionic relaxation frequency (ω), and the polarizability can be reformulated using the Debye-type relaxation frequency dependence as:

$$\alpha_{||,\perp} = \alpha_{||,\perp}^\infty + \frac{\alpha_{||,\perp}^0 - \alpha_{||,\perp}^\infty}{1 + \omega^2\tau_{||,\perp}^2} \tag{3}$$

where

$$\tau_{||,\perp} = \epsilon_0\frac{(1 - L_{||,\perp})\epsilon_e + L_{||,\perp}\epsilon_p}{(1 - L_{||,\perp})\kappa_e + L_{||,\perp}\kappa_{p,||,\perp}}, \tag{4}$$

$$\alpha_{||,\perp}^\infty = \frac{4\pi ab^2}{3}\epsilon_0\epsilon_e \frac{\epsilon_p - \epsilon_e}{\epsilon_e + (\epsilon_p - \epsilon_e)L_{||,\perp}} \tag{5}$$

and

$$\alpha^0{}_{||,\perp} = \frac{4\pi ab^2}{3}\epsilon_0\epsilon_e \frac{\kappa_{p,||,\perp} - \kappa_e}{\kappa_e + (\kappa_{p,||,\perp} - \kappa_e)L_{||,\perp}}. \tag{6}$$

According to O'konski's model,[29] the EDL produces an effective particle conductivity, $\kappa_{p,||,\perp}$. This can be formulated using the surface conductivity κ^S and the effective length $\xi_{||,\perp}$ of particles:[30]

$$\kappa_{p,||,\perp} = \kappa_{GO} + \frac{\kappa^S}{\xi_{||,\perp}} \tag{7}$$

where κ_{GO} is the conductivity of GO itself excluding the effect of EDL. Since GO is a dielectric material, κ_{GO} is negligible and the equations can be reduced to:

$$\kappa_{p,\perp} = \frac{\kappa^S}{a} \text{ and } \kappa_{p,||} = \frac{2\kappa^S}{b} \tag{8}$$

For a two-dimensional particle, the depolarized factor is approximately given by:

$$L_{||} \approx 1 - \frac{\pi a}{2b} \text{ and } L_{\perp} = \frac{\pi a}{4b} \tag{9}$$

Here, the surface conductivity $\kappa^S = \mu_s\sigma_s$ near the GO surface is determined by the electrical mobility (μ_s) and the surface charge density (σ_s). Once the physical properties ϵ_e, κ_e and κ^S are determined, the anisotropic polarizability, $\Delta\alpha = \alpha_\perp - \alpha_{||}$, can be calculated using Eq. (3).

GO has many carboxyl and hydroxyl groups on the basal plane, resulting in the negative zeta potentials via protonation of these functional groups, and therefore, the majority of the ions in EDL are H_3O^+. The mobility of H_3O^+ ions is approximately the same as the mobility of H^+ ions owing to proton transport,[31] which is about $3.6 \cdot 10^{-7}$ m^{2}V^{-1}S^{-1}. The surface charge density of GO can be approximated using the zeta potential,[32] which is mostly in the range of -70 to -40 mV for aqueous GO dispersions. The corresponding surface charge density is approximated as -0.1 to -0.01 Cm^{-2}. Hence, the maximum conductivity is estimated to be roughly $3.6 \cdot 10^{-8}$ S^{-1}. Thus, from Eq. (8), the effective conductivities, $\kappa_{p,||,\perp}$, are calculated as $4.5 \cdot 10^{-2}$ and 72 S^{-1}, respectively.

From these values of the conductivities of particles and solvent, the theoretical anisotropy of polarizability of GO particle can be calculated using Eq. (3). Shen *et al.* reported that the anisotropy of the polarizability for their GO dispersion with 3.2 μm mean diameter and 0.1 vol.-% was calculated as:[17]

$$\Delta\alpha = \alpha_{||} - \alpha_\perp = -1.5 \cdot 10^{-26} \text{ Fm}^2. \tag{10}$$

Here, $\Delta\alpha$ is a theoretical value, but $\Delta\alpha$ can be experimentally determined as well, using electro-optical measurements. The birefringence (Δn) and the electric field (E) can be related using the Kerr coefficient (K) as $\Delta n = K\lambda E^2$. In a GO solution, $\Delta n = \Delta n_{SAT} \cdot \Phi \cdot S(E)$. Here, Δn_{SAT} is a constant, Φ is the volume fraction, and $S(E)$ is the order parameter of GO particles as a function of E. When the interparticle interactions are neglected, the order parameter is defined using Boltzmann distribution, $f(\theta, E)$, as:

$$S(E) = \int_0^\pi \left(\frac{3}{2}\cos^2\theta - \frac{1}{2} \right) f(\theta, E) \sin\theta d\theta \tag{11}$$

Here, $f(\theta, E)$ is the Boltzmann distribution with a potential:

$$U(\theta) = -\frac{1}{2}\Delta\alpha E^2 \cos^2\theta. \tag{12}$$

Hence,

$$S(E) = \frac{\int_0^\pi \left(\frac{3}{2}\cos^2\theta - \frac{1}{2} \right) e^{-A\cos^2\theta} \sin\theta d\theta}{\int_0^\pi e^{-A\cos^2\theta} \sin\theta d\theta} \tag{13}$$

where

$$A = \frac{\Delta\alpha}{2k_B T}E^2. \tag{14}$$

When E is small, this reduces to:

$$S(E) \cong \frac{1}{2}\int_0^\pi \left(\frac{3}{2}\cos^2\theta - \frac{1}{2} \right)\left(1 - A\cos^2\theta \right) \sin\theta d\theta = -\frac{\Delta\alpha}{15k_B T}E^2. \tag{15}$$

Hence, the polarizability and the Kerr coefficient can be written as:

$$\Delta\alpha \cong -\frac{15k_B T \Delta n}{\Delta n_{SAT}\Phi E^2} \tag{16}$$

and

$$K \cong -\Delta n_{SAT}\frac{\Delta\alpha\Phi}{15k_B T\lambda} \tag{17}$$

This equation is valid when the inter-particle interaction is negligible. Shen *et al.* reported that $\Delta\alpha$ for their 0.025 vol.-% GO sample was experimentally obtained to be $-2.1{\cdot}10^{-26}$ Fm^2. This is of the same order as the theoretical value shown in Eq. (10), indicating that the theoretical calculation agrees well with the experimental result.

Straley and Van der Beek *et al.* introduced Onsager's reorientational entropy into the field-induced Maxwell–Boltzmann distribution function for dispersed particles to obtain the Kerr coefficient as:[33,34]

$$K \approx -\Delta n_{SAT}\frac{\Delta\alpha}{15k_B T\lambda}\frac{\Phi}{1 - \Phi/\Phi_{IB}} \tag{18}$$

Here, the last term, $(1 - \Phi/\Phi_{IB})^{-1}$, comes from Onsager's inter-particle interaction, where Φ_{IB} is the biphasic transition concentration. If the concentration is very low and the inter-particle interaction is negligible, $(1 - \Phi/\Phi_{IB})^{-1}$ approaches 1 and Eq. (18) reduces to Eq. (17). However, when the concentration is close to Φ_{IB} or in biphase, the nematic inter-particle interaction enhances the Kerr coefficient.

3. Large Kerr coefficient of aqueous GO dispersions

Shen *et al.* demonstrated the electric-field-induced birefringence in the low-concentration nematic phase, the biphase, and the isotropic phase (Figs. 2a and 2b).[17,26] Chemical reduction and electrolysis are observed only under the application of a low-frequency electric field (below 0.5 kHz) with a sufficiently high amplitude,[2] but these can be avoided by applying a 10 kHz electric field, even without any insulation layer. As shown in Fig. 2a, clear birefringent bright pattern is induced by applying a 5 Vmm^{-1} electric field, which is roughly three orders of magnitude weaker than that for conven-

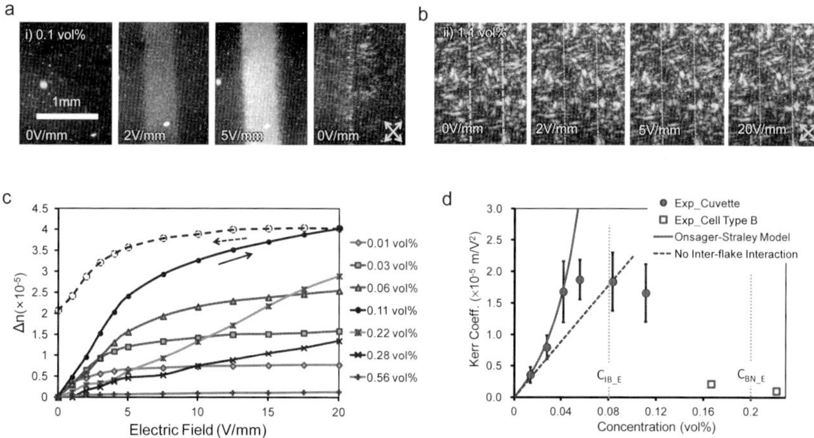

Fig. 2. (a) Field-induced birefringence generated by applying 10 kHz electric fields to a cell with an aqueous 0.1 vol.-% GO dispersion. After switched off, the field-induced birefringence almost disappeared.(b) In the same cell structure with a 1.1 vol.-% GO LC, no change was detected up to 20 Vmm^{-1}. (c) Field-induced-birefringence curves for the GO dispersions with varying concentrations. Part of the hysteresis curve is shown for the 0.11 vol.-% sample. (d) Kerr coefficients measured using a cuvette filled with a GO dispersion. Below C_{IB_E} the Onsager–Straley model fitted well with the experimental results. (Reproduced from Ref. 17)

tional molecular LC switching. When the voltage is switched off, the field-induced birefringence slowly disappears. In contrast, no change is observed in a nematic GO cell up to 20 Vmm^{-1} (Fig. 2b).

The field-induced birefringence is plotted for GO dispersions with varying concentration in Fig. 2c, where the vertical axis represents the induced birefringence obtained by subtracting the initial birefringence. The field-induced birefringence curves do not exhibit a Frederiks transition, and have a large hysteresis. The curve slope depends sensitively on the GO concentration.[35,36] Since $\Delta n = \Delta n_{SAT} \cdot S \cdot \Phi$, Δn increases as the concentration is increased to 0.1 vol.-%. However, it decreases when the concentration is increased beyond 0.1 vol.-%, and the sensitivity to external fields quickly becomes muted. The nematic GO (0.56 vol.-% in Fig. 2c) is almost unresponsive to the applied voltage up to 20 Vmm^{-1}.

The Kerr coefficient is shown in Fig. 2d as a function of the GO concentration. The Kerr coefficient was measured using a cuvette with parallel electrodes on two opposite walls and a beam-path length of 5 mm for an accurate measurement.[17] As shown in Fig. 2d, the maximum value of Kerr coefficient reaches approximately $1.8{\cdot}10^{-5}$ mV^{-2} near the biphasic phase transition concentration. Note that the Kerr coefficients of a typical Kerr material, nitrobenzene, is of the order of 10^{-12} mV^{-2} and that of aqueous 2D gibbsite platelet suspensions is of the order of 10^{-9} mV^{-2}.[37] The largest Kerr coefficient except the GO dispersion was reported to be about 10^{-6} mV^{-2} for thermal rubidium vapour.[38] Blue-phase LCs, which are known to have the largest Kerr coefficient in molecular LC phase, have a Kerr coefficient of the order of $10^{-9} - 10^{-8}$ mV^{-2}.[20,39,40] Thus, the Kerr coefficient of GO-LCs of the order of 10^{-5} mV^{-2} is extraordinarily large compared to those of any other Kerr materials.

As explained in the previous section, the theoretical $\Delta\alpha$ is expected to be roughly $-1.5 \cdot 10^{-26}$ Fm^2, which is two or three orders of magnitude larger than that of any other plate-like or rod-like particles.[30] Here, the negative value of $\Delta\alpha$ indicates that the normal direction of the GO plane is likely to be aligned perpendicular to the electric field. Using the theoretical $\Delta\alpha$ obtained above, the Kerr coefficients can be theoretically estimated using either the Straley or the van der Beek model (Eq. (18)) or the usual Boltzmann distribution (Eq. (17)) as a function of concentration as shown in Fig. 2d. The curve based on the Onsager–Straley model accords better with the experimental results below the biphasic transition concentration than the Boltzmann distribution model (Eq. (17)). This implies that Onsager's nematic inter-particle interaction significantly encourages the sensitivity to external fields in isotropic phase. However, the same nematic interactions in nematic phase desensitize the electro-optical response.

4. Ionic effect on the electro-optical switching

Ion concentration is known to primarily influence the electro-optical performance in GO-LC. S.-H. Hong *et al.* performed systematic experiments to clarify the ionic effect on the electro-optical performance.[26] As ionic additives, they selected neutral NaCl, acidic HCl, and basic NaOH. Excessive addition of NaCl and HCl causes partial flocculation of the GO contents and a decrease in the absolute value of zeta potential. On the other hand, excessive addition of NaOH brings about partial reduction of GO with a noticeable color change from bright brown to dark brown. Hence, they performed the ionic addition experiments in the ionic concentration range from zero to 10^{-3} M for all ionic additives, in which the unwanted side-effects can be avoided.

Usually, aqueous GO dispersions are acidic due to the protonation of functional groups. According to their experiment, the pH of a pure 0.1 wt.-% GO dispersion was 3.7, as shown in Fig. 3a. This corresponds to $2 \cdot 10^{-4}$ M H^+ ions. The pH of GO dispersions depends on the GO concentration and the density of the functional groups. The pH varies largely from 3.7 to 6.1 upon addition of up to 10^{-3} M NaOH, but the addition of HCl results in relatively little variation because of the low pH of the initial GO dispersion. Addition of NaCl does not cause a meaningful change in pH. Figure 3b shows the solution conductivities of GO dispersions with various ionic additives and the theoretical conductivities of the electrolytes without GO. The GO solution without any ionic additives has a bulk conductivity compara-

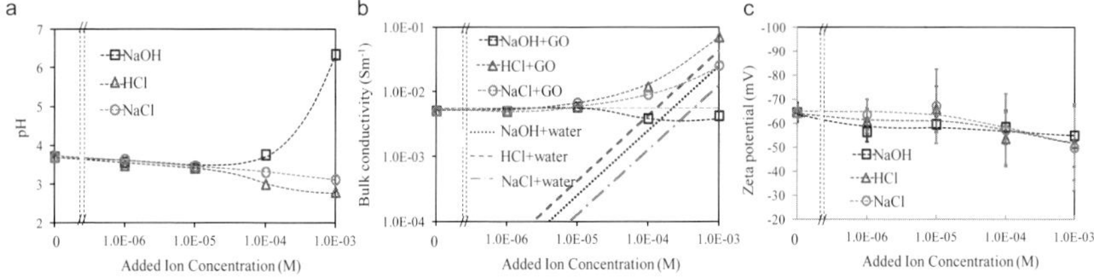

Fig. 3. (a) The pH values, (b) solution conductivities, and (c) zeta potentials for GO solutions with various ionic additives. The solid lines in (a) are the theoretical conductivities of the pure electrolyte without GO. (Reproduced from Ref. 26 with permission. Copyright 2014 American Chemical Society.)

ble to that of solutions with $10^{-4} - 10^{-3}$ M electrolyte concentrations. This is well-matched with the pH of the pure GO dispersion in Fig. 3a. One can notice that the NaOH-GO solution has the lowest conductivity of the three sets of GO solutions in the entire range of ionic concentrations. Addition of NaCl or HCl to a GO solution increases the ionic concentration, but the addition of NaOH does not cause the increase in the ionic concentration because the added OH^- ions are mostly neutralized by H^+ ions presenting in the GO dispersions. As a result, H^+ ions in solution are mostly replaced by Na^+ upon adding NaOH. The ionic mobility of Na^+ is lower than that of H^+, and hence, the conductivity of the GO solutions is slightly decreased by adding NaOH, unlike the other ionic additives (Fig. 3b). The absolute values of zeta potentials decreased slightly upon the addition of ions for all the ionic additives, as shown in Fig. 3c. The absolute values of zeta potentials are high enough to sustain a stable colloid.[41,42]

The electric field-induced birefringence is significantly influenced by the ionic addition,[17] as indicated in Fig. 4. Figure 4a shows the cell geometry

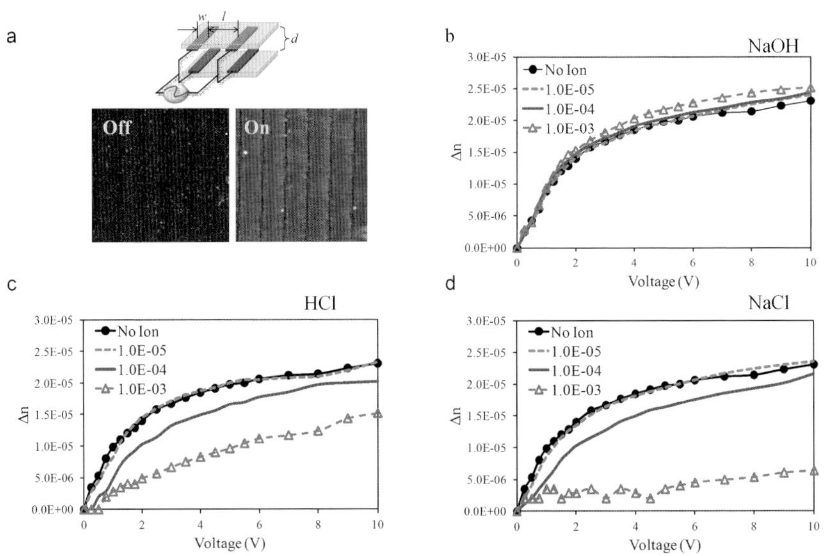

Fig. 4. The electro-optical experimental results; (a) The cell configuration: $l = 500$ μm, $w = 10$ μm, and $d = 300$ μm. Photographs with and without applied voltage. (b) – (d) The birefringence as a function of applied voltage for NaOH-GO dispersions (b), HCl-GO dispersions (c), and NaCl-GO dispersions (d). (Reproduced from Ref. 26 with permission. Copyright 2014 American Chemical Society.)

used and the polarized optical microscopic images without and with electric fields. The initial dark state with no electric field becomes bright by activation of the voltage. Figures 4b to 4d show the birefringence with increasing voltage of the three sets of GO solutions with different ions added. Interestingly, the addition of HCl or NaCl to GO dispersions decreased the electro-optic response, but the addition up to 10^{-3} M NaOH slightly enhanced the electro-optic response.

The dynamic response also depends on the ionic addition, as shown in Fig. 5. As shown in Fig. 5a, when the voltage was applied, the normalized birefringence increased within 0.3 s. for a pure GO dispersion. The addition of up to 10^{-3} M NaOH does not cause any significant change in the dynamic response. However, the addition of just 10^{-4} M HCl significantly slows the dynamic response, and the relaxation time constant increases three-fold compared to that of the solution with no added ions, as indicated in Fig. 5c. In contrast, the off response does not show any significant change with the addition of ions for all types of ions (Figs. 5b and 5c). This implies that the slow on-response time of the HCl-GO solution attributes to the weakened driving force rather than the increasing viscosity. The driving force for the electro-optical switching arises from the anisotropic polarizability of GO, and the addition of HCl weakens the anisotropy of GO polarizability. However, the addition of NaOH does not bring about the same result due to the ionic neutralization.

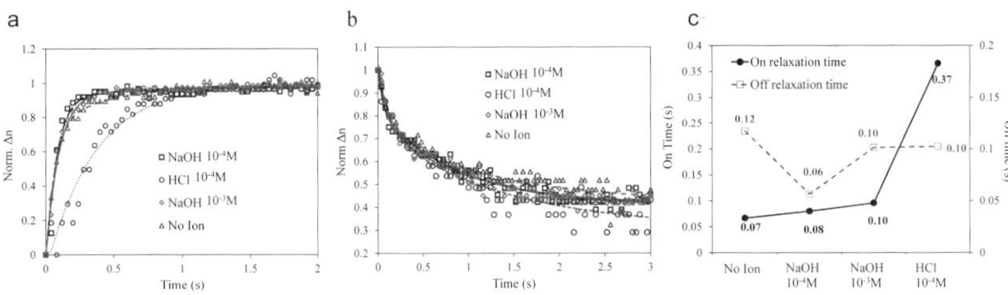

Fig. 5. The dynamic electro-optic response of the GO dispersions; (a) The turn-on response and (b) the turn-off response of the field-induced birefringence; and (c) the corresponding relaxation time constant. (Reproduced from Ref. 26 with permission. Copyright 2014 American Chemical Society.)

The Kerr coefficient is plotted as a function of ionic concentration in Fig. 6. The Kerr coefficients in Fig. 6 are one order smaller than those in the previous chapter,[17] possibly due to different cell geometries and the smaller

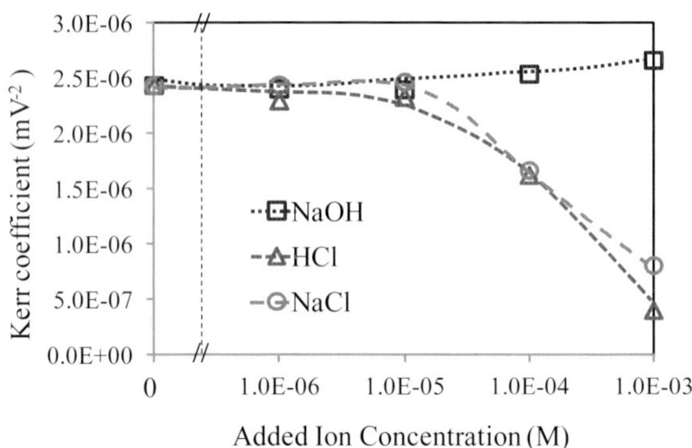

Fig. 6. The optical Kerr coefficient of GO dispersions with various ionic additives. (Reproduced from Ref. 26 with permission. Copyright 2014 American Chemical Society.)

GO size.[26] The sensitivity to electric fields decreases with increasing ionic concentration for the HCl-GO and NaCl-GO solutions but it increases for the NaOH-GO solutions.

According to the Maxwell–Wagener–O'konski model, the electric polarizability of a spheroidal particle in a colloidal solution can be calculated as shown in Sec. 2 of this chapter. For a pure GO dispersion with no added ions, $\kappa^S = \mu_s \sigma_s$ can be determined as follows. A pure GO dispersion without ionic additives exhibits pH 3.7, which corresponds to a H^+ concentration of $2 \cdot 10^{-4}$ M. The H^+ ions are supplied by the negatively-charged functional groups on the surface of GO particles. Dividing the total H^+ ion density in the water by the total surface area of GO flakes in a unit volume of a 0.1 wt.-% GO dispersion, the surface charge density of GO flakes that supply the bulk H^+ ions can be approximated to be 0.02 Cm^{-2}. In the pure GO dispersion without ionic additives, μ_s is the mobility of H^+ ions and is $3.6 \cdot 10^{-7}$ $m^2 V^{-1} S^{-1}$. Using the values of $\kappa^S = \mu_s \sigma_s$, $\Delta\alpha$ for the pure GO dispersion is $1.8 \cdot 10^{-27}$ Fm^2.

The Kerr coefficient can be expressed as:[17,26,37]

$$|K| = \frac{\Delta n}{\lambda E^2} = \frac{\Delta n_{SAT} \phi_W D_e S(E)}{\lambda D_{GO} E^2} \tag{19}$$

Here, ϕ_w, D_{GO}, D_e and $S(E)$ are the weight concentration of GO in the sample, the density of GO particles, the density of water, and the order parameter, respectively. Δn_{SAT} is the specific birefringence when $S = 1$ and $\phi_w = 1$. From Eqs. (19) and (15), the Kerr coefficient can be simplified as:[17,26]

$$K = -\frac{\Delta n_{SAT}\phi_w D_e}{15\lambda D_{GO}k_B T}\Delta\alpha \tag{20}$$

Using the experimental value of K and the theoretical value of $\Delta\alpha$ for the pure GO dispersion, one can estimate Δn_{SAT} from Eq. (20), which is calculated to be $9.27 \cdot 10^{-2}$. Since the optical refractive index of GO particles is not influenced by the ionic concentration in dispersion, Δn_{SAT} is supposed to be the same in all the GO dispersions with different ionic strengths. Using Eq. (20) and the experimental value of K, one can calculate $\Delta\alpha$ as a function of the ionic additive concentration, which is plotted in Fig. 7a. One can notice that the addition of ions decreases $\Delta\alpha$, which is the main cause of the desensitization of electro-optical response upon adding the ions.

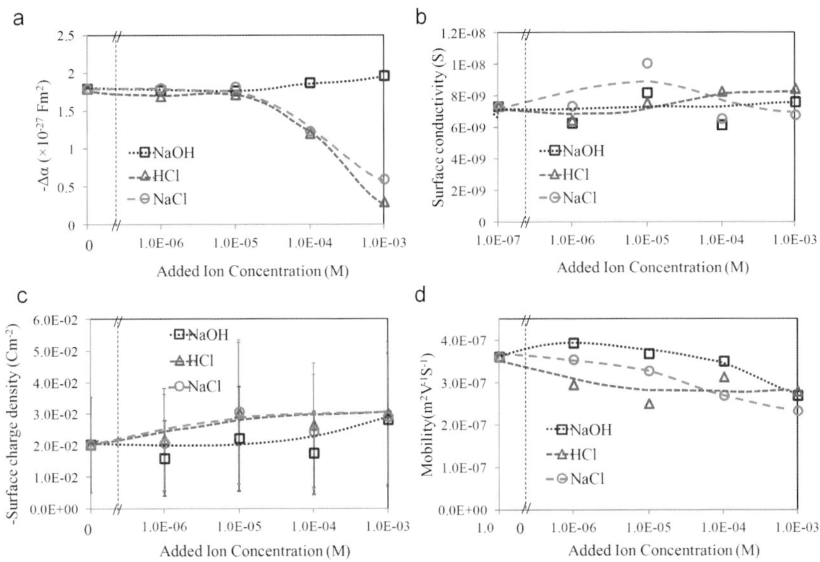

Fig. 7. (a) The anisotropy of polarizability and (b) the surface conductivity of GO dispersions as a function of ionic concentration. (c) The surface charge density and (d) mobility of GO particles as a function of ionic concentration. (Reproduced from Ref. 26 with permission. Copyright 2014 American Chemical Society.)

Using Eq. (3) and the values of $\Delta\alpha$ (Fig. 7a) and bulk conductivity (κ_e shown in Fig. 3b), the surface conductivity, κ^S, of GO particles is plotted, as shown in Fig. 7b. Interestingly, the surface conductivity on GO dispersion is almost constant with varying ionic concentration. Mantegazza *et al.* also reported that the surface conductivity in the electrical double layer is insensitive to the ionic strength when the surface charge density is in the order of 10^{-1} Sm^{-1}.[43] Thus, one can notice that the decrease in the Kerr coefficient of GO dispersions upon the addition of ions attributes to the increasing bulk conductivity rather than the modification of EDL on the GO surface. Similarly, the slight increase in Kerr coefficient of GO dispersions added by NaOH is also explained by the slight decrease in the bulk conductivity due to the ionic neutralization.

Directly calculating the surface charge density using the Grahame equation gives the same conclusion. The Grahame equation is expressed as:[26,32,44]

$$\sigma_s = \left(2\epsilon_0\epsilon_r k_B T N_0 \cdot 10^3 \sum |A^\pm|_S\right)^{1/2}, \tag{21}$$

where the molar concentration of ion A near the surface is $|A^\pm|_S = |A^\pm|_\infty e^{\pm \frac{eV_0}{k_B T}} - |A^\pm|_\infty$. The $A^\pm$ variables are the ionic concentrations of Na$^+$, Cl$^-$, H$^+$, or OH$^-$ in the GO dispersion, and the subscripts S and ∞ indicate the surface area and bulk area, respectively. The parameters e, ϵ_r, N_0 and V_0 represent the elementary positive charge, dielectric constant of pure water, Avogadro's number, and the surface potential, respectively. All of the variables were known except V_0, which is difficult to determine. By substituting the value of σ_s and $A = $ H$^+$ in Eq. (21), one can obtain $V_0 \approx 2.55 \cdot \zeta$ for the pure GO dispersion. Assuming this relationship is valid for the other dispersions, one can calculate σ_s for the other dispersions as shown in Fig. 7c. Using the surface conductivity and the surface charge density in Figs. 7b and c, the surface charge mobility can be simply calculated as shown in Fig. 7d. The result shows that the surface charge densities and the ionic mobility exhibit the opposite trends and they compensate for each other, giving rise to the nearly constant surface conductivity.

The mobility seems to weakly depend on the ion types. The addition of NaOH does not cause a meaningful difference from addition of other ions. This result indicates that the cation exchange capacity for H$^+$ ions in the EDL is quite high, and H$^+$ ions are not likely to be replaced by other ions.

Since $\kappa_{p,||}$ is much smaller than $\kappa_{p,\perp}$ from the definition, $\alpha_\perp$ is always much greater than $\alpha_{||}$, and as a result, $\Delta\alpha \sim \alpha_\perp$, approximately. When the frequency is lower than the resonance frequency and $\kappa_e \ll \kappa_{p,\perp}$, the anisotropic polarizability can be approximately reduced as:

$$\Delta\alpha \approx \alpha_\perp^0 \approx -\frac{4\pi ab^2}{3}\epsilon_0\epsilon_e \left(\frac{\kappa_{p,\perp}}{\kappa_e + L_\perp \kappa_{p,\perp}}\right). \tag{22}$$

For example, Hong *et al.* calculated these properties for their GO sample; $\kappa_{p,\perp} =\sim 6 \gg \kappa_e = (6\cdot10^{-3}-7\cdot10^{-2}) > L_\perp \kappa_{p,\perp} =\sim 1.5\cdot10^{-3}$.[45] Hence, the bracket in the right side of Eq. (22) is approximately reduced to $\kappa_{p,\perp}/\kappa_e$. Hence, $\Delta\alpha \sim \kappa_{p,\perp}/\kappa_e$. Figure 7b shows that $\kappa_{p,\perp}$ is almost constant. Therefore, $K \sim \Delta\alpha \sim \kappa_e^{-1}$. Figure 8 shows more or less good correlation between K and κ_e^{-1}. One can conclude that the Kerr coefficient is mainly influenced by the bulk ionic concentration in the GO dispersion with ionic additives.

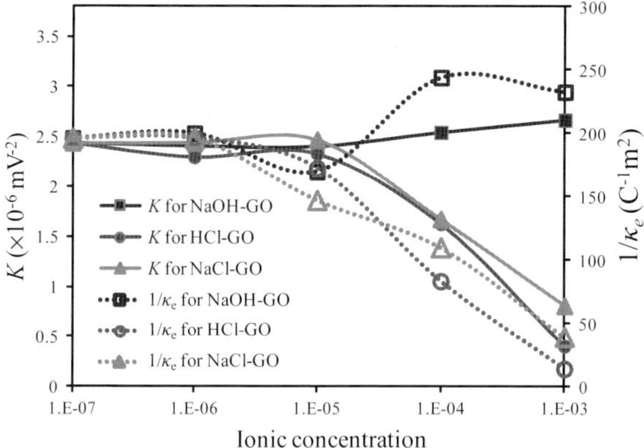

Fig. 8. Correlation between K (filled data set, left axis) and κ_e^{-1} (open data set, right axis). (Reproduced from Ref. 26 with permission. Copyright 2014 American Chemical Society.)

Summarizing, the effect of ionic additives on the electro-optical sensitivity can be illustrated as shown in Fig. 9. A GO particle supplies the dispersion with H^+ ions, and the supplied H^+ ions construct an EDL around the GO particle and acidify the GO dispersion (Fig. 9a). When an electric field is applied, a large dipole-moment is transiently achieved due to the large difference between the surface and bulk conductivities (Fig. 9b). When acidic HCl or neutral NaCl ions are added, the bulk charge density and the bulk conductivity will also increase due to increasing bulk ionic concentrations (Figs. 9c and 9d), which results in the decrease in the polarization of the GO particle. The zeta potential of the dispersions just slightly changes when the ions are added up to 10^{-3} M, indicating that the EDL is just weakly influenced by the ionic addition. Hence, the surface conductivity is nearly maintained. The addition of NaOH does not

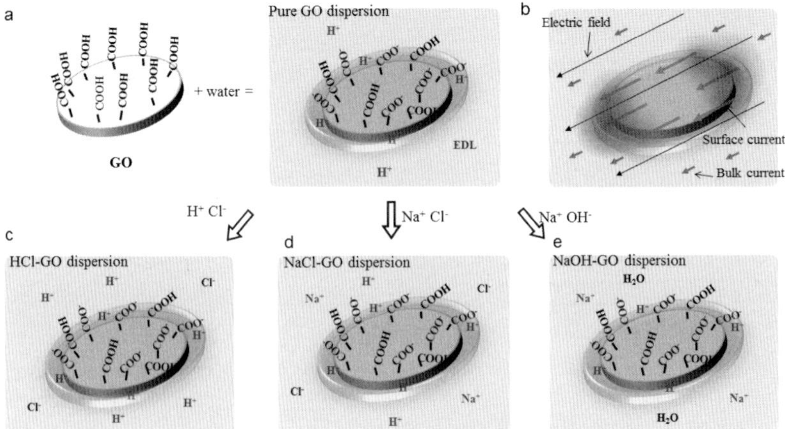

Fig. 9.   Simple illustration that explains the phenomenon observed in an ion-added GO dispersion. (a) GO akes supplies H^+ ions to water, which forms the electrical double layer (EDL). (b) Large difference between the surface and bulk conductivities causes a large polarization. (c, d) In the HClGO and NaClGO dispersions, the bulk ionic strength increases. (e) In the NaOHGO dispersion, H^+ ions in the solvent are replaced by Na^+ ions. (Reproduced from Ref. 26 with permission. Copyright 2014 American Chemical Society.)

increase the total number of ions in the solvent (Fig. 9e), but H^+ ions are replaced by Na^+ ions with lower mobility, resulting in the slight decrease in the bulk conductivity. As a result, the addition of NaOH slightly enhances the electro-optical sensitivity, unlike the addition of NaCl or HCl.

5. GO size effect on the electro-optical switching

In liquid crystal displays, the maximum transmittance is obtained when the optical retardation ($d\Delta n$), where d is the light-path length, is higher than the half of the light wavelength ($\lambda/2$).[46] However, Δn in GO dispersions is quite low and is directly proportional to the GO concentration. Therefore, we need to use a GO dispersion with high concentration in order to develop an electro-optical device. As we discussed in Sec. 3 of this chapter, nematic GO dispersions with high GO concentrations do not respond to the application of electric fields due to strong inter-particle frictions.[17] The electrical switching of GO dispersions is achieved through the rotational motion of individual GO particles. When the spacing between neighboring GO particles is short, the rotational motion of GO particles can be easily suppressed. Hence, the increase in GO concentration desensitizes the electrical sensitivity of the GO dispersion. This can be a serious limitation for electro-optical devices using GO dispersions.

It was reported that the GO particle size can influence both the friction of the rotational motion of the individual GO particles and the electro-optical sensitivity.[27] Ahmad *et al.* systematically studied the GO size effect on the electro-optical performance of GO dispersions. They used GO dispersions with different mean size by ultra-sonicating large sized GO particles for varying time.[27] Four GO dispersions with different particle mean sizes ranging from 7.95 μm to 0.075 μm were used in their experiments (Fig. 10).

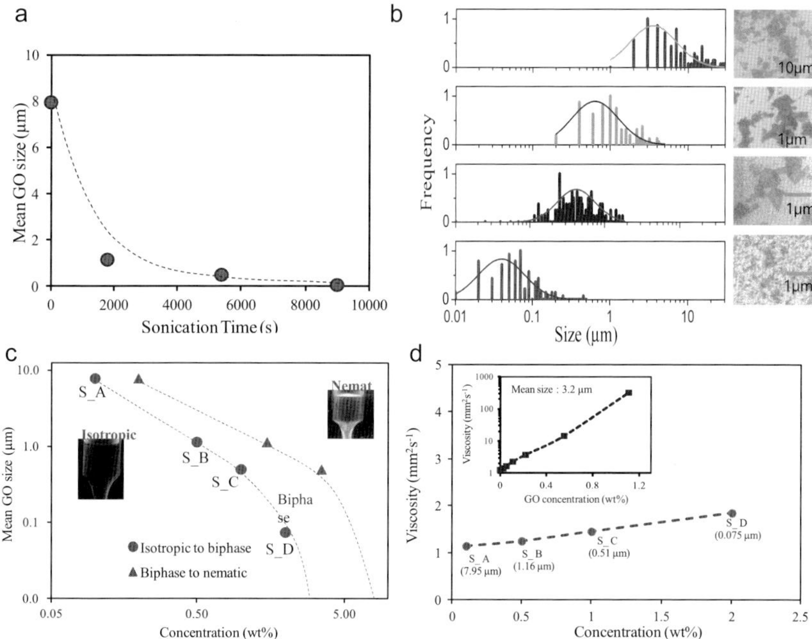

Fig. 10. (a) Mean GO size as a function of ultra-sonication time. (b) GO size distributions for four selected GO dispersions and SEM images. (c) Phase diagram of GO dispersions as functions of the mean GO particle size and concentration. (d) Viscosity of the four samples on the isotropic to biphasic transition line. The inset curve is for a fixed GO size. (Reproduced from Ref. 27.)

As the GO concentration increases in aqueous dispersions, the phase changes from isotropic to biphasic and from biphasic to nematic.[4,17] The

GO dispersion with larger sized particles exhibits the phase transition at the lower concentration. Figure 10c shows the phase sequences for the four selected samples with varying concentration, which clearly shows the dependency of the phase transition as a function of the mean size of particle.[17] The GO dispersion with the large flake size of 7.95 μm exhibited the nematic phase even at 0.2 wt.-%, whereas the GO dispersion with the mean size of 0.075 μm was biphasic even at 3.5 wt.-%. According to the Onsager type excluded volume theory, the phase transition concentration sensitively depends on the aspect ratio of the particles, which is the origin of the tendency shown in Fig. 10c.[11,13,14] The width of the biphasic region depends on the polydispersity of the particles.[14] They selected four samples on the border between the isotropic to biphasic phase (the circles in Fig. 10c). The samples, labelled as S_A to S_D, have the highest concentration in the isotropic region, hence these do not show nematic ordering (Fig. 10c).

The viscosity of the samples is shown in Fig. 10d. The viscosity curve exhibits weakly increasing trend with concentration, which shows a clear contrast to the curve with dramatic increase in the inset. The viscosity curve in the inset in Fig. 10d was obtained using GO dispersions with fixed particle size of 3.2 μm as a function of GO concentrations.[17] In the inset curve, the viscosity of 1 wt.-% GO dispersion is about three orders of magnitude larger than that of sample S_C with the same concentration of 1 wt.-%. The comparison of these two curves indicates that the particle size is the most crucial factor for the interparticle interaction. Note that all the samples S_A to S_D belong to the isotropic phase, whereas the 1 wt.-% sample presented in the inset is in the nematic phase. According to Onsager's theory, the nematic phase arises from the interparticle steric interaction causing packed assembly, and the interparticle steric interaction hinders the free rotation of the GO particles. Usually, the spacing between neighboring particles decreases as the concentration increases, which results in an increase in the rotational friction of the particles and in the viscosity. However, the rotational friction is still sufficiently low for smaller GO particles to allow free rotation at high concentration. This brings about the high-concentration isotropic phase for the small sized GO disperses, such as S_C and S_D samples. Hence, the viscosity of S_C and S_D is much lower that the GO sample with the same concentration and the larger size.

The electro-optical response of the selected GO dispersions is shown in Fig. 11. In the cell shown in Fig. 11d, the distance between two neighboring wires is approximately 1 mm, which is several orders magnitude larger than that used in usual in-plane switching LC devices. When an electric signal

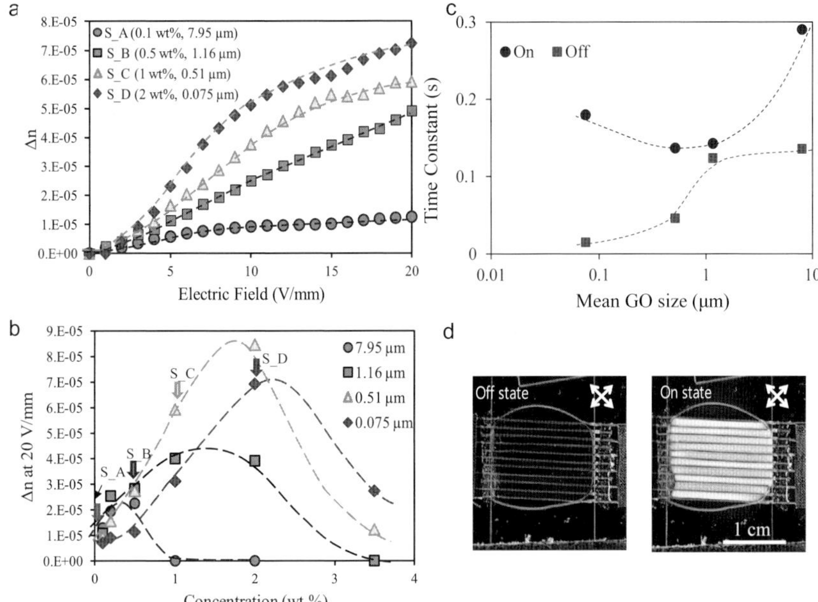

Fig. 11. (a) Birefringence as a function of applied electric field for the GO dispersions S_A to S_D. (b) The birefringence at 20 Vmm^{-1} for GO dispersions with different GO sizes. (c) Time constants for each dynamic response and the applied single exponential curve fits. (d) The left and right images are the 'field off' and 'field on' states, respectively, under crossed polarizers. (Reproduced from Ref. 27.)

with 10 kHz was tuned off and on, the cell filled with the S_C GO sample displayed dark and bright states, respectively, as shown in Fig. 11d. Since the GO sample is in the isotropic phase, the cell looks dark under the crossed polarizers without application of fields. On the other hand, the GO particles align and exhibit electric field-induced birefringence when applying the electric signal.

The birefringence for the cells is plotted as a function of the applied electric fields, as shown in Fig. 11a.[27] The curves are similar in shape, but the higher birefringence appears in the sample with the higher GO concentration. Figure 11b shows the birefringence at 20 Vmm^{-1} as a function of GO concentration for different flake sizes. All the curves exhibit a peak birefringence at a certain concentration; below the peak concentration, the birefringence increases with increasing concentration and above the peak concentration, it decreases with increasing concentration. The arrow for each curve indicates the samples of S_A to S_D, which are on the border of the isotropic to biphasic transition concentration. The electric sensitivity increases up to a low-concentration biphasic state. As the concentration increases further to high-concentration biphasic and nematic phases, the electrical sensitivity decreases rapidly. The maximum birefringence increases as the mean GO size decreases to 0.51 μm, and the maximum birefringence is obtained for the 2 wt.-% GO dispersion with a mean size of 0.51 μm. However, further decrease in the particle size reduces the maximum birefringence; the GO dispersion of 0.075 μm has a lower value of maximum birefringence than that of the GO dispersion of 0.51 μm. According to the theoretical analysis discussed in Sec. 2, the electrical polarizability decreases as the GO particle size decreases. Hence, the decrease in the particle size may bring about the decrease in the polarizability as well as the decrease in the interparticle friction. In particular, when GO particles are smaller than about 100 nm, the former predominantly influences the electro-optical sensitivity, and the electrical sensitivity decreases with the decreasing size of GO particle. Thus, the maximum birefringence is obtained in the GO dispersion with a mean size of approximately 500 nm.

The dynamic response time is also important for actual electro-optical applications.[46] The switching on and off relaxation time constants are plotted as a function of the mean particle size for the samples, S_A to S_D, shown in Fig. 11c.[17,27] The off time constant monotonically increases as the mean GO size increases. The off response is related with the rotational diffusive relaxation of the GO particles, that is, the rotational viscosity. Hence, the monotonic decrease in the off time constant implies that the rotational viscosity decreases monotonically as the mean GO size decreases. Meanwhile, the switching-on time constant decreases up to the 500 nm sample and increases again above 500 nm. The switching on response time of liquid crystals is proportional to $\gamma_1/\Delta\alpha$ (γ_1 is the rotational viscosity), where $\Delta\alpha$ is the anisotropy of polarizability for the GO particles. The rotational viscosity decreases with the decreasing mean GO size, but $\Delta\alpha$ also decreases due to the decreasing aspect ratio. Hence, the GO dispersion of the smallest GO particles has weaker driving force compared to the other larger GO particles, giving rise to the slow on-response time. However, when the mean GO size is larger than 500 nm, the contribution of the anisotropy of polarizability is not significant, whereas the increase in rotational viscosity contributes more to the dynamic response. As a result, S_A with the largest GO particles has the longest response time.

6. Centrifugal cleaning effect on the electro-optical performance

Usually, aqueous GO dispersions are synthesized by Hummers method or modified Hummers method.[47] In the early stage of the Hummers method, graphite oxide dispersion with bright yellow color is obtained. Then, about 10 to 15 cycles of centrifuge cleaning processes are performed to obtain quality single layered GO dispersion. During the centrifuge process, thick graphite particles are exfoliated into thin single layered GO particles. The scanning electronic microscopic and atomic-force microscopic images in Fig. 12a are taken of the GO dispersion after 4 and 14 cleaning cycles, respectively. As the number of the centrifugal cleaning cycles increases, the mean thickness and diameter of GO particles are decreased due to the exfoliation and crumbling. Figure 12b shows the mean GO size for the sample after 4, 8, 10, and 14 times of cleaning cycles. After the 14 times of centrifugal cleaning process, most GO particles become single-layered.[25]

For each centrifugal cleaning cycle, the supernatant liquid is replaced by fresh deionized distilled water. Hence, the conductivity and acidity of the supernatant liquid after each centrifugal cleaning also varies, as well indicated in Figs. 12c and 12d. The conductivity of supernatant water decreases gradually with the increasing number of cleaning cycles, which indicates that the residual salts of oxidizing reagents are quickly removed. The pH value also increases and saturates near pH 7. In fact, GO dispersion itself has quite a low pH value even after the full set of cleaning cycles as shown in Fig. 3a, but the supernatant liquid becomes almost neutral.

Thus, the centrifugal cleaning results in two significant modifications in the properties of GO dispersions. The supernatant liquid containing ions is replaced by fresh deionized distilled water in every centrifugal cleaning, and so, the ion concentration keeps decreasing. In addition, water molecules penetrate into the stacked graphite oxide and exfoliate it into single layer GO sheets. In fact, these two modifications are connected to each other; the residual acidic ions promote aggregation of GO flakes and disturb the exfoliation, and hence, the elimination of the ions promotes the exfoliation. As shown in Figs. 12c and 12d, the conductivity and pH of supernatant water almost reach the saturation level after about 10 cycles of centrifugal cleaning processes.

The electro-optical responses of the GO dispersions also depend on the numbers of centrifuge cleaning cycles, as shown in Fig. 13.[25] The GO dispersion with no cleaning does not respond at all to the external fields. The

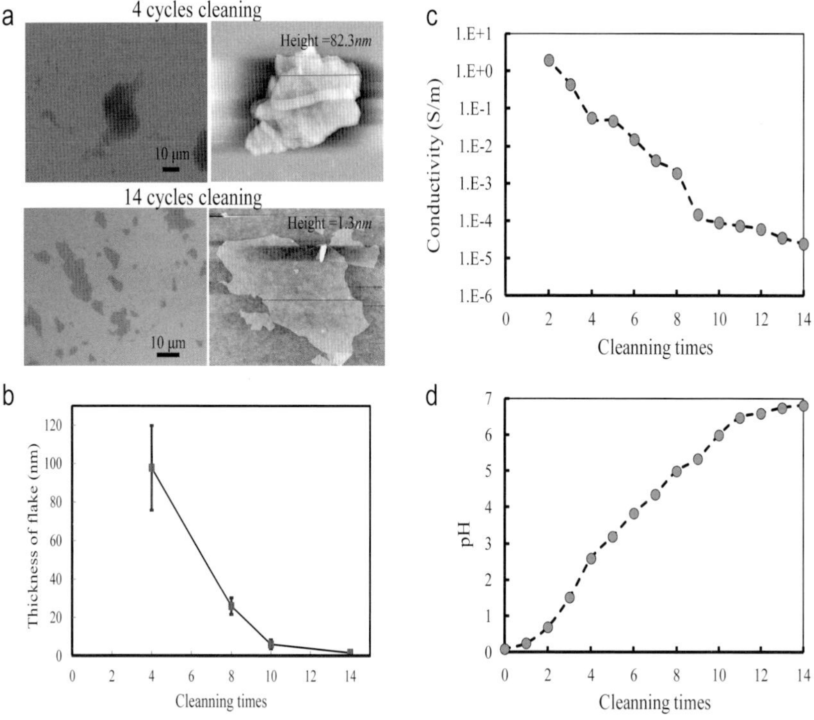

Fig. 12. (a) SEM and AFM images for the GO sample after 4 and 14 cleaning cycles. (b) The particle-size distributions for the dispersions after 4, 8, 10, and 14 times of cleaning cycles. (c) Conductivity and (d) pH values of supernatant liquid of GO solutions as a function of the number of centrifugal cleaning cycles. (Reproduced from Ref. 25, Copyright 2014, with permission from Elsevier.)

GO dispersion after the fourth cleaning cycle starts to weakly respond to external fields, but the maximum birefringence at 10 Vmm^{-1} is very low. The conductivity of the supernatant water of the sample is over 10^{-2} S and the pH value is less than 3 (Fig. 12), which indicate that a large amount of residual ions remain in the dispersion. The electro-optic sensitivity to external field reaches the maximum level after 11 times of cleaning processes, as shown in Fig. 13. This phenomenon attributes to both of the decreasing ionic concentration and the decreasing thickness of GO particles.

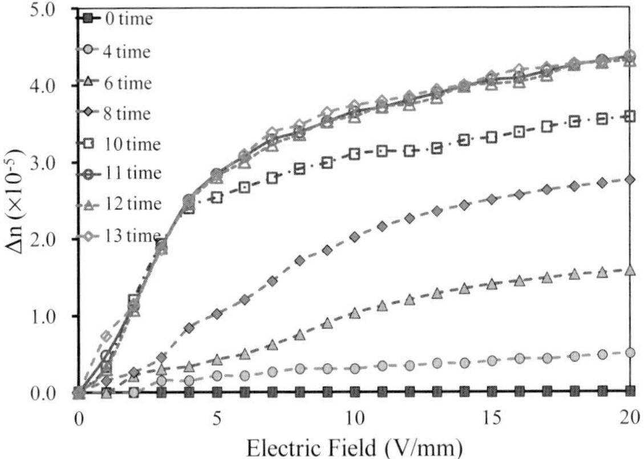

Fig. 13. The birefringence as a function of applied field for the cells with GO dispersions with an increasing number of cleaning cycles. (Reproduced from Ref. 25, Copyright 2014, with permission from Elsevier.)

Maxwell–Wagner polarization for an anisotropic colloid particle shown in Eq. (3) can be approximately written as:[17]

$$\alpha_{||,\perp} = \frac{4\pi ab^2}{3}\epsilon_0\epsilon_e \frac{\kappa_{p,||,\perp} - \kappa_e}{\kappa_e + (\kappa_{p,||,\perp} - \kappa_e)L_{||,\perp}} \tag{23}$$

When the ionic concentration is sufficiently low, κ_e (solvent conductivity) is much smaller than both $\kappa_{p,\perp}$ and $\kappa_{p,||}$ (effective particle conductivity), and Eq. (23) can be simplified as:

$$\alpha_{||} \approx \frac{4\pi ab^2}{3}\epsilon_0\epsilon_e, \tag{24}$$

$$\alpha_{\perp} \approx \frac{4\pi ab^2}{3}\epsilon_0\epsilon_e \frac{1}{L_{\perp}} \tag{25}$$

and

$$\Delta\alpha \equiv \alpha_{\perp} - \alpha_{||} \approx \frac{4\pi ab^2}{3}\epsilon_0\epsilon_e\left(\frac{4b}{\pi a} - 1\right) \equiv \Delta\alpha_0 \tag{26}$$

Here, $\Delta\alpha$ does not depend on either κ_e or κ_p, but it depends on the aspect ratio (b/a) of the GO flakes. That is, when the residual ion concentration in a GO dispersion is less than approximately 10^{-5} M, further decrease in the residual ion concentration does not improve the anisotropic polarizability of GO particles. However, when the residual ion concentration increases,

κ_e will approach $\kappa_{p,||}$ (but κ_e is still much smaller than $\kappa_{p,||}$, due to the large electric conductivity in the electrical double layer on GO basal plane) and Eq. (23) becomes:

$$\alpha_{||} \approx \frac{4\pi a b^2}{3} \epsilon_0 \epsilon_e \left(1 - \frac{\kappa_e}{\kappa_{p,||}} \right), \tag{27}$$

$$\alpha_{\perp} \approx \frac{4\pi a b^2}{3} \epsilon_0 \epsilon_e \frac{1}{L_{\perp}} \left(1 - \frac{\kappa_e}{L_{\perp}\kappa_{p,\perp|}} \right) \tag{28}$$

and

$$\Delta\alpha \approx \Delta\alpha_0 - \frac{4\pi a b^2}{3} \epsilon_0 \epsilon_e \left(\frac{\kappa_e}{L_{\perp}^2 \kappa_{p,\perp}} \right) \tag{29}$$

$\Delta\alpha$ decreases with increasing κ_e, and when $\kappa_e \sim L_{\perp} \cdot \kappa_{p,\perp} \sim 10 - 2$ Sm^{-1}, $\Delta\alpha$ approaches zero. It is evident that $\Delta\alpha$ decreases in the range of the ionic strength from 10^{-5} to 10^{-2} M because of the increase in κ_e. Hence, both the anisotropic polarizability and the aspect ratio are involved in the sharp increase in the sensitivity of the electro-optic response during the centrifugal cleaning process.

7. Dielectrophoretic migration of GO particles

In the electro-dynamic response of GO dispersions, more than two different dynamic mechanisms are involved in the relaxation processes of on and off responses. During the switch-on response, the rotational motion of GO flakes with a fast time constant is responsible for the field-induced birefringence. In Fig. 14, the electro-optical dynamic response curves are fitted to an equation with two exponential terms by assuming that two different relaxation processes, the rotational mode and the translational mode, are involved.

The translational migration of GO flakes with a larger time constant, which is roughly two orders of magnitude larger than that of the fast mode, is detected directly in POM observations (Fig. 15). The area between two neighbouring electrodes becomes fully bright within 10 s. For the following hundreds and thousands of seconds, depending on the concentration, GO flakes slowly moves towards the electrodes, indicating that electric-field gradient causes the migration of GO. Considering that the frequency of the applied voltage is 10 kHz (the same migration was observed up to 7 MHz), the migration results from the dielectrophoretic force that is proportional to $\nabla \mathbf{E}^2$. Dielectrophoresis does not accompany swirling flows that disturbs

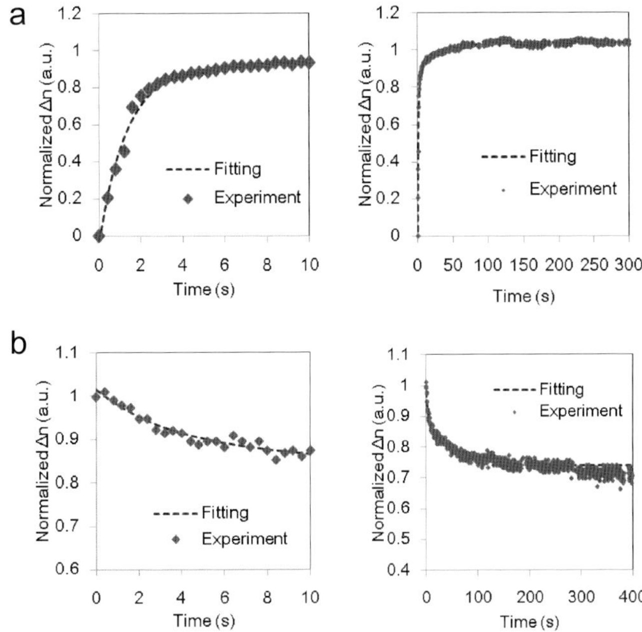

Fig. 14. The electro-optical dynamic response curves of GO dispersions for (a) switching on and (b) switching off.

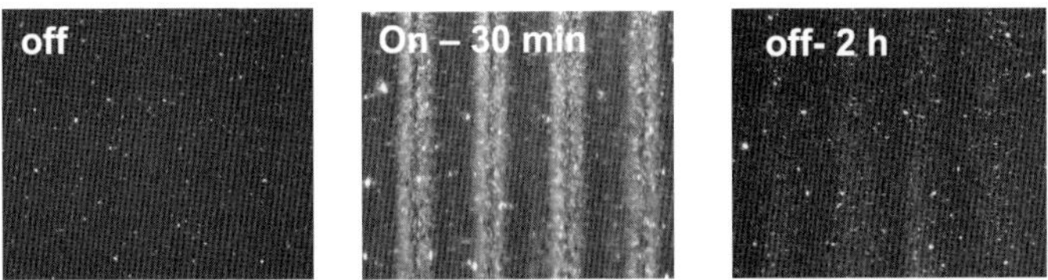

Fig. 15. The dielectrophoretic migration was observed microscopically. Prolonged application of fields induced dense nematic condensation near electrode. After turning off, the density modulation was released slowly.

the control over the density distribution and orientational orderings of the GO flakes.

Similar to field-driven dynamics, the diffusive process involved in turning the electric fields off also has two relaxation modes, rotational and migrational diffusions (Fig. 14), which also have time constants that are different by roughly one or two orders of magnitude.

The dielectrophoretic manipulation of GO particles can be used to directly deposit GO particles on a certain area,[48] to achieve a site-selective deposition,[49] and to fabricate electronic devices.[50]

8. Electro-optical devices using GO dispersions

The abundant electro-dynamics in GO dispersions enables one to fabricate electro-optical GO devices. The electro-optical switching device was already discussed in Fig. 11, in which the order parameter of GO particles is controlled by applying high frequency electric signals. On the other hand, the director of nematic GO is not switchable owing to high inter-flake friction as shown in Fig. 2b, but the director of the field-induced GO alignment in low concentration is controllable, as shown in Fig. 16a.[17] The director of the field-induced GO is easily rotatable by changing the electric field direction, which exhibits an optical switching behaviour similar to that of a typical nematic LC device. In order to change the field direction, four

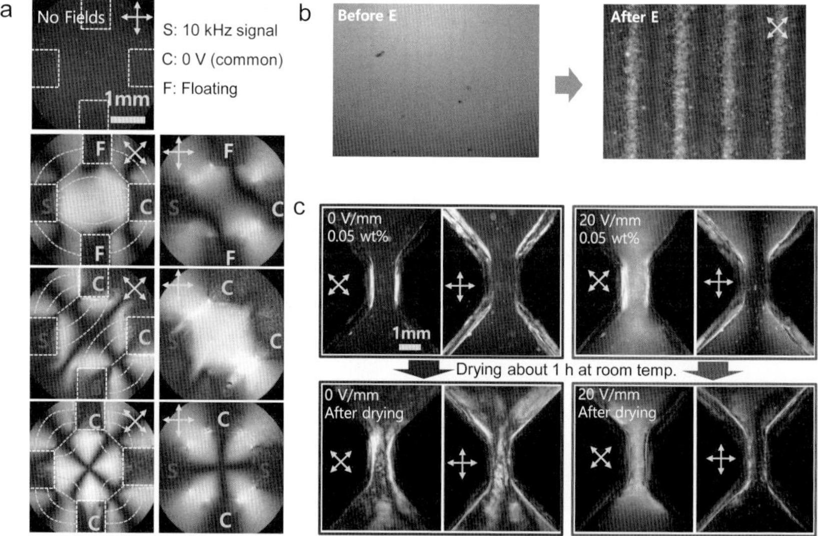

Fig. 16. (a) The director of the field-induced GO alignment rotates with changes in field direction. (b) A GO density grating was fabricated 30 min. after applying electric fields with spatial modulation of amplitude. (c) The isotropic GO phase turned into the LC phase as the water evaporated. While the GO on the substrate without fields exhibited a deformed LC director (left), the GO on the substrate with fields exhibited a well-controlled, uniform nematic LC phase (right). (Reproduced from Ref. 17)

electrodes were used in the experiment shown in Fig. 16a.[17] The switching of the GO alignment direction is somewhat different from that shown in Fig. 11, the switching of the order parameter. The switching speed of the director rotation is quicker than that of the order parameter control.

Using the dielectrophoretic migration of GO flakes, a GO density grating can be fabricated (Fig. 16b). Prolonged application of electric field with periodic intensity modulation can induce the GO density grating. The periodic density grating of GOs is discernible without polarisers because of light absorption by GO (Fig. 16b). The induced birefringence persisted for more than 2 h after the fields were turned off, indicating that the high-density region is actually in the nematic phase.

Shen *et al.* reported an electrically aligned, high-concentration nematic GO by evaporating some of the water in isotropic GO dispersion under the application of electric fields (Fig. 16c). An isotropic 0.1 wt.-% aqueous GO dispersion was released between two electrodes on an uncovered substrate and left in ambient conditions to evaporate the water. As the water evaporated, the isotropic phase transited into nematic phase. The field-induced uniform GO alignment was sustained after it transited into the nematic phase, and the uniform GO LC alignment was not disturbed even after the fields were switched off. On the other hand, the cell dried without electric fields exhibited many brushes indicating disordered LC alignment (the left of Fig. 4c).

In this way, the exceptionally high aspect ratio of GO flakes and the EDL containing large amount of H^+ ions provide an important tool to manipulate the order parameter, director orientation, and density distribution of GO particles in isotropic aqueous GO dispersions via application of electric fields.

References

1. Z. Xu and C. Gao, Graphene chiral liquid crystals and macroscopic assembled fibres, *Nat. Commun.* **2**, 571 (2011).
2. J. E. Kim, T. H. Han, S. H. Lee, J. Y. Kim, C. W. Ahn, J. M. Yun and S. O. Kim, Graphene oxide liquid crystals, *Angew. Chem.* **50**(13), 3043–3047 (2011).
3. F. Guo, F. Kim, T. H. Han, V. B. Shenoy, J. Huang and R. H. Hurt, Hydration-responsive folding and unfolding in graphene oxide liquid crystal phases, *ACS Nano.* **5**(10), 8019–8025 (2011).
4. B. Dan, N. Behabtu, A. Martinez, J. S. Evans, D. V. Kosynkin, J. M. Tour, M. Pasquali and I. I. Smalyukh, Liquid crystals of aqueous, giant graphene

oxide flakes, *Soft Matter.* **7**(23), 11154 (2011).

5. K. E. Lee, J. E. Kim, N. U. Maiti, J. Lim, J. O. Hwang, J. Shim, J. J. Oh, T. Yun and S. O. Kim, Liquid crystal size selection of large-size graphene oxide for size-dependent n- doping and oxygen reduction calalysis, *ACS Nano.* **8**, 9073–9080 (2014).

6. P. Kumar, U. N. Maiti, K. E. Lee and S. O. Kim, Rheological properties of graphene oxide liquid crystal, *Carbon.* **80**, 453–461 (2014).

7. Y. Zhu, S. Murali, W. Cai, X. Li, J. W. Suk, J. R. Potts and R. S. Ruoff, Graphene and graphene oxide: synthesis, properties, and applications, *Adv. Mater.* **22**(35), 3906–3924 (2010).

8. K. P. Loh, Q. Bao, G. Eda and M. Chhowalla, Graphene oxide as a chemically tunable platform for optical applications, *Nat. Chem.* **2**, 1015–1024 (2010).

9. D. R. Dreyer, S. Park, C. W. Bielawski and R. S. Ruoff, The chemistry of graphene oxide, *Chem. Soc. Rev.* **39**(1), 228–240 (2010).

10. Y. Yoon, K. Lee, S. Kwon, S. Seo, H. Yoo, S. Kim, Y. Shin, Y. Park, D. Kim, J.-Y. Choi and H. Lee, Vertical alignments of graphene sheets spatially and densely piled for fast ion diffusion in compact supercapacitors, *ACS Nano.* **8**(5), 4580–4590 (2014).

11. L. Onsager, The effect of shape on the interaction of colloidal particles, *L. Ann. N.Y. Acad. Sci.* **51**, 627–659 (1949).

12. P. A. Forsyth Jr., S. Marcelja, D. J. Mitchell and B. W. Ninham, Onsager transition in hard plate fluid, *J. Chem. Soc., Faraday Trans. 2.* **73**, 84–88 (1977).

13. F. M. van der Kooij and H. N. W. Lekkerkerker, Formation of nematic liquid crystals in suspensions of hard colloidal platelets, *J. Phys. Chem. B.* **102**, 7829–7832 (1998).

14. M. A. Bates and D. Frenkel, Nematic–isotropic transition in polydisperse systems of infinitely thin hard platelets, *J. Chem. Phys.* **110**(13), 6553–6559 (1999).

15. D. A. Dikin, S. Stankovich, E. J. Zimney, R. D. Piner, G. H. Dommett, G. Evmenenko, S. T. Nguyen and R. S. Ruoff, Preparation and characterization of graphene oxide paper, *Nature.* **448**(7152), 457–460 (2007).

16. S. H. Aboutalebi, M. M. Gudarzi, Q. B. Zheng and J.-K. Kim, Spontaneous formation of liquid crystals in ultralarge graphene oxide dispersions, *Adv. Funct. Mater.* **21**(15), 2978–2988 (2011).

17. T.-Z. Shen, S.-H. Hong and J.-K. Song, Electro-optical switching of graphene oxide liquid crystals with an extremely large Kerr coefficient, *Nat. Mater.* **13**, 394–399 (2014).

18. Z. Xu and C. Gao, Aqueous liquid crystals of graphene oxide, *ACS Nano.* **5**(4), 2908–2915 (2011).

19. D. Demus, J. W. Goodby, G. W. Gray and H. W. Spiess, eds., *Handbook of Liquid Crystals, Vol. 1, Chap. 7.* vol. 1, Wiley-VCH, Weinheim, Germany (1998).

20. Y. Hasakado, H. Kikuchi, T. Nagamura and T. Kajiyama, Large electro-optic Kerr effect in polymer-stabilized liquid-crystalline blue phase, *Adv. Mater.* **17**(1), 96–98 (2005).

21. I. Dierking, G. Scalia, P. Morales and D. LeClere, Aligning and reorienting carbon nanotubes with nematic liquid crystals, *Adv. Mater.* **16**(11), 865–869 (2004).

22. I. Dierking, G. Scalia and P. Morales, Liquid crystal–carbon nanotube dispersions, *J. Appl. Phys.* **97**(4), 044309 (2005).

23. W. Tie, S. S. Bhattacharyya, Y. J. Lim, S. W. Lee, T. H. Lee, Y. H. Lee and S. H. Lee, Dynamic electro-optic response of graphene/graphitic flakes in nematic liquid crystals, *Opt. Express.* **21**(17), 19867–19879 (2013).

24. C. Zakri, C. Blanc, E. Grelet, C. Zamora-Ledezma, N. Puech, E. Anglaret and P. Poulin, Liquid crystals of carbon nanotubes and graphene, *Philos. Trans. A Math. Phys. Eng. Sci.* **371**(1988), 20120499 (2013).

25. T.-Z. Shen, S.-H. Hong and J.-K. Song, Effect of centrifugal cleaning on the electro-optic response in the preparation of aqueous graphene-oxide dispersions, *Carbon.* **80**, 560–564 (2014).

26. S.-H. Hong, T.-Z. Shen and J.-K. Song, Electro-optical characteristics of aqueous graphene oxide dispersion depending on ion concentration, *J. Phys. Chem. C.* **118**(45), 26304–26312 (2014).

27. R. T. Ahmad, S. H. Hong, T. Z. Shen and J. K. Song, Optimization of particle size for high birefringence and fast switching time in electro-optical switching of graphene oxide dispersions, *Opt. Express.* **23**(4), 4435–4440 (2015).

28. D. A. Saville, T. Bellini, V. Degiorgio and F. Mantegazza, An extended Maxwell–Wagner theory for the electric birefringence of charged colloids, *J. Chem. Phys.* **113**(16), 6974 (2000).

29. C. T. O'Konski, Electric properties of macromolecules. v. theory of ionic polarization in polyelectrolytes, *J. Phys. Chem.* **64**, 605–619 (1960).

30. I. Dozov, E. Paineau, P. Davidson, K. Antonova, C. Baravian, I. Bihannic and L. J. Michot, Electric-field-induced perfect anti-nematic order in isotropic aqueous suspensions of a natural beidellite clay, *J. Phys. Chem. B.* **115**(24), 7751–7765 (2011).

31. X. M. Dong, T. Kimura, J.-F. Revol and D. G. Gray, Effects of ionic strength on the isotropic-chiral nematic phase transition of suspensions of cellulose crystallites, *Langmuir.* **12**(8), 2076–2082 (1996).

32. B. Konkena and S. Vasudevan, Understanding aqueous dispersibility of graphene oxide and reduced graphene oxide through pka measurements, *J. Phys. Chem. Lett.* **3**(7), 867–872 (2012).

33. D. van der Beek, A. Petukhov, P. Davidson, J. Ferré, J. Jamet, H. Wensink, G. Vroege, W. Bras and H. Lekkerkerker, Magnetic-field-induced orientational order in the isotropic phase of hard colloidal platelets, *Phys. Rev. E.* **73**(4), 041402 (2006).

34. J. P. Straley, The gas of long rods as a model for lyotropic liquid crystals, *Mol. Cryst. Liq. Cryst.* **22**(3-4), 333–357 (1973).

35. L. Rao, J. Yan, S.-T. Wu, Y.-C. Lai, Y.-H. Chiu, H.-Y. Chen, C.-C. Liang, C.-M. Wu, P.-J. Hsieh, S.-H. Liu and K.-L. Cheng, Critical field for a hysteresis-free BPLC device, *J. Display Technol.* **7**(12), 627–629 (2011).

36. K.-M. Chen, S. Gauza, H. Xianyu and S.-T. Wu, Hysteresis effects in blue-phase liquid crystals, *J. Display Technol.* **6**(8), 318–322 (2010).

37. M. L. Jimenez, L. Fornasari, F. Mantegazza, M. C. Mourad and T. Bellini, Electric birefringence of dispersions of platelets, *Langmuir.* **28**(1), 251–258 (2012).

38. A. K. Mohapatra, M. G. Bason, B. Butscher, K. J. Weatherill and C. S. Adams, A giant electro-optic effect using polarizable dark states, *Nat. Phys.* **4**(11), 890–894 (2008).

39. Y. Haseba, H. Kikuchi, T. Nagamura and T. Kajiyama, Large electro-optic Kerr effect in nanostructured chiral liquid-crystal composites over a wide temperature range, *Adv. Mater.* **17**, 2311–2315 (2005).

40. Y. Chen, D. Xu, S.-T. Wu, S.-i. Yamamoto and Y. Haseba, A low voltage and submillisecond-response polymer-stabilized blue phase liquid crystal, *Appl. Phys. Lett.* **102**(14), 141116 (2013).

41. X. Wang, H. Bai and G. Shi, Size fractionation of graphene oxide sheets by ph-assisted selective sedimentation, *J. Am. Chem. Soc.* **133**(16), 6338–6342 (2011).

42. D. Li, M. B. Muller, S. Gilje, R. B. Kaner and G. G. Wallace, Processable aqueous dispersions of graphene nanosheets, *Nat. Nanotechnol.* **3**(2), 101–105 (2008).

43. F. Mantegazza, T. Bellini, M. Buscaglia, V. Degiorgio and D. A. Saville, Electrokinetic properties of colloids of variable charge. III. observation of a Maxwell–Wagner relaxation mechanism by high-frequency electric-birefringence spectroscopy, *J. Chem. Phys.* **113**(16), 6984 (2000).

44. J. N. Israelachivili, *Intermolecular and Surface Forces, Third edition, Chap. 14.* Elsevier, Waltham, USA (2011).

45. S.-H. Hong, T.-Z. Shen and J.-K. Song, Flow-induced ordering of particles and flow velocity profile transition in a tube flow of graphene oxide dispersions, *Liq. Cryst.* **42**(2), 261–269 (2014).

46. K. H. Kim and J. K. Song, Technical evolution of liquid crystal displays, *NPG Asia mater.* **1**(1), 29–36 (2009).

47. W. S. Hummers and R. E. Offema, Preparation of graphite oxide, *J. Am. Chem. Soc.* **80**(6), 1339–1339 (1958).

48. S. Hong, S. Jung, S. Kang, Y. Kim, X. Chen, S. Stankovich, S. R. Ruoff and S. Baik, Dielectrophoretic deposition of graphite oxide soot particles, *J. Nanosci. Nanotechnol.* **8**(1), 424–427 (2008).

49. B. R. Burg, F. Lütolf, J. Schneider, N. C. Schirmer, T. Schwamb and D. Poulikakos, High-yield dielectrophoretic assembly of two-dimensional graphene nanostructures, *Appl. Phys. Lett.* **94**(5), 053110 (2009).

50. A. Vijayaraghavan, C. Sciascia, S. Dehm, A. Lombardo, A. Bonetti, A. C. Ferrari and R. Krupke, Dielectrophoretic assembly of high-density arrays of individual graphene devices for rapid screening, *ACS Nano.* **3**(7), 1729–1734 (2009).

Chapter 26

Liquid crystalline phases in suspensions of pigments in non-polar solvents

Susanne Klein,[a,*] Robert M. Richardson[b] and Alexey Eremin[c]

[a] *HP Labs, Bristol, UK*
[b] *H. H. Wills Physics Laboratory, University of Bristol, UK*
[c] *Soft Matter Lab, Otto van Guericke University, Magdeburg, Germany*
[*] *susanne.klein@hpe.com*

We will discuss colloid suspensions of pigments and compare their electro-optic properties with those of traditional dyed low molecular weight liquid crystal systems. There are several potential advantages of colloidal suspensions over low molecular weight liquid crystal systems: a very high contrast because of the high orientational order parameter of suspensions of rod shaped nano-particles, the excellent light fastness of pigments as compared to dyes and high colour saturations resulting from the high loading of the colour stuff. Although a weak 'single-particle' electro-optic response can be observed in dilute suspensions, the response is very much enhanced when the concentration of the particles is sufficient to lead to a nematic phase. Excellent stability of suspensions is beneficial for experimental observation and reproducibility, but it is a fundamental necessity for display applications. We therefore discuss a method to achieve long term stability of dispersed pigments and the reasons for its success. Small angle X-ray scattering was used to determine the orientational order parameter of the suspensions as a function of concentration and the dynamic response to an applied electric field. Optical properties were investigated for a wide range of pigment concentrations. Electro-optical phenomena, such as field-induced birefringence and switching, were characterised. In addition, mixtures of pigment suspensions with small amounts of ferrofluids show promise as future magneto-optical materials.

Contents

847

1. Introduction

We live in a connected world. The number of active mobile phones has been predicted to exceed the number of people on our planet in 2014.[1] Every mobile phone has a display. But these are not the only displays which surround us. When we look around our homes we will find computers, televisions, radios, weighing scales, hobs, clocks, game consoles, thermometers etc., all equipped with displays. Often these displays will be liquid crystal displays, so far one of the most successful display technologies ever. But what is a liquid crystal display?

A standard liquid crystal display consists of a number of layers as can be seen in Fig. 1. Its active part is the combination of the polarisers and the liquid crystal which form a light valve. Light passing the first polariser is polarised, i.e. only one vibration mode is transmitted.

Depending on the orientation of the liquid crystal director this mode stays untouched or is changed. The second polariser, the analyser, blocks or transmits the light depending on its orientation and its state of polarisation as can be seen in Fig. 2. In a nematic liquid crystal, the orientation of the director can be changed by an applied field, hence the device can switch

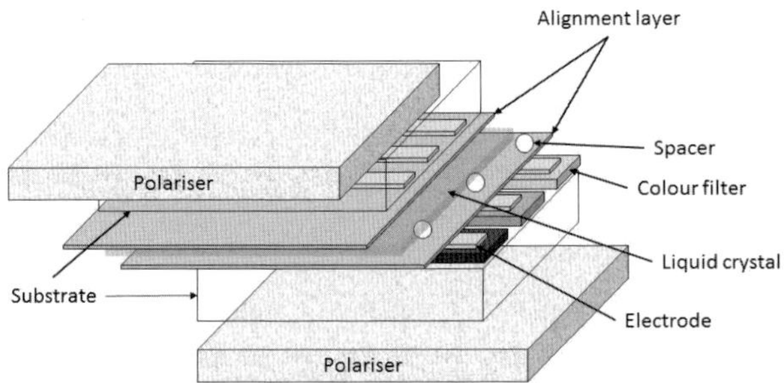

Fig. 1. The layout of a commercially available liquid crystal display. The polarisers in combination with the liquid crystal form the light switch. The alignment layers guarantee a uniform orientation of the liquid crystal and therefore reliable switching. Colour is generated by opening or closing the light valves in front of the colour filters. Not shown are the pixel borders which would surround the unit shown in the figure.

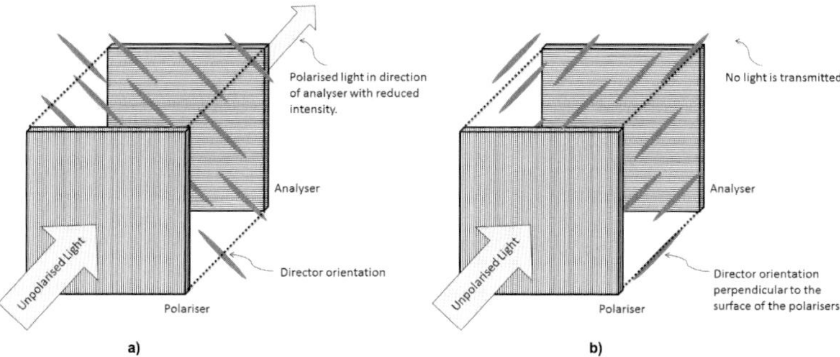

Fig. 2.   Operational principle of a liquid crystal light valve: whether light is transmitted or not depends on the orientation of the liquid crystal molecules and the resulting birefringence. The first polariser transmits only one out of many possible polarisations which are always perpendicular to the beam direction. In Fig. 2a the liquid crystal molecules are oriented in such a way that incident light experiences a birefringent material and its polarisation direction is rotated until it is parallel to the transmission direction of the second polariser. In Fig. 2b the liquid crystal is re-oriented by an electric field. It acts now as a single refractive index material and leaves the light polarisation unchanged. This polarisation is blocked by the second polariser. No light is transmitted.

from transmission to blocking. Colour is generated by opening or closing the light valve on top of Red, Green, and Blue (RGB) colour filters. The unit depicted in Fig. 1 is called a pixel. The pixel size is dependent upon the application. The higher the resolution (i.e. the higher the number of pixels), the smaller is the pixel size. There is no real physical constraint on the size of the pixel. The major constraint is the data flow and, coupled with it, the refresh rate. The higher the product of the number of pixels and the refresh rate, the more data has to be channelled to each line in the display. Processors powering modern, high resolution displays with a refresh rate of 100 Hz and more have to cope with a considerable data rate.

Even though the liquid crystal display is extremely successful, one of its major drawbacks is light efficiency. Only roughly one quarter of the light incident onto the display is transmitted when the display appears white; that is, when all light valves are open. Since polarisers not only polarise but also absorb, about 40% of the incident light passes the first polariser.[a] An ideal combination of the spectral transmittance of the RGB colour filters would transmit roughly 80% of the light reaching them[2] when all the light valves are open. The second polariser then absorbs a further 20% of the transmitted light, assuming that the light is polarised parallel to

---

[a]www.edmundoptics.com/optics/polarizers/linear-polarizers/high-contrast-linear-polarizing-film/3435.

the analyser, which leaves about 25% of the incident light. Other sources of light loss are the electrodes, pixel boundaries and reflections at interfaces, which are not included in the calculation. Consequently images are only visible when the display is illuminated by a very strong backlight. Still the transmitted light is so weak that liquid crystal displays perform poorly in outdoor conditions. On a sunny day, a full colour liquid crystal display will appear dark to the observer. It is not possible to use this kind of display in reflective mode. In reflective mode the light has to pass the stack twice and only about 16% of the incident light would be reflected, another 9% less than in the transmitting configuration.

A major step to improve light efficiency is the removal of polarisers and colour filters. By removing these three layers and incorporating the colour into the LC layer, the light efficiency can be improved to 50% transmission which would make it possible to use the display in reflective mode, see for example.[3,4] As a result a much lighter, cheaper and optically more versatile display could be built.

2. Guest-host systems

Thirty years ago, research into so called 'guest-host systems' was very active. In a guest-host system dyes are dissolved into a liquid crystalline host to replace the combination of polarisers and colour filters. The 'rod' like dye molecules slot into the nematic matrix and are rotated when the director is reoriented by applying an electric field. The dye molecules act like antennae. When the transition moment is parallel to the electric field vector of the electromagnetic wave,[3–5] the light can couple into the transition moment and the colour matching to the frequency of the dye molecule is absorbed. Electric field vectors perpendicular to the transition moment stay completely unaffected by the dye molecule. Ideally the dye could be switched from absorbing to non-absorbing, i.e. from coloured to transparent. A measure of the efficiency of this mechanism is the so called dichroic ratio.

The dichroic ratio is defined as $DR = A_{||}/A_{\perp}$, where $A_{||}$ and $A_{\perp}$ are optical absorbances of the aligned dye doped into a liquid crystal, measured for light polarised parallel and perpendicular to the director of the liquid crystal.[5] Conventionally $A_{||}$ and $A_{\perp}$ are measured at the maximum absorption band of the dye. However for a dye with a wide absorption spectrum or a black dye, the dichroic ratio is evaluated over the whole visible spectrum:[5]

$$DR = \frac{\int A_{||}(\lambda)\,\mathrm{d}\lambda}{\int A_{\perp}(\lambda)\,\mathrm{d}\lambda} \tag{1}$$

where $A_{||}(\lambda)$ and $A_{\perp}(\lambda)$ are the absorbance of the dye parallel and perpendicular to the director at a wavelength λ. To account for the photopic response of the human eye to colour, the photopic dichroic ratio (DR_{vs}) can be defined as

$$DR_{vs} = \frac{\int A_{||}(\lambda)\,V(\lambda)\mathrm{d}\lambda}{\int A_{\perp}(\lambda)\,V(\lambda)\mathrm{d}\lambda} \tag{2}$$

where $V(\lambda)$ is the value of the photopic luminosity efficiency function at a wavelength λ.[5] The dichroic ratio depends strongly on the orientational order parameter (defined in Chap. 2, Eq. (1); we use the same definition of the angle β in this chapter, cf. Fig. 3) of the dye molecules and is mainly limited by the order parameter of the host. The relationship between dichroic ratio and order parameter follows from a simple picture. When a photon interacts with a dye molecule, the probability of absorption depends on $\cos^2 \delta$,

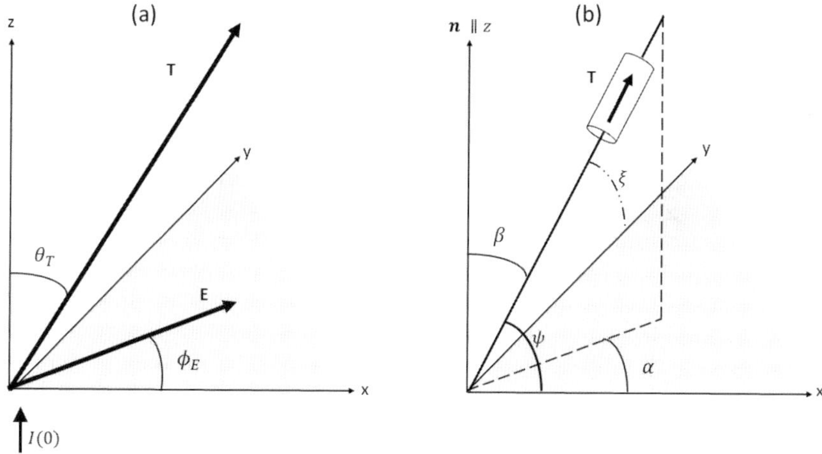

Fig. 3. Part (a) shows a single fixed orientation of the transition dipoles. Light is travelling along the z-direction. The dipoles are aligned along the direction marked T which lies in the xz plane. **E** is the direction of the electric field in the x, y plane, ϕ_E is the angle of the initial polarisation and θ_T is the angle between the transition moment and the z axis. Part (b) shows a particle with a longitudinal transition dipole and the angles that define its orientation. β is the angle between the long particle axis and the director, **n**, and α is the angle between the projection of the long particle axis into the xy plane and the x axis.

where δ is the angle between the transition dipole and the electric field. For a solution of aligned dye molecules, the absorption, A, is a function of the linear attenuation coefficient of the pure dye for light polarised parallel to the transition dipole, $k_\parallel$, the volume fraction of dye in the solution, Φ, and the cell path length, L,

$$A = -\ln \frac{I}{I_0} = -\ln T = k_\parallel \Phi L \cos^2 \delta \tag{3}$$

where T is the transmission. The equation shows that changing the orientation of the dye molecules will not lead to a sudden on/off of the absorption but to a rather soft transition. This is an intrinsic feature of guest-host systems. In general, there is a distribution of orientations of the dye molecules, therefore the mean value of $\cos^2 \delta$ is used. The average is taken over the distribution of the orientations of the transition dipoles. For an isotropic liquid, $\langle \cos^2 \delta \rangle = 1/3$, so it is possible to relate the above equation to the familiar Beer-Lambert Law:

$$A = -\ln \frac{I}{I_0} = \varepsilon c L \tag{4}$$

with $\varepsilon c = (k_\parallel \Phi)/3$, where ε is the molar absorption coefficient and c is the molar concentration. For an aligned nematic, the value of $\langle \cos^2 \delta \rangle$ may be expressed in terms of the orientational order parameter for the different geometries of polarisation and director. For a polarisation parallel to the director, it is easy to show that $\delta = \beta$, leading to an absorption,

$$A_\parallel = k_\parallel \Phi L \langle \cos^2 \beta \rangle = k_\parallel \Phi L \frac{2S + 1}{3} \tag{5}$$

For a polarisation perpendicular to the director, $\cos \delta = \sin \alpha \sin \beta$ and $\langle \sin^2 \alpha \rangle = 1/2$, resulting in

$$A_\perp = k_\parallel \Phi L \left\langle \frac{\sin^2 \beta}{2} \right\rangle = k_\parallel \Phi L \frac{1 - S}{3} \tag{6}$$

The dichroic ratio is therefore

$$DR = \frac{A_\parallel}{A_\perp} = \frac{2S + 1}{1 - S} \tag{7}$$

A high contrast device requires a high dichroic ratio material. A barely acceptable value is 10 which implies an order parameter of 0.75. This is high for a low molecular weight nematic liquid crystal. Thus an exceptionally high order parameter host and a favourable coupling between the host nematic and the guest dye are required for a useful device.

3. Pigments instead of dyes

The simplest definition of a pigment is a dye which does not dissolve, but it can be much more. The dye molecules within an anisometric pigment crystallite are often aligned relative to a particle axis and their transition dipoles are therefore also aligned. Colloidal suspensions of such dichroic pigments have properties different from a guest host system:

(1) The particles may be large enough to self-shield so that some of the absorbing material in a particle is 'hidden' from the incident light. This suggests a venetian blind type of display but this possibility has not yet been exploited.

(2) The anisotropy of the optical properties may be modified by the shape of the particles. This is known as the 'form' effect, another parameter influencing the transmittance.[6]

(3) An electrically switchable liquid crystalline phase can be achieved by suspending dichroic particles in an isotropic solvent. This avoids the difficulties of making stable suspensions in nematic hosts. It can also lead to high order parameters and hence to high optical contrast between different states.

In the following we will concentrate on particles that are small relative to the wavelength of the light (nano-particles) in order to avoid scattering. This is justified because scattering intensity is proportional to V_{1P}^2/λ^4 where V_{1P} is the volume of a single particle and λ the wavelength. Absorption tends to follow V_{1P}/λ. In this section, we examine the changes in transmission that can be expected from changing the orientation of the director of a nematic suspension of dichroic pigment particles.

Consider a suspension of dichroic particles occupying the region bounded by the $z = 0$ and $z = L$ planes. A beam of light, travelling in the positive z direction, is incident on this material. Initially we consider that all the transition dipoles perfectly aligned in the direction, $\mathbf{T}$, which lies in the xz plane as shown on the left of Fig. 3a. The polarisation is defined by the direction of the electric field, $\mathbf{E}$, which lies in the xy plane. The light will propagate along the z direction as two mutually incoherent beams with orthogonal polarisations. The intensity of each beam on entry (near $z=0$) is defined by the initial polarisation angle, ϕ_E

$$I(0) = I_x(0) + I_y(0) \quad I_x(0) = I(0)\cos^2\phi_E \quad I_y(0) = I(0)\sin^2\phi_E \quad (8)$$

The beam with polarisation along the y axis is not attenuated because its electric field is perpendicular to transition dipole. The other is attenuated at a rate determined by the attenuation coefficient and the angle between the transition dipole and the z axis, θ_T. The total intensity of the light when it leaves the material is then:

$$I(L) = I(0)\left\{\cos^2\phi_E e^{-k_{\parallel}\Phi\sin^2\theta_T L} + \sin^2\phi_E\right\} \tag{9}$$

Thus an unpolarised incident beam becomes polarised along the y axis. If the alignment of the particles, and consequently their transition dipoles, is not perfect then both the internal beams will be attenuated and the total intensity leaving the suspension becomes:

$$I(L) = I(0)\left\{\cos^2\phi_E e^{-k_{\parallel}\Phi\langle\cos^2\psi\rangle L} + \sin^2\phi_E e^{-k_{\parallel}\Phi\langle\cos^2\xi\rangle L}\right\} \tag{10}$$

where ψ is the angle between the transition dipole and the x axis and ξ is the angle between the transition dipole and the y axis. The angle brackets indicate averages over all the transition dipoles. These quantities will depend on the orientation of the director, $\mathbf{n}$, and the orientational order parameter, S, of the transition dipoles. It is useful to calculate them for particular cases of transition dipoles embedded in anisotropic particles.

We first consider a uniaxial distribution of rod shaped particles with the transition dipoles along the rod axes, as shown in Fig. 3b. For the case of homeotropic alignment, with the director along z, the angles are

$$\langle\cos^2\psi\rangle = \langle\cos^2\alpha\rangle\langle\sin^2\beta\rangle \text{ and } \langle\cos^2\xi\rangle = \langle\sin^2\alpha\rangle\langle\sin^2\beta\rangle \tag{11}$$

which reduces to a single decay for any incident polarisation, because all directions perpendicular to z are equivalent.

$$I_H(L) = I(0)e^{-k_{\parallel}\Phi(1-S)L/3} = I(0)e^{-A_0(1-S)} \tag{12}$$

where $A_0 = k_{\parallel}\Phi L/3$ is the absorption of an isotropic suspension. The absorption of the homeotropically aligned suspension is therefore,

$$A_{HR} = A_0(1-S) \tag{13}$$

For planar alignment of these rods, we choose the director to lie along the x axis. In this case, the directions perpendicular to z are not equivalent and so there are two separate intensity decays (for $S \neq 0$)

$$I_P(L) = I(0)\left\{\cos^2\phi_E e^{-A_0(2S+1)} + \sin^2\phi_E e^{-A_0(1-S)}\right\} \tag{14}$$

For unpolarised incident light, an expansion of the exponentials gives to first order

$$I_P(L) \approx I(0)e^{-A_0(1+S/2)} \tag{15}$$

Therefore the absorption of a planar aligned suspension is $A_{PR} = A_0(1 + S/2)$. Similar calculations may be performed for a uniaxial distribution of discs with transition dipoles distributed perpendicular to the disc axes. For homeotropic alignment of the discs, with the director along z,

$$A_{HD} = A_0 \left(S/2 + 1 \right) \tag{16}$$

For a planar alignment of the discs with the director along the x axis

$$A_{PD} \approx A_0 \left(1 - S/4 \right) \tag{17}$$

We can now estimate the ratios of absorptions, the so called device field response, for reflective displays based on switching from random alignment, or planar alignment of the director, to homeotropic alignment using an applied field as illustrated in Fig. 4 (adapted from Ref. 7). Table 1 shows the device field response, D, for rods and discs discussed above with assumed values of the order parameters. For a discotic system, the particles' orientational order parameter, S, is typically between $-1/2$ and 0 since the long axes tend to be perpendicular to the director.

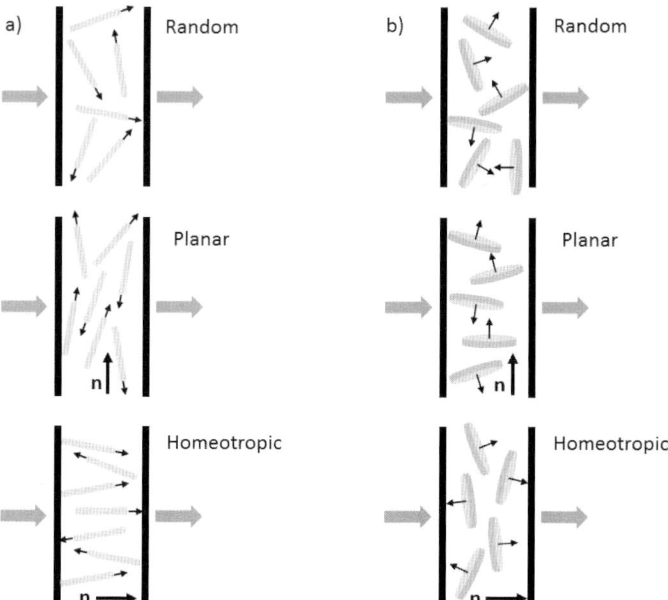

Fig. 4. Different director configurations for dispersions of rod-shaped (a) and disc-shaped (b) particles (adapted from Ref. 7). The director describes the mean orientation of the long particle axis of rods and the mean orientation of the plate normal for plates.

Table 1. Device field response as a function of order parameter and particle shape.

	Rods with a transition dipole along the long rod axis		Discs with a transition dipole in plane	
Order parameter of particles, S	random to homeotropic, $D_1 = \frac{A_{HR}}{A_0}$	planar to homeotropic $D_2 = \frac{A_{HR}}{A_{PR}}$	random to homeotropic $D_3 = \frac{A_{HD}}{A_0}$	planar to homeotropic $D_4 = \frac{A_{HD}}{A_{PD}}$
1.0	0.0	0.0		
0.9	0.1	0.07		
-0.45			0.78	0.70
-0.5			0.75	0.67

These calculations show that the values of the field response ratios for rods are very different from one and do suggest that a high contrast display could be made based on the reorientation of nanorods with a transition dipole along their long axes. The field responses for the discs cases are much weaker. It is clear that the best optical response to the application of an electric field will be achieved using a suspension of rods with high orientational order parameter. This may be achieved by forming a nematic phase of rods in an isotropic liquid or by suspending rods in a small-molecule nematic phase.

4. Stable suspensions and their preparation

To see any of the effects discussed above we need stable colloidal suspensions. A colloidal suspension is stable when the thermal energy is high enough to counteract the attractive forces between the particles which would cause aggregation and the gravitational force which would cause sedimentation. The attractive forces are dependent on the materials of the particle and the suspension medium and the particle dimensions. For parallel, side-by-side rod shaped particles the Van der Waals attractive potential given by the approximate formula[8]

$$E(x) \approx \frac{\sqrt{R}}{24x^{3/2}} LA \tag{18}$$

where A is the effective Hamaker constant for combination of the particle materials and surrounding medium, R is the radius of the rod and L is its length. This formula holds for small gaps, x.

    The plot in Fig. 5 shows that the smaller the distance between two particles is the stronger the attraction. To prevent particles from coming into the attractive range, they have to be either charged or their surface

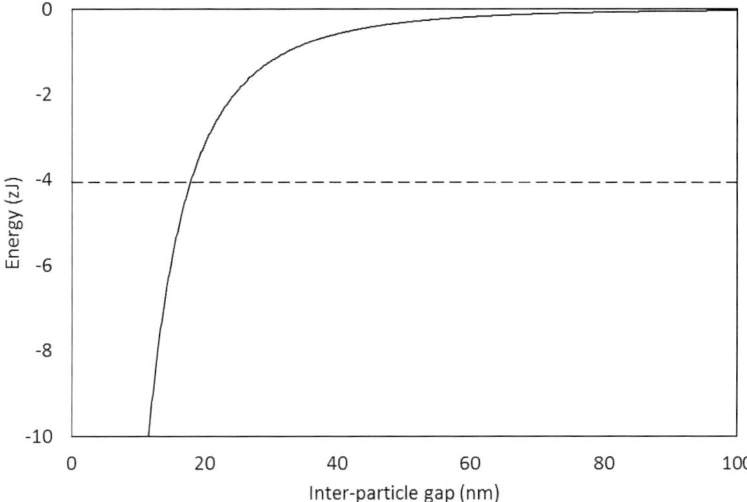

Fig. 5. Showing the Van der Waals attractive potential energy as for two parallel, side-by-side nanorods as a function of the gap between them. They have a length of length 300 nm and radius 30 nm for an effective Hamaker constant of 10 zJ. The horizontal line represents kT. (Calculated using formula C.3.b.1 in Ref. 8.)

has to be treated in such a way that a fluffy barrier stops the particles from coming too close. Charged particles are surrounded by a cloud of counter ions. The thickness of this cloud is described by the Debye screening length κ^{-1} (in Chap. 3 this was denoted λ_D)with

$$\kappa^{-1} = \sqrt{\frac{\varepsilon \varepsilon_0 k_B T}{2e^2 N_A c_I}} \tag{19}$$

where e is the elemental charge, c_I is the ionic strength of the electrolyte, N_A is the Avogadro constant, $k_B T$ is the thermal energy, ε is the relative permittivity of the medium, and ε_0 is the permittivity of vacuum. From the equation it becomes clear that the stronger the electrolyte, i.e. the more charge is present, the smaller the Debye screening length.

On the other hand in non-polar solvents the Debye screening length is big, that means if the particles were charged no further stabilization would be necessary. However charging of particles in non-polar solvents is difficult because of the local neutralization by counter ions. Steric stabilization is generally more effective. If polymer chains are attached to the surface of the pigments and the solvent swells those chains they extend to their full length. When two polymer stabilized particles approach each other two scenarios can occur: a) the polymer chains overlap. The increased polymer concentration creates a repulsive osmotic pressure and the particles will move apart if this pressure is higher than the attractive van der Waals force. b) If the pressure is not high enough the polymer chains will compress thus reducing the entropy of the polymer chains which will again lead to a separation of the particles.

Electrostatic repulsion and steric stabilization occur often in parallel, but in non-polar solvents steric stabilization is the dominant mechanism.

All objects experience gravitational force, which means there is a tendency for dense particles to sink. The particles will be accelerated downwards until this acceleration is balanced by the friction between the particle and the surrounding liquid, the so called drag force. The particles will then travel at so called terminal velocity which is given, for example for a sphere of radius, a, by:

$$v_t = \frac{2a^2 \Delta \rho g}{9\eta} \tag{20}$$

where $\Delta \rho$ is the difference in density between particle and medium and η is the viscosity. Sedimentation is partly counteracted by Brownian motion, a random motion caused by the collision of the particle and the thermally fluctuating molecules in the liquid and by the tendency of diffusion to create a uniform particle concentration. The equilibrium thickness of the sediment is given by:

$$h = \frac{k_B T}{\Delta \rho V_p g} \tag{21}$$

where V_p is the volume of a particle. If the sedimentation thickness is substantially greater than the particle dimension, the suspension is said to be stable against sedimentation.

The pigments are generally supplied as dry powders. To prepare suspensions the clusters in the powder have to be broken up, ideally into single particles, and the particles have to be stabilized by a surface treatment to avoid aggregation in the solvent.

A very successful method is milling of the pigments in a solvent in combination with a dispersant. Depending on the pigment the amount of dispersant needed varied between 10 to 40% of the weight of pigment. We found that for dodecane as a solvent and for 20 to 30 wt% of pigment the Solsperse dispersant 11200 (Lubrizol) is the most effective one. Suspensions with less than 20w/w% of pigment were prepared by stepwise dilution of the mill base. When the particles were prepared for suspension in a liquid crystal, the particles were milled in a solvent mixture with a similar dielectric constant to the liquid crystal (5CB for example has an isotropic dielectric constant $\varepsilon_{iso} = \frac{\varepsilon_\parallel + 2\varepsilon_\perp}{3} = 10.83$ at $25°C^{b}$) and a low boiling point. The pigments were then transferred to the liquid crystal and the milling solvent was evaporated.

One of the test pigments was Novoperm Carmine HF3C (Clariant, Frankfurt am Main, Germany) which is a blue shade benzimidazolone pigment (C.I. Pigment Red 176). It has a rod like shape with an average length of 230 ± 70 nm and an average diameter of 46 ± 20 nm, see Fig. 6.

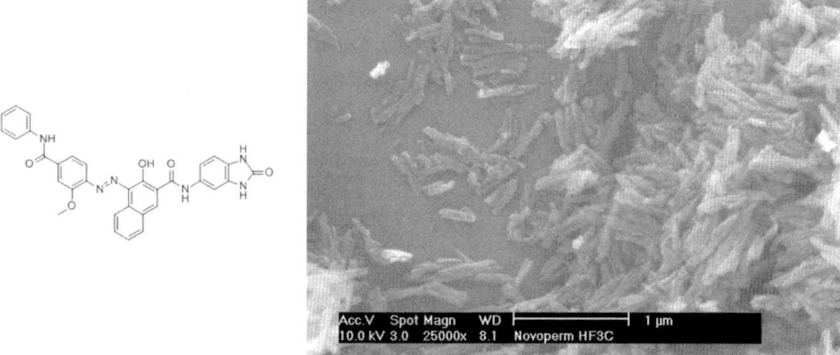

Fig. 6. Structural formula of the dye forming C.I. Pigment Red 176 and a scanning electron micrograph of Novoperm Carmine HF3C. The particles visible on the right hand side are crystallites, i.e. nano-sized pigments

All milled suspension showed Schlieren texture in between crossed polarisers indicating a nematic phase. The particle size was determined by dynamic light scattering in a Malvern Nanosizer and showed that milling did not break the primary particles.

Another test pigment was Permanent Rubine L4B01 (C.I. Pigment Red 57:1). This pigment from Clariant is a calcium laked BONS red pigment and its primary particle shape is that of a flake with an average width of 131 ± 17 nm, average length 282 ± 227 nm and a thickness of roughly 10 nm (Fig. 7). With the same procedure and the same stabilizers as for Novoperm Carmine HF3C stable suspensions were achieved as well.

The third test pigment was Graphtol Carmine, another elongated shaped particle, with colour index Pigment Red 185. Graphtol Carmine belongs to the same chemical group of benzimidazolone pigments as Novoperm Carmine HF3C but is more lath shaped with an average length of 330 nm, width of 66 nm, and a thickness of 11 nm.

---

[b]http://liqcryst.chemie.uni-hamburg.de/en/lc_1264.php.

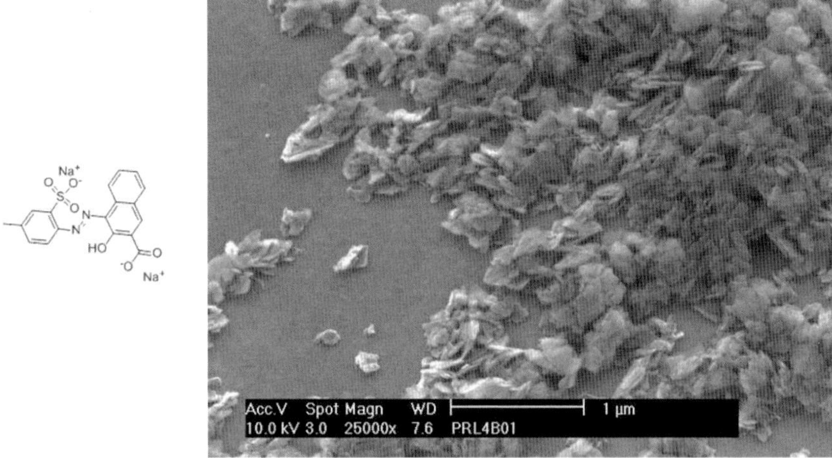

Fig. 7. Structural formula of the dye forming C.I. Pigment Red 7:1 and a scanning electron micrograph of Permanent Rubine L4B01. It is obvious that the crystallites are flakes.

5. Optical characterization

Since the driving force behind the research into pigment suspensions in non-polar solvents is the desire to create a display without the need of colour filters the ideal suspension would switch between a coloured and a clear state when an electric field is applied. To make the suspension useful for display application a threshold is necessary as well, i.e. the particles would only re-orient when a voltage higher than the threshold was applied. Gradual re-orientation would deteriorate the optical performance of any display.

Traditionally the dichroic ratio is defined as in equation (7). The absorbances are measured in at the maximum absorption band, parallel and perpendicular to the director of the liquid crystal.

In the case of pigment suspensions we cannot use this definition since two problems are encountered: a) Pigment suspensions in isotropic solvents are very hard to align without any applied fields. Instead of switching the director between parallel and perpendicular to the light polarisation, the director is switched between unaligned and perpendicular to the light polarisation. b) Suspensions above 10 wt% of pigment are so strongly absorbent that their electro-optical response is hard to quantify.

For suspensions of 5 wt% and less the absorbance of the suspension is low enough to measure changes of the spectrum when a field is applied. The suspensions are filled into glass cells which consist of two parallel glass substrate coated with ITO (indium tin oxide). The ITO coating allows the application of an electric field. The ITO layer was coated with an insulating layer to prevent electro-chemical reactions during the experiments. Figure 8a shows a small change in the absorption spectrum of Permanent Rubine L4B01 in dodecane as reported in Ref. 9. The difference between the two spectra is minute but still visible by eye. Figure 8b shows the device field response, which is the absorbance recorded when a field was applied, divided by the absorbance without a field. The device field response decreases with increasing amplitude which indicates that the transition dipole aligns more and more with the electric field lines and therefore more perpendicular to the electromagnetic field of the illuminating light. At the maximum amplitude of 2 V/μm it has not yet plateaued out which is suggesting that the orientational order parameter is increasing but has not yet reached a maximum. No threshold is observed either.

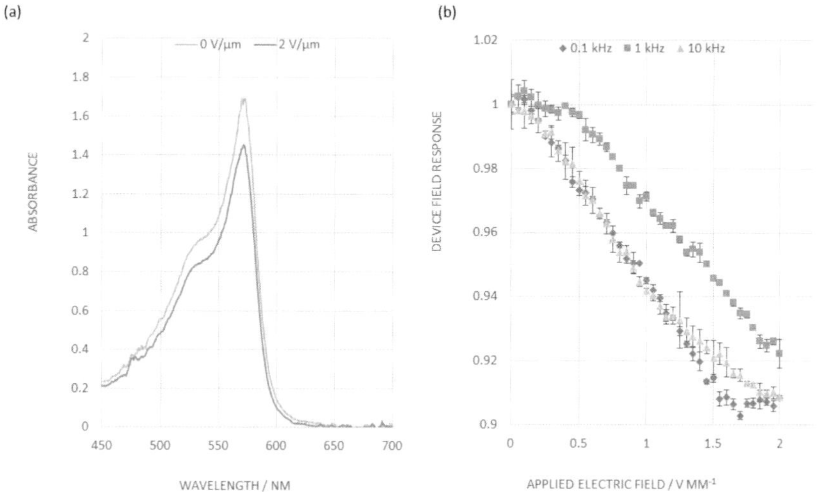

Fig. 8. (a) Shows the visible absorption spectrum for a 5 wt% suspension of Permanent Rubine L4B01 with an applied field of an amplitude of 2 V/μm and a frequency of 1 kHz (square wave) and without a field. (b) The device field response as a function of applied electric field and varying frequency.

5.1. *Birefringence*

Form-anisotropy of colloidal particles affects optical properties of dispersions and results in such optical phenomena as birefringence and dichroism. Birefringence (Fig. 9) was found in various types of colloidal systems such as dispersions of clay particles, fd- and tobacco mosaic viruses.[10–12] It is attributed to the orientational order of anisometric colloidal particles resulting in the formation of lyotropic mesophases. The magnitude of the birefringence is of the order of magnitude of 10^{-3}, which is much smaller than in common thermotropic liquid crystals, and it strongly depends on the volume fraction of the dispersant. Birefringence can also be induced by external stimuli such as shear flow, electric or magnetic fields (Fig. 9b).

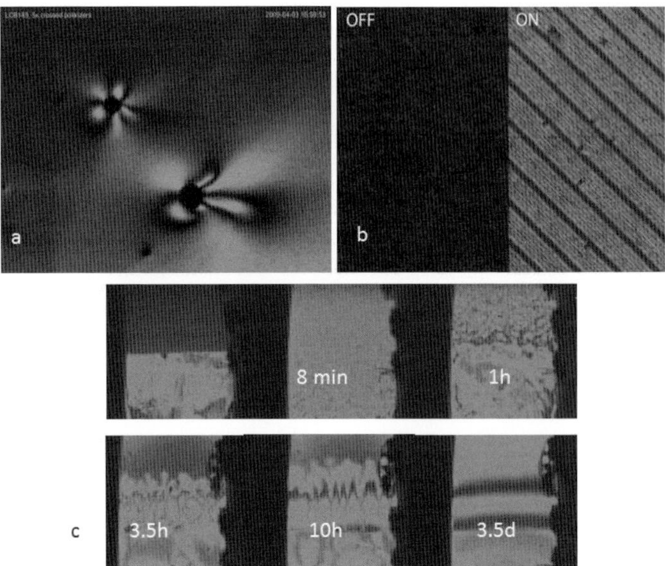

Fig. 9. Birefringence in colloidal dispersions imaged by polarising microscopy: a) Schlieren texture in a thin sample of 35 wt% Novoperm Carmine HF3C dispersion; b) optical switching in 10 wt% Novoperm Carmine HF3C dispersion confined in a cell with interdigitated electrodes. The left side image is without electric field and the right image is made under an electric field ($E_{pp} = 2.4$ V/μm, $f = 100$ Hz). c) Polarisation microscopy pictures of an I-N phase separated goethite sample 9% volume fraction in a 250 mT field (adopted from Ref. 10).

Due to their high viscosity birefringent dispersions with a high volume fraction of pigment particles show only a weak optical response in an electric field, either dichroism or birefringence. Isotropic dispersions with small volume fractions are very susceptible to the fields. Field-induced birefringence was demonstrated in thin cells with interdigitated comb-electrodes and under an action of the AC electric field (Fig. 9b). Maximal response was observed at the frequency of 50 Hz. At low frequency, the refractive index difference Δn decreases. In DC fields, transient birefringence is observed after switching the field on. Field-induced birefringence increases nearly linearly with the volume fraction of the pigment particles (Fig. 10).

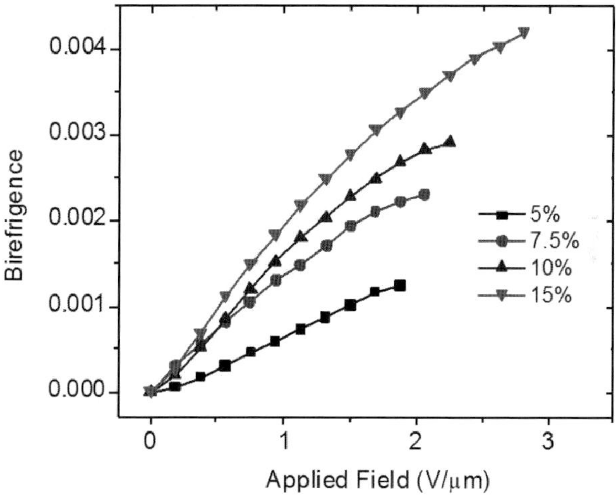

Fig. 10. Dependence of the birefringence on an applied 50 Hz electric field for different weight fractions of Novoperm Carmine HF3C.

The mechanism of the orientational effect is still unclear. It does not seem to be a simple Kerr effect[13] since the increase in birefringence is not proportional to the square of the applied electric field. The transient behaviour of the field-induced birefringence in DC fields suggests that shear flow may be involved in the alignment process. An electric field induces electric current of charged entities of the free surfactant in the dispersion. Additionally, the permanent dipole moment of the particles may contribute to the particle alignment.

5.2. *Magneto-optical response*

Pigment dispersions of Novoperm Carmine HF3C do not show any significant response to a magnetic field. The Cotton-Moutton effect has been observed in strong magnetic fields in the range of 10–20T. Binary mixtures of non-magnetic rod-shaped pigment particles with magnetic spherical particles of a ferrofluid exhibit magnetically induced birefringence at field strengths as low as 50 - 700 mT (Fig. 11). The volume fraction of the ferrofluid in these systems does not exceed 1%. This behaviour can be attributed to the Onsager-Lekkerkerker-Effect where the magnetic particles form chains in a magnetic field. Steric interactions between the magnetic chains and the non-magnetic pigment particles induce the alignment of the latter.[14,15] At small volume fractions ϕ_m of the magnetic component, the birefringence grows linearly with ϕ_m.

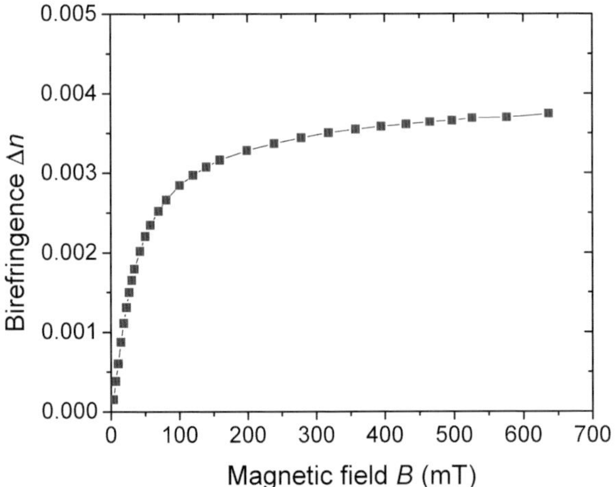

Fig. 11. Birefringence as a function of magnetic field in a binary mixture of 5 v.-% of Novoperm Carmine HF3C and 0.9 v.-% of the ferrofluid APG935 (Ferrotech, Germany) (adapted from Ref. 17).

6. Determination of the order parameter via X-ray scattering

X-rays are electromagnetic radiation with a wavelength between 0.01 and 10 nm. Visible light for example covers the wavelength range from 380 to 750 nm. The small wavelength of X-rays makes it possible to explore a wide range of structures, from the spacing of atoms in a crystal to the shape and orientation of macromolecules or nanoparticles.

Some of the incident X-ray waves are scattered elastically and coherently by the electrons in the sample. The scattered waves interfere to give a diffraction pattern which contains information on the sample structure. The distribution of the electron density in the sample is connected to the diffraction pattern by a Fourier transform. For nanoparticles, Bragg peaks arise from their internal periodic structure while the shape and local packing of the particles determine the distribution of the scattering at low scattering vectors ($\mathbf{Q}$). In principle, it is possible to use any anisotropic scattering feature to determine the orientational order parameter of nanoparticles in suspension. The low Q scattering from a rod shaped particle is predominantly a streak that is perpendicular to the rod axis. In an unaligned or isotropic suspension of rods, this gives an isotropic low Q signal but in a well aligned sample, the scattering becomes more intense in a direction at right angles to the director of the rod axes. Thus, the low Q scattering is useful for a qualitative assessment of the rods' orientational order. It can be seen in Fig. 12 although partially obscured by the beamstop. However, there are several contributing factors to the low Q scattering: particle dimensions, their polydispersity, their local packing in concentrated suspensions and their orientational order. It is impossible to separate these influences in order to determine the orientational order parameter accurately and reliably.

The Bragg scattering from the internal structure of the particles provides a much more reliable route to the orientational order parameter. Bragg scattering is the coherent scattering of X-rays by periodic structures. The intensity of scattering signal on the detector is given by

$$I(\mathbf{W}) = |F(\mathbf{Q})|^2 |Z(\mathbf{Q})|^2 \tag{22}$$

$F(\mathbf{Q})$ is the Fourier transform of the scattering length density distribution associated with a single repeating unit, such as a unit cell in a crystal, and $Z(\mathbf{Q})$ is the Fourier transform of the lattice or ordered arrangement of the repeating units. Assuming that the repeating units are arranged in parallel planes separated by a distance d, Bragg peaks, i.e. constructive interference of the scattered waves, will occur when

$$Q = \frac{n2\pi}{d} \tag{23}$$

The integer n indicates the order of reflection. The intensity of the Bragg is modulated by the structure factor $F(\mathbf{Q})$. Broadening of the peaks occurs because of distortion of the lattice and the limited size of the crystalline domains. The distribution of the Bragg scattering around a ring at constant $|\mathbf{Q}|$ is determined by the orientational order of the particles. If the orientation of the diffracting planes within the particle is known, the particle order parameter may be determined from by analysing the intensity

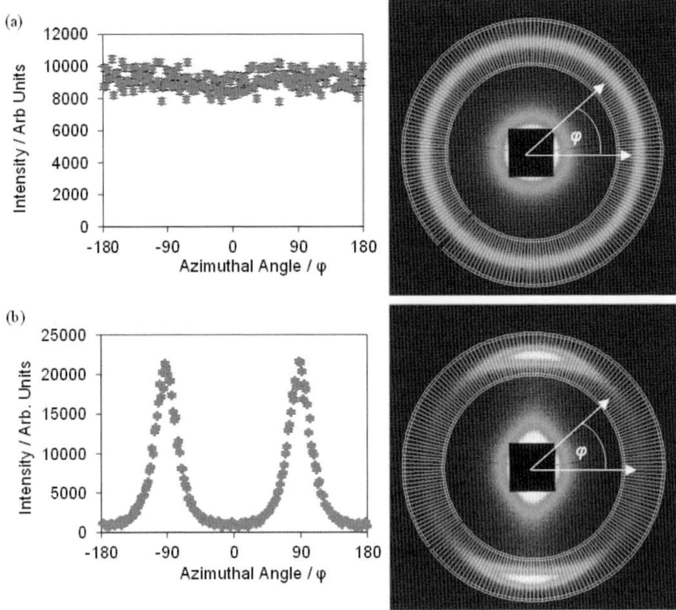

Fig. 12. Showing the extraction of the azimuthal angular variation of the intensity of a Bragg peak from a suspension of 25 wt% Permanent Rubine L4B01 in dodecane with the accompanying two dimensional scattering plot including data bins (a) at 0 Vμm^{-1} and (b) at 2 Vμm^{-1} with frequency of 1 kHz.

distribution on a ring. For example, Fig. 13 shows the lattice planes in Permanent Rubine platelets which are oriented perpendicular to the plate normal.

Experimental Measurement

Nanoparticle suspensions are contained in thin walled glass capillaries (diameters 1.5 mm) placed between two electrodes insulated with Kapton tape to reduce sparking. A horizontal electric field perpendicular to the X-ray beam is generated. The field strength could be varied up to 2 V/μm and a frequency of 1 kHz was found to be most effective in inducing alignment. The beamline I22 at the Diamond Light Source synchrotron[c] was used with a sample-detector distance of 1 m and a wavelength of 1.0 Å to record the Bragg peaks as a function of applied fields. In Fig. 14 the schematic set up is shown.

---

[c]http://www.diamond.ac.uk/Beamlines.html.

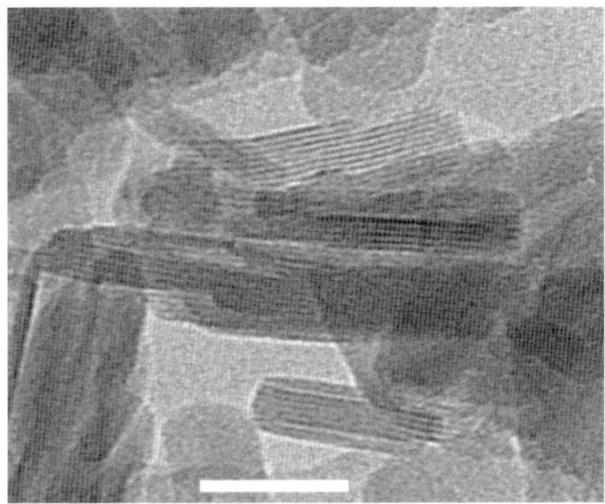

Fig. 13. Bright field transmission electron micrograph of Permanent Rubine L4B01 platelets showing spacing of 18 Å corresponding to a Bragg peak at 0.35 Å^{-1}. (Scale bar 35.1 nm)

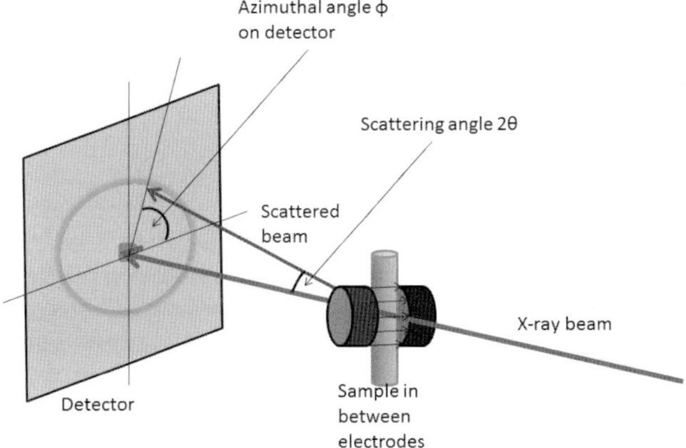

Fig. 14. Experimental set up: The sample filled in a capillary is placed between two insulated electrodes. The applied field is perpendicular to the monochromatic and collimated X-ray beam incident on the sample. The plane of the detector is perpendicular to the direction of the beam. The scattered beam deviates from the original direction by an angle 2θ which defines the magnitude of the scattering vector, $\mathbf{Q}$, of a point on the detector.

In general the particles are not aligned when the suspensions are flowed into capillaries. Each Bragg peak from the crystalline structure in the particles forms a uniform ring, the so called Debye-Scherrer ring. A single particle could give a Bragg peak, perpendicular to the crystal planes, at a point on the detector with azimuthal angle, φ. The different orientations of the particles do not lead to different Q values, since the distance between the lattice planes is fixed, but to Bragg peaks at different φ values. When the orientation of the particles is isotropic a uniform ring will be formed. When the particles become aligned the intensities in some intervals of φ will increase and in others decrease, see Fig. 12. Aligning the particles with a field causes two distinctive crescent shaped areas on the Debye-Scherrer ring. The scattering order parameter $\overline{P_{2,S}}$ is calculated by

$$\overline{P_{2,S}} = \int_0^\pi f(\varphi) \left(\frac{3}{2} \cos^2 \varphi - \frac{1}{2} \right) \sin \varphi \, \mathrm{d}\varphi \tag{24}$$

where $f(\varphi)$ is the normalised distribution of intensity around the ring. For uniaxial distributions, there is a simple relationship between the scattering order parameter and that of the particles.[16] In the case of Permanent Rubine L4B01, Fig. 13 shows the platelet normal is also perpendicular to the crystal planes so the order parameter for the platelet normals is simply

$$S = \overline{P_{2,S}} \tag{25}$$

Figure 4b illustrates the relationship between the director and the platelet normal for three different order parameters. In the case of Permanent Rubine L4B01, the applied field leads to planar director alignment.

The orientational order parameter values for three different suspensions in dodecane are shown in Fig. 15. The 10 wt% suspensions of the three different pigments show the same trend. Increasing field strengths result in a more negative particle order parameter, i.e. the suspensions are more and more aligned with the platelet normal perpendicular to the field. No threshold was observable. The suspension responded to all applied field strengths immediately. The order parameter vs. particle concentration shows steady increase over 0 wt% to 20 wt% then a sudden decrease (i.e. more negative) at about 25 wt%, which is the onset of Schlieren texture when observed under a polarisation microscope. Suspensions above 25 wt% become difficult to handle. Their viscosity is so high that it is either very difficult or impossible to fill them into glass capillaries.

An isotropic to liquid crystalline phase transition could not be identified with certainty, probably because the polydispersity of the particles makes it continuous rather than sharp. All suspensions prepared with the three different pigment particles show Schlieren texture above 25 wt%. Permanent Rubine L4B01 and Novoperm Carmine HF3C show a sudden jump in the orientational order parameter at 25 wt%; for Graphtol Carmine a similar jump occurs at 30 wt%. The combination of Schlieren texture and a jump in order parameter hints that the system is predominantly nematic at higher concentrations.

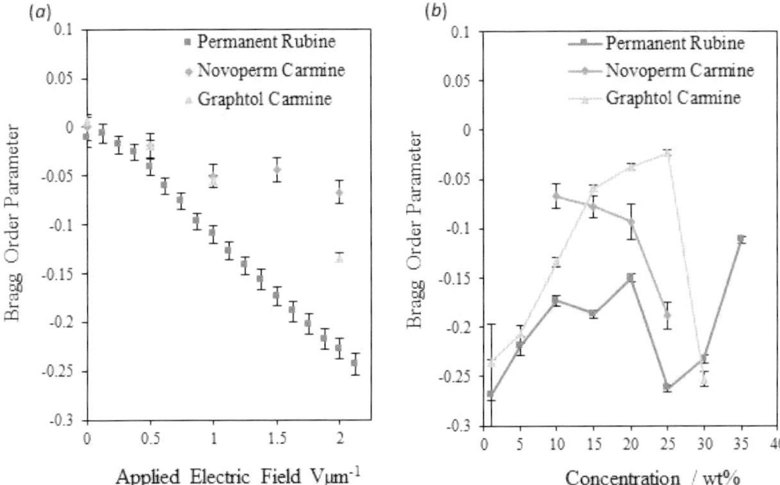

Fig. 15.   Showing the orientational order parameter for 10 wt% Permanent Rubine L4B01, Novoperm Carmine H3FC and Graphtol Carmine for (a) increasing applied electric field (b) varying concentration at a constant field of 1.5 Vμm^{-1} for Permanent Rubine L4B01 and 2 Vμm^{-1} for both Carmine pigments at a frequency of 1 kHz. The line are guides only.

7. Conclusions

These studies have shown that it is possible to prepare a stable suspension of anistropic pigment particles which has high orientational order and may be reconfigured by application of an electric field. The field response of the optical absorption is consistent with the field induced change in the director distribution and the order parameter. The remaining challenge is to make a monodispersed pigment with the transition dipole along the long axis of a rod so that high contrast response can be achieved.

References

1. J. Pramis, Number of mobile phones to exceed world population by 2014, *Digital Trends* (2013).
2. R. W. Sabnis, Color filter technology for liquid crystal displays, *Displays.* **20**(3), 119–129 (1999).
3. P. Malik, P. Kumar and K. Raina, Guest host polymer dispersed liquid crystal display device: role of dichroic dye, *Proceeding of ASID.* p. 173, (2006).
4. T. Uchida, H. Seki, C. Shishido and M. Wada, Guest-host interactions in

nematic liquid crystals with negative dielectric anisotropy, *Electron Devices, IEEE Transactions on.* **26**(9), 1373–1374 (1979).

5. B. Bahadur and M. Tilton, *Liquid crystals: applications and uses.* vol. 3, World Scientific (1992).

6. S. Klein and R. M. Richardson, The optical response of polarizer-free liquid crystal systems: dye molecules versus nano-particles, *HP Labs technical report,* (2006).

7. R. J. Greasty, *Orientational Order in Pigment Particle Suspensions.* PhD thesis, University of Bristol, (2012).

8. V. A. Parsegian, *Van der Waals forces: a handbook for biologists, chemists, engineers, and physicists.* Cambridge University Press, (2005).

9. R. J. Greasty, R. M. Richardson, S. Klein, D. Cherns, M. R. Thomas, C. Pizzey, N. Terrill and C. Rochas, Electro-induced orientational ordering of anisotropic pigment nanoparticles, *Philosophical Transactions of the Royal Society a-Mathematical Physical and Engineering Sciences.* **371**(1988), (2013).

10. E. van den Pol, A. Lupascu, P. Davidson and G. J. Vroege, The isotropic-nematic interface of colloidal goethite in an external magnetic field, *J. Chem. Phys.* **133**(16), (2010).

11. E. van den Pol, A. V. Petukhov, D. M. E. Thies-Weesie and G. J. Vroege, Simple rectangular columnar phase of goethite nanorods and its martensitic transition to the centered rectangular columnar phase, *Langmuir.* **26**(3), 1579–1582 (2010).

12. D. van der Beek, P. Davidson, H. H. Wensink, G. J. Vroege and H. N. W. Lekkerkerker, Influence of a magnetic field on the nematic phase of hard colloidal platelets, *Phys. Rev. E.* **77**(3), (2008).

13. J. Kerr, A new relation between electricity and light: Dielectrified media birefringent, *The London, Edinburgh, and Dublin Philosophical Magazine and Journal of Science.* **50**(332), 337–348 (1875).

14. S. Kredentser, O. Buluy, P. Davidson, I. Dozov, S. Malynych, V. Reshetnyak, K. Slyusarenko and Y. Reznikov, Strong orientational coupling in two-component suspensions of rod-like nanoparticles, *Soft Matter.* **9**(20), 5061–5066 (2013).

15. K. Slyusarenko, V. Reshetnyak and Y. Reznikov, Magnetic field control of the ordering of two-component suspension of hard rods, *Philosophical Transactions of the Royal Society a-Mathematical Physical and Engineering Sciences.* **371**(1988), (2013).

16. R. Lovell and G. R. Mitchell, Molecular-orientation distribution derived from an arbitrary reflection, *Acta Crystallographica Section A.* **37**(Jan), 135–137 (1981).

17. K. May, A. Eremin, R. Stannarius, S. D. Peroukidis, S. H. L. Klapp and S. Klein, Colloidal Suspensions of Rodlike Nanocrystals and Magnetic Spheres under an External Magnetic Stimulus: Experiment and Molecular Dynammics Simulation, *Langmuir,* **32**(20), 5085–5093 (2016).

Chapter 27

Cholesteric liquid crystal formation in suspensions of cellulose nanocrystals

Camilla Honorato-Rios,[a] Johanna Bruckner,[a] Christina Schütz,[b]
Sammy Wagner,[a] Zornitza Tosheva,[a] Lennart Bergström[b,*] and
Jan P. F. Lagerwall[a,†]

[a]*University of Luxembourg, Physics & Materials Science Research Unit,
162a, avenue de la faiencerie, 1511 Luxembourg, Luxembourg*
[b]*Stockholm University, Department of Materials and
Environmental Chemistry, Stockholm, Sweden*
**lennart.bergstrom@mmk.su.se, †jan.lagerwall@lcsoftmatter.com*

With the strong current trend in nanotechnology to focus on sustainably produced nanomaterials, cellulose nanocrystals (CNC) are emerging as a particularly interesting candidate. They are mechanically strong, optically transparency and birefringent, have low weight and low thermal expansion coefficient. A most desirable feature of CNC is that aqueous suspensions form cholesteric liquid crystal phases already at low concentration, and when dried into thin solid films, the periodicity of the helical structure can be reduced to the range of visible selective reflection, in practice making the film a photonic crystal paper.

We begin the chapter by briefly explaining how CNC is extracted from cellulose-rich bioresources, followed by a summary of the typical characteristics in terms of dimensions and surface charge, and how these depend on the production method. The current understanding of the phase diagram of CNC suspensions is then discussed, from the low-concentration regime around the isotropic-cholesteric transition to the less well understood regime where the system is kinetically arrested in a non-equilibrium state. We discuss the influences on phase behavior and cholesteric pitch of the solvent and its ionic strength. Finally, we discuss the production of photonic crystal films and we give a brief outlook.

Contents

1. Why the current interest in cellulose nanocrystals?

The thin rods of crystalline cellulose referred to as cellulose nanocrystals—or CNC—constitute one of the most inspiring nanoparticle classes being studied today, in particular from a liquid crystal science point of view. Cellulose is inherently mainly hydrophilic and due to the surface charges introduced during extraction, CNC is easily dispersed in water. Already at very low volume fraction, the combination of a slender rod shape of high aspect ratio (L/D, length divided by diameter) with a unichiral material (cellulose) making up the rod leads to the spontaneous development of a cholesteric (chiral nematic) phase. While the equilibrium pitch is typically in the range of tens of μm, it can shrink to the submicron range during drying of a suspension into a cellulose film, giving the final object the beautiful (and useful) iridescent colors characteristic of short-pitch cholesteric structures. Today's research on CNC spans from fundamental soft matter physics, aiming to answer, e.g., the question of how chirality is transferred from the cellulose molecular structure to the helical structure of the macroscopic cholesteric phase (typically consisting of 90-98% water), to projects that aim to develop, for instance, paper-like photonic crystals or light-weight but mechanically robust composites.

CNC is not a new material. In the 1950s, Rånby and Ribi were the first to produce the nanocrystals via controlled sulfuric acid hydrolysis of wood and cotton cellulose fibers and study the colloidal suspensions.[1,2] The nanorods were found to be approximately 5-10 nm wide and 50-60 nm long, as determined by X-ray diffraction. Marchessault *et al.*[3] reported that, beyond a critical concentration in water, CNC forms a birefringent gel. It then took another three decades until Gray and co-workers[4] demonstrated that the phase formed by CNC produced by sulfuric acid hydrolysis is chiral nematic.

One major reason for the current strong interest in CNC is the fact that this is a sustainably produced nanoparticle, derived from renewable bioresources and not from oil (in contrast to CNTs and many other nanoparticles), with very attractive mechanical and optical properties. The individual CNC rods are transparent across the visible spectrum, they have low density and excellent mechanical strength, and the surface provides a defined chemistry of primary and secondary hydroxyl groups which open the toolbox for specific surface modifications. Another important reason is that the advantages of liquid crystalline self-assembly in advanced materials science is more and more recognized, opening for many applications far beyond displays and related devices.[5] CNC thus appears to be a uniquely attractive nanomaterial, from the scale of the individual nanorod to the bulk macroscopic phase, with few—if any—competitors that cover such a broad spectrum. At the same time, many aspects remain poorly understood, especially from a physics/physical chemistry perspective, turning CNC research into a highly fertile ground for liquid crystal scientists.

This chapter aims to introduce the field of CNC research, with a particular emphasis on the liquid crystal science aspects. In recent years a number of excellent reviews of the nanocellulose field have appeared,[6–14] most of which focus on the chemical engineering aspects. We encourage readers to consult these for more details.

2. Raw materials, extraction procedure and variability in CNC characteristics

Cellulose nanocrystals have been isolated from an extensive variety of cellulosic sources, including wood, bacteria, algae and tunicate.[15–19] The process starts with purification and homogenization pretreatments, followed by separation and removal of the more accessible defect-rich regions to liberate rodlike crystalline cellulose sections. The pretreatment of wood and other plants involves the removal of matrix materials such as hemicelluloses and lignin, using chemical and/or mechanical processes. The pretreatment for bacterial cellulose consists mainly in the removal of bacteria and other media from the suspension. When the cellulose source is algae, the pretreatment ensures the removal of algal wall matrix material. For tunicate, finally, the pretreatment involves the isolation of the mantel formed by highly crystalline cellulose microfibrils (tunicin) and the removal of the protein matrix.[12,20,21] The cellulose source has a major impact on the dimensions of the final CNC rods, as summarized in Table 1.

Table 1. Length and width (nm) of CNC from different cellulose sources, all extracted using H_2SO_4 hydrolysis.

	Length (nm)	Width (nm)	Reference
Wood pulp	100-300	3-10	9, 18-20
Bacterial cellulose	500-2000	20-70	5, 10
Tunica	1000	10-80	10, 21
Cotton	100-400	5-10	10, 21-23

The isolation of the nanocrystals can be performed by mechanical treatment, enzymatic hydrolysis or acid hydrolysis,[22-24] the latter being the most common. Different strong acids, e.g., hydrochloric acid, sulfuric acid, nitric acid, phosphoric acid, hydrobromic acid, and mixtures of organic acids, have been reported to successfully release crystalline cellulosic nanoparticles.[14] The choice of acid used during hydrolysis has a major effect on the surface properties of the nanocrystals; crystals produced with hydrochloric acid (HCl) exhibit poor colloidal stability, because HCl leaves the CNC surface with uncharged OH-groups.[25] In contrast, sulfuric acid (H_2SO_4) hydrolysis is very effective, introducing sulfate half-ester groups at the CNC surface[26] which ensure good colloidal stability in aqueous media. Also the ratio of acid to cellulose during hydrolysis is important for controlling the properties.[16] For instance, with a five-fold increase of the volume of sulfuric acid for the same amount of cotton cellulose source, Honorato-Rios *et al.*[27] raised the resulting CNC surface charge from 23 mmol kg^{-1} to 37 mmol kg^{-1}.

3. Current understanding of liquid crystalline phase behavior of CNC suspensions

The vast majority of investigations of the liquid crystalline phase behavior of CNC suspensions has dealt with aqueous suspensions of CNC with charged surface groups, produced via, in most cases, H_2SO_4 hydrolysis. There is thus a strong emphasis on this class of CNC suspension in the following summary. Various methods are now available, however, for converting CNC to be compatible with other solvents (see Sec. 5), suggesting that we may soon see more data on suspensions in organic solvents. The existing reports already hint at some very interesting differences between aqueous and non-aqueous dispersion, hence this is an exciting field for future research.

3.1. *From cholesteric-isotropic phase coexistence to non-equilibrium kinetic arrest*

Many studies have been devoted to establish the phase behavior of CNC suspensions of different types in the low-concentration regime where the suspensions go from isotropic phase around 1 wt%, via biphasic cholesteric-isotropic coexistence from some 3-5 wt% to $\sim 6 - 10$ wt%, beyond which the system is fully liquid crystalline. Because the mass fraction of CNC (with density greater than water) is higher in the liquid crystal than in the isotropic phase (see Chap. 2), the former separates from the latter if a vial in the two-phase regime is left standing for some time, on the order of days, cf. Fig. 1. While the phase separation can be detected rather soon, it can be a matter of months until equilibrium is reached, hence an early inspection will frequently overestimate the fraction of liquid crystalline phase.[28] Longer rods preferentially fractionate to the liquid crystal phase, while shorter reside primarily in the isotropic fraction, as already noted by Gray and co-workers.[23]

It is important to realize that only a small fraction of the liquid crystal phase diagram of aqueous CNC suspensions has been experimentally investigated.[9] This is because the same feature of CNC that is key to the

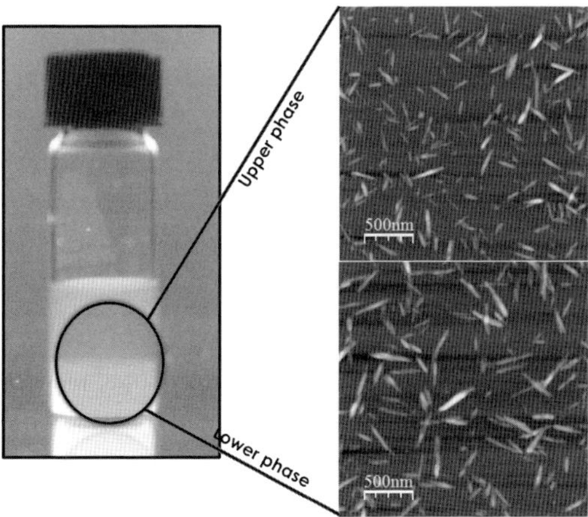

Fig. 1. Gravity-driven macroscopic phase separation in a 5 wt% suspension of cotton-derived CNC, in the two-phase regime of its phase diagram, the lower-density isotropic fraction residing on top of the higher-density cholesteric fraction. On the right, Atomic Force Microscopy images of the rods extracted from each fraction are shown, revealing the expected fractionation between longer rods in the liquid crystalline fraction and shorter in the isotropic one. Source: C. Honorato-Rios.

liquid crystal formation at low mass fraction—the slender rod shape—also promotes kinetic arrest into a non-equilibrium state, recognized through its gel-like appearance, already at an overall mass fraction of some 10-20 wt%. While there are indications that the local mass fraction can be much higher at the onset of kinetic arrest,[29] it is in practice very challenging to explore the equilibrium phase diagram at high CNC content. This is why most studies have focused on the low-concentration equilibrium range dominated by cholesteric-isotropic coexistence. Sometimes kinetic arrest sets in before the whole system is cholesteric but in many cases there is a window of some 5 wt% of complete cholesteric behavior that can be investigated.

From a liquid crystal characterization point of view, the kinetic arrest is clearly a nuisance, as it severely limits the range in which we can study the equilibrium phase diagram experimentally. However, from an application point of view, this tendency to 'freeze' the self-assembled cholesteric structure prior to any other phase transition, most conspicuously crystallization of the macroscopic phase, is in fact extremely valuable. It is thanks to the kinetic arrest that dry films can be produced after evaporating the solvent that fully retain the self-assembled structure, at least on a qualitative level. This is in stark contrast to surfactant-based lyotropic liquid crystals, with which it is much more difficult to harvest the self-assembled structure in form of any durable solvent-free material. We will come back to this aspect at the end of this chapter. First, we will discuss the considerable differences in terms of phase diagram and kinetic arrest that are found depending on CNC source and production method.

3.2. *Effect of CNC dimensions and surface charge on the thresholds for liquid crystallinity and kinetic arrest*

The various thresholds in mass (volume) fraction, w_0 (ϕ_0) for initial phase separation, w_1 (ϕ_1) for complete liquid crystallinity, and w_k (ϕ_k) for kinetic arrest, depend strongly on CNC aspect ratio and surface charge. As motivated in Chap. 2, basic Onsager theory suggests that $w_0(\phi_0)$ and $w_1(\phi_1)$ should be inversely proportional to the aspect ratio of the suspended rods.[30] This prediction often finds support in experimental data, at least qualitatively, when comparing different CNC, derived from e.g. wood,[4,31,32] cotton,[23,33] bacteria[7,18,34] and tunicate.[21,35]

Cellulose nanocrystals derived from bacterial cellulose and tunicin have significantly larger rod aspect ratios than other CNC, in the range of 50-150, and onset concentrations of liquid crystallinity below $w \sim 0.5$ wt% have been reported.[18,21,34] Araki *et al.* reported extraordinarily low values for $w_0 \approx 0.1$ wt% as well as $w_k \approx 1.5$ wt% for bacterial cellulose with an aspect ratio of about 100.[34] The threshold w_1 for complete liquid crystallinity could be estimated by extrapolation to ~ 1.7 wt%, but no data points were given, as this was already in the practical non-equilibrium range. In contrast, CNC from wood, cotton or paper, often with an aspect ratio in the range of 10-50, requires a substantially greater mass fraction to reach any of the thresholds. Using CNC derived from wood pulp, Schütz and co-workers[28] could study the complete biphasic regime with volume fractions ϕ between 1.7 and 5.2 vol% (between 2.5 wt.% and 8.0 wt%), as well as a small range of fully developed cholesteric order until kinetic arrest set in around $\phi \approx 6.5$ vol% (about 10 wt%).

Also polydispersity appears to have a strong impact. For CNC obtained from filter paper hydrolysis, with aspect ratio in the range of 13-50, Dong *et al.* reported a biphasic regime in the range 5-13 wt%,[33] whereas Shafiei-Sabet *et al.* found the biphasic region of their wood-derived CNC with aspect ratio in the narrower range of 13-20 to be 3-7 wt%.[36] As mentioned above, longer CNC rods appear to accumulate in the anisotropic phase and the shorter rods in the isotropic fraction.[18,23] This type of liquid crystal-driven rod fractionation has been used successfully to fractionate carbon nanotubes.[37]

Beck-Candanedo *et al.*[16] varied the H_2SO_4 hydrolysis time in preparation of CNC from black spruce, thereby tuning the rod aspect ratio between 23 and 31, finding a corresponding variation in w_0 between 7 wt% and 5 wt%, qualitatively in line with the Onsager predictions. However, the relation appears to be the opposite when comparing with the data of Shafiei-Sabet *et al.*,[36] which was also based on sulfuric acid-hydrolyzed black spruce CNC, with a low value of $w_0 \approx 3$ wt% despite their aspect ratio of only 13-20. What such a discrepancy demonstrates is that there are many aspects that need to be considered in order to understand the phase behavior of CNC.

Variations in surface charge will also influence the phase behavior. In the study of Beck-Candanedo *et al.*, the nanocrystals with higher aspect ratio also showed lower surface charge density, a result of the shorter hydrolysis time. In principle a high surface charge density means a greater effective volume fraction ϕ for the same mass fraction w, since the electrostatic repulsion yields an excluded volume that is greater than the physical volume of the cellulose itself. However, the matter is complicated by the fact that the charged CNC also brings with it counter ions into solution, increasing the ionic strength and thus leading to greater screening of the electric charge, which reduces the electrostatic effect on the excluded volume. This also means that the ϕ/w ratio decreases as more CNC is added to the suspension. Because of this latter aspect one almost never sees, in the biphasic regime of CNC suspensions, the linear increase predicted by Onsager for the liquid crystal–to–isotropic sample fraction as the CNC mass fraction is increased.[33]

When sulfuric acid was used during the CNC preparation, it has been reported that the sulfation degree of CNC has an important effect on w_0/ϕ_0 and on w_k/ϕ_k.[38,39] With more sulfate groups, the CNC has a tendency to develop a liquid crystalline phase at lower concentrations, a trend we can relate to the increased effective rod volume that comes with the increased surface charge. Note that the effect on aspect ratio, which would promote the opposite effect since the increase in effective radius r_{eff} leads to decreased aspect ratio, is dwarfed by the former effect because the change in aspect ratio scales as r_{eff} whereas the change in volume scales as r_{eff}^2. Shafiei *et al.*[36] studied the influence of the degree of sulfation on the rheology of wood derived CNC suspensions for a broad concentration range using two different acid-to-pulp ratios in order to increase the sulfate group content. The produced rods had similar dimensions with aspect ratios in the range of 10-20, giving the possibility to independently examine the effects of surface charge on the suspensions. With CNC produced with a higher acid-to-pulp ratio, thus with greater surface charge, $w_0 \approx 3$ wt% and $w_k \approx 12$ wt%, respectively. When using less acid, the onset concentration to liquid crystallinity increased to $w_0 \approx 4$ wt% but the onset concentration of kinetic arres decreased to $w_k \approx 10$ wt%.

3.3. *Effect of added salts on the thresholds for liquid crystallinity and kinetic arrest*

As just mentioned, the linear increase predicted by Onsager for the volume fraction of the cholesteric phase as the CNC mass fraction is increased within the biphasic regime is almost never seen in practice, as the CNC addition affects the ionic strength. This effect was elegantly circumvented in a study by Dong *et al.*,[33] where they added hydrochloric acid at different concentration for different CNC mass fraction, calculated as to yield a constant concentration of counterions throughout the entire biphasic region. In this way, the ionic strength during the phase separation remained constant, and a linear dependency between cholesteric volume fraction and cellulose mass fraction was in fact obtained.

In general, the effect of the ionic strength and its influence on the phase separation can be well investigated by adding electrolytes to CNC suspensions.[33,34,40] For a fix total mass fraction of CNC produced from filter paper, the threshold w_0 increased from $\sim$5 wt% to $\sim$8 wt% as the concentration of added NaCl increased to 2 mM. Hirai *et al.*[18] also reported an increase in w_0 for bacterial CNC with addition of an electrolyte (0 to 5.0 mM). Dong and Gray[41] reported a detailed study on the influence of counterions (H^+, Na^+, K^+ and Cs^+). A cholesteric phase was formed with all different counterions, but w_0 depended on the counterion associated to the surface of cellulose nanocrystals. For identical w ($> w_0$ for all samples) the cholesteric volume fraction decreased in the order $H^+ > Na^+ > K^+ > Cs^+$.

One study[42] using mono- and divalent counter ions concluded that the divalent Ca^{2+} present more negative influence on the colloidal stability of CNC suspensions than monovalent Na^+, which was attributed to the stronger screening effect and specific adsorption of Ca^{2+} on the CNC surface. It could, however, also be due to a kind of 'crosslinking' effect, which only occurs for di-or trivalent ions (this effect was studied in the formation of hydrogels[43]). Dong and Grey[41] concluded that the divalent counterions Ca^{2+} and Ba^{2+} are very efficient in inducing kinetic arrest and thus effectively counteracting liquid crystal formation.

4. Chirality transfer in CNC suspensions

While it is clear that the origin of chirality of the lyotropic cholesteric phases formed by CNC suspensions is the cellulose, it is far from obvious *how* the transfer of chirality from asymmetric carbons in the molecule structure to the macroscopic scale of the liquid crystal phase occurs. It appears that the mechanism of chirality transfer involves multiple steps, the first being a geometric effect where the CNC nanorod acquires a uniformly right-handed twisted morphology,[a] as recently confirmed by careful AFM studies on wood-derived CNC.[44] Earlier the same right-handed twist was observed in CNC derived from tunicate.[45] Apparently this twisted morphology is then transferred to the helical modulation of the macroscopic phase (which, notably, has the opposite handedness compared to the twist of individual rods, left- rather than right-handed).

---

[a]It should be mentioned, however, that only in 5-10% of 100 investigated particles the twist could be clearly visualized in the cited study.

At the moment one can only speculate about the exact mechanism of this latter transfer, where steric interactions between twisted rods is an obvious possibility. But also the directional modulation of the electrostatic repulsion along the twisted rod may be important, at least when using electrostatically stabilized CNC in water. Hydrogen bond networks in the water may also participate in the transfer of chirality. Considering that the average separation distance between rods is about 40 nm at w_0,[28] where fingerprint patterns due to the helical modulation can clearly be detected, it seems reasonable to assume that some long-range interaction is involved. Below we will discuss CNC dispersion in non-aqueous solvents, and it turns out that also then cholesteric phases develop, possibly indicating that the steric effect dominates, at least in the high-CNC-mass fraction regime studied in those cases.

All experimental studies report a pitch decrease with increasing CNC content. This trend has been confirmed for multiple cellulose sources, including bacteria, cotton, filter paper and wood.[18,28,33,46,47] When, in a wood derived CNC suspension, the CNC content was increased from 7 wt% to 13 wt%, the pitch decreased from ∼20 μm to ∼10 μm.[16] In all these cases, however, the CNC is electrostatically charged and thus the change in CNC mass fraction also changes the ionic strength. It is thus not obvious that the pitch decrease is simply a result of increasing concentration of chiral material, but it may also be related to varying electrostatic screening effects.

An indication that electrostatic interactions are important for the chirality transfer from rod to phase is the fact that the ionic strength of the solvent clearly affects the helical modulation, leading to a pitch in cholesteric CNC suspensions that continuously changes, even within the biphasic regime.[28] This is in direct contrast to the case of cholesteric collagen suspensions, not bearing any electric charge on the surface, where the pitch is independent of concentration until 100% liquid crystallinity is reached.[48] Within the tactoids in the biphasic regime the rod concentration is not expected to change with overall CNC mass fraction, hence the cellulose content within a local liquid crystal phase does not change. It is the total fraction of liquid crystal in the overall sample that increases as the CNC fraction is raised within the biphasic regime. Therefore, the changing pitch within this regime suggests that it is the increasing concentration of counter ions as more CNC is added that drives the pitch change.

An even more clearcut demonstration of the influence of the electrostatic repulsion on the chirality transfer is the strong change in helix pitch upon addition of salt at constant CNC content.[33,34] In suspensions of CNC derived from bacterial cellulose, addition of NaCl resulted in a decrease of the pitch from $\sim$16.5 μm to $\sim$12 μm as the concentration of electrolyte increased to $\sim$1 mM.[18] Surprisingly, in that study the pitch versus electrolyte concentration trend reversed for higher concentrations, and the final values of $\sim$19 μm were reached at an NaCl concentration of 2.0 mM. An explanation of this non-monotonic behavior has not been proposed.

The change in counter ion concentration immediately affects the range of electrostatic repulsion but indirectly it affects, in fact, also the steric interactions. As discussed by Araki and Kuga,[34] the electrostatic repulsion creates a 'padding' around each rod of excluded volume, which may 'hide' the twisted rod morphology to some extent, thus leading to more effective chirality transfer at high ionic strength, whether achieved by increasing the CNC concentration or by adding other ions. Indeed, both options reduce the measured pitch, as described in some more detail in the following overview of available experimental data.

Also the geometrical characteristics of the CNC rods seem to play an important role for the helical twisting. Beck-Candanedo *et al.*[16] found that the pitch increases as the length of the rods increases in suspensions having the same CNC content. For spruce-derived CNC, as the average length increased from $\sim$100 nm to $\sim$140 nm (with aspect ratio in the range of 23-31), the pitch at the same cellulose mass fraction rose from 7 μm to 18 μm. Therefore, it was concluded that longer rods exhibit less tendency to develop the twisted chiral nematic structure, although—as will be emphasized in a moment—the experimental data unfortunately do not allow a clearcut conclusion.

At present this is a purely empirical observation without any proposed explanation for the effect. One may speculate that the greater rod length affects the elastic constants of the phase, rendering twist less favorable, or that defects in the twisted morphology of individual long rods may counteract efficient chirality transfer. This is clearly an important topic for future research, where computer simulations may be particularly revealing, as this allows tuning of only a single parameter at a time, which is very difficult to achieve in experiments. For instance, the increase in rod length in the study of Beck-Candanedo *et al.* coincided with a decrease in surface charge, as a result of the modified production procedure, which affects geometrical properties as well as the concentration of charged surface groups. With decreasing surface charge the concentration of counter ions is reduced, hence the 'padding' about each rod is greater, and then also the Araki–Kuga explanation might apply for the greater pitch for longer rods. This means that it may in fact not be so much the different rod length, but rather the different surface charge that is key to the difference in pitch. Even worse, it is not clarified what effect CNC length polydispersity has on the CNC pitch, and also this will vary when preparing CNC with different lengths, as done in the study by Beck-Candanedo *et al.* Typically, the shorter the average rod length, the lower the polydispersity. This example highlights the difficulty in carrying out systematic studies concerning structure–property relations for CNC.

Comparing CNC from two different cellulose sources, wood (aspect ratio 20-40) and bacterial cellulose (aspect ratio 50-90), the wood derived CNC presented a pitch of 15 μm compared to bacterial cellulose with a pitch of 16.5 μm. The concentration of both suspensions was 3 wt%.[4,18] The authors did not publish the surface charge in these cases.

One should point out that it is not trivial to achieve reliable pitch data in CNC suspensions, because a single sample often shows a considerable variation of pitch throughout its volume. In fact, there is not a great deal of data available on equilibrium pitch of CNC suspensions, and most data are based on microscopy observation of suspensions filled into glass capillaries. It appears that the capillary walls can have a considerable effect both on orientation of the helix and the actual pitch length, thereby constituting a considerable potential source of errors. Schütz *et al.*[28] recently conducted a combined laser and x-ray scattering study of the helix pitch in suspensions of wood-derived CNC, finding considerably smaller pitch values than in many earlier reports, changing from about 15 μm to 2 μm as the CNC fraction was changed from $\phi \approx 2.5$ vol% to $\phi \approx 6.5$ vol% (from ~ 4wt% to ~ 10wt%).

5. Dispersion of CNC in non-aqueous media

While CNC suspensions are typically prepared with water as solvent, there are many other solvents which are capable, in principle, of supporting the formation of lyotropic liquid crystalline phases.[49] It is known from various lyotropic systems, that the choice of solvent may significantly alter the phase behavior as well as the properties of the liquid crystal.[50–55] In regard to this, two intriguing questions arise: first, is it possible to disperse CNC effectively, and at sufficient concentration to form a lyotropic liquid crystal phase, in solvents other than water, possibly after appropriate surface modification? And, second, does the change of solvent then influence the macroscopic properties of the CNC suspension?

The main focus has so far been on the dispersion of CNC in non-polar solvents, which is particularly challenging. The sulfate half-ester groups resulting from H_2SO_4-based extraction, which are so useful for aqueous dispersion, are of no help if the water is replaced with a nonpolar organic solvent. The surface groups are generally not ionized, as the weak electrostatic screening in a low dielectric permittivity solvent leads to counter ion condensation, incapacitating the electrostatic repulsion mechanism. The situation is further aggravated by the inability of many organic solvent molecules to be a good hydrogen-bonding partner, resulting in strong attraction between the cellulose particles, with a consequent rapid aggregation that prevents the formation of a colloidal suspension.

This non-dispersability of CNC in non-polar organic solvents is a regrettable restriction, considering the potential for using CNC as a renewable resource in the development of composite materials,[56–59] many of which would involve components that are not soluble or dispersible in water. In an attempt to enhance their versatility as functional nanomaterial and thereby to vastly broaden their application range, several investigations have thus been devoted to identifying appropriate surface modification schemes for making CNC compatible with organic solvents.[8,60,61] Two general approaches can be distinguished, where the CNC surface is modified by an appropriately designed molecule, often a polymer of low molar mass, either by physical adsorption or by grafting (covalent attachment), cf. Fig. 2.

Starting with the physical adsorption approach, Heux *et al.*[63] demonstrated stable dispersion in cyclohexane and toluene of CNC produced using H_2SO_4 hydrolysis followed by adsorption of an ethoxylated phosphoric ester of nonylphenol with the commercial name BNA (Fig. 2a), acting as surfactant. In both organic solvents, they could reach a concentration sufficient to develop a cholesteric phase. A subsequent study[67] investigated systematically the influence of the CNC aspect ratio on the liquid crystalline phase diagram in non-polar solvents, finding that, similar to observations in aqueous dispersions, the pitch increased with increasing aspect ratio. As expected, the onset concentration increases with decreasing aspect ratio. Zhou *et al.*[66] demonstrated successful dispersion in toluene of CNC modified by adsorbed xyloglucan oligosaccharide-poly(ethylene glycol)-polystyrene triblock copolymer (Fig. 2b). Adsorption of quarternery ammonium salts (Fig. 2c) onto CNC bearing carboxylic groups[68] has also been used to prepare stable dispersions in toluene.[64]

For chemical modification the functional surface groups introduced by the acid hydrolysis-based extraction process are key, the unmodified hy-

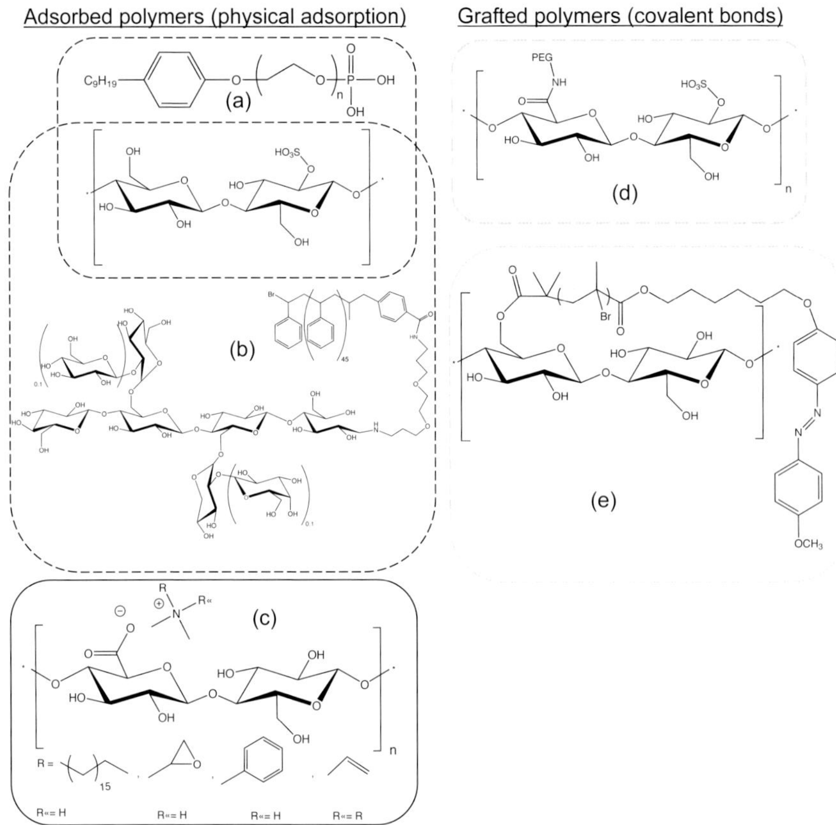

Fig. 2. Schematic representation of CNC modifications via polymer adsorption (a-c) and polymer grafting (d and e), allowing suspension in organic solvents with formation of liquid crystalline phase.[62–66] CNCs are derived from sulfuric acid hydrolysis (dashed boxes) and via TEMPO-mediated oxidation with subsequent hydrochloric acid hydrolysis (continuous line). See main text for further details.

droxyl groups resulting from HCl extraction being a convenient starting point. A post treatment by chlorosilanes, halogenated acetic acids, isocyanates or epoxides can then be used to introduce silylated, carboxymethylated, urethane linkages or ethers, respectively, onto the CNC surface.[8,60] Araki and coworkers[62] sterically stabilized the CNC with poly(ethylene glycol) (PEG) bound via an amide to the surface of the CNC (Fig. 2d), allowing dispersion in chloroform. Xu *et al.*[65] reported the polymer-modified CNC in Fig. 2e, finding lyotropic liquid crystal formation in chlorobenzene, and even thermotropic liquid crystalline behavior.

The common use of surfactants for dispersing CNC in nonpolar solvents results in a three-component system, making it difficult to compare directly with conventional CNC/water suspensions. In case of dispersion in polar but non-aqueous solvents, which do not necessarily require further functionalization of the CNC or the addition of surfactants, a more immediate comparision is possible. However, also this type of solvent exchange is not trivial. Due to the preparation process, CNC is always suspended in water to start with. Therefore, the first step of preparing non-aqueous CNC suspensions is to replace the water. As a simple thermal evaporation of the solvent leads to agglomeration of the CNC rods, making it impossible to redisperse them in other solvents, two main protocols have been explored for replacing the water. The first one is to freeze-dry the aqueous CNC suspension followed by a redispersion of the CNC in the desired solvent.[57] The second approach is to perform a solvent exchange by repeated centrifugation, removal of the supernatant solvent and redispersion in the non-aqueous solvent.[69] A comperative study performed by Tian *et al.*[70] applied both methods to aqueous CNC suspensions of the same source. Redispersion of the CNC in the polar solvent DMSO as well as the apolar solvent toluene showed that the solvent exchange method seems to be the preferable one, because freeze drying still leads to some CNC agglomeration.

A second important issue for the dispersion of CNC in non-aqueous solvents is the previous treatment and consequently the state of the CNC surface. Espionsa *et al.*[25] isolated CNC from cotton by acid hydrolysis with hydrochloric acid, sulfuric acid and phosphoric acid and redispersed them in polar (water, DMF, DMSO) and apolar (THF) solvents. They found that dispersion in the apolar solvent THF is not possible with any of the prepared CNC types. For the CNC prepared by hydrolysis with sulfuric or phosphoric acid a good dispersion in all of the polar solvents was detected, whereas the CNC prepared with hydrochloric acid agglomerated in any solvent except DMF. The explanation given by the authors for these differences is that the CNC prepared by hydrolysis with hydrochloric acid exhibits pronounced hydrogen bonding, causing strong interactions between individual CNC nanorods that lead to agglomeration. In contrast, the charged sulfate or phosphate surface groups after hydrolysis with sulfuric or phosphoric acid provide electrostatic stabilization of the CNC suspension also in these non-aqueous but polar solvents.

A further approach to modify the CNC for compatibility with non-aqueous polar solvents is to dissociate the sulfate surface groups by treatment with a base, as was done by Cheung *et al.*[71] The authors found that CNC treated in this way readily disperses in polar organic solvents, such as DMSO, formamide, N-methylformamide and DMF, whereas untreated CNC precipitated within minutes. Their explanation for this observation was that the neutralization decreased inter-particle hydrogen bonding, yielding more efficient dispersion of the treated CNC. But they went one step further by also considering the influence of the solvent, concluding that solvents capable of forming strong hydrogen bonds are more favorable for the dispersion of the base treated CNC than non-hydrogen bonding solvents.

The influence of the solvent on the dispersibility of modified and unmodified CNC was investigated by Blachechen *et al.*[56] by using ethyl acetate, DMF and THF as solvents. Based on the observed good dispersion of CNC in DMF, they concluded that a high relative permittivity as well as a high viscosity of the solvent is favorable for an effective suspension, as both factors decrease the probability of CNC aggregation. Okura *et al.*[72] investigated the dispersibility of CNC in 21 different polar and apolar organic solvents by looking for shear-induced birefringence in the samples. Also these authors found some correlation between good CNC dispersibility and high relative permittivity and high viscosity of the solvent. However, this rule did not apply strictly to all investigated solvents. They detected a clearer correlation with the acceptor and donor numbers of the solvents which indicate the Lewis acidity or basicity of the solvents, respectively. Only solvents with large acceptor and donor numbers, which are usually called amphoteric solvents, are able to form suspensions of pristine CNC. The reason for this is a strong interaction of the solvents with the hydroxyl groups on the CNC surface.

A good dispersibility of freeze-dried CNC in DMF, DMSO and formamide was observed by Viet *et al.*[73] However, upon the addition of 4Å mole sieve to extract any excess water the suspensions started to precipitate. Thus, the authors proposed that traces of water within the suspensions might be helpful for the stability of CNC in non-aqueous suspensions.

Coming to the question of how the liquid crystal phase properties are affected by the solvent exchange, not too much data exist. It is primarily CNC dispersed in nonpolar organic solvents that has been investigated in this respect. The first striking observation when comparing the few published studies on these systems with those on aqueous CNC suspensions, is the much higher threshold values $w_0(\phi_0)$, $w_1(\phi_1)$ and apparently also $w_k(\phi_k)$. For the latter we are not aware of any published direct measurements, but we can infer indirectly from the high reported mass fractions for equilibrium phases that $w_k(\phi_k)$ must be very high. In the study by Elazzouzi-Hafraoui *et al.*[67] involving cotton-based CNC compatibilized for dispersion in cyclohexane using surfactant (Fig. 2a), w_0 values between 16 and 21 wt% and w_1 values between 32 and 40 wt% were reported. Surprisingly, according to the earlier paper by the same team,[63] where the equilibrium liquid crystal range was reported to lie between $w_0 \approx 32$ wt% and $w_1 \approx 37$ wt%, birefringence could easily be shear-induced already at concentrations of about 1 wt% or lower. This is indeed remarkable considering that the CNC mass fraction was about 1/30 of the threshold value for spontaneous cholesteric phase formation.

The cholesteric pitch reported for these systems[67] was on the order of a few microns, decreasing from about 6 μm at $w_0 \approx 21$ wt% to less than 3 μm at $w_1 \approx 40$ wt% for a CNC type with average rod length just above 100 nm, and an aspect ratio of about 7. For longer rods they reported substantially shorter pitch values than the corresponding short-rod CNC towards the isotropic side of the biphasic regime, whereas the pitch values were more similar towards the completely liquid crystalline end. The authors write that these pitch values are much shorter than in aqueous suspension, but this comparison is somewhat misleading. First, because the pitch values they report as typical for aqueous suspension are remarkably high, an order of magnitude greater than the data by Schütz *et al.*,[28] for aqueous suspension, second, because the cyclohexane dispersion contains an order of magnitude more CNC than the corresponding aqueous system, and it is, after all, the CNC that is the source of chirality. The pitch of cyclohexane-suspended CNC at w_1 reported by Elazzouzi-Hafraoui *et al.*[67] is about 1.5 times smaller than that of water-suspended CNC at w_1 reported by Schütz *et al.*,[28] which must be considered a rather small difference considering that the former value was obtained for 8 times as much cellulose in the system.

What is also of considerable interest in the study by Elazzouzi-Hafraoui *et al.*[67] is that the pitch is reported to decrease continuously throughout the biphasic regime, in contrast to the case of collagen studied by Mosser *et al.*[48] This is mysterious, as the variation of CNC mass fraction in cyclohexane suspension does not lead to changed effective rod appearance, as in the case of aqueous systems where the ionic strength and consequent electrostatic screening is affected, as discussed above. Yet the mass fraction of CNC in a cholesteric tactoid should not—as already mentioned—change within the biphasic regime, leaving this concentration dependence of the pitch in the cyclohexane suspensions unexplained.

Zhou *et al.* investigated the pitch for CNC dispersed in toluene with the aid of xyloglucan oligosaccharide-poly(ethylene glycol)-polystyrene triblock copolymer (Fig. 2b) for a single sample with a CNC mass fraction of 11 wt%. They found a considerably longer pitch of about 17 μm.[66] compared to the one reported by Elazzouzi-Hafraoui *et al.*[67]

For the case of non-aqueous polar solvents, the question of liquid crystalline phase behavior of CNC remains largely unanswered at the present date. Up to now only the dispersibility and not the properties of the suspensions were investigated. This is an interesting and challenging task for future research.

6. Drying CNC suspensions into solid photonic crystal films

Pure CNC films with a helical internal arrangement of the rod-like cellulose nanoparticles can be obtained by drying a CNC suspension. As mentioned in the beginning of this chapter, the fact that the system is kinetically arrested during evaporation of the solvent long before any transition to a macroscopic crystal phase sets in, ensures that the self-assembled cholesteric liquid crystal helical order persists all the way until the film is fully dry, a most beneficial property of CNC suspensions. The pitch is reduced through the drying process to the submicron range, thus giving the final film striking iridescent Bragg reflection, see Fig. 3. As attractive as this property of

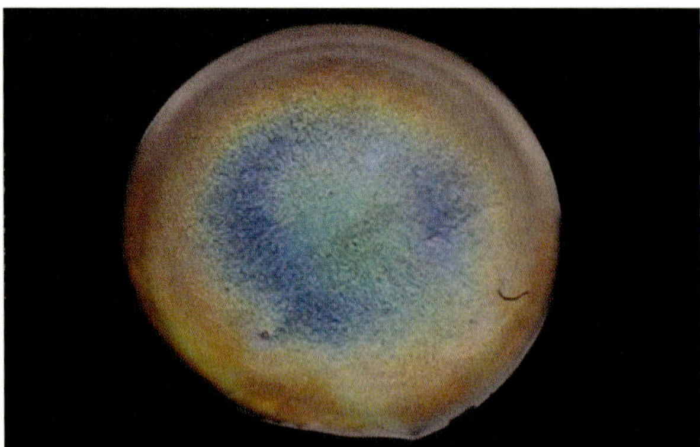

Fig. 3.   Iridescent colors (as seen by the naked eye, without crossed polarizers; the film is on a black table) from a 25 mm diameter CNC film, obtained by drying a droplet of a liquid crystalline suspension on a circular cover glass slide. The radial variation in color shows that the structure is not homogeneous across the film.

CNC films is, the local variations in color show that the control of the final structure is not yet sufficient for use in concrete applications. In this case the helix orientation was quite uniformly vertical (obtained by using a fully liquid crystalline CNC suspension at the start; see the following section) but a uniform structure throughout the film was not achieved, resulting in the variations from long to short to longer reflection wavelengths, going from the edge to the center of the film.

Dried CNC films are usually obtained by drop casting or spin coating and then removing the water by evaporation. During the evaporation the volume of the CNC suspension decreases and the CNC volume fraction increases, which rather soon results in kinetic arrest at the surface of the drop, yielding a thin gel-like film along the top in which the rod-like particles are locked in a non-equilibrium state. The arrangement of this state can be amorphous or ordered depending on the history as well as on the properties of the initial CNC suspension.[9] Dumanli *et al.* used an elegant method based on measuring the reflectance value at the CNC suspension–air interface to monitor the CNC volume fraction during drying, finding the surprisingly high value of about 40% at the onset of kinetic arrest.[29]

In our recent review on the physics of CNC suspensions[9] we pointed out that the equilibrium and non-equilibrium stages of the drying process must be considered separately in order to gain control of the reflection color of the final film. This view was confirmed by recent studies by Mu and Gray[74] and by Dumanli *et al.*,[29] who independently demonstrated that at least two separate stages can be identified in the drying process. Each stage influences the final pitch of the film. In a first stage, as the bulk suspension is in an equilibrium cholesteric phase (a thin top layer may already be kinetically arrested), the pitch decreases continuously as the volume fraction of CNC increases due to the evaporation of the solvent. Mu and Gray demonstrated that shortening the pitch within this equilibrium stage does not necessarily give the same result for the final dried film. They added glucose to the CNC suspension, which turned out to reduce the equilibrium pitch, but it also reduced w_k, thus limiting the range in which the equilibrium cholesteric pitch could shrink with increasing CNC content. The end result was a dry film with *longer* pitch than without the glucose addition, clearly demonstrating the importance of equilibrium pitch as well as kinetic arrest in determining the structure of the final CNC film.

Via in-situ spectroscopic monitoring, Dumanli *et al.* showed that the pitch first decreases relatively rapidly from a value of several microns to a stage where the reflection wavelength is in the green (in their particular experiment), after which the pitch continuous to decrease for another five hours or so, but at a much reduced rate. The authors did not discuss an interpretation of this process in detail, but it could be that the rapid decrease represents the equilibrium cholesteric phase whereas the much slower decrease reflects a phase when the kinetically arrested state permeates throughout the bulk. Finally, they detected a discontinuous reduction in reflection color by some 50-70 nm, after which no further change took place. The authors explained the final jump with the change in average refractive index as the final water leaves the sample. As the CNC cannot collapse entirely from the state frozen-in during kinetic arrest, the final film contains voids in which the refractive index reduces from the $n \approx 1.3$ of water to $n = 1$ of air.

An ongoing debate remains concerning the radial color variation in the dry films. Surprisingly, in Fig. 3 a blue-reflecting ring and thus the smallest pitch is found at an intermediate distance between the center and the edge of the film. At the center a green reflection is found, revealing a slightly longer pitch, whereas at the edge red reflection is observed. Even if the reason for the colour variation is not clear, the red-shift towards the outside may be due to the more rapid evaporation of the thinnest part of the initial droplet which thus first enters into the glassy state.[75]

There is a clear need for continued careful studies of the drying process similar to that of Dumanli *et al.*, where temperature and humidity are both controlled and the reflection wavelength spectrum is continuously monitored throughout the process. The analysis is complicated by the concentration gradient in the film during the drying, the topmost regime losing water the fastest and thus entering the kinetically arrested state early, while the bulk is still in the equilibrium state. Beyond this point, further evaporation of the water is slowed down, as the water from the bulk must diffuse through the gel-like top film. There are several indications that the temperature during drying can be used to tune the final film color[29,32] but the understanding of how it influences the process is yet incomplete.

7. Techniques to control the orientation of the cholesteric helix in CNC suspensions and dried films

In most attempts to apply the self-assembled helical order of CNC suspensions, a uniform orientation of the helix, and preferably also a means to choose this orientation, is required. In many studies, care has not been taken to ensure this, and as a result, films prepared by drying a suspension exhibit a mosaic texture reflecting a separation into domains with random helix orientations. Two approaches have been demonstrated to provide the necessary control of helix orientation, either using a magnetic field or by relying on the top and bottom interfaces of a fully liquid crystalline droplet to impose a uniform vertical helix alignment.

Kimura *et al.*[35] showed in two different experiments that it is possible, on the one hand, to align the helix axis in the magnetic field direction after applying a static magnetic field of at least 1 T over a few hours (Fig. 4) and, on the other hand, to unwind the helix by applying a rotating magnetic field (5 T, 10 rpm). The underlying physical reason for this control of the helix formation is the anisotropic diamagnetic character of CNC (the susceptibility $\chi_\parallel$ parallel to the director $\mathbf{n}$ is smaller than $\chi_\perp$, perpendicular to $\mathbf{n}$), yielding an alignment of the director perpendicular to the field. This means that the cholesteric helix axis must align along the field direction. Placing the sample between crossed polarizers it is easy to see the fingerprint texture, uniformly aligned with the stripes perpendicular to the direction along which the magnetic field was applied. The alignment works best in the lower concentration regime of cholesteric phase formation, which most likely is related to the lower viscosity compared to that of higher concentrated suspensions. In general, the achieved uniform helix orientation may not be stable after taking the suspension out of the magnetic field, as thermal fluctuations may then reorient the helix randomly. The time scale of such

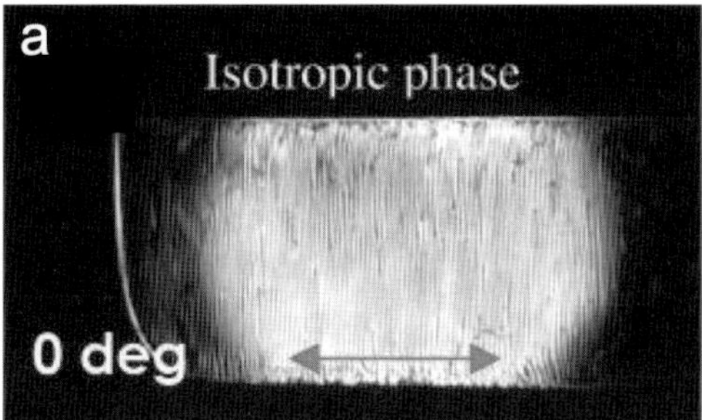

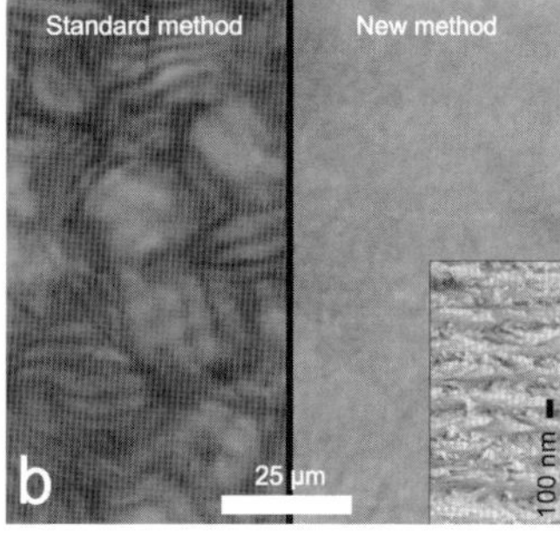

Fig. 4. Two methods of aligning the cholesteric helix uniformly in CNC suspensions. (a) After exposure to to a 12 T magnetic field for 18 h, a fingerprint texture develops in the equilibrium cholesteric phase with stripes perpendicular to the field direction. Reprinted with permission from Ref. 35. Copyright (2005) American Chemical Society. (b) By drying a fully liquid crystalline suspension (right) rather than a suspension starting out in the biphasic regime (left), the helix aligns perpendicular to the film plane, yielding a uniform selective reflection color. The inset shows an electron microscopy image of the fractured film. Copyright (2014) Wiley. Used with permission from Ref. 75.

reorientation is however rather large, typically on the order of several hours, hence magnetic field alignment is certainly a viable approach.

The other approach, presented by Park *et al.*,[75] is much simpler. The authors recognized that the mosaic texture of most CNC films reported in the literature has its origin in the fact that the starting suspension is typically of very low concentration, placing it either in the fully isotropic regime[76–78] of the phase diagram or towards the low-concentration end of the biphasic regime.[32,76,79–81] As a consequence, tactoids will form during the drying process, and as these are surrounded by an isotropic fluid environment, the helix in the tactoid can form in any direction. As tactoids grow during the drying process they eventually meet, but they often do not merge easily,[31,48] as a certain interfacial tension between adjacent tactoids must be overcome. Considering the slow dynamics of CNC suspensions and the relatively fast drying process, a locking-in of the random arrangement of helix axes, coming from nucleation of many different tactoids, takes place, and the final film gets a more or less useless mosaic texture.

By raising the concentration of the starting suspension to w_1, the formation of tactoids is avoided. In this case, the cholesteric phase permeating throughout the droplet is exposed to only two interfaces: to the bottom substrate and to the air above. Both these interfaces promote an alignment of the director $\mathbf{n}$ along the interface. Because we are dealing with large droplets, with diameter on the order of cm, the curvature of the droplet's top surface is negligible and the two interfaces are thus both practically horizontal. As a consequence, the helix aligns perpendicularly to the interfaces, meaning vertically, which is exactly the orientation we desire for photonic applications. This simple procedure removed the mosaic texture and yielded a uniform color over macroscopic areas, cf. Fig. 4.

References

1. B. Rånby, Aqueous colloidal solutions of cellulose micelles, *Acta Chem. Scand.* **3**(5), 649–650 (1949).
2. B. G. Rånby and E. Ribi, Über den feinbau der zellulose, *Experientia.* **VI**(1), 12–14 (1950).
3. R. Marchessault, F. Morehead, and N. Walter, Liquid crystal systems from fibrillar polysaccharides, *Nature* (1959).
4. J. Revol, H. Bradford, J. Giasson, R. Marchessault, and D. Gray, Helicoidal self-ordering of cellulose microfibrils in aqueous suspension, *Int J Biol Macromol.* **14**(3), 170–172 (1992).
5. J. P. F. Lagerwall and G. Scalia, A new era for liquid crystal research: Ap-

plications of liquid crystals in soft matter nano-, bio- and microtechnology, *Curr. Appl. Phys.* **12**(6), 1387–1412 (2012).

6. J. Kelly, M. Giese, K. Shopsowitz, W. Hamad, and M. Maclachlan, The development of chiral nematic mesoporous materials., *Acc Chem Res.* **47**(4), 1088–1096 (2014).

7. Y. Huang, C. Zhu, J. Yang, Y. Nie, C. Chen, and D. Sun, Recent advances in bacterial cellulose, *Cellulose.* **21**(1), 1–30 (2014).

8. Y. Habibi, Key advances in the chemical modification of nanocelluloses., *Chem. Soc. Rev.* **43**(5), 1519–1542 (2014).

9. J. P. F. Lagerwall, C. Schütz, M. Salajkova, J. Noh, J. H. Park, G. Scalia, and L. Bergström, Cellulose nanocrystal-based materials: from liquid crystal self-assembly and glass formation to multifunctional thin films, *NPG Asia Mater.* **6**(1), e80 (2014).

10. D. Klemm, F. Kramer, S. Moritz, T. Lindstrom, M. Ankerfors, D. Gray, and A. Dorris, Nanocelluloses: A new family of nature-based materials, *Angew Chem Int Edit.* **50**(24), 5438–5466 (2011).

11. S. J. Eichhorn, Cellulose nanowhiskers: promising materials for advanced applications, *Soft Matter.* **7**(2), 303–315 (2011).

12. R. Moon, A. Martini, J. Nairn, J. Simonsen, and J. Youngblood, Cellulose nanomaterials review: structure, properties and nanocomposites, *Chem. Soc. Rev.* **40**(7), 3941–3994 (2011).

13. S. Eichhorn, A. Dufresne, M. Aranguren, N. Marcovich, J. Capadona, S. Rowan, C. Weder, W. Thielemans, M. Roman, S. Renneckar, W. Gindl, S. Veigel, J. Keckes, H. Yano, K. Abe, M. Nogi, A. Nakagaito, A. Mangalam, J. Simonsen, A. Benight, A. Bismarck, L. Berglund, and T. Peijs, Review: current international research into cellulose nanofibres and nanocomposites, *J. Mater. Sci.* **45**(1), 1–33 (2010).

14. Y. Habibi, L. Lucia, and O. J. Rojas, Cellulose nanocrystals: Chemistry, self-assembly, and applications, *Chem. Rev.* **110**(6), 3479–3500 (2010).

15. N. van der Wel, C. Putman, S. van Noort, and A. de Grooth, BG Emons, Atomic force microscopy of pollen grains, cellulose microfibrils, and protoplasts, *Protoplasma* (1996).

16. S. Beck-Candanedo, M. Roman, and D. Gray, Effect of reaction conditions on the properties and behavior of wood cellulose nanocrystal suspensions, *Biomacromolecules.* **6**(2), 1048–1054 (2005).

17. A. Bondeson, Daniel Mathew and K. Oksman, Optimization of the isolation of nanocrystals from microcrystalline cellulose by acid hydrolysis, *Cellulose* (2006).

18. A. Hirai, O. Inui, F. Horii, and M. Tsuji, Phase separation behavior in aqueous suspensions of bacterial cellulose nanocrystals prepared by sulfuric acid treatment, *Langmuir.* **25**(1), 497–502 (2009).

19. M. N. Angles and A. Dufresne, Plasticized starch/tunicin whiskers nanocomposites. 1. structural analysis, *Macromolecules.* **33**(22), 8344–8353 (2000).

20. M. Hubbe, O. Rojas, L. Lucia, and M. Sain, Cellulosic nanocomposites: a review, *BioResources.* **3**(3), 929–980 (2008).

21. M. Khandelwal and A. H. Windle, Self-assembly of bacterial and tunicate

cellulose nanowhiskers, *Polymer.* **54**(19), 5199–5206 (2013).

22. Y. Qing, R. Sabo, J. Y. Zhu, U. Agarwal, Z. Cai, and Y. Wu, A comparative study of cellulose nanofibrils disintegrated via multiple processing approaches, *Carbohydr. Polym.* (2013).

23. X. Dong, J. Revol, and D. Gray, Effect of microcrystallite preparation conditions on the formation of colloid crystals of cellulose, *Cellulose.* **5**(1), 19–32 (1998).

24. P. B. Filson, B. E. Dawson-Andoh, and D. Schwegler-Berry, Enzymatic-mediated production of cellulose nanocrystals from recycled pulp, *Green Chemistry* (2009).

25. S. C. Espinosa, T. Kuhnt, E. J. Foster, and C. Weder, Isolation of thermally stable cellulose nanocrystals by phosphoric acid hydrolysis, *Biomacromolecules.* **14**, 1223–1230 (2013).

26. S. Beck, M. Méthot, and J. Bouchard, General procedure for determining cellulose nanocrystal sulfate half-ester content by conductometric titration, *Cellulose.* **22**(1), 101–116 (2015).

27. C. Honorato-Rios, A. Kuhnhold, J. R. Bruckner, R. Dannert, T. Schilling, and J. P. Lagerwall, Equilibrium liquid crystal phase diagrams and detection of kinetic arrest in cellulose nanocrystal suspensions, *Frontiers in Materials*, **3**(21), DOI:10.3389/fmats.2016.00021 (2016).

28. C. Schütz, M. Agthe, A. Fall, K. Gordeyeva, V. Guccini, M. Salajková, T. Plivelic, J. Lagerwall, G. Salazar-Alvarez, and L. Bergström, Rod packing in chiral nematic cellulose nanocrystal dispersions studied by small-angle x-ray scattering and laser diffraction., *Langmuir.* **31**(23), 6507–6513 (2015).

29. A. Dumanli, G. Kamita, J. Landman, H. van der Kooij, B. Glover, J. Baumberg, U. Steiner, and S. Vignolini, Controlled, bio-inspired self-assembly of cellulose-based chiral reflectors., *Adv. Opt. Mater.* **2**(7), 646–650 (2014).

30. L. Onsager, The effects of shape on the interaction of colloidal particles, *Ann. N. Y. Acad. Sci.* **51**(4), 627–659 (1949).

31. J. Revol, L. Godbout, X. Dong, D. Gray, H. Chanzy, and G. Maret, Chiral nematic suspensions of cellulose crystallites - phase-separation and magnetic-field orientation, *Liq. Cryst.* **16**(1), 127–134 (1994).

32. S. Beck, J. Bouchard, G. Chauve, and R. Berry, Controlled production of patterns in iridescent solid films of cellulose nanocrystals, *Cellulose.* **20**(3), 1401–1411 (2013).

33. X. Dong, T. Kimura, J. Revol, and D. Gray, Effects of ionic strength on the isotropic-chiral nematic phase transition of suspensions of cellulose crystallites, *Langmuir.* **12**(8), 2076–2082 (1996).

34. J. Araki and S. Kuga, Effect of trace electrolyte on liquid crystal type of cellulose microcrystals, *Langmuir.* **17**(15), 4493–4496 (2001).

35. F. Kimura, T. Kimura, M. Tamura, A. Hirai, M. Ikuno, and F. Horii, Magnetic alignment of the chiral nematic phase of a cellulose microfibril suspension, *Langmuir.* **21**(5), 2034–2037 (2005).

36. S. Shafiei-Sabet, Y. Hamad, Wadood, and G. Hatzikiriakos, Savvas, Rheology of nanocrystalline cellulose aqueous suspensions, *Langmuir.* **28**(49), 17124–17133 (2012).

37. S. J. Zhang, I. A. Kinloch, and A. H. Windle, Mesogenicity drives fractionation in lyotropic aqueous suspensions of multiwall carbon nanotubes, *Nano. Lett.* **6**(3), 568–572 (2006).

38. M. Bercea and P. Navard, Shear dynamics of aqueous suspensions of cellulose whiskers, *Macromolecules* (2000).

39. W. Orts, L. Godbout, R. Marchessault, and J. Revol, Enhanced ordering of liquid crystalline suspensions of cellulose microfibrils: A small angle neutron scattering study, *Macromolecules.* **31**(17), 5717–5725 (1998).

40. A. B. Fall, S. B. Lindström, O. Sundman, L. Ödberg, and L. Wågberg, Colloidal stability of aqueous nanofibrillated cellulose dispersions, *Langmuir* (2011).

41. X. Dong and D. Gray, Effect of counterions on ordered phase formation in suspensions of charged rodlike cellulose crystallites, *Langmuir.* **13**(8), 2404–2409 (1997).

42. L. Zhong, S. Fu, X. Peng, H. Zhan, and R. Sun, Colloidal stability of negatively charged cellulose nanocrystalline in aqueous systems, *Carbohydr. Polym.* (2012).

43. C. H. Yang, M. X. Wang, H. Haider, J. H. Yang, J.-Y. Sun, Y. M. Chen, J. Zhou, and Z. Suo, Strengthening alginate/polyacrylamide hydrogels using various multivalent cations, *ACS Appl. Mater. Interfaces* (2013).

44. I. Usov, G. Nyström, J. Adamcik, S. Handschin, C. Schütz, A. Fall, L. Bergström, and R. Mezzenga, Understanding nanocellulose chirality and structure-properties relationship at the single fibril level., *Nat. Commun.* **6**, 7564 (2015).

45. S. J. Hanley, J.-F. Revol, L. Godbout, and D. G. Gray, Atomic force microscopy and transmission electron microscopy of cellulose from micrasterias denticulata; evidence for a chiral helical microfibril twist, *Cellulose.* **4**(3), 209–220 (1997).

46. S. Shafeiei-Sabet, W. Y. Hamad, and S. G. Hatzikiriakos, Influence of degree of sulfation on the rheology of cellulose nanocrystal suspensions, *Rheol Acta.* **52**(8-9), 741–751 (2013).

47. E. E. Urena-Benavides, G. Ao, V. A. Davis, and C. L. Kitchens, Rheology and phase behavior of lyotropic cellulose nanocrystal suspensions, *Macromolecules.* **44**(22), 8990–8998 (2011).

48. G. Mosser, A. Anglo, C. Helary, Y. Bouligand, and M. Giraud-Guille, Dense tissue-like collagen matrices formed in cell-free conditions., *Matrix Biol.* **25**(1), 3–13 (2006).

49. T. L. Greaves and C. J. Drummond, Solvent nanostructure, the solvophobic effect and amphiphile self-assembly in ionic liquids, *Chem. Soc. Rev.* **42**, 1096–1120 (2013).

50. P. Alexandridis, P. Holmqvist, and B. Lindman, *Colloids Surfaces A: Physicoehem. Eng. Aspects.* **129–130**, 3–21 (1997).

51. P. K. Bhowmik, A. K. Nedeltchev, and H. Han, Synthesis, thermal and lyotropic liquid crystalline properties of protic ionic salts, *Liq. Cryst.* **35**(6), 757–764 (2008).

52. Y.-m. Dong, W. Mao, H.-w. Wang, Y.-q. Zhao, X.-j. Li, D.-x. Bi, L.-l. Yang,

Q. Ge, and X. Fang, Measurement of critical concentration for mesophase formation of chitosan derivatives in both aqueous and organic solutions, *Polym. Int.* **55**, 1444–1449 (2006).

53. M. Kolbel, T. Beyersdorff, C. Tschierske, S. Diele, and J. Kain, Thermotropic and lyotropic liquid crystalline phases of rigid aromatic amphiphiles, *Chem. -Eur. J.* **6**(20), 3821–3837 (2000).

54. A. K. Nedeltchev, H. Han, P. K. Bhowmik, and L. Ma, Solution, thermal and optical properties of new poly(pyridinium salt)s derived from conjugated quinoline diamines, *Journal of Polymer Science Part A: Polymer Chemistry.* **49**, 1907–1918 (2011).

55. K. Oyamada, K. Terao, M. Suwa, S. Kitamura, and T. Sato, Lyotropic liquid crystallinity of amylose tris(alkylcarbamates): Cholesteric and smectic phase formation in different solvents, *Macromol.* **46**, 4589–4595 (2013).

56. L. S. Blachechen, J. P. de Mesquita, E. L. de Paula, and D. F. S. Pereira, Fabiano V Petri, Interplay of colloidal stability of cellulose nanocrystals and their dispersibility in cellulose acetate butyrate matrix, *Cellulose.* **20**, 1329–1342 (2013).

57. N. Marcovich, M. L. Auad, N. E. Bellesi, S. R. Nutt, and M. I. Aranguren, Cellulose micro/nanocrystals reinforced polyurethane, *J. Mater. Res.* **21**, 870 (2006).

58. S. Noorani and A. Simonsen, John Sundar, Nano-enabled microtechnology: polysulfone nanocomposites incorporating cellulose nanocrystals, *Cellulose.* **14**, 577–584 (2007).

59. J. Sapkota, M. Jorfi, C. Weder, and E. J. Foster, Reinforcing poly(ethylene) with cellulose nanocrystals, *Macromol. Rapid Commun.* **35**, 1747 – 1753 (2014).

60. S. Eyley and W. Thielemans, *Nanoscale.* **6**, 7764–7779 (2014).

61. B. L. Peng, N. Dhar, H. L. Liu, and K. C. Tam, Chemistry and applications of nanocrystalline cellulose and its derivatives: A nanotechnology perspective, *Can. J. Chem. Eng.* **89**(5), 1191–1206 (2011).

62. J. Araki, M. Wada, and S. Kuga, Steric stabilization of a cellulose microcrystal suspension by poly (ethylene glycol) grafting, *Langmuir.* **17**(1), 21–27 (2001).

63. L. Heux, G. Chauve, and C. Bonini, Nonflocculating and chiral-nematic self-ordering of cellulose microcrystals suspensions in nonpolar solvents, *Langmuir.* **16**(21), 8210–8212 (2000).

64. M. Salajkova, A. Berglund, Lars, and Q. Zhou, Hydrophobic cellulose nanocrystals modified with quaternary ammonium salts, *J. Mater. Chem.* **22**(37), 19798–19805 (2012).

65. Q. Xu, J. Yi, X. Zhang, and H. Zhang, *Eur. Polym. J.* **44**, 2830–2837 (2008).

66. Q. Zhou, H. Brumer, and T. Teeri, Self-organization of cellulose nanocrystals adsorbed with xyloglucan oligosaccharide—poly (ethylene glycol)—polystyrene triblock copolymer, *Macromolecules.* **42**(15), 5430–5432 (2009).

67. S. Elazzouzi-Hafraoui, J.-L. Putaux, and L. Heux, Self-assembling and chiral nematic properties of organophilic cellulose nanocrystals, *J. Phys. Chem. B.* **113**(32), 11069–11075 (2009).

68. A. Isogai, T. Saito, and H. Fukuzumi, TEMPO-oxidized cellulose nanofibers, *Nanoscale.* **3**(1), 71–85 (2011).

69. G. Siqueira, J. Bras, and A. Dufresne, *Langmuir.* **26**(1), 402–411 (2010).

70. C. Tian, S. Fu, Y. Habibi, and L. A. Lucia, Polymerization topochemistry of cellulose nanocrystals: A function of surface dehydration control, *Langmuir.* **30**, 14670–14679 (2014).

71. C. C. Y. Cheung, M. Giese, J. A. Kelly, W. Y. Hamad, and M. J. MacLachlan, Iridescent chiral nematic cellulose nanocrystal/polymer composites assembled in organic solvents, *ACS Macro Lett.* pp. 1016–1020 (2013).

72. H. Okura, M. Wada, and T. Serizawa, Dispersibility of HCl-treated cellulose nanocrystals with water-dispersible properties in organic solvents, *Chem. Lett.* **43**, 601–603 (2014).

73. D. Viet, S. Beck-Candanedo, and D. Gray, Dispersion of cellulose nanocrystals in polar organic solvents, *Cellulose.* **14**(2), 109–113 (2007).

74. X. Mu and D. Gray, Formation of chiral nematic films from cellulose nanocrystal suspensions is a two-stage process., *Langmuir.* **30**(31), 9256–9260 (2014).

75. J. H. Park, J. Noh, C. Schütz, G. Salazar-Alvarez, G. Scalia, L. Bergström, and J. P. F. Lagerwall, Macroscopic control of helix orientation in films dried from cholesteric liquid-crystalline cellulose nanocrystal suspensions, *ChemPhysChem.* **15**(7), 1477–1484 (2014).

76. S. Beck, J. Bouchard, and R. Berry, Controlling the reflection wavelength of iridescent solid films of nanocrystalline cellulose, *Biomacromolecules.* **12**(1), 167–172 (2011).

77. J. Majoinen, E. Kontturi, O. Ikkala, and G. Gray, Derek, SEM imaging of chiral nematic films cast from cellulose nanocrystal suspensions, *Cellulose.* **19**(5), 1599–1605 (2012).

78. J. Pan, W. Hamad, and S. Straus, Parameters affecting the chiral nematic phase of nanocrystalline cellulose films, *Macromolecules.* **43**(8), 3851–3858 (2010).

79. S. Beck, J. Bouchard, and R. Berry, Dispersibility in water of dried nanocrystalline cellulose, *Biomacromolecules.* **13**(5), 1486–1494 (2012).

80. Y. P. Zhang, V. P. Chodavarapu, A. G. Kirk, and M. P. Andrews, Nanocrystalline cellulose for covert optical encryption, *Proc. SPIE: Organic Photonic Materials and Devices XIV*, **8258**, p. 825808 (2012).

81. Y. P. Zhang, P. Chodavarapu, Vamsy, G. Kirk, Andrew, and P. Andrews, Mark, Structured color humidity indicator from reversible pitch tuning in self-assembled nanocrystalline cellulose films, *Sensor. Actuat. B-Chem.* **176**, 692–697 (2013).